Nancy Jane Baker
Box 199

Quantum Chemistry

This book is part of

THE ALLYN AND BACON CHEMISTRY SERIES

and was developed under the co-consulting editorship of

DARYLE H. BUSCH

HARRISON SHULL

Second Edition

QUANTUM CHEMISTRY

IRA N. LEVINE

Brooklyn College
City University of New York

Allyn and Bacon, Inc.
Boston • London • Sydney • Toronto

Library of Congress Cataloging in Publication Data

Levine, Ira N   date
    Quantum chemistry.

    (*Allyn and Bacon chemistry series*)
    First published in 1970 as v. 1 of Quantum chemistry,
with special title: *Quantum mechanics and molecular
electronic structure.*
    Bibliography: p.
    1.   Quantum chemistry.

QD462.L48   541'.28   74-4545

ISBN· 0-205-04305-4
Fourth printing . . . July, 1977

To my students: Andrew Auerbach, Joseph Barbuto, David Baron, Sene Bauman, Howard Becker, Michael Beitchman, Anna Berne, Mark Blackman, Toby Block, Allen Bloom, Paul Brumer, Lynn Caporale, Richard Carter, Joseph D'Amore, Barry DuRon, Myron Elgart, Stephen Engel, Larry Filler, Seymour Fishman, Donald Franceschetti, Tobi Eisenstein Fried, Joel Friedman, Kenneth Friedman, Mark Freilich, Michael Freshwater, Aryeh Frimer, Mark Froimowitz, Paul Gallant, Stephen Goldman, Neil Goodman, Roy Goodman, Isaac Gorbaty, Michael Gross, Sheila Handler, Warren Hirsch, Richard Hom, Fu-juan Hsu, Leonard Itzkowitz, Abraham Karkowsky, Michael Kittay, Barry Kohn, David Kurnit, Athanasios Ladas, Alan Lambowitz, Stephen Lemont, Elliot Lerner, Joel Liebman, Steven Lipp, Dennis Lynch, Louis Maresca, Allen Marks, Ira Michaels, Paul Mogolesko, Irving Nadler, Stuart Nagourney, Harold Nelson, Eli Pines, Jerry Polesuk, Arlene Gallanter Pollin, James Pollin, Robert Richman, Bruce Rosenberg, Robert Rundberg, Edward Sachs, David Schaeffer, Gary Schneier, Neil Schweid, Judith Rosenkranz Selwyn, Gunnar Senum, Steven Shaya, Allen Sheffron, Lawrence Shore, Alvin Silverstein, Barry Siskind, Jerome Solomon, Henry Sperling, David Trauber, King-hung Tse, Alan Waldman, Robert Washington, Ken Zaner.

Contents

Preface

This book is intended for first-year graduate and advanced undergraduate introductory courses in quantum chemistry. It covers quantum mechanics and molecular electronic structure. This is the second edition of the book published previously as *Quantum Chemistry*, Volume I. (The second edition of Volume II is being published by Wiley–Interscience as an independent book under the title *Molecular Spectroscopy*.)

In the second edition, the text has been revised to bring material up to date, to clarify explanations, and to correct errors. The treatment of semiempirical methods has been expanded to include the CNDO, INDO, and MINDO methods; advances made in *ab initio* work have been included. A new section (15.11) on chemical reactions has been added; this discusses *ab initio* and semiempirical calculation of reaction surfaces, frontier orbitals, and the Woodward–Hoffmann rules.

I have tried to make explanations clear and complete, without glossing over difficult or subtle points. Derivations are given with enough detail to make them easy to follow, and resort to the frustrating phrase "it can be shown that" is avoided wherever possible. The aim is to give students a solid understanding of the physical and mathematical aspects of quantum mechanics and molecular electronic structure. The book is designed to be useful to students in all branches of chemistry, not just future quantum chemists. However, the presentation is such that those who do go on in quantum chemistry will have a good foundation and won't be hampered by misconceptions.

One of the major obstacles faced by many chemistry students in learning quantum mechanics is their unfamiliarity with much of the required mathematics. In this text I have included detailed treatments of operators, differential equations, simultaneous linear equations, and other needed topics. Rather than putting all the mathematics in an introductory chapter or in a series of appendices, I have integrated the mathematics with the physics and chemistry. Immediate application of the mathematics to solving some quantum-mechanical problem should provide better motivation for the student than would be provided by studying the mathematics separately. I have also kept in mind the limited physics background of many chemistry students by reviewing topics they are likely to be unclear on.

A large number of problems of varying degrees of difficulty are included, together with answers for many of them.

The first edition benefited from the critical comments of Professors James Bolton, Melvyn Feinberg, David Goldberg, Harry King, and Harrison Shull. Professors Uldis Blukis, Melvyn Feinberg, and Joel Liebman made suggestions for the second edition. I wish to thank these people and several anonymous reviewers.

I would appreciate receiving any suggestions that readers may have for improving the book.

I. N. L.

Quantum Chemistry

CHAPTER
1

The Schroedinger Equation

1.1 The Historical Background of Quantum Mechanics

In the late 19th century, investigations of electric discharge tubes and natural radioactivity showed that atoms and molecules are composed of charged particles. Electrons have a negative charge. The proton has a positive charge equal in magnitude but opposite in sign to the electron charge and is 1836 times as heavy as the electron. The third constituent of atoms, the neutron (discovered in 1932), is neutral and slightly heavier than the proton.

Starting in 1909, Rutherford, Geiger, and Marsden carried out a series of experiments in which they passed a beam of alpha particles through a thin metal foil and observed the deflections of the particles by allowing them to fall on a fluorescent screen. Alpha particles are positively charged helium nuclei obtained from natural radioactive decay. Rutherford observed that most of the alpha particles passed through the foil essentially undeflected, but, surprisingly, a few underwent large deflections, some being deflected backwards. To get large deflections, one needs a very close approach between the charges, so that the Coulombic repulsive force is great. If the positive charge were spread throughout the atom (as J. J. Thomson had proposed in 1904), once the high-energy alpha particle penetrated the atom, the repulsive force would fall off, becoming zero at the center of the atom, according to classical electrostatics. Hence Rutherford concluded that such large deflections could occur only if the positive charge were concentrated in a tiny, heavy nucleus.

An atom contains a tiny (10^{-13} to 10^{-12} cm radius) heavy nucleus consisting of neutrons and Z protons, where Z is the atomic number. Outside the nucleus there are Z electrons. The charged particles interact according to Coulomb's law. (The nucleons are held together in the nucleus by strong, short-range nuclear forces which will not concern us.) The radius of an atom is about one angstrom (1 Å $\equiv$ 10^{-8} cm) as shown, for example, by results from the kinetic theory of gases. Molecules have more than one nucleus.

The chemical properties of atoms and molecules are determined by their electronic structure and so the question arises as to the nature of the motions and energies of the electrons. Since the nucleus is much more massive than the electron, we expect the motion of the nucleus to be slight compared to the electrons' motions.

In 1911 Rutherford proposed his "planetary" model of the atom in which the electrons revolved about the nucleus in various orbits, just as the planets revolve about the sun. However, there is a fundamental difficulty with this model. According to classical electromagnetic theory, an accelerated charged particle radiates energy in the form of electromagnetic (light) waves. An electron circling the nucleus at constant speed is being accelerated, since the direction of its velocity vector is continually changing. Hence the electrons in the Rutherford model should continually lose energy by radiation and therefore would spiral in toward the nucleus. Thus, according to classical (19th century) physics, the Rutherford atom is unstable and would collapse.

A possible way out of this difficulty was proposed by Bohr in 1913, when he applied the concept of quantization of energy to the hydrogen atom. Energy quantization was first introduced into physics in 1900 by Planck, who derived the observed intensity distribution of light emitted by a hot solid (blackbody radiation) starting from the assumption that the solid radiated energy in integral multiples of hv, where v is the radiation's frequency and h is a proportionality constant (called *Planck's constant*) equal to 6.6×10^{-27} erg·sec. In 1905, Einstein pointed out that the dependence of the kinetic energy of the electrons emitted in the photoelectric effect on the frequency of the light shining on the emitting metal could be explained by viewing light as made up of particle-like entities (*photons*), with each photon having an energy

$$E_{\text{photon}} = hv \tag{1.1}$$

Thus light can show particle-like behavior in addition to the wave-like behavior evidenced by diffraction.

Bohr assumed that the energy of the electron in a hydrogen atom was quantized, with the electron constrained to move only on one of a number of allowed circles. When an electron makes a transition from one orbit (stationary state) to another, a quantum of light of frequency

$$v = \Delta E/h \tag{1.2}$$

is absorbed or emitted, where ΔE is the energy difference between the two states (conservation of energy). With the assumption that an electron making a transition from a free (ionized) state to one of the bound orbits emits a photon whose frequency is an integral multiple of one-half the classical frequency of revolution of the electron in the bound orbit, Bohr used Newtonian mechanics to derive a formula for the hydrogen-atom energy levels. Using (1.2), he obtained agreement with the observed hydrogen spectrum. However, attempts to fit the helium spectrum using the Bohr theory failed. Moreover, the theory could not account for chemical bonds in molecules.

The basic difficulty in the Bohr model arises from the use of classical Newtonian mechanics to describe the electronic motions in atoms. The evidence of atomic spectra, which show discrete frequencies, indicates that only certain energies of motion are allowed; i.e., the electronic energy is "quantized." However, Newtonian mechanics allows a continuous range of energies. Quantization does occur in wave motion; for example, the fundamental and overtone frequencies of a violin string. Hence de Broglie suggested in 1923 that the motion of electrons might have a wave aspect; i.e., that an electron of mass m and speed v would have a wavelength λ associated with it, such that

$$\lambda = \frac{h}{mv} = \frac{h}{p} \tag{1.3}$$

where p is the linear momentum. de Broglie arrived at Eq. (1.3) by reasoning in analogy with photons. The energy of any particle (including a photon) can be expressed, according to Einstein's special theory of relativity, as $E = mc^2$, where c is the speed of light. Using (1.1), we get $mc^2 = hv = hc/\lambda$, so that $\lambda = h/mc = h/p$ for a photon traveling at speed c. Equation (1.3) is then the corresponding relation for an electron.

In 1927, Davisson and Germer experimentally confirmed de Broglie's hypothesis by observing diffraction effects by reflecting electrons from metals. In 1932, Stern observed the same effects with helium atoms and hydrogen molecules, thus verifying that the wave effects are not peculiar to electrons, but result from some general law of motion for microscopic particles. (The electron microscope is a practical application of the wave properties of electrons.)

Thus electrons behave in some respects like particles, and in other respects like waves. We are faced with the apparently contradictory "wave-particle duality" of matter (and of light). How can an electron be both a particle, which is a localized entity, and a wave, which is nonlocalized? The answer is that an electron is neither a wave nor a particle, but something else. An accurate pictorial description of an electron's behavior is impossible using the wave or particle concepts of classical physics. The concepts of classical physics have been developed from experience in the macroscopic world and do not provide a proper description of the microscopic world.

Although both photons and electrons show an apparent "duality," they are not the same kinds of entities. Photons always travel at speed c and have zero rest mass; electrons always have $v < c$ and a nonzero rest mass. Photons must always be treated relativistically, but electrons whose speed is not too high can be treated nonrelativistically.

1.2 The Uncertainty Principle

Let us consider what effect the wave-particle duality has on attempts to measure simultaneously the x coordinate and the x component of linear momentum of a microscopic "particle." We start with a beam of particles with momentum p, traveling in the y direction, and we let the beam fall on a narrow slit. Behind this slit is a photographic plate. See Fig. 1.1.

Particles that pass through the slit of width w have an uncertainty w in their x coordinate at the time of going through the slit. Calling this spread in x values, Δx, we have $\Delta x = w$.

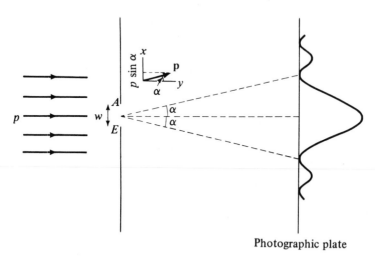

FIGURE 1.1   *Diffraction of electrons by a slit.*

Since microscopic "particles" have wave properties, they are diffracted by the slit producing (as would a light beam) a diffraction pattern on the plate. The height of the graph in Fig. 1.1 is a measure of the number of particles reaching a given point. The diffraction pattern indicates that when the particles were diffracted by the slit, their direction of motion was changed so that part of their momentum was transferred to the x direction. The x component of momentum is given by the projection of the momentum vector in the x direction. A particle deflected upward by an angle α has an x component of momentum $p \sin \alpha$. A particle deflected downward by an angle α has an x component of momentum $-p \sin \alpha$. Since most of the particles undergo deflections in the range $-\alpha$ to α, where α is the angle to the first minimum in the diffraction pattern, we shall take one-half the spread of momentum values in the central diffraction peak as a measure of the uncertainty Δp_x in the x component of momentum: $\Delta p_x = p \sin \alpha$.

Hence

$$\Delta x \, \Delta p_x = pw \sin \alpha \qquad (1.4)$$

The angle α at which the first diffraction minimum occurs is readily calculated. The condition for the first minimum is that the difference in the distances traveled by particles passing through the slit at its upper edge and particles passing through the center of the slit be equal to $\frac{1}{2}\lambda$, where λ is the wavelength of the associated wave. Waves originating from the top of the slit are then exactly out of phase with waves originating from the center of the slit and they cancel each other. Waves originating from a point in the slit at a distance d below the slit midpoint cancel with waves originating at a distance d below the top of the slit. Drawing AC in Fig. 1.2 so that $AD = CD$, we have the difference in path length as BC. The

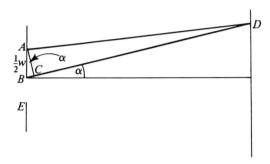

FIGURE 1.2 *Calculation of first diffraction minimum.*

distance from the slit to the screen is large compared with the slit width. Hence AD and BD are nearly parallel. This makes the angle ACB essentially a right angle, so that angle $BAC = \alpha$. The path difference BC is then $\frac{1}{2}w \sin \alpha$. Setting BC equal to $\frac{1}{2}\lambda$, we have $w \sin \alpha = \lambda$, and Eq. (1.4) becomes $\Delta x \, \Delta p_x = p\lambda$. The wavelength λ is given by the de Broglie relation $\lambda = h/p$, so that $\Delta x \, \Delta p_x = h$. Since the uncertainties have not been precisely defined, the equality sign is not really justified; instead we write:

$$\Delta x \, \Delta p_x \approx h \qquad (1.5)$$

indicating that the product of the uncertainties in x and p_x is of the order of magnitude of Planck's constant. In Section 5.1 we will give a precise statistical definition of the uncertainties and a precise inequality to replace (1.5).

Although we have demonstrated (1.5) for only one experimental setup, its validity is general. No matter what attempts are made, the wave-particle duality of microscopic "particles" imposes a limit on our ability to measure simultaneously the position and momentum of such particles. The more precisely we determine the position, the less accurate is our determination of momentum. (In Fig. 1.1, $\sin \alpha = \lambda/w$, so that narrowing the slit increases the spread of the diffraction pattern.) This limitation is called the *uncertainty principle* and was discovered in 1927 by Heisenberg.

Because of the wave-particle duality, the act of measurement introduces an uncontrollable disturbance in the system being measured. We started with particles having a precise value of p_x (namely zero); by imposing the slit, we measured the x coordinate of the particles to an accuracy w, but this measurement introduced an uncertainty into the p_x values of the particles. The measurement changed the state of the system.

1.3 The Time-Dependent Schroedinger Equation

Classical mechanics is applicable only to macroscopic particles. For microscopic "particles" we require a new form of mechanics which we will call *quantum mechanics* (or *wave mechanics*). We now consider some of the contrasts between classical and quantum mechanics. For simplicity we deal with a one-particle, one-dimensional system.

In classical mechanics the motion of the particle is governed by Newton's second law:

$$F = m\frac{d^2x}{dt^2} \tag{1.6}$$

where F is the force acting on the particle, m is its mass, and t is the time. Equation (1.6) contains the second derivative of the coordinate x with respect to time. To solve it we must carry out two integrations. This introduces two arbitrary constants c_1 and c_2 into the solution, so that

$$x = g(t, c_1, c_2) \tag{1.7}$$

where g is some function of time. We now ask, what information must we possess at a given time t_0 to be able to predict the future motion of the particle? If we know that at t_0 the particle is at point x_0, we have

$$x_0 = g(t_0, c_1, c_2) \tag{1.8}$$

Since we have two constants to determine, we need more information. Differentiating (1.7) we have

$$\frac{dx}{dt} = v = \frac{d}{dt}g(t, c_1, c_2)$$

where v is the particle's velocity. If we also know that at time t_0 the particle has velocity v_0, then we have the additional relation

$$v_0 = \frac{d}{dt}g(t, c_1, c_2)\Big|_{t=t_0} \tag{1.9}$$

We may then use (1.8) and (1.9) to solve for c_1 and c_2 in terms of x_0 and v_0. Knowing c_1 and c_2, we can use Eq. (1.7) to predict the exact future motion of the particle.

The word *state* in classical mechanics means a specification of the position and velocity of each particle of the system at some instant of time, plus specification of the forces acting on the particles. According to Newton's second law, given the state of a system at any time, its future state and future motions are exactly determined. The impressive success of Newton's laws in explaining planetary motions led many philosophers to use Newton's laws as an argument for philosophical determinism. The mathematician and astronomer Laplace (1749–1827) assumed that the universe consisted of nothing but particles which obeyed Newton's laws. Therefore, given the state of the universe at some instant, the future motion of everything in the universe was completely determined. A super-being able to know the state of the universe at any instant could, in principle, calculate all future motions.

However, the Heisenberg uncertainty principle shows that we cannot determine simultaneously the exact position and velocity of a microscopic particle, so that the very knowledge required by classical mechanics for predicting the future motions of a system cannot be obtained. We must be content in quantum mechanics with something less than complete prediction of the exact future motion.

Our approach to quantum mechanics will be to *postulate* the basic principles and then use these postulates to deduce experimentally testable consequences such as the energy levels of atoms. To describe the *state* of a system in quantum mechanics, we postulate the existence of a function of the coordinates called the *wave function* (or *state function*) Ψ. Since the state will, in general, change with time, Ψ is a function of time also. For a one-particle, one-dimensional system, we have: $\Psi = \Psi(x, t)$. The wave function contains all possible information about a system so that instead of speaking of "the state described by the wave function Ψ," we simply say, "the state Ψ." Newton's second law tells us how to find the future state of a classical-mechanical system from knowledge of the present state. To find the future state of a quantum-mechanical system from knowledge of the present state, we want an equation which tells us how the wave function changes with time. This equation is postulated to be:

$$-\frac{\hbar}{i}\frac{\partial\Psi(x,t)}{\partial t} = -\frac{\hbar^2}{2m}\frac{\partial^2\Psi(x,t)}{\partial x^2} + V(x,t)\Psi(x,t) \qquad \textbf{(1.10)}$$

where the constant $\hbar$ ("h-bar") is defined as

$$\hbar \equiv \frac{h}{2\pi} \qquad \textbf{(1.11)}$$

The concept of the wave function and the equation governing its change with time were discovered in 1926 by the Austrian physicist Schroedinger (1887–1961). In this equation, known as the *time-dependent Schroedinger equation* (or the *Schroedinger wave equation*), $i = \sqrt{-1}$, m is the mass of the particle, and $V(x,t)$ is the potential-energy function of the system. (Recall from classical mechanics that if the force acting on the particle is $F(x,t)$, then V is defined by

$$\frac{\partial V(x,t)}{\partial x} = -F(x,t)$$

and V may be obtained by an integration.) The time-dependent Schroedinger equation contains the first derivative of the wave function with respect to time and allows us to calculate the future wave function (state) at any time, if we know the wave function at time t_0.

The wave function contains all the information we can possibly know about the system it describes. What information does Ψ give us about the result of a measurement of the x coordinate of the particle? We cannot expect Ψ to involve the definite specification of position that the state of a classical-mechanical system does. The correct answer to this question was provided by Born shortly after

Schroedinger discovered the Schroedinger equation. Born postulated that

$$|\Psi(x,t)|^2\,dx \tag{1.12}$$

gives the *probability* at time t of finding the particle in the region of the x axis lying between x and $x+dx$. In (1.12), the bars denote the absolute value and dx is an infinitesimal length on the x axis. The function $|\Psi(x,t)|^2$ is the *probability density* for finding the particle at various places on the x axis. (A review of probability is given in Section 1.5.) For example, suppose that at some particular time t_0 the particle is in a state characterized by the wave function ae^{-bx^2}, where a and b are real constants. If we measure the particle's position at time t_0, we might get any value of x, because the probability density $a^2e^{-2bx^2}$ is nonzero everywhere. Of course, values of x in the region around $x=0$ are more likely to be found than other values, since $|\Psi|^2$ is a maximum at the origin.

To make a precise connection between $|\Psi|^2$ and experimental measurements, we would take a large number of identical noninteracting systems, each of which was in the same state Ψ. We then make a measurement of position in each system. If we had n systems and made n measurements, and if dn_x denotes the number of measurements for which we found the particle between x and $x+dx$, then dn_x/n is the probability for finding the particle between x and $x+dx$. Thus

$$\frac{dn_x}{n} = |\Psi|^2\,dx$$

and a graph of $(1/n)\,dn_x/dx$ versus x gives the probability density $|\Psi|^2$. It might be thought that we could find the probability-density function by taking one system which was in the state Ψ and repeatedly carrying out measurements of the particle's position. This procedure will not do because the process of measurement generally changes the state of a system; we saw an example of this in our discussion of the uncertainty principle (Section 1.2).

Quantum mechanics is basically *statistical* in nature. Knowing the state, we cannot predict the result of a position measurement with certainty; we can only predict the *probabilities* of various possible results. The Bohr theory of the hydrogen atom specified the precise path of the electron and is therefore not a correct quantum-mechanical picture.

Quantum mechanics does not say that an electron is distributed over a large region of space as a wave is distributed. Rather, it is the probability patterns (wave functions) used to describe the electron's motion that behave like waves and satisfy a wave equation.

The reader might ask how the wave function gives us information on other properties (e.g., momentum) besides the position. We postpone discussion on this point until later chapters.

The postulates of, say, thermodynamics (the first, second, and third laws of thermodynamics) are stated in terms of macroscopic experience and hence are fairly readily understood. The postulates of quantum mechanics are stated in terms of the microscopic world and appear quite abstract. You should not expect to have a full understanding of the postulates of quantum mechanics at first reading. As we treat various examples, understanding of the postulates will increase. (We have not yet introduced all the postulates of quantum mechanics. Further postulates will be introduced later.)

It may bother the reader that we wrote down the Schroedinger equation without any attempt to prove its plausibility. By using analogies between geometrical optics and classical mechanics on the one hand, and wave optics and quantum mechanics on the other hand, one can show the plausibility of the Schroedinger equation. Geometrical optics is an approximation to wave optics, valid when the wavelength of the light is much less than the size of the apparatus. (Recall its use in treating lenses and mirrors.) Likewise, classical mechanics is an approximation to wave mechanics, valid when the particle's wavelength is much less than the size of the apparatus. One can make a plausible guess as to how to get the proper equation for quantum mechanics from classical mechanics based on the known relation between the equations of geometrical and wave optics. Since most chemists are not particularly familiar with optics, these arguments have been omitted. In any case, such analogies can only make the Schroedinger equation seem *plausible*; they cannot be used to *derive* or *prove* this equation. The Schroedinger equation is a *postulate* of the theory, to be tested by agreement of its predictions with experiment. (Details of the reasoning that led Schroedinger to his equation are given in *Jammer*, Section 5.3. References with the author's name italicized are listed in the Bibliography.)

Quantum mechanics provides the law of motion for microscopic particles. Experimentally, macroscopic objects obey classical mechanics. Hence, for quantum mechanics to be a valid theory, it should reduce to classical mechanics as we make the transition from microscopic to macroscopic particles. Quantum effects are associated with the de Broglie wavelength $\lambda = h/mv$. Since h is very small, the de Broglie wavelength of macroscopic objects is essentially zero. Thus in the limit $\lambda \to 0$ we expect the time-dependent Schroedinger equation to reduce to Newton's second law.[1] We can prove this to be so (see Problem 7.19).

1.4 The Time-Independent Schroedinger Equation

The time-dependent Schroedinger equation (1.10) is rather formidable looking. Fortunately, for many applications of quantum mechanics to chemistry, it is not necessary to deal with this equation; instead, the simpler time-independent Schroedinger equation is used. We now derive the time-independent from the time-dependent Schroedinger equation, for the one-particle, one-dimensional case.

We begin by restricting ourselves to the special case where the potential energy V is not a function of time but depends only on x. The time-dependent Schroedinger equation reads

$$-\frac{\hbar}{i}\frac{\partial \Psi(x,t)}{\partial t} = -\frac{\hbar^2}{2m}\frac{\partial^2 \Psi(x,t)}{\partial x^2} + V(x)\Psi(x,t) \qquad (1.13)$$

---

[1] A similar situation holds in the relation between special relativity and classical mechanics. In the limit $v/c \to 0$, where c is the velocity of light, special relativity reduces to classical mechanics. The form of quantum mechanics that we will develop will be nonrelativistic. A complete integration of relativity with quantum mechanics has not been achieved.

We will look for those solutions of (1.13) that can be written as the product of a function of time and a function of x:

$$\Psi(x,t) = f(t)\psi(x) \tag{1.14}$$

Note that we use capital psi for the time-dependent wave function and lower case psi for the factor which depends only on the coordinate x. States corresponding to wave functions of the form (1.14) possess certain properties (to be discussed shortly) which make them of great interest. Taking partial derivatives of (1.14) we have

$$\frac{\partial \Psi(x,t)}{\partial t} = \frac{df(t)}{dt}\psi(x), \qquad \frac{\partial^2 \Psi(x,t)}{\partial x^2} = f(t)\frac{d^2\psi(x)}{dx^2}$$

so that Eq. (1.13) becomes

$$-\frac{\hbar}{i}\frac{df(t)}{dt}\psi(x) = -\frac{\hbar^2}{2m}f(t)\frac{d^2\psi(x)}{dx^2} + V(x)\psi(x)f(t)$$

$$-\frac{\hbar}{i}\frac{1}{f(t)}\frac{df(t)}{dt} = -\frac{\hbar^2}{2m}\frac{1}{\psi(x)}\frac{d^2\psi(x)}{dx^2} + V(x) \tag{1.15}$$

where we divided by $f\psi$. In general, we expect the quantity to which each side of (1.15) is equal, to be a certain function of x and t. However, the right side of (1.15) does not depend on t, so that the function which each side of (1.15) is equal to, must be independent of t. The left side of (1.15) is independent of x, so that this function must also be independent of x. Since the function is independent of both variables, x and t, it must be a constant. We call this constant E.

Equating the left side of (1.15) to E, we get

$$\frac{df(t)}{f(t)} = -\frac{iE}{\hbar}dt$$

Integrating both sides of this equation with respect to t, we have

$$\ln f(t) = -iEt/\hbar + C$$

where C is an arbitrary constant of integration. Hence

$$f(t) = e^C e^{-iEt/\hbar} = A e^{-iEt/\hbar}$$

where the arbitrary constant A has replaced e^C. Since A can be included as a factor in the function $\psi(x)$ which multiplies $f(t)$, there is no loss in generality in omitting it from $f(t)$. Thus we take

$$f(t) = e^{-iEt/\hbar}$$

Equating the right side of (1.15) to E, we have

$$-\frac{\hbar^2}{2m}\frac{d^2\psi(x)}{dx^2} + V(x)\psi(x) = E\psi(x) \tag{1.16}$$

$$\frac{d^2\psi(x)}{dx^2} + \frac{8\pi^2 m}{h^2}[E-V(x)]\psi(x) = 0$$

Equation (1.16) is the *time-independent Schroedinger equation* for a single particle of mass m moving in one dimension.[2]

What is the significance of the constant E? Since E occurs as $[E-V(x)]$, E has the same dimensions as V, i.e., E has the dimensions of energy. In fact, we postulate that E is the energy of the system. (This is a special case of a more general postulate to be discussed in a later chapter.) Thus for cases where the potential energy is a function of x only, there exist wave functions of the form

$$\Psi(x,t) = e^{-iEt/\hbar}\psi(x) \tag{1.17}$$

and these wave functions correspond to states of constant energy E. Much of our attention in the next few chapters will be devoted to finding the solutions of (1.16) for various systems.

The wave function in (1.17) is complex, but the quantity that is experimentally observable is the probability density $|\Psi(x,t)|^2$. The square of the absolute value of a complex quantity is given by the product of the quantity with its complex conjugate, the complex conjugate being formed by replacing i with $-i$ wherever it occurs.[3] Thus

$$|\Psi|^2 = \Psi^*\Psi$$

where the star denotes the complex conjugate. For the wave function (1.17), we have

$$\begin{aligned}
|\Psi(x,t)|^2 &= [e^{-iEt/\hbar}\psi(x)]^*e^{-iEt/\hbar}\psi(x) \\
&= e^{iEt/\hbar}\psi^*(x)e^{-iEt/\hbar}\psi(x) \\
&= e^0\psi^*(x)\psi(x) = \psi^*(x)\psi(x) \\
|\Psi(x,t)|^2 &= |\psi(x)|^2
\end{aligned} \tag{1.18}$$

[In deriving (1.18), we assumed that E is a real number so that $E = E^*$. This fact will be proved in Section 7.2.] Hence for states of the form (1.17), the probability density is given by $|\psi(x)|^2$ and does not change with time. Such states are called *stationary states*. Since the physically significant quantity is $|\Psi(x,t)|^2$, and since for stationary states $|\Psi(x,t)|^2 = |\psi(x)|^2$, the function $\psi(x)$ is often called the wave function, although the complete wave function of a stationary state is obtained by multiplying $\psi(x)$ by $e^{-iEt/\hbar}$. The term "stationary state" should not mislead the reader into thinking that a particle in a stationary state is at rest. What is stationary is the probability density $|\Psi|^2$, not the particle itself.

We will mostly be concerned with states of constant energy (stationary states) and hence will usually deal with the time-independent Schroedinger equation (1.16). For simplicity we will refer to this equation as "the Schroedinger equation." Note that the Schroedinger equation contains *two* unknowns, the allowed energies E and the allowed wave functions ψ. To solve for two unknowns, we need to impose

---

[2] Schroedinger actually developed the time-independent equation before the time-dependent equation. The relevant papers are: E. Schroedinger, *Ann. Physik*, **79**, 361, 489 (1926); **80**, 437 (1926); **81**, 109 (1926).

[3] A review of complex numbers is provided in Section 1.6.

additional conditions (called boundary conditions) on ψ besides requiring that it satisfy (1.16); the boundary conditions determine the allowed energies, since it turns out that only certain values of E allow ψ to meet the boundary conditions. This will become clearer when we discuss specific examples in later chapters.

The units we will use will be cgs Gaussian units. (See *Coulson, Electricity*, p. 243.) In this system, the units of length, mass, and time, are the centimeter, gram, and second, respectively. Force is measured in dynes and energy in ergs. Coulomb's law for the magnitude of the force acting between two charges q_1 and q_2 separated by a distance r_{12} in vacuum is $F = q_1 q_2 / r_{12}^2$. In this equation, the charge is in statcoulombs (also called electrostatic units of charge, esu).

In 1960, an official international body recommended the use of the International System (SI) of units. SI units are essentially the rationalized mks system. Since most of the literature and textbooks in quantum chemistry do not use SI units at present, this book is not in SI units. (For converting Gaussian units and equations to their SI equivalents, see the Appendix.)

1.5 Probability

Probability plays a fundamental role in quantum mechanics. In this section we review the mathematics of probability.

There has been much controversy about the proper definition of probability. One definition is the following: If an experiment has n equally probable outcomes, m of which are favorable to the occurrence of a certain event A, then the probability that A occurs is m/n. Note that this definition is circular since it specifies equally *probable* outcomes, whereas *probability* is what we are attempting to define. It is simply assumed that we can recognize equally probable outcomes. An alternative definition is based on actually performing the experiment many times. Suppose we perform the experiment N times and that in M of these trials the event A occurs. The probability of A occurring is then defined as

$$\lim_{N \to \infty} \frac{M}{N}$$

Thus if we toss a coin repeatedly, the fraction of heads will approach 1/2 as we increase the number of tosses.

For example, suppose we pick a card at random from a deck and ask for the probability of drawing a heart. There are 52 cards and hence 52 equally probable outcomes. Since there are 13 hearts, there are 13 favorable outcomes. Hence $m/n = 13/52 = 1/4$. The probability for drawing a heart is 1/4. (Alternatively, we say the odds are 3 to 1 against drawing a heart.)

Sometimes we ask for the probability of two related events both occurring. For example, we may ask for the probability of drawing two hearts from a 52-card deck, assuming we do not replace the first card after it is drawn. There are 52 possible outcomes of the first draw, and for each of these possibilities there are 51 possible second draws. We have $52 \cdot 51$ possible outcomes. Since there are 13 hearts, there are $13 \cdot 12$ different ways to draw two hearts. The desired probability is $13 \cdot 12/52 \cdot 51 = 1/17$. This calculation illustrates the theorem: The probability that two events A and B both occur is the probability that A occurs, multiplied by the conditional probability that B then occurs, calculated with the assumption that A occurred. Thus if A is the probability of drawing a heart on the first draw, the probability of A is 13/52. The probability of drawing a heart on the second draw, given that the first draw yielded a heart, is 12/51 since there remain 12 hearts in the deck. The probability of drawing two hearts is then $(13/52)(12/51) = 1/17$ as found previously.

In quantum mechanics we must deal with probabilities involving a continuous variable; e.g., the x coordinate. It doesn't make much sense to talk about the probability of a particle being found *at* a particular point such as $x = 0.5000 \ldots$, since there are an infinite number of points on the x axis and for any finite number of measurements we make, the probability of getting *exactly* $0.5000 \ldots$ is vanishingly small. Instead we talk of the probability of finding the particle in a small interval of the x axis lying between x and $x + dx$, dx being an infinitesimal element of length. This probability will naturally be proportional to the length of the small interval, dx, and will vary for different regions of the x axis. Hence the probability that the particle will be found between x and $x + dx$ is equal to $g(x)\,dx$, where $g(x)$ is some function which tells how the probability varies over the x axis. The function $g(x)$ is called the *probability density* since it is a probability per unit length. Since probabilities are real, nonnegative numbers, $g(x)$ must be a real function that is everywhere nonnegative. The wave function Ψ can take on negative and complex values and is not a probability density. Quantum mechanics postulates that the probability density is given by $|\Psi|^2$.

What is the probability that the particle lies in some finite region of space $a \leqslant x \leqslant b$? To find this probability we sum up the probabilities of finding the particle in all the infinitesimal regions lying between a and b. This is just the definition of the definite integral

$$\int_a^b |\Psi|^2 \, dx \tag{1.19}$$

A probability of 1 represents certainty. Since it is certain that the particle is somewhere on the x axis, we have the requirement

$$\int_{-\infty}^{\infty} |\Psi|^2 \, dx = 1 \tag{1.20}$$

When Ψ satisfies (1.20), it is said to be *normalized*.

1.6   Complex Numbers

We have seen that the wave function can be complex, so we now review some properties of complex numbers.

If i is $\sqrt{-1}$ then we may write a complex number z as $z = x + iy$ where x and y are real numbers; x and y are called the real and imaginary parts of z: $x = \mathrm{Re}\,(z), y = \mathrm{Im}\,(z)$. A convenient representation of z is as a point in the complex

FIGURE 1.3   *Plot of a complex number z = x + iy.*

plane (Fig. 1.3) where the real part of z is plotted on the horizontal axis and the imaginary part on the vertical axis. This diagram immediately suggests defining two quantities which characterize the complex number z: the distance r of the point z from the origin is called the *absolute value* or modulus of z; the angle θ that the radius vector to the point z makes with the positive horizontal axis is called the *phase* or argument of z. We have

$$|z| = r = (x^2 + y^2)^{1/2}, \qquad \tan\theta = y/x$$
$$x = r\cos\theta, \qquad\qquad y = r\sin\theta$$

So we may write z as

$$z = r\cos\theta + ir\sin\theta = re^{i\theta} \tag{1.21}$$

since (Problem 4.10)

$$e^{i\theta} = \cos\theta + i\sin\theta \tag{1.22}$$

The *complex conjugate* of z, z^*, is defined as

$$z^* = x - iy = re^{-i\theta} \tag{1.23}$$

If z is a real number, its imaginary part is zero. Thus z is real if and only if $z = z^*$. Taking the complex conjugate twice, we get z back again, $(z^*)^* = z$. Forming the product of z and its complex conjugate we have

$$zz^* = x^2 + y^2 = r^2 = |z|^2 \tag{1.24}$$

For the product and quotient of two complex numbers $z_1 = r_1 e^{i\theta_1}$ and $z_2 = r_2 e^{i\theta_2}$, we have

$$z_1 z_2 = r_1 r_2 e^{i(\theta_1 + \theta_2)}, \qquad \frac{z_1}{z_2} = \frac{r_1}{r_2} e^{i(\theta_1 - \theta_2)} \tag{1.25}$$

It is easy to prove, either directly from the definition of complex conjugate or from (1.25), that the complex conjugate of a product is the product of the complex conjugates:

$$(z_1 z_2)^* = z_1^* z_2^* \tag{1.26}$$

Likewise

$$\left(\frac{z_1}{z_2}\right)^* = \frac{z_1^*}{z_2^*}, \qquad (z_1+z_2)^* = z_1^* + z_2^*, \qquad (z_1-z_2)^* = z_1^* - z_2^* \qquad (1.27)$$

For the absolute values of products and quotients, it follows from (1.25) that

$$|z_1 z_2| = |z_1||z_2|, \qquad \left|\frac{z_1}{z_2}\right| = \frac{|z_1|}{|z_2|} \qquad (1.28)$$

Therefore if ψ is a complex wave function we have

$$|\psi^2| = |\psi|^2 = \psi^*\psi \qquad (1.29)$$

We now obtain a formula for the nth roots of unity. We may take the phase of the number 1 to be 0 or 2π or 4π, etc.; hence

$$1 = e^{i2\pi k} \qquad (1.30)$$

where k is any integer, zero, negative, or positive. Now consider the number ω where

$$\omega = e^{i2\pi k/n} \qquad (1.31)$$

n being a positive integer. Using (1.25) n times, we see that $\omega^n = 1$. Thus ω is an nth root of unity. There are n different complex nth roots of unity, and taking n successive values of the integer k gives us all of them:

$$\omega = e^{i2\pi k/n}, \qquad k = 0, 1, 2, ..., n-1 \qquad (1.32)$$

Any other value of k besides those in (1.32) gives a number whose phase differs by an integral multiple of 2π from one of the numbers in (1.32) and hence is not a different root.

PROBLEMS

1.1 Express each of the following units in terms of the fundamental units (cm, g, sec) of the Gaussian system: (a) dynes; (b) ergs; (c) statcoulombs.

1.2 Calculate the force acting on an alpha particle passing a gold atomic nucleus at a distance of 0.0030 Å.

1.3 (a) Calculate the de Broglie wavelength of an electron moving at a speed 1/137th the speed of light. (b) Would you expect m in Eq. (1.3) to be the particle's rest mass or its relativistic mass?

1.4 Obtain the trajectory as a function of time for a classical-mechanical particle moving in one dimension and subject to a constant force F. Assume that at time t_0 the particle was at x_0 and had velocity v_0.

1.5 What important probability-density function occurs in (a) the kinetic theory of gases? (b) the analysis of random errors of measurement?

1.6 Which of the following functions meet all the requirements of a probability-density function: (a) e^{ix}; (b) xe^{-x^2}; (c) e^{-x^2}?

1.7 If the peak in the mass spectrum of C_2F_6 at mass number 138 is 100 units high, calculate the heights of the peaks at mass numbers 139 and 140. Isotopic abundances: C^{12}—98.89%, C^{13}—1.11%, F^{19}—100%.

1.8 In bridge, each of the four players (A, B, C, D) receives 13 cards. Suppose A and C have 11 of the 13 spades between them. What is the probability that the remaining two spades are distributed so that B and D have one spade apiece?

1.9 When J. J. Thomson investigated electrons in cathode-ray tubes, he observed the behavior expected for particles obeying classical mechanics. (a) Electrons are accelerated through a potential difference of 1000 volts and passed through a collimating slit of width 0.100 cm. Calculate the diffraction angle α in Fig. 1.1. Use (6.121) and $\sin\alpha \approx \alpha$ for small α. (b) What slit width is needed to give $\alpha = 1.00°$ for 1000-volt electrons?

1.10 The density of lead is 11 g/cm³. If lead atoms were cubes, what would be the length of each edge?

1.11 Verify that

$$\sin\theta = \frac{e^{i\theta} - e^{-i\theta}}{2i}, \qquad \cos\theta = \frac{e^{i\theta} + e^{-i\theta}}{2}$$

1.12 Find the cube roots of unity.

1.13 Find the absolute value and the phase of (a) i; (b) $ae^{i\pi/3}$; (c) $1 - 2i$.

CHAPTER
2

The Particle in a Box

2.1 Differential Equations

Since the Schroedinger equation is a differential equation, we will review the mathematics of differential equations. In this section, we consider only *ordinary* differential equations, which are those involving only one independent variable. Our differential equation will involve some sort of relation between an independent variable x, a dependent variable $y(x)$, and the first, second, ..., nth derivatives of y. We have

$$f(x, y, y', y'', ..., y^{(n)}) = 0 \qquad (2.1)$$

where f indicates some functional relation. An example is

$$y^{(iv)} + x(y')^2 + \sin x \cos y = 3e^x \qquad (2.2)$$

The *order* of a differential equation is the order of the highest derivative that occurs. Thus (2.1) is of nth order, while (2.2) is of fourth order.

A special kind of differential equation is the *linear* differential equation, which has the form

$$A_n(x) y^{(n)} + A_{n-1}(x) y^{(n-1)} + \cdots + A_0(x) y = g(x) \qquad (2.3)$$

where the A's are various functions of x. A differential equation that cannot be put in the form (2.3) is *nonlinear*. If $g(x) = 0$ in (2.3), the linear differential equation is said to be *homogeneous*; otherwise it is *inhomogeneous*. The one-dimensional Schroedinger equation (1.16) is a linear homogeneous differential equation of second order.

By dividing by the coefficient of y'', we can put any linear homogeneous second-order differential equation into the form

$$y'' + P(x)\,y' + Q(x)\,y = 0 \qquad (2.4)$$

Suppose we have two independent functions y_1 and y_2, each of which satisfies (2.4). By independent, we mean that y_2 is not simply a multiple of y_1. Then the general solution of (2.4) is

$$y = c_1 y_1 + c_2 y_2 \qquad (2.5)$$

where c_1 and c_2 are arbitrary constants. This is readily verified by substituting (2.5) into (2.4):

$$c_1 y_1'' + c_2 y_2'' + P(x)\,c_1 y_1' + P(x)\,c_2 y_2' + Q(x)\,c_1 y_1 + Q(x)\,c_2 y_2$$
$$= c_1 [y_1'' + P(x)\,y_1' + Q(x)\,y_1] + c_2 [y_2'' + P(x)\,y_2' + Q(x)\,y_2]$$
$$= c_1 \cdot 0 + c_2 \cdot 0 = 0$$

where the fact that y_1 and y_2 satisfy (2.4) has been used.

In general, the general solution of a differential equation of nth order has n arbitrary constants. To fix these constants, we may have *boundary conditions*, which are conditions that specify the value of y or various of its derivatives at a point or points. Thus if y represents the displacement of a vibrating string held fixed at two points, we know y must be zero at these points. We will discuss appropriate boundary conditions for the Schroedinger equation later.

An important case is the linear homogeneous second-order differential equation with *constant coefficients*:

$$y'' + py' + qy = 0 \qquad (2.6)$$

where p and q are constants. To solve (2.6) let us tentatively assume a solution of the form $y = e^{sx}$. (We are looking for a function whose derivatives when multiplied by constants will cancel out the original function. The exponential function repeats itself when differentiated, and is thus the correct choice.) Substitution in (2.6) gives

$$s^2 e^{sx} + pse^{sx} + qe^{sx} = 0$$
$$s^2 + ps + q = 0 \qquad (2.7)$$

Equation (2.7) is called the *auxiliary equation*. It is a quadratic equation with two roots s_1 and s_2 which, provided s_1 and s_2 are not equal, give two independent solutions to (2.6). Thus the general solution of (2.6) is

$$y = c_1 e^{s_1 x} + c_2 e^{s_2 x} \qquad (2.8)$$

2.2 Particle in a One-Dimensional Box

Having obtained the solution of one kind of differential equation, let us look at a case where we can use this solution to solve the Schroedinger equation. We consider a particle in a one-dimensional box. By this we mean a particle subjected to a potential-energy function that is infinite everywhere along the x axis except for a line segment of length l, where the potential energy is zero. Such a system may seem physically unreal, but we shall later see that this model can be applied with some success to certain conjugated molecules; see Section 15.8. We put the origin at the left end of the line segment (Fig. 2.1).

We have three regions to consider. For regions I and III, the potential energy V equals infinity; the Schroedinger equation (1.16) for these regions is:

$$\frac{d^2\psi}{dx^2} + \frac{2m}{\hbar^2}(E - \infty)\psi = 0$$

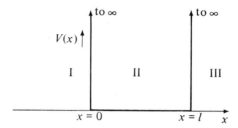

FIGURE 2.1   Potential energy for the particle in a one-dimensional box.

Neglecting E in comparison with ∞, we have

$$\frac{d^2\psi}{dx^2} = \infty\psi, \qquad \psi = \frac{1}{\infty}\frac{d^2\psi}{dx^2}$$

and we conclude that ψ is zero outside the box:

$$\psi_\mathrm{I} = 0, \qquad \psi_\mathrm{III} = 0 \tag{2.9}$$

For region II, x between zero and l, the potential energy V is zero, and the Schroedinger equation (1.16) becomes

$$\frac{d^2\psi_\mathrm{II}}{dx^2} + \frac{2m}{\hbar^2}E\psi_\mathrm{II} = 0 \tag{2.10}$$

where m is the mass of the particle and E is its total energy. We recognize (2.10) as a linear homogeneous second-order differential equation with constant coefficients. The auxiliary equation (2.7) gives

$$s^2 + 2mE\hbar^{-2} = 0$$

$$s = \pm(-2mE)^{1/2}\hbar^{-1} \tag{2.11}$$

The energy E is equal to the potential energy, which is zero, plus the kinetic energy, which is positive, so E is positive, and it is convenient to rewrite (2.11) as

$$s = \pm i(2mE)^{1/2}/\hbar \tag{2.12}$$

Using (2.8), we have

$$\psi_\mathrm{II} = c_1 e^{i(2mE)^{1/2}x/\hbar} + c_2 e^{-i(2mE)^{1/2}x/\hbar} \tag{2.13}$$

Temporarily, let

$$\theta = (2mE)^{1/2}x/\hbar \qquad (2.14)$$

$$\psi_{\mathrm{II}} = c_1 e^{i\theta} + c_2 e^{-i\theta} \qquad (2.15)$$

Using (1.22), we have

$$\psi_{\mathrm{II}} = c_1 \cos\theta + ic_1 \sin\theta + c_2 \cos\theta - ic_2 \sin\theta$$

$$= (c_1 + c_2) \cos\theta + (ic_1 - ic_2) \sin\theta$$

$$= A \cos\theta + B \sin\theta$$

where A and B are new arbitrary constants. Hence

$$\psi_{\mathrm{II}} = A \cos[\hbar^{-1}(2mE)^{1/2}x] + B \sin[\hbar^{-1}(2mE)^{1/2}x] \qquad (2.16)$$

Now we determine A and B by applying boundary conditions. It seems reasonable to postulate that the wave function will be continuous, i.e., it will make no sudden jumps in value. If ψ is to be continuous at the point $x = 0$, then ψ_{I} and ψ_{II} must approach the same value at $x = 0$:

$$\lim_{x \to 0} \psi_{\mathrm{I}} = \lim_{x \to 0} \psi_{\mathrm{II}}$$

$$0 = \lim_{x \to 0} \{A \cos[\hbar^{-1}(2mE)^{1/2}x] + B \sin[\hbar^{-1}(2mE)^{1/2}x]\}$$

$$0 = A$$

We have evaluated one arbitrary constant, and we now have

$$\psi_{\mathrm{II}} = B \sin[(2\pi/h)(2mE)^{1/2}x] \qquad (2.17)$$

Applying the continuity condition at $x = l$, we get

$$B \sin[(2\pi/h)(2mE)^{1/2}l] = 0 \qquad (2.18)$$

B cannot be zero, because this would make the wave function zero everywhere—we would have an empty box. Therefore

$$\sin[(2\pi/h)(2mE)^{1/2}l] = 0$$

The zeros of the sine function occur at $0, \pm\pi, \pm2\pi, \pm3\pi, \dots$. Hence

$$(2\pi/h)(2mE)^{1/2}l = \pm n\pi \qquad (2.19)$$

We must, however, reject the value zero for n because it gives

$$(2\pi/h)(2mE)^{1/2} = 0$$

which, from Eq. (2.17), would make the wave function zero. Therefore

$$(4\pi^2/h^2)(2mE)l^2 = n^2\pi^2$$

$$E = n^2 \frac{h^2}{8ml^2}, \qquad n = 1, 2, 3, \dots \qquad (2.20)$$

Only the energy values (2.20) allow ψ to satisfy the boundary condition of continuity at $x = l$. Application of a boundary condition has forced us to the conclusion that the values of the energy are quantized; this is in striking contrast to the classical result that the particle in the box can have any nonnegative energy. Note also that there is a minimum value, greater than zero, for the energy of the particle. Substitution of (2.19) into (2.17) gives for the wave function

$$\psi_{\mathrm{II}} = B \sin\left(\frac{n\pi x}{l}\right), \qquad n = 1, 2, 3, \ldots \tag{2.21}$$

[The use of the negative sign in front of $n\pi$ does not give us another independent solution. Since $\sin(-\theta) = -\sin\theta$ we would simply get a constant, -1, times the solution with the plus sign.]

The constant B in Eq. (2.21) is still arbitrary. To fix its value, we use the normalization requirement, Eq. (1.20):

$$\int_{-\infty}^{\infty} |\Psi|^2 \, dx = \int_{-\infty}^{\infty} |\psi|^2 \, dx = 1$$

$$\int_{-\infty}^{0} |\psi_{\mathrm{I}}|^2 \, dx + \int_{0}^{l} |\psi_{\mathrm{II}}|^2 \, dx + \int_{l}^{\infty} |\psi_{\mathrm{III}}|^2 \, dx = 1$$

$$|B|^2 \int_{0}^{l} \sin^2\left(\frac{n\pi x}{l}\right) dx = 1 = |B|^2 \frac{l}{2}$$

where the integral was evaluated by using

$$2 \sin^2 t = 1 - \cos 2t \tag{2.22}$$

We obtain

$$|B| = \left(\frac{2}{l}\right)^{1/2}$$

Note that we have determined only the absolute value of B. B could be $-\sqrt{2/l}$ as well as $+\sqrt{2/l}$. Moreover, B need not be a real number—we could use any complex number with absolute value $\sqrt{2/l}$, i.e., all we can say is that $B = (2/l)^{1/2} e^{i\alpha}$ where α is the phase of B. (See Section 1.6.) Choosing the phase to be zero, we finally write

$$\psi_{\mathrm{II}} = \left(\frac{2}{l}\right)^{1/2} \sin\left(\frac{n\pi x}{l}\right), \qquad n = 1, 2, 3, \ldots \tag{2.23}$$

Graphs of the wave functions and the probability densities are shown in Figs. 2.2 and 2.3.

Note that there are points (called *nodes*) where the wave function is zero. For each increase of one in the value of n (n is called a *quantum number*) we find one more node. The existence of nodes in ψ and $|\psi|^2$ may seem surprising. Thus for $n = 2$, Fig. 2.3 says that there is zero probability of finding the particle in the center of the box at $x = l/2$. How can the particle get from one side of the box to the other without at any time being found in the center? This apparent paradox arises from

FIGURE 2.2   *Graphs of ψ for the three lowest energy particle-in-a-box states.*

attempting to understand the motion of microscopic particles using our everyday experience of the motions of macroscopic particles. However, as stated in Chapter 1, electrons and other microscopic "particles" cannot be fully and correctly described in terms of concepts of classical physics drawn from the macroscopic world.

Figure 2.3 shows that the probability of finding the particle at various places in the box is quite different from the classical result. Classically, a particle of fixed energy in a box bounces back and forth elastically between the two walls, moving at constant speed. Thus it is equally likely to be found at any point in the box. Quantum mechanically, we find a maximum in probability at the center of the box for the lowest energy level. As we go to higher energy levels with more nodes, the maxima and minima of probability come closer together, and the variations in probability along the length of the box ultimately become undetectable. For high quantum numbers we approach the classical result of uniform probability density. This result, that in the limit of large quantum numbers quantum mechanics goes over into classical mechanics, is known as the *Bohr correspondence principle*. Since Newtonian mechanics is valid for macroscopic bodies (moving at speeds much less than the speed of light), we expect nonrelativistic quantum mechanics to give the same answer as classical mechanics for macroscopic bodies. Because of the extremely small magnitude of Planck's constant, quantization of energy is unobservable for macroscopic bodies. Since the mass of the particle and the length of the box squared appear in the denominator of Eq. (2.20), a macroscopic object in a macroscopic box having a macroscopic energy of motion would have a huge value for n, and hence, according to the correspondence principle, would show classical behavior.

We have a whole set of wave functions, each one corresponding to a different value of the energy and characterized by the quantum number n, which may have integral values from one up. Let the subscript i denote a particular wave function

FIGURE 2.3   *Graphs of ψ² for the lowest particle-in-a-box states.*

with the value n_i for its quantum number:

$$\psi_i = \left(\frac{2}{l}\right)^{1/2} \sin\left(\frac{n_i \pi x}{l}\right), \qquad 0 < x < l$$

$$\psi_i = 0 \qquad\qquad\qquad \text{elsewhere}$$

Since the wave function has been normalized, we have

$$\int_{-\infty}^{\infty} \psi_i^* \psi_j \, dx = 1 \qquad \text{if } i = j \tag{2.24}$$

We now ask for the value of this integral when we use wave functions corresponding to *different* energy levels, i.e.:

$$\int_{-\infty}^{\infty} \psi_i^* \psi_j \, dx = \int_0^l \left(\frac{2}{l}\right)^{1/2} \sin\left(\frac{n_i \pi x}{l}\right) \left(\frac{2}{l}\right)^{1/2} \sin\left(\frac{n_j \pi x}{l}\right) dx, \qquad n_i \neq n_j$$

Let $t = \pi x / l$.

$$\int_{-\infty}^{\infty} \psi_i^* \psi_j \, dx = \frac{2}{l} \int_0^\pi \sin n_i t \sin n_j t \, dt \cdot \frac{l}{\pi}$$

The integral may be evaluated with the identity

$$\sin n_i t \sin n_j t = \tfrac{1}{2} \cos(n_i - n_j)t - \tfrac{1}{2} \cos(n_i + n_j)t \tag{2.25}$$

Hence

$$\int_{-\infty}^{\infty} \psi_i^* \psi_j \, dx = \frac{2}{\pi} \int_0^\pi \tfrac{1}{2} \cos(n_i - n_j)t \, dt - \frac{2}{\pi} \int_0^\pi \tfrac{1}{2} \cos(n_i + n_j)t \, dt = 0$$

since $\sin m\pi = 0$ for m an integer. We thus have

$$\int_{-\infty}^{\infty} \psi_i^* \psi_j \, dx = 0, \qquad i \neq j \tag{2.26}$$

We say that ψ_i and ψ_j are *orthogonal* to each other for $i \neq j$. We can combine (2.24) and (2.26) by writing

$$\int_{-\infty}^{\infty} \psi_i^* \psi_j \, dx = \delta_{ij} \tag{2.27}$$

The symbol δ_{ij} is called the Kronecker delta (after a mathematician); it equals one whenever the two indices i and j are equal, and equals zero when i and j are unequal:

$$\delta_{ij} = \begin{cases} 0 & \text{for } i \neq j \\ 1 & \text{for } i = j \end{cases} \tag{2.28}$$

The property of the wave functions illustrated in (2.27) is called *orthonormality*. We proved orthonormality only for the particle-in-a-box wave functions; we shall later prove it more generally.

A more rigorous way to look at the particle in a box with infinite walls is to first treat the particle in a box with a finite jump in potential energy at the walls, and then take the limit as the jump in potential energy becomes infinite. The results, when the limit is taken, will be the same as we have obtained.

Another related problem is a particle in a one-dimensional box with walls of finite height *and* finite thickness. A plot of the potential energy looks like Fig. 2.4. Classically, a particle in the box of Fig. 2.4 would not be able to escape from the box unless it had an energy greater than the height of the potential-energy barrier V_0. However, the quantum-mechanical solution[1] (which we omit) shows that there is a finite probability for a particle of total energy less than V_0 to be found outside the box. This phenomenon is called *tunneling*. The escape of alpha particles from a radioactive nucleus involves tunneling.

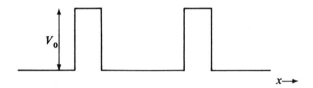

FIGURE 2.4 *Potential energy for a particle in a box of finite height and thickness.*

2.3 The Free Particle in One Dimension

By a free particle, we mean a particle subject to no forces whatever. For a free particle, the potential energy remains constant no matter what the value of x is. Since the choice of the zero level of energy is arbitrary, we may set $V(x) = 0$. The Schroedinger equation (1.16) becomes

$$\frac{d^2\psi}{dx^2} + \frac{2m}{\hbar^2} E\psi = 0 \qquad (2.29)$$

Equation (2.29) is the same as Eq. (2.10) (except for the boundary conditions); therefore the general solution of (2.29) is (2.13):

$$\psi = c_1 e^{i(2mE)^{1/2}x/\hbar} + c_2 e^{-i(2mE)^{1/2}x/\hbar} \qquad (2.30)$$

What boundary condition might we impose? It seems reasonable to postulate (since $\psi^*\psi \, dx$ represents a probability) that ψ will remain finite as x goes to $\pm\infty$. If the energy E is less than zero, then this boundary condition will be violated, since for $E < 0$ we have

$$i(2mE)^{1/2} = i(-2m|E|)^{1/2} = i \cdot i \cdot (2m|E|)^{1/2} = -(2m|E|)^{1/2}$$

and therefore the first term in (2.30) will become infinite as x approaches minus infinity. Similarly, if E is negative, the second term in (2.30) becomes infinite as x approaches plus infinity. Thus the boundary condition requires

$$E \geqslant 0 \qquad (2.31)$$

---

[1] *Kauzmann*, p. 195.

for the free particle. The wave function is oscillatory and is a linear combination of a sine and a cosine term [Eq. (2.16)]. For the free particle, we do not get quantization of the energy; all nonnegative energies are allowed. Since we set $V = 0$, the energy E is in this case all kinetic energy. If we attempt to evaluate the arbitrary constants c_1 and c_2 by normalization, we will find that the integral $\int_{-\infty}^{\infty} \psi^*(x)\psi(x)\, dx$ is divergent. In other words, the free-particle wave function is not normalizable in the usual sense. This is to be expected on physical grounds since there is no reason for the probability of finding the free particle to approach zero as x goes to $\pm\infty$.

The free-particle problem represents an unreal situation, since we could not actually have a particle that had no interaction with any other particle in the universe.

PROBLEMS

2.1 Solve $y''(x) + y'(x) - 2y(x) = 0$.

2.2 (a) For the case of equal roots of the auxiliary equation, $s_1 = s_2 = s$, we have found only one independent solution of the linear homogeneous second-order differential equation: e^{sx}. Verify that xe^{sx} is the second solution in this case. (b) Solve $y''(x) - 2y'(x) + y(x) = 0$.

2.3 Consider a macroscopic object of mass 1.0 g moving with speed 1.0 cm/sec in a one-dimensional box of length 1.0 cm; find the quantum number n.

2.4 Consider a particle with quantum number n moving in a one-dimensional box of length l. (a) Find the probability of finding the particle in the left quarter of the box. (b) For what value of n is this probability a maximum? (c) What is the limit of this probability for $n \to \infty$? (d) What principle is illustrated in (c)?

2.5 An extremely crude picture of an electron in an atom or molecule treats it as a particle in a one-dimensional box whose length is of the order of the size of atoms and molecules. (a) For an electron in a box of length 1.0 Å, calculate, in ergs and in eV, the separation between the two lowest energy levels. (b) Calculate the wavelength of a photon corresponding to a transition between these two levels. (c) In what portion of the electromagnetic spectrum is this wavelength?

2.6 Write down the time-dependent wave function for a free particle with energy E.

2.7 For the particle in a one-dimensional box of length l, we could have put the coordinate origin at the center of the box. Find the wave functions and energy levels for this choice of origin.

2.8 Sketch rough graphs of ψ and of ψ^2 for the $n = 4$ and $n = 5$ particle-in-a-box states.

2.9 Integrals involving trigonometric functions can often be evaluated using the identities of Problem 1.11. Use the complex-exponential form of the sine function to verify Eq. (2.27) for the particle-in-a-box wave functions.

CHAPTER

3

Operators

3.1 Operators

We now develop the theory of quantum mechanics in a more general fashion than previously. We begin by writing the one-particle, one-dimensional time-independent Schroedinger equation (1.16) in the form

$$\left[-\frac{\hbar^2}{2m}\frac{d^2}{dx^2} + V(x)\right]\psi(x) = E\psi(x) \tag{3.1}$$

The entity in brackets in (3.1) is an *operator*. Equation (3.1) suggests that we have an energy operator, which, operating on the wave function, gives us the wave function back again, but multiplied by the allowed values of the energy. We therefore discuss operators.

An *operator* is simply a rule whereby given some function we can find another, corresponding function. For example, let $\hat{D}$ be the operator that differentiates a function with respect to x. (We use a circumflex to indicate an operator.) Provided $f(x)$ is differentiable, we have as the result of operating on $f(x)$ with $\hat{D}$: $\hat{D}f(x) = f'(x)$. For example, $\hat{D}(x^2 + 3e^x) = 2x + 3e^x$. If $\hat{3}$ is the operator that multiplies a function by 3, then $\hat{3}(x^2 + 3e^x) = 3x^2 + 9e^x$. If SQRT is the operator that takes the square root of a function, then $\text{SQRT}(x^2 + 3e^x) = (x^2 + 3e^x)^{1/2}$.

We define the *sum* of two operators $\hat{A}$ and $\hat{B}$ by the equation

$$(\hat{A} + \hat{B})f(x) \equiv \hat{A}f(x) + \hat{B}f(x) \tag{3.2}$$

For example

$$(\hat{D} + \hat{3})(x^2 + 3e^x) = (2x + 3e^x) + (3x^2 + 9e^x) = 2x + 3x^2 + 12e^x$$

We define the *product* of two operators $\hat{A}$ and $\hat{B}$ by the equation

$$\hat{A}\hat{B}f(x) \equiv \hat{A}[\hat{B}f(x)] \tag{3.3}$$

In other words, we first operate on $f(x)$ with the operator on the right of the operator product, and then we take the resulting function and operate on it with the operator on the left of the operator product. For example,

$$\hat{3}\hat{D}f(x) = \hat{3}[\hat{D}f(x)] = \hat{3}f'(x) = 3f'(x) \tag{3.4}$$

For this example it would have made no difference in the final result whether we first applied one operator or the other. In general, we cannot assume that $\hat{A}\hat{B}$ and $\hat{B}\hat{A}$ have the same effect. Consider, for example, the operators d/dx and $\hat{x}$:

$$\hat{D}\hat{x}f(x) = \frac{d}{dx}[xf(x)] = f(x) + xf'(x) = (\hat{1}+\hat{x}\hat{D})f(x) \tag{3.5}$$

$$\hat{x}\hat{D}f(x) = \hat{x}\left[\frac{d}{dx}f(x)\right] = xf'(x)$$

Thus $\hat{A}\hat{B}$ and $\hat{B}\hat{A}$ are different operators in this case.

We can develop an *operator algebra* as follows. If $\hat{A}$ and $\hat{B}$ are two operators such that $\hat{A}f = \hat{B}f$ for all functions f, we say that $\hat{A}$ and $\hat{B}$ are equal: $\hat{A} = \hat{B}$. For example, (3.5) shows that

$$\hat{D}\hat{x} = \hat{1} + \hat{x}\hat{D} \tag{3.6}$$

The operator $\hat{1}$ (multiplication by one) is the *unit operator*. The operator $\hat{0}$ (multiplication by zero) is the *null operator*. We usually omit the circumflex over operators that are simply multiplication by a constant. We can transfer operators from one side of an operator equation to the other (Problem 3.28); thus (3.6) is equivalent to

$$\hat{D}\hat{x} - \hat{x}\hat{D} - 1 = 0$$

where we have omitted circumflexes over the null and unit operators.

Operators obey the associative law of multiplication:

$$\hat{A}(\hat{B}\hat{C}) = (\hat{A}\hat{B})\hat{C} \tag{3.7}$$

The proof of (3.7) is outlined in Problem 3.2. As an example, let $\hat{A} = d/dx$, $\hat{B} = \hat{x}$, $\hat{C} = \hat{3}$. We have, using (3.6):

$$(\hat{A}\hat{B}) = \hat{D}\hat{x} = 1 + \hat{x}\hat{D}, \qquad [(\hat{A}\hat{B})\hat{C}]f = (1+\hat{x}\hat{D})3f = 3f + 3xf'$$

$$(\hat{B}\hat{C}) = 3\hat{x}, \qquad [\hat{A}(\hat{B}\hat{C})]f = \hat{D}(3xf) = 3f + 3xf'$$

The major difference between operator algebra and ordinary algebra is that numbers obey the commutative law of multiplication, but operators do not necessarily do so; $ab = ba$ if a and b are numbers, but $\hat{A}\hat{B}$ and $\hat{B}\hat{A}$ are not necessarily equal operators. We define the *commutator* $[\hat{A}, \hat{B}]$ of the operators $\hat{A}$ and $\hat{B}$ as the operator $\hat{A}\hat{B} - \hat{B}\hat{A}$:

$$[\hat{A}, \hat{B}] \equiv \hat{A}\hat{B} - \hat{B}\hat{A} \tag{3.8}$$

If $\hat{A}\hat{B} = \hat{B}\hat{A}$ we say that $\hat{A}$ and $\hat{B}$ *commute*. Since it makes no difference in what order we apply the operators $\hat{3}$ and d/dx, we have

$$\left[\hat{3}, \frac{d}{dx}\right] = \hat{3}\frac{d}{dx} - \frac{d}{dx}\hat{3} = 0$$

From Eq. (3.6) we have

$$\left[\frac{d}{dx}, \hat{x}\right] = \hat{D}\hat{x} - \hat{x}\hat{D} = 1 \tag{3.9}$$

The *square* of an operator is defined as the product of the operator with itself: $\hat{A}^2 = \hat{A}\hat{A}$. Let us find the square of the differentiation operator:

$$\hat{D}^2 f(x) = \hat{D}(\hat{D}f) = \hat{D}f' = f''$$

$$\hat{D}^2 = \frac{d^2}{dx^2} \tag{3.10}$$

As another example, the square of the operator that takes the complex conjugate of a function is equal to the unit operator, since taking the complex conjugate twice gives the original function. The nth power of an operator $(n = 1, 2, 3, ...)$ is defined to mean applying the operator n times in succession.

It turns out that the operators occurring in quantum mechanics are linear. $\hat{A}$ is a *linear operator* if and only if it has the following two properties:

$$\hat{A}[f(x)+g(x)] = \hat{A}f(x) + \hat{A}g(x) \tag{3.11}$$

$$\hat{A}[cf(x)] = c\hat{A}f(x) \tag{3.12}$$

where f and g are arbitrary functions, and c is an arbitrary constant. Examples of linear operators are: $\hat{x}^2$, d/dx, and d^2/dx^2; the square-root operator SQRT is nonlinear.

Equation (2.3) defines the form of a linear differential equation. Using the differentiation operator $\hat{D}$, we can rewrite (2.3) as:

$$[A_n(x)\hat{D}^n + A_{n-1}(x)\hat{D}^{n-1} + \cdots + A_0(x)] y(x) = g(x) \tag{3.13}$$

The operator in brackets in (3.13) is linear.

Useful identities in linear-operator manipulations are

$$(\hat{A}+\hat{B})\hat{C} = \hat{A}\hat{C} + \hat{B}\hat{C} \tag{3.14}$$

$$\hat{A}(\hat{B}+\hat{C}) = \hat{A}\hat{B} + \hat{A}\hat{C} \tag{3.15}$$

The proof of the distributive law (3.14) follows from the definition of the product and sum of operators; we have

$$[(\hat{A}+\hat{B})\hat{C}] f(x) = (\hat{A}+\hat{B})(\hat{C}f) = \hat{A}(\hat{C}f) + \hat{B}(\hat{C}f)$$

$$= \hat{A}\hat{C}f + \hat{B}\hat{C}f = (\hat{A}\hat{C}+\hat{B}\hat{C})f$$

To gain facility in operator manipulations, we will work out the square of $d/dx + \hat{x}$. We have

$$(\hat{D}+\hat{x})^2 f(x) = (\hat{D}+\hat{x})[(\hat{D}+\hat{x})f] = (\hat{D}+\hat{x})(f'+xf)$$
$$= f'' + f + xf' + xf' + x^2 f = (\hat{D}^2 + 2\hat{x}\hat{D} + \hat{x}^2 + 1) f(x)$$
$$(\hat{D}+\hat{x})^2 = \hat{D}^2 + 2\hat{x}\hat{D} + \hat{x}^2 + 1$$

Let us repeat this calculation, using only operator equations:

$$(\hat{D}+\hat{x})^2 = (\hat{D}+\hat{x})(\hat{D}+\hat{x}) = \hat{D}(\hat{D}+\hat{x}) + \hat{x}(\hat{D}+\hat{x})$$
$$= \hat{D}^2 + \hat{D}\hat{x} + \hat{x}\hat{D} + \hat{x}^2 = \hat{D}^2 + \hat{x}\hat{D} + 1 + \hat{x}\hat{D} + \hat{x}^2$$
$$= \hat{D}^2 + 2x\hat{D} + x^2 + 1$$

where (3.14), (3.15), and (3.6) have been used, and the circumflex over the operator "multiplication by x" has been omitted.

Although we have considered only operators and functions in one dimension, x, we can readily extend all we have said to operators and functions in several dimensions.

3.2 Eigenfunctions and Eigenvalues

Suppose that the effect of operating on some function $f(x)$ with the operator $\hat{A}$ is simply to multiply $f(x)$ by a certain constant k. We then say that $f(x)$ is an *eigenfunction* of $\hat{A}$, with *eigenvalue* k. We have[1]

$$\hat{A}f(x) = kf(x) \tag{3.16}$$

(*Eigen* is a German word meaning *characteristic*. "Eigenvalue" is a hybrid word; it has been suggested that "characteristicwert" would be just as suitable.) As an example of (3.16), e^{2x} is an eigenfunction of the operator d/dx with eigenvalue 2:

$$(d/dx)e^{2x} = 2e^{2x}$$

Let us find all the eigenfunctions and eigenvalues of d/dx. Equation (3.16) becomes:

$$\frac{df(x)}{dx} = kf(x) \tag{3.17}$$

$$df/f = k\,dx \tag{3.18}$$

$$\ln f = kx + \text{constant}$$

$$f = e^{\text{constant}}e^{kx}$$

$$f = ce^{kx} \tag{3.19}$$

---

[1] As part of the definition, we shall require that $f(x)$ is not identically zero. By this we mean that although $f(x)$ may vanish at various points, it is not everywhere zero.

The eigenfunctions of d/dx are given by (3.19). The eigenvalues are k, which can be any number whatever and (3.17) will still be satisfied. The eigenfunctions contain an arbitrary multiplicative constant c. This is true for the eigenfunctions of any linear operator, as is easily shown: Using (3.12) and (3.16), we have

$$\hat{A}(cf) = c\hat{A}f = ckf = k(cf) \tag{3.20}$$

Thus if $f(x)$ is an eigenfunction of $\hat{A}$ with eigenvalue k, so is $cf(x)$. With each different value of k in (3.19), we get a different eigenfunction; eigenfunctions with the same value of k, but different values of c, are not independent of each other. One final point: Suppose we impose the boundary condition that the solutions of (3.17) remain finite as x goes to plus or minus infinity. Since k can be complex, we write it as: $k = a + ib$, where a and b are real numbers. We then have $f(x) = ce^{ax}e^{ibx}$. The factor e^{ax} goes to infinity as x goes to infinity if a is positive; it goes to infinity as x goes to minus infinity if a is negative. Hence the boundary conditions require that $a = 0$, and we have pure imaginary eigenvalues, $k = ib$.

3.3 Operators and Quantum Mechanics

We now consider the relationship between operators and quantum mechanics. Comparing Eq. (3.1) with (3.16), we see that the Schroedinger equation is an eigenvalue problem. The values of the energy E are the eigenvalues; the eigenfunctions are the wave functions ψ; the operator whose eigenfunctions and eigenvalues are desired is $-(\hbar^2/2m)\,d^2/dx^2 + V(x)$. This operator is called the *Hamiltonian operator* for the system.

Sir William Rowan Hamilton (1805–1865) devised an alternative form of Newton's equations of motion involving a function H, the Hamiltonian function for the system. For a system where the potential energy is a function of the coordinates only, the total energy remains constant with time, i.e., E is conserved. We shall restrict ourselves to such conservative systems. For conservative systems, the classical-mechanical Hamiltonian function turns out to be simply the total energy expressed in terms of coordinates and conjugate momenta. For Cartesian coordinates x, y, z, the conjugate momenta are the components of linear momentum in the x, y, and z directions: p_x, p_y, and p_z.

Let us consider what the classical-mechanical Hamiltonian function is for a particle of mass m moving in one dimension, and subject to a potential energy $V(x)$. The Hamiltonian function is equal to the energy, which is composed of kinetic and potential energies. The familiar form of the kinetic energy, $\frac{1}{2}mv_x^2$, will not do, however, since we must express the Hamiltonian as a function of coordinates and momenta, not velocities. Since $v_x = p_x/m$, the form of the kinetic energy we want is $p_x^2/2m$. The Hamiltonian function is:

$$H = \frac{p_x^2}{2m} + V(x) \tag{3.21}$$

The time-independent Schroedinger equation (3.1) indicates that corresponding to the Hamiltonian function (3.21) we have a quantum-mechanical operator

$$-\frac{\hbar^2}{2m}\frac{d^2}{dx^2} + V(x) \tag{3.22}$$

whose eigenvalues are the possible values of the system's energy. This correspondence between physical quantities in classical mechanics and operators in quantum mechanics is general. It is a fundamental postulate of quantum mechanics that to every physical property (e.g., the energy, the x coordinate, the momentum) there corresponds a quantum-mechanical operator. We further postulate that the operator corresponding to the property F is obtained by writing down the classical-mechanical expression for F as a function of Cartesian coordinates and corresponding momenta, and then making the following replacements. Each Cartesian coordinate q is replaced by the operator multiplication by that coordinate:

$$\hat{q} = q \cdot \tag{3.23}$$

Each Cartesian component of linear momentum p_q is replaced by the operator

$$\hat{p}_q = \frac{\hbar}{i}\frac{\partial}{\partial q} = -i\hbar\frac{\partial}{\partial q} \tag{3.24}$$

In (3.24), $i = \sqrt{-1}$, and $\partial/\partial q$ is the operator for the partial derivative with respect to the coordinate q.

Consider some examples. The operator corresponding to the x coordinate is multiplication by x:

$$\hat{x} = x \cdot \tag{3.25}$$

Also

$$\hat{y} = y \cdot \tag{3.26}$$

$$\hat{z} = z \cdot \tag{3.27}$$

The operators for the components of linear momentum are:

$$\hat{p}_x = \frac{\hbar}{i}\frac{\partial}{\partial x}, \qquad \hat{p}_y = \frac{\hbar}{i}\frac{\partial}{\partial y}, \qquad \hat{p}_z = \frac{\hbar}{i}\frac{\partial}{\partial z} \tag{3.28}$$

For the operator corresponding to p_x^2, we have

$$\hat{p}_x^2 = \left(\frac{\hbar}{i}\frac{\partial}{\partial x}\right)^2 = \frac{\hbar}{i}\frac{\partial}{\partial x}\frac{\hbar}{i}\frac{\partial}{\partial x} = -\hbar^2\frac{\partial^2}{\partial x^2} \tag{3.29}$$

with similar expressions for $\hat{p}_y^2$ and $\hat{p}_z^2$.

Now consider the potential-energy and kinetic-energy operators in one dimension. Suppose we had a system with the potential-energy function $V(x) = ax^2$, where a is a constant. Replacing x with $x\cdot$, we see that the potential-energy operator is simply multiplication by ax^2:

$$\hat{V}(x) = ax^2 \cdot \tag{3.30}$$

In general, we have for any potential-energy function:

$$\hat{V}(x) = V(x) \cdot \tag{3.31}$$

The classical-mechanical expression for the kinetic energy T is

$$T = p_x^2/2m \tag{3.32}$$

Replacing p_x by the corresponding operator, we have

$$\hat{T} = -\frac{\hbar^2}{2m}\frac{\partial^2}{\partial x^2} = -\frac{\hbar^2}{2m}\frac{d^2}{dx^2} \tag{3.33}$$

where (3.29) has been used, and the partial derivative becomes an ordinary derivative in one dimension. The classical-mechanical Hamiltonian (3.21) is

$$H = T + V \tag{3.34}$$

The corresponding quantum-mechanical Hamiltonian (or energy) operator is

$$\hat{H} = \hat{T} + \hat{V} = -\frac{\hbar^2}{2m}\frac{d^2}{dx^2} + V(x) \tag{3.35}$$

which agrees with (3.22). Note that all these operators are linear.

How are the quantum-mechanical operators related to the corresponding properties of a system? Each such operator has its own set of eigenfunctions and eigenvalues. If φ_i is an eigenfunction of $\hat{F}$ with eigenvalue a_i, we have [Eq. (3.16)]

$$\hat{F}\varphi_i = a_i \varphi_i \tag{3.36}$$

(The subscript indicates that we have a whole set of possible eigenfunctions and eigenvalues: $i = 1, 2, 3, \ldots$.) The operator $\hat{F}$ is usually a differential operator and (3.36) is a differential equation whose solutions give the eigenfunctions and eigenvalues. It is postulated that the eigenvalues a_i are the only values of the property F that the system can have; i.e., *a measurement of property F will necessarily yield one of the values* a_i. For example, the only values possible for the energy of a system are the eigenvalues of the energy (i.e., Hamiltonian) operator $\hat{H}$. Using ψ for the eigenfunctions of $\hat{H}$, we have for the eigenvalue equation (3.36):

$$\hat{H}\psi_i = E_i \psi_i \tag{3.37}$$

Using the Hamiltonian (3.35), we obtain for a one-dimensional, one-particle system:

$$\left[-\frac{\hbar^2}{2m}\frac{d^2}{dx^2} + V(x) \right]\psi_i = E_i\psi_i \tag{3.38}$$

which is the time-independent Schroedinger equation, (3.1). Thus our postulates about operators are consistent with our previous work. We will later provide further justification of the choice (3.24) for the momentum operator, by showing that in the limiting transition to classical mechanics this choice yields $p_x = m(dx/dt)$, as it should. (See Problem 7.19.)

In Chapter 1 we postulated that the state of a quantum-mechanical system is specified by a state function $\Psi(x, t)$, which contains all the information we can know about the system. How does Ψ give us information about the property F? We postulate that *if Ψ is an eigenfunction of $\hat{F}$ with eigenvalue a_i, then a measurement of F is certain to yield the value a_i.* Consider, for example, the energy. The eigenfunctions of the energy operator are the solutions $\psi(x)$ of the time-independent Schroedinger equation (3.38). Suppose the system is in a stationary state with state function [Eq. (1.17)]

$$\Psi(x,t) = e^{-iEt/\hbar}\psi(x) \tag{3.39}$$

Is $\Psi(x,t)$ an eigenfunction of the energy operator $\hat{H}$? We have

$$\hat{H}\Psi(x,t) = \hat{H}e^{-iEt/\hbar}\psi(x) \tag{3.40}$$

$\hat{H}$ contains no derivatives with respect to time, and therefore does not affect the exponential factor in (3.40). We have

$$\hat{H}\Psi(x,t) = e^{-iEt/\hbar}\hat{H}\psi(x) = Ee^{-iEt/\hbar}\psi(x) = E\Psi(x,t)$$

$$\hat{H}\Psi = E\Psi \tag{3.41}$$

where (3.37) was used. Hence, for a stationary state, $\Psi(x,t)$ is an eigenfunction of $\hat{H}$, and we are certain to obtain the value E when we measure the energy.

As an example of another property, consider momentum. The eigenfunctions φ of $\hat{p}_x$ are found by solving

$$\hat{p}_x\varphi = k\varphi$$

$$\frac{\hbar}{i}\frac{d\varphi}{dx} = k\varphi \tag{3.42}$$

We find (Problem 3.25):

$$\varphi = Ae^{ikx/\hbar} \tag{3.43}$$

where A is an arbitrary constant. To keep φ finite for large $|x|$, the eigenvalues k must be real. Thus the eigenvalues of $\hat{p}_x$ are all the real numbers

$$-\infty < k < \infty \tag{3.44}$$

which is reasonable. It might seem surprising that the operator for the physical property momentum involves the imaginary number i. Actually, the presence of i in $\hat{p}_x$ insures that the eigenvalues k are real; recall that the eigenvalues of d/dx are imaginary (Section 3.2).

Now consider the momentum of a particle in a box. The state function for a particle in a stationary state in a one-dimensional box is [Eqs. (3.39), (2.20), and (2.23)]:

$$\Psi(x,t) = e^{-iEt/\hbar}\left(\frac{2}{l}\right)^{1/2}\sin\left(\frac{n\pi x}{l}\right) \tag{3.45}$$

$$E = n^2h^2/8ml^2 \tag{3.46}$$

Do we have a definite value of p_x, i.e., is $\Psi(x,t)$ an eigenfunction of $\hat{p}_x$? Looking at the eigenfunctions of $\hat{p}_x$, we see that there is no numerical value of the real constant k that will make the exponential function in (3.43) become a sine function, as in (3.45). Hence Ψ is not an eigenfunction of $\hat{p}_x$. We can verify this directly; we have

$$\hat{p}_x \Psi = \frac{\hbar}{i} \frac{\partial}{\partial x} e^{-iEt/\hbar} \left(\frac{2}{l}\right)^{1/2} \sin\left(\frac{n\pi x}{l}\right) = \frac{n\pi\hbar}{il} e^{-iEt/\hbar} \left(\frac{2}{l}\right)^{1/2} \cos\left(\frac{n\pi x}{l}\right)$$

Since $\hat{p}_x \Psi \neq \text{constant} \cdot \Psi$, the state function Ψ is not an eigenfunction of $\hat{p}_x$. How about p_x^2? We have [Eq. (3.29)]:

$$\hat{p}_x^2 \Psi = -\hbar^2 \frac{\partial^2}{\partial x^2} e^{-iEt/\hbar} \left(\frac{2}{l}\right)^{1/2} \sin\left(\frac{n\pi x}{l}\right) = \frac{n^2\pi^2\hbar^2}{l^2} e^{-iEt/\hbar} \left(\frac{2}{l}\right)^{1/2} \sin\left(\frac{n\pi x}{l}\right)$$

$$\hat{p}_x^2 \Psi = \frac{n^2 h^2}{4l^2} \Psi \tag{3.47}$$

Hence a measurement of p_x^2 will always give the result $n^2 h^2 / 4l^2$ when the particle is in the stationary state with quantum number n. This should come as no surprise: The potential energy in the box is zero, so that the Hamiltonian is

$$\hat{H} = \hat{T} + \hat{V} = \hat{T} = \hat{p}_x^2 / 2m \tag{3.48}$$

We then have [Eq. (3.41)]:

$$\hat{H}\Psi = E\Psi = \frac{\hat{p}_x^2}{2m} \Psi$$

$$\hat{p}_x^2 \Psi = 2mE\Psi = 2m \frac{n^2 h^2}{8ml^2} \Psi = \frac{n^2 h^2}{4l^2} \Psi \tag{3.49}$$

in agreement with (3.47). The only possible value for p_x^2 is

$$p_x^2 = n^2 h^2 / 4l^2 \tag{3.50}$$

Equation (3.50) suggests that a measurement of p_x would necessarily yield one of the two values $\pm \frac{1}{2} nh/l$, corresponding to the particle moving to the right or to the left in the box. This plausible suggestion is not accurate. An analysis using the methods of Chapter 7 shows that there is a high probability that the measured value will be close to one of the two values $\pm \frac{1}{2} nh/l$, but that any value consistent with (3.44) can result from a measurement of p_x for the particle in a box; see Problem 7.30.

Comparing the free-particle wave function (2.30) with the eigenfunctions (3.43) of $\hat{p}_x$, we note the following physical interpretation: The first term in (2.30) corresponds to positive momentum and represents motion in the $+x$ direction, while the second term in (2.30) corresponds to negative momentum and represents motion in the $-x$ direction.

We postulated that a measurement of the property F can only give a result that is one of the eigenvalues of the operator $\hat{F}$. If the state function Ψ happens to be an eigenfunction of $\hat{F}$ with eigenvalue a, we are certain to get a in a measurement of F. However, suppose that Ψ is not one of the eigenfunctions of $\hat{F}$; what then?

We still assert that *we will get one of the eigenvalues of $\hat{F}$ when we measure F, but we cannot say for certain which eigenvalue will be obtained.* We will later see (Chapter 7) that the *probabilities* for obtaining each of the possible eigenvalues of $\hat{F}$ can be predicted.

3.4 The Three-Dimensional Many-Particle Schroedinger Equation

Up to now we have restricted ourselves to one-dimensional, one-particle systems. The operator formalism developed in the last section enables us to extend our work to three-dimensional many-particle systems. The time-dependent Schroedinger equation for the time development of the state function is postulated to be [*cf.* Eq. (1.10)]:

$$ih\frac{\partial \Psi}{\partial t} = \hat{H}\Psi \tag{3.51}$$

while the time-independent Schroedinger equation for the energy eigenfunctions and eigenvalues is

$$\hat{H}\psi = E\psi \tag{3.52}$$

For a one-particle, three-dimensional system, the classical-mechanical Hamiltonian is

$$H = T + V = \frac{1}{2m}(p_x^2 + p_y^2 + p_z^2) + V(x, y, z) \tag{3.53}$$

Introducing the quantum-mechanical operators [Eq. (3.29)], we have for the Hamiltonian operator

$$\hat{H} = -\frac{\hbar^2}{2m}\left(\frac{\partial^2}{\partial x^2} + \frac{\partial^2}{\partial y^2} + \frac{\partial^2}{\partial z^2}\right) + V(x, y, z) \tag{3.54}$$

The operator in parentheses in (3.54) is called the *Laplacian operator* ∇^2 (read as "del squared"):

$$\nabla^2 \equiv \frac{\partial^2}{\partial x^2} + \frac{\partial^2}{\partial y^2} + \frac{\partial^2}{\partial z^2} \tag{3.55}$$

The one-particle, three-dimensional time-independent Schroedinger equation is then

$$-\frac{\hbar^2}{2m}\nabla^2\psi + V\psi = E\psi \tag{3.56}$$

Now consider a three-dimensional system with n particles. Let particle i have mass m_i and coordinates (x_i, y_i, z_i), where $i = 1, 2, 3, ..., n$. The kinetic energy is the sum of the kinetic energies of the individual particles:

$$T = \frac{1}{2m_1}(p_{x_1}^2 + p_{y_1}^2 + p_{z_1}^2) + \frac{1}{2m_2}(p_{x_2}^2 + p_{y_2}^2 + p_{z_2}^2) + \cdots + \frac{1}{2m_n}(p_{x_n}^2 + p_{y_n}^2 + p_{z_n}^2) \tag{3.57}$$

where p_{x_i} is the x-component of the linear momentum of particle i, etc. The kinetic-energy operator is

$$\hat{T} = -\frac{\hbar^2}{2m_1}\left(\frac{\partial^2}{\partial x_1^2} + \frac{\partial^2}{\partial y_1^2} + \frac{\partial^2}{\partial z_1^2}\right) - \cdots - \frac{\hbar^2}{2m_n}\left(\frac{\partial^2}{\partial x_n^2} + \frac{\partial^2}{\partial y_n^2} + \frac{\partial^2}{\partial z_n^2}\right) \tag{3.58}$$

$$\hat{T} = -\sum_{i=1}^{n}\frac{\hbar^2}{2m_i}\nabla_i^2 \tag{3.59}$$

$$\nabla_i^2 \equiv \frac{\partial^2}{\partial x_i^2} + \frac{\partial^2}{\partial y_i^2} + \frac{\partial^2}{\partial z_i^2} \tag{3.60}$$

We will restrict ourselves to cases where the potential energy depends only on the $3n$ coordinates:

$$V = V(x_1, y_1, z_1, \ldots, x_n, y_n, z_n) \tag{3.61}$$

The Hamiltonian operator for an n-particle three-dimensional system is then:

$$\hat{H} = -\sum_{i=1}^{n}\frac{\hbar^2}{2m_i}\nabla_i^2 + V(x_1, \ldots, z_n) \tag{3.62}$$

and the time-independent Schroedinger equation is

$$\left[-\sum_{i=1}^{n}\frac{\hbar^2}{2m_i}\nabla_i^2 + V(x_1, \ldots, z_n)\right]\psi = E\psi \tag{3.63}$$

where the time-independent wave function is a function of the $3n$ coordinates of the n particles:

$$\psi = \psi(x_1, y_1, z_1, \ldots, x_n, y_n, z_n) \tag{3.64}$$

The Schroedinger equation (3.63) is a linear partial differential equation.

As an example, consider a system of two particles interacting so that the potential energy is inversely proportional to the distance between them, with c being the proportionality constant. The Schroedinger equation (3.63) becomes:

$$\left[-\frac{\hbar^2}{2m_1}\left(\frac{\partial^2}{\partial x_1^2} + \frac{\partial^2}{\partial y_1^2} + \frac{\partial^2}{\partial z_1^2}\right) - \frac{\hbar^2}{2m_2}\left(\frac{\partial^2}{\partial x_2^2} + \frac{\partial^2}{\partial y_2^2} + \frac{\partial^2}{\partial z_2^2}\right)\right.$$
$$\left. + \frac{c}{[(x_1 - x_2)^2 + (y_1 - y_2)^2 + (z_1 - z_2)^2]^{1/2}}\right]\psi = E\psi \tag{3.65}$$

$$\psi = \psi(x_1, y_1, z_1, x_2, y_2, z_2) \tag{3.66}$$

Although (3.65) looks formidable, we will solve it in Chapter 6.

For a one-particle, one-dimensional system, the Born postulate [Eq. (1.12)] states that $|\Psi(x, t)|^2\,dx$ is the probability of observing the particle between x and $x + dx$ at time t. We extend this postulate as follows. For a three-dimensional, one-particle system, the quantity

$$|\Psi(x, y, z, t)|^2\,dx\,dy\,dz \tag{3.67}$$

is the probability of finding the particle in the infinitesimal region of space with the

x coordinate lying between x and $x+dx$, the y coordinate lying between y and $y+dy$, and the z coordinate lying between z and $z+dz$. Since the total probability of finding the particle is 1, the normalization condition is

$$\int_{-\infty}^{\infty} \int_{-\infty}^{\infty} \int_{-\infty}^{\infty} |\Psi|^2 \, dx \, dy \, dz = 1 \tag{3.68}$$

For a three-dimensional n-particle system, we postulate that

$$|\Psi(x_1, y_1, z_1, x_2, y_2, z_2, \ldots, x_n, y_n, z_n, t)|^2 \, dx_1 \, dy_1 \, dz_1 \, dx_2 \, dy_2 \, dz_2 \cdots dx_n \, dy_n \, dz_n \tag{3.69}$$

is the probability at time t of simultaneously finding particle 1 in the infinitesimal rectangular box at (x_1, y_1, z_1) with edges dx_1, dy_1, dz_1, particle 2 in the infinitesimal box at (x_2, y_2, z_2) with edges $dx_2, dy_2, dz_2, \ldots$, particle n in the infinitesimal box at (x_n, y_n, z_n) with edges dx_n, dy_n, dz_n. The total probability of finding all the particles is 1, and the normalization condition is

$$\int_{-\infty}^{\infty} \int_{-\infty}^{\infty} \int_{-\infty}^{\infty} \cdots \int_{-\infty}^{\infty} \int_{-\infty}^{\infty} \int_{-\infty}^{\infty} |\Psi|^2 \, dx_1 \, dy_1 \, dz_1 \cdots dx_n \, dy_n \, dz_n = 1 \tag{3.70}$$

It is customary in quantum mechanics to denote integration over the full range of all the coordinates of a system by $\int dq$ or $\int d\tau$. A shorthand way of writing (3.68) or (3.70) is

$$\int |\Psi|^2 \, d\tau = 1 \tag{3.71}$$

Although (3.71) may look like an indefinite integral, it is understood to be a definite integral; the integration variables and their ranges are understood from the context in which the integral appears.

Since $|\Psi|^2 = |\psi|^2$ for a stationary state, we have for a stationary state:

$$\int |\psi|^2 \, d\tau = 1 \tag{3.72}$$

3.5 The Particle in a Three-Dimensional Box

For the present, we confine ourselves to one-particle problems. In this section we consider the three-dimensional case of the problem solved in Section 2.2, the particle in a box.

There are many possible shapes for a three-dimensional box. The box we consider is a rectangular parallelepiped with edges of length a, b, and c. We choose our coordinate system so that one corner of the box lies at the origin and the box lies in the first octant of space. Within the box, the potential energy is zero; outside the box it is infinite:

$$V(x, y, z) = 0 \quad \text{in the region} \begin{cases} 0 < x < a \\ 0 < y < b \\ 0 < z < c \end{cases} \tag{3.73}$$

$$V = \infty \quad \text{elsewhere}$$

We conclude at once that the wave function is zero outside the box. Within the box, we have zero for the potential-energy operator and the Schroedinger equation is [Eq. (3.56)]:

$$-\frac{\hbar^2}{2m}\left(\frac{\partial^2\psi}{\partial x^2}+\frac{\partial^2\psi}{\partial y^2}+\frac{\partial^2\psi}{\partial z^2}\right)=E\psi \tag{3.74}$$

To solve (3.74), we start by assuming that the solution can be written as the product of a function of x alone times a function of y alone times a function of z alone:

$$\psi(x,y,z)=f(x)g(y)h(z) \tag{3.75}$$

It might seem that this assumption throws away solutions which are not of the form (3.75). However, it can be shown mathematically, that if we can find solutions of the form (3.75) that satisfy the boundary conditions, then there are no other solutions of the Schroedinger equation that will satisfy the boundary conditions. The method we are using to solve (3.74) is called, for obvious reasons, *separation of variables*.

From (3.75) we find

$$\frac{\partial^2\psi}{\partial x^2}=f''(x)g(y)h(z), \qquad \frac{\partial^2\psi}{\partial y^2}=f(x)g''(y)h(z), \qquad \frac{\partial^2\psi}{\partial z^2}=f(x)g(y)h''(z)$$

$$\tag{3.76}$$

We then substitute (3.75) and (3.76) into (3.74) to obtain

$$f''gh+fg''h+fgh''+2m\hbar^{-2}Efgh=0 \tag{3.77}$$

Dividing (3.77) by fgh, we have

$$\frac{f''}{f}+\frac{g''}{g}+\frac{h''}{h}+\frac{2m}{\hbar^2}E=0 \tag{3.78}$$

$$\frac{f''(x)}{f(x)}=-\frac{g''(y)}{g(y)}-\frac{h''(z)}{h(z)}-\frac{2mE}{\hbar^2} \tag{3.79}$$

Let $k_x\equiv f''/f$. Since k_x equals $f''(x)/f(x)$, it must be independent of y and z. Equation (3.79) shows that k_x equals $-g''(y)/g(y)-h''(z)/h(z)-2mE/\hbar^2$, and hence k_x must be independent of x. Being independent of x, y, and z, the quantity k_x must be a constant, and we have

$$f''(x)/f(x)=k_x \tag{3.80}$$

Since x, y, and z occur symmetrically in (3.78), we can use the same argument to conclude that

$$g''(y)/g(y)=k_y, \qquad h''(z)/h(z)=k_z \tag{3.81}$$

where k_y and k_z are two more constants. What do we know about the k's? If we substitute (3.80) and (3.81) into (3.78), we find:

$$k_x+k_y+k_z=-2mE\hbar^{-2} \tag{3.82}$$

Looking at (3.82) we decide to change the form of our constants by defining three new constants, as follows:

$$k_x = -2mE_x\hbar^{-2}, \qquad k_y = -2mE_y\hbar^{-2}, \qquad k_z = -2mE_z\hbar^{-2} \qquad (3.83)$$

where E_x, E_y, and E_z are constants having the dimensions of energy. Equation (3.82) becomes:

$$E_x + E_y + E_z = E \qquad (3.84)$$

Using (3.83) in (3.80)–(3.81), we have

$$\frac{d^2f(x)}{dx^2} + \frac{2m}{\hbar^2}E_x f(x) = 0 \qquad (3.85)$$

$$\frac{d^2g(y)}{dy^2} + \frac{2m}{\hbar^2}E_y g(y) = 0 \qquad (3.86)$$

$$\frac{d^2h(z)}{dz^2} + \frac{2m}{\hbar^2}E_z h(z) = 0 \qquad (3.87)$$

We have converted the partial differential equation in three variables into three ordinary differential equations. What are the boundary conditions on (3.85)? Since the wave function vanishes outside the box, continuity of ψ requires that it vanish on the walls of the box. In particular ψ must be zero on the wall of the box lying in the yz plane, where $x = 0$, and it must be zero on the parallel wall of the box, where $x = a$. Therefore

$$f(0) = 0, \qquad f(a) = 0 \qquad (3.88)$$

Now compare Eq. (3.85) with Eq. (2.10) in Section 2.2, dealing with the particle in a one-dimensional box. The equations are the same in form, with E_x in (3.85) corresponding to E in (2.10). Are the boundary conditions the same? Yes, except that we have $x = a$ instead of $x = l$ as the second point where the independent variable vanishes. Thus we can use the work in Section 2.2 to write down as the solution [see Eqs. (2.23) and (2.20)]:

$$f(x) = \left(\frac{2}{a}\right)^{1/2} \sin\left(\frac{n_x \pi x}{a}\right) \qquad (3.89)$$

$$E_x = \frac{n_x^2 h^2}{8ma^2}, \qquad n_x = 1, 2, 3, \ldots \qquad (3.90)$$

The same reasoning applied to the y and z equations gives

$$g(y) = \left(\frac{2}{b}\right)^{1/2} \sin\left(\frac{n_y \pi y}{b}\right), \qquad h(z) = \left(\frac{2}{c}\right)^{1/2} \sin\left(\frac{n_z \pi z}{c}\right) \qquad (3.91)$$

$$E_y = \frac{n_y^2 h^2}{8mb^2}, \qquad n_y = 1, 2, 3, \ldots \qquad (3.92)$$

$$E_z = \frac{n_z^2 h^2}{8mc^2}, \qquad n_z = 1, 2, 3, \ldots \qquad (3.93)$$

From (3.84) we have for the energy:

$$E = \frac{h^2}{8m}\left(\frac{n_x^2}{a^2} + \frac{n_y^2}{b^2} + \frac{n_z^2}{c^2}\right) \tag{3.94}$$

From (3.75) we have for the wave function in the box

$$\psi(x, y, z) = \left(\frac{8}{abc}\right)^{1/2} \sin\left(\frac{n_x \pi x}{a}\right)\sin\left(\frac{n_y \pi y}{b}\right)\sin\left(\frac{n_z \pi z}{c}\right) \tag{3.95}$$

There are three quantum numbers, n_x, n_y, n_z; we can attribute this to the three-dimensional nature of the problem. The three quantum numbers vary independently of one another.

Since the x, y, and z factors in the wave function are each independently normalized, the wave function is normalized:

$$\int_{-\infty}^{\infty}\int_{-\infty}^{\infty}\int_{-\infty}^{\infty} |\psi|^2 \, dx \, dy \, dz = \int_0^a |f(x)|^2 \, dx \int_0^b |g(y)|^2 \, dy \int_0^c |h(z)|^2 \, dz = 1$$

Suppose that $a = b = c$, i.e., we have a cube. The energy levels are then

$$E = (h^2/8ma^2)(n_x^2 + n_y^2 + n_z^2) \tag{3.96}$$

Let us tabulate some of the allowed energies of a particle confined to a cube with infinitely strong walls:

$n_x n_y n_z$	111	211	121	112	122	212	221	113	131	311	222	
$E(8ma^2/h^2)$	3	6	6	6	9	9	9	11	11	11	12	(3.97)

Observe that states with different quantum numbers may have the same energy. Thus the states with the quantum numbers $(2, 1, 1)$, $(1, 2, 1)$, and $(1, 1, 2)$ each have the same energy. However, referring to Eq. (3.95) we see that these three sets of quantum numbers give three different, independent wave functions and therefore do represent different states of the system. When two or more independent wave functions correspond to states with the same energy eigenvalue, we have *degeneracy*. The *degree* of degeneracy of an energy level is the number of states that have that energy. Thus the second-lowest energy level of the particle in a cube is threefold degenerate. We got the degeneracy when we made the edges of the box equal; degeneracy is generally related to the *symmetry* of the system. Usually one doesn't find degeneracy in one-dimensional problems.

3.6 Degeneracy

Let us prove an important theorem about the wave functions of an n-fold degenerate energy level. We have n independent wave functions $\psi_1, \psi_2, ..., \psi_n$. Let W be the energy of the degenerate level:

$$\hat{H}\psi_1 = W\psi_1, \quad \hat{H}\psi_2 = W\psi_2, ..., \hat{H}\psi_n = W\psi_n \tag{3.98}$$

We wish to prove that any linear combination

$$\varphi \equiv c_1\psi_1 + c_2\psi_2 + \cdots + c_n\psi_n \qquad (3.99)$$

of the n wave functions of the *degenerate* level is an eigenfunction of the Hamiltonian with eigenvalue W, i.e., we must show $\hat{H}\varphi = W\varphi$ or

$$\hat{H}[c_1\psi_1 + c_2\psi_2 + \cdots + c_n\psi_n] = W[c_1\psi_1 + c_2\psi_2 + \cdots + c_n\psi_n] \qquad (3.100)$$

Since the Hamiltonian is a linear operator, we can apply Eq. (3.11) $n-1$ times to the left side of (3.100), obtaining:

$$\hat{H}[c_1\psi_1 + c_2\psi_2 + \cdots + c_n\psi_n] = \hat{H}c_1\psi_1 + \hat{H}c_2\psi_2 + \cdots + \hat{H}c_n\psi_n \qquad (3.101)$$

Using Eqs. (3.12) and (3.98), we have:

$$\hat{H}[c_1\psi_1 + c_2\psi_2 + \cdots + c_n\psi_n] = c_1\hat{H}\psi_1 + c_2\hat{H}\psi_2 + \cdots + c_n\hat{H}\psi_n$$
$$= c_1 W\psi_1 + c_2 W\psi_2 + \cdots + c_n W\psi_n$$
$$\hat{H}[c_1\psi_1 + c_2\psi_2 + \cdots + c_n\psi_n] = W[c_1\psi_1 + c_2\psi_2 + \cdots + c_n\psi_n] \qquad (3.102)$$

Q.E.D.

Since any linear combination of the wave functions corresponding to a degenerate energy level is an eigenfunction of $\hat{H}$ with the same eigenvalue, we can construct an infinite number of different wave functions for any degenerate energy level. Actually, we are only interested in eigenfunctions that are linearly independent. The n functions $f_1, ..., f_n$ are said to be *linearly independent* if the equation $c_1 f_1 + \cdots + c_n f_n = 0$ can only be satisfied with all the constants $c_1, ..., c_n$ equal to zero. This means that no member of the set of functions can be expressed as a linear combination of the remaining members. For example, the functions $f_1 = 3x$, $f_2 = 5x^2 - x$, $f_3 = x^2$ are not linearly independent since $f_2 = 5f_3 - \frac{1}{3}f_1$. The functions $g_1 = 1$, $g_2 = x$, $g_3 = x^2$ are linearly independent since none of them can be written as a linear combination of the other two. The *degree of degeneracy* of an energy level is equal to the number of linearly independent wave functions corresponding to that value of the energy.

3.7 Average Values

Consider the physical property F. In Section 3.3 we pointed out that when the state function Ψ is not an eigenfunction of the operator $\hat{F}$, a measurement of F will give one of a number of possible values. We now consider the average value of the property F for a system whose state is Ψ.

To determine the average value of F experimentally, we do the following. (Recall the discussion in Section 1.3.) We take a large number of separate systems, each in the same state Ψ, and we make a measurement of F in each system. The *average value* of F is defined as the arithmetic mean of the observed values. Let $f_1, f_2, ..., f_N$ be the observed values of F. The symbol for the average value is $\langle F \rangle$ or $\bar{F}$, and we have

$$\langle F \rangle = \bar{F} = \frac{\sum_{i=1}^{N} f_i}{N} \qquad (3.103)$$

where N (the number of systems) is very large.

Instead of summing over the observed values of F, we can sum over all possible values of F, multiplying each possible value by the number of times it is observed, to obtain the equivalent expression

$$\langle F \rangle = \frac{\sum_f n_f f}{N} \tag{3.104}$$

where n_f is the number of times the value f is observed. An example will make this clear. Suppose a class of 9 students takes a quiz that has 5 questions, and that the students' grades are: 0, 20, 20, 60, 60, 80, 80, 80, 100. Calculating the average grade according to (3.103), we have

$$\frac{1}{N} \sum_{i=1}^{N} f_i = \frac{0+20+20+60+60+80+80+80+100}{9} = 56 \tag{3.105}$$

To calculate the average grade according to (3.104), we sum over the possible grades, which are: 0, 20, 40, 60, 80, 100. We have

$$\frac{1}{N} \sum_f n_f f = \frac{1(0)+2(20)+0(40)+2(60)+3(80)+1(100)}{9} = 56 \tag{3.106}$$

We can write (3.104) as

$$\langle F \rangle = \sum_f \left(\frac{n_f}{N} \right) f \tag{3.107}$$

Since N is very large, n_f/N is the probability of observing the value f (see Section 1.5); denoting this probability by P_f, we have

$$\langle F \rangle = \sum_f P_f f \tag{3.108}$$

Now consider the average value of the x coordinate for a one-particle one-dimensional system in the state $\Psi(x, t)$. x takes on a continuous range of values, and the probability of observing the particle between x and $x+dx$ is $|\Psi|^2 dx$. The summation over the infinitesimal probabilities is equivalent to an integration, so that (3.108) becomes

$$\langle x \rangle = \int_{-\infty}^{\infty} x |\Psi(x, t)|^2 dx \tag{3.109}$$

For the one-particle three-dimensional case, the probability of finding the particle in the volume element at point (x, y, z) with edges dx, dy, dz is

$$|\Psi(x, y, z, t)|^2 dx \, dy \, dz \tag{3.110}$$

If we want the probability that the particle is between x and $x+dx$, we must integrate (3.110) over all possible values of y and z, since the particle can have any values for its y and z coordinates while its x coordinate lies between x and $x+dx$. Hence, in the three-dimensional case (3.109) becomes:

$$\langle x \rangle = \int_{-\infty}^{\infty} \left[\int_{-\infty}^{\infty} \int_{-\infty}^{\infty} |\Psi(x, y, z, t)|^2 \, dy \, dz \right] x \, dx$$

$$\langle x \rangle = \int_{-\infty}^{\infty} \int_{-\infty}^{\infty} \int_{-\infty}^{\infty} |\Psi(x, y, z, t)|^2 x \, dx \, dy \, dz \tag{3.111}$$

Now consider the average value of some physical property $F(x, y, z)$ that is a function of the particle's coordinates. An example is the potential energy $V(x, y, z)$. Reasoning along the same lines that gave us (3.111), we have for the average value of F:

$$\langle F(x, y, z) \rangle = \int_{-\infty}^{\infty} \int_{-\infty}^{\infty} \int_{-\infty}^{\infty} |\Psi(x, y, z, t)|^2 F(x, y, z) \, dx \, dy \, dz \quad \textbf{(3.112)}$$

$$\langle F(x, y, z) \rangle = \int_{-\infty}^{\infty} \int_{-\infty}^{\infty} \int_{-\infty}^{\infty} \Psi^* F \Psi \, dx \, dy \, dz \quad \textbf{(3.113)}$$

The form (3.113) might seem like a bit of whimsy, as it is no different from (3.112). In a moment we will see its significance.

In general, the property F depends on both coordinates *and* momenta:

$$F = F(x, y, z, p_x, p_y, p_z) \quad \textbf{(3.114)}$$

for the one-particle three-dimensional case. How do we find the average value of F? We *postulate* that

$$\langle F \rangle = \int_{-\infty}^{\infty} \int_{-\infty}^{\infty} \int_{-\infty}^{\infty} \Psi^* F\left(x, y, z, \frac{\hbar}{i} \frac{\partial}{\partial x}, \frac{\hbar}{i} \frac{\partial}{\partial y}, \frac{\hbar}{i} \frac{\partial}{\partial z}\right) \Psi \, dx \, dy \, dz \quad \textbf{(3.115)}$$

$$\langle F \rangle = \int_{-\infty}^{\infty} \int_{-\infty}^{\infty} \int_{-\infty}^{\infty} \Psi^* \hat{F} \Psi \, dx \, dy \, dz \quad \textbf{(3.116)}$$

where $\hat{F}$ is the quantum-mechanical operator for the property F. [Later, we will provide some justification for this postulate, by using (3.116) to show that the time-dependent Schroedinger equation reduces to Newton's second law in the transition from quantum to classical mechanics; see Problem 7.19.] For the *n*-particle case, we postulate that

$$\langle F \rangle = \int \Psi^* \hat{F} \Psi \, d\tau \quad \textbf{(3.117)}$$

where $\int d\tau$ indicates integration over the full range of the $3n$ coordinates. The state function in (3.117) must be normalized, since we took $\Psi^* \Psi$ as the probability density. It is important to have the operator properly sandwiched between Ψ^* and Ψ; the quantities $\hat{F} \Psi^* \Psi$ and $\Psi^* \Psi \hat{F}$ are not the same as $\Psi^* \hat{F} \Psi$, unless $\hat{F}$ is a function of coordinates only.

For a stationary state we have

$$\Psi^* \hat{F} \Psi = e^{iEt/\hbar} \psi^* \hat{F} e^{-iEt/\hbar} \psi = e^0 \psi^* \hat{F} \psi = \psi^* \hat{F} \psi \quad \textbf{(3.118)}$$

since $\hat{F}$ contains no time derivatives and does not affect the time factor. Hence for a stationary state:

$$\langle F \rangle = \int \psi^* \hat{F} \psi \, d\tau \quad \textbf{(3.119)}$$

Consider the special case where Ψ is an eigenfunction of $\hat{F}$: $\hat{F} \Psi = k \Psi$. Equation (3.117) becomes:

$$\langle F \rangle = \int \Psi^* \hat{F} \Psi \, d\tau = \int \Psi^* k \Psi \, d\tau = k \int \Psi^* \Psi \, d\tau = k \quad \textbf{(3.120)}$$

since Ψ is normalized. The result (3.120) is reasonable, since k is the only possible value we can find for F when we make a measurement.

From Eq. (3.117) it readily follows that the average value of a sum is the sum of the average values:

$$\langle F+G \rangle = \langle F \rangle + \langle G \rangle \tag{3.121}$$

where F and G are any two properties. However, it is not necessarily true that the average value of a product is the product of the average values:

$$\langle FG \rangle \neq \langle F \rangle \langle G \rangle \tag{3.122}$$

The term *expectation value* is often used instead of average value. The expectation value is not necessarily one of the possible values we might observe; e.g., American families average 2.2 children.

Consider some average values for the particle in a three-dimensional box. For the average value of the x coordinate, Eqs. (3.119) and (3.75) give

$$\langle x \rangle = \int \int \int f^* g^* h^* x f g h \, dx \, dy \, dz \tag{3.123}$$

$$\langle x \rangle = \int_0^a x |f(x)|^2 \, dx \int_0^b |g(y)|^2 \, dy \int_0^c |h(z)|^2 \, dz = \int_0^a x |f(x)|^2 \, dx$$

since $g(y)$ and $h(z)$ are separately normalized. For the lowest energy state, Eq. (3.89) gives

$$\langle x \rangle = \frac{2}{a} \int_0^a x \sin^2 \left(\frac{\pi x}{a} \right) dx = \frac{a}{2} \tag{3.124}$$

where we used (2.22) to evaluate the integral. A glance at Fig. 2.3 shows that (3.124) is reasonable. For the average value of p_x, we have

$$\langle p_x \rangle = \int \int \int f^* g^* h^* \frac{\hbar}{i} \frac{\partial}{\partial x} [f(x) g(y) h(z)] \, dx \, dy \, dz$$

$$\langle p_x \rangle = \frac{\hbar}{i} \int_0^a f^*(x) f'(x) \, dx \int_0^b |g(y)|^2 \, dy \int_0^c |h(z)|^2 \, dz$$

$$\langle p_x \rangle = \frac{\hbar}{i} \int_0^a f(x) f'(x) \, dx = \frac{\hbar}{2i} f^2(x) \Big|_0^a = 0 \tag{3.125}$$

where (3.88) was used. The result is reasonable, since the particle is just as likely to be headed in the $+x$ direction as in the $-x$ direction.

3.8 Requirements for an Acceptable Wave Function

In solving the particle in a box, we required ψ to be continuous. We now discuss other requirements the wave function must satisfy.

Since $\psi^* \psi \, dq$ is a probability, we want to be able to normalize the wave function by choosing a suitable *normalization constant* as a multiplier of the wave function. However, we can do this only if the integral over all space $\int \psi^* \psi \, dq$ exists. If this integral exists we say that ψ is *quadratically integrable*; thus we generally demand that ψ be quadratically integrable. The important exception is a particle that is not bound. Thus the wave functions for the unbound states of the hydrogen atom and for a free particle are not quadratically integrable.

Since $\psi^* \psi$ is the probability density, it must be single-valued; it would be embarrassing if our theory gave two different values for the probability of finding a particle at a certain point. If we demand that ψ be single-valued, then surely $\psi^* \psi$ will be single-valued. It is possible to have ψ multivalued [e.g., $\psi(q) = -1, +1, i$] and still have $\psi^* \psi$ single-valued. We will, however, demand single-valuedness for ψ.

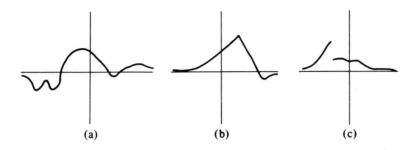

(a)   (b)   (c)

FIGURE 3.1 *Function (a) is continuous and its first derivative is continuous. Function (b) is continuous but its first derivative has a discontinuity. Function (c) is discontinuous.*

In addition to demanding that ψ be continuous, we generally also require that all the partial derivatives $\partial \psi / \partial x$, $\partial \psi / \partial y$, etc., be continuous. (See Fig. 3.1.) Referring back to Section 2.2, however, we note that for the particle in a box there is a discontinuity in the derivative of the wave function at the walls of the box; ψ and $d\psi/dx$ are zero everywhere outside the box, but from Eq. (2.23) we see that $d\psi/dx$ does not become zero at the walls. The discontinuity in ψ' is due to the infinite jump in potential energy at the walls of the box. For a box with walls of finite height, ψ' is continuous at the walls.

In line with the requirement of quadratic integrability, it is sometimes stated that we require the wave function to be finite everywhere, including infinity. However, this is usually a much stronger requirement than quadratic integrability, and, in fact, it turns out that some of the relativistic wave functions for the hydrogen atom are infinite at the origin, but are quadratically integrable; occasionally one encounters nonrelativistic wave functions that are infinite at the origin. Thus the fundamental requirement is quadratic integrability, rather than finiteness.

We require that the eigenfunctions of any operator representing a physical quantity meet the above requirements. A function meeting these requirements is said to be *well behaved*.

PROBLEMS

3.1 Let $\hat{D} = d/dx$. Verify that

$$(\hat{D}+x)(\hat{D}-x) = \hat{D}^2 - x^2 - 1$$

3.2 By repeated application of the definition of the product of two operators show that

$$[(\hat{A}\hat{B})\hat{C}]f = \hat{A}[\hat{B}(\hat{C}f)]$$

$$[\hat{A}(\hat{B}\hat{C})]f = \hat{A}[\hat{B}(\hat{C}f)]$$

thus proving associativity, Eq. (3.7).

3.3 (a) Show that $(\hat{A}+\hat{B})^2 = (\hat{B}+\hat{A})^2$, for any two operators (linear or nonlinear). (b) Under what condition is

$$(\hat{A}+\hat{B})^2 = \hat{A}^2 + 2\hat{A}\hat{B} + \hat{B}^2$$

3.4 What do you suppose we mean by the zeroth power of an operator?

3.5 Classify these operators as linear or nonlinear: (a) $3x^2\,d^2/dx^2$; (b) $(\ )^2$; (c) $\int dx$; (d) exp; (e) $\sum_{x=1}^{n}$.

3.6 (a) Give an example of an operator that satisfies Eq. (3.11) but does not satisfy (3.12). (b) Give an example of an operator that satisfies (3.12) but not (3.11).

3.7 Prove that the product of two linear operators is a linear operator.

3.8 Verify the commutator identity: $[\hat{A}, \hat{B}] = -[\hat{B}, \hat{A}]$.

3.9 Evaluate

$$\left[\frac{d^2}{dx^2}, ax^2 + bx + c\right]$$

3.10 (a) If $\hat{A}$ is linear, show that

$$\hat{A}(bf+cg) = b\hat{A}f + c\hat{A}g \qquad (3.126)$$

where b and c are constants and f and g are functions. (b) If (3.126) is true, show that $\hat{A}$ is linear.

3.11 Evaluate the commutators: (a) $[\hat{x}, \hat{p}_x]$; (b) $[\hat{x}, \hat{p}_x^2]$; (c) $[\hat{x}, \hat{p}_y]$; (d) $[\hat{x}, \hat{V}(x, y, z)]$; (e) $[\hat{x}, \hat{H}]$, where the Hamiltonian operator is given by Eq. (3.54); (f) $[\hat{x}\hat{y}\hat{z}, \hat{p}_x^2]$.

3.12 The *Laplace transform operator* $\hat{L}$ is defined by

$$\hat{L}f(x) = \int_0^\infty e^{-px}f(x)\,dx$$

(a) Is $\hat{L}$ linear? (b) Evaluate $\hat{L}(1)$; (c) Evaluate $\hat{L}e^{ax}$, assuming that $p > a$.

3.13 We define the *translation operator* $\hat{T}_h$ by

$$\hat{T}_h f(x) = f(x+h) \qquad (3.127)$$

(a) Is $\hat{T}_h$ a linear operator? (b) Evaluate $(\hat{T}_1^2 - 3\hat{T}_1 + 2)x^2$.

3.14 We define the operator $e^{\hat{A}}$ by the equation

$$e^{\hat{A}} = \hat{1} + \hat{A} + \frac{\hat{A}^2}{2!} + \frac{\hat{A}^3}{3!} + \cdots = \sum_{k=0}^\infty \frac{\hat{A}^k}{k!} \qquad (3.128)$$

Show that $e^{\hat{D}} = \hat{T}_1$ where $\hat{D} = d/dx$, and $\hat{T}_1$ is defined by (3.127).

3.15 Which of the following functions are eigenfunctions of d^2/dx^2? (a) e^x; (b) x^2; (c) $\sin x$; (d) $3\cos x$; (e) $\sin x + \cos x$. Give the eigenvalue for each eigenfunction.

3.16 For the particle confined to a box with dimensions a, b, and c, find the following values for the state with quantum numbers n_x, n_y, n_z. (a) $\langle x \rangle$; (b) $\langle y \rangle$, $\langle z \rangle$. Use symmetry considerations and the answer to part (a). (c) $\langle p_x \rangle$; (d) $\langle x^2 \rangle$. Is $\langle x^2 \rangle = \langle x \rangle^2$? Is $\langle xy \rangle = \langle x \rangle \langle y \rangle$?

3.17 For the particle in a cubic box, what is the degree of degeneracy of the energy levels with the following values of $8ma^2E/h^2$? (a) 12; (b) 14; (c) 27.

3.18 Find the eigenfunctions of

$$-\frac{\hbar^2}{2m}\frac{d^2}{dx^2}$$

If the eigenfunctions are to remain finite for $x \to \pm \infty$, what are the allowed eigenvalues?

3.19 If ψ is a normalized wave function, what are its cgs units for (a) the one-particle one-dimensional case; (b) the one-particle three-dimensional case; (c) the n-particle three-dimensional case.

3.20 Which of the following are sets of linearly independent functions? (a) x, x^2, x^6; (b) 8, x, x^2, $3x^2 - 1$; (c) $\sin x$, $\cos x$; (d) $\sin z$, $\cos z$, $\tan z$; (e) $\sin x$, $\cos x$, e^{ix}; (f) $\sin^2 x$, $\cos^2 x$, 1; (g) $\sin^2 x$, $\cos^2 y$, 1.

3.21 The wave function of a particle in a three-dimensional box is an eigenfunction of which of these operators? (a) $\hat{p}_x$; (b) $\hat{p}_x^2$; (c) $\hat{p}_z^2$; (d) $\hat{x}$.

3.22 Which of the following functions, when multiplied by a normalization constant, would be acceptable one-dimensional wave functions for a bound particle? (a) e^{-x}; (b) e^{-x^2}; (c) xe^{-x^2}; (d) ie^{-x^2}; (e) $f(x) = e^{-x^2}$ for $x < 0$, $f(x) = 2e^{-x^2}$ for $x \geq 0$.

3.23 Solve the one-particle three-dimensional time-independent Schroedinger equation for the free particle.

3.24 If ψ is an unnormalized wave function, and N is a constant such that $N\psi$ is normalized, express $|N|$ in terms of ψ.

3.25 Fill in the details leading to (3.43) and (3.44) as the eigenfunctions and eigenvalues of $\hat{p}_x$.

3.26 Give the quantum-mechanical operators for the following physical quantities. (a) p_y^3; (b) $xp_y - yp_x$; (c) $(xp_y - yp_x)^2$.

3.27 For an n-particle three-dimensional system in the state Ψ, what is the probability of finding particle 1 with x coordinate between 0 and 2?

3.28 Prove that if $\hat{A} + \hat{B} = \hat{C}$, then $\hat{A} = \hat{C} - \hat{B}$.

3.29 Prove that Eq. (3.15) holds for linear operators.

3.30 The terms "state" and "energy level" are not synonymous in quantum mechanics. For the particle in a cubic box, consider the energy range $E < 15h^2/8ma^2$. (a) How many states lie in this range? (b) How many energy levels lie in this range?

CHAPTER

4

The Harmonic Oscillator

4.1 Power-Series Solution of Differential Equations

So far, we have considered only cases where the potential energy $V(x)$ is a constant. This makes the Schroedinger equation a second-order linear homogeneous differential equation with *constant* coefficients, which we know how to solve. However, we want to deal with the wave equation for cases in which V varies with x. A useful approach in this case is to attempt a power-series solution of the differential equation.

To illustrate the method consider the differential equation

$$y''(x) + c^2 y(x) = 0 \tag{4.1}$$

where c^2 is a real, positive number. Of course this differential equation has *constant* coefficients, but we can solve it with the power-series method if we want. Let us first obtain the solution by using the auxiliary equation, which is $s^2 + c^2 = 0$. We find $s = \pm ic$. Recalling the work in Section 2.2 [Eqs. (2.10) and (4.1) are the same], we get trigonometric solutions when the roots of the auxiliary equation are pure imaginary:

$$y = A \cos(cx) + B \sin(cx) \tag{4.2}$$

where A and B are the constants of integration. A different form of (4.2) is sometimes useful, namely

$$y = D \sin(cx + e) \tag{4.3}$$

where D and e are arbitrary constants. Using the formula for the sine of the sum of two angles, we can show that (4.3) is equivalent to (4.2).

Now let us solve (4.1) using the power-series method. We start by assuming that the solution can be expanded in a Taylor series (see Problem 4.8) about $x = 0$, i.e., we assume that

$$y(x) = \sum_{n=0}^{\infty} a_n x^n = a_0 + a_1 x + a_2 x^2 + a_3 x^3 + \cdots \tag{4.4}$$

where the a's are coefficients to be determined so as to satisfy (4.1). Differentiating (4.4), we have

$$y'(x) = a_1 + 2a_2 x + 3a_3 x^2 + \cdots = \sum_{n=1}^{\infty} na_n x^{n-1} \tag{4.5}$$

where we have assumed that term-by-term differentiation is valid for the series. (This is not always true for infinite series.) For y'' we have

$$y''(x) = 2a_2 + 3(2)a_3 x + \cdots = \sum_{n=2}^{\infty} n(n-1)a_n x^{n-2} \tag{4.6}$$

Substituting (4.4) and (4.6) into (4.1), we get

$$\sum_{n=2}^{\infty} n(n-1)a_n x^{n-2} + \sum_{n=0}^{\infty} c^2 a_n x^n = 0 \tag{4.7}$$

We want to combine the two sums in (4.7). Provided certain conditions are met, we can add two infinite series term by term to get their sum:

$$\sum_{j=0}^{\infty} b_j x^j + \sum_{j=0}^{\infty} c_j x^j = \sum_{j=0}^{\infty} (b_j + c_j) x^j \tag{4.8}$$

To apply (4.8) to the two sums in (4.7), we want the summation limits in each sum to be the same and the powers of x to be the same. We therefore make a change of summation index in the first sum in (4.7), setting $n = k + 2$.

$$\sum_{n=2}^{\infty} n(n-1)a_n x^{n-2} = \sum_{k=0}^{\infty} (k+2)(k+1)a_{k+2} x^k \tag{4.9}$$

$$\sum_{n=2}^{\infty} n(n-1)a_n x^{n-2} = \sum_{n=0}^{\infty} (n+2)(n+1)a_{n+2} x^n \tag{4.10}$$

Sometimes students are puzzled as to how (4.10) follows from (4.9). The point is that the summation index is a *dummy variable*; i.e., it makes no difference what letter we use to denote this variable. An example will make this clear. Consider the two sums

$$\sum_{i=1}^{3} c_i x^i \quad \text{and} \quad \sum_{j=1}^{3} c_j x^j \tag{4.11}$$

Because only the dummy variables in the two sums differ, the sums are equal to each other. This is easy to see if we write them out:

$$\sum_{i=1}^{3} c_i x^i = c_1 x + c_2 x^2 + c_3 x^3 \quad \text{and} \quad \sum_{j=1}^{3} c_j x^j = c_1 x + c_2 x^2 + c_3 x^3$$

In going from (4.9) to (4.10) we simply changed the symbol denoting the summation index from k to n.

The integration variable in a definite integral is also a dummy variable, since the value of a definite integral is unaffected by what letter we use for this variable. Thus

$$\int_a^b f(x)\, dx = \int_a^b f(t)\, dt \tag{4.12}$$

Using (4.10) in (4.7) we find, after applying (4.8),

$$\sum_{n=0}^{\infty} [(n+2)(n+1)a_{n+2} + c^2 a_n] x^n = 0 \tag{4.13}$$

If (4.13) is to be true for all values of x, then the coefficient of each power of x must vanish. To see this, consider the equation

$$\sum_{j=0}^{\infty} b_j x^j = 0 \tag{4.14}$$

Putting $x = 0$ in (4.14) shows that $b_0 = 0$. Taking the first derivative of (4.14) with respect to x, and then putting $x = 0$, shows that $b_1 = 0$. Taking the nth derivative and putting $x = 0$, gives $b_n = 0$. Thus from (4.13) we have

$$(n+2)(n+1)a_{n+2} + c^2 a_n = 0 \tag{4.15}$$

$$a_{n+2} = -\frac{c^2}{(n+1)(n+2)} a_n \tag{4.16}$$

An equation like (4.16) is called a *recursion relation*. Using (4.16), if we know the value of a_0 we can find $a_2, a_4, a_6, \ldots$. If we know a_1, we can find $a_3, a_5, a_7, \ldots$. Since there is no restriction on the values of a_0 and a_1, they are arbitrary constants which we denote by A and Bc:

$$a_0 = A, \qquad a_1 = Bc \tag{4.17}$$

Using (4.16) we find for the coefficients

$$a_0 = A, \qquad a_2 = -\frac{c^2 A}{1 \cdot 2}, \qquad a_4 = \frac{c^4 A}{4 \cdot 3 \cdot 2 \cdot 1}, \qquad a_6 = -\frac{c^6 A}{6!}, \ldots$$

$$a_{2k} = (-1)^k \frac{c^{2k} A}{(2k)!}, \qquad k = 0, 1, 2, 3, \ldots \tag{4.18}$$

$$a_1 = Bc, \qquad a_3 = -\frac{c^3 B}{2 \cdot 3}, \qquad a_5 = \frac{c^5 B}{5 \cdot 4 \cdot 3 \cdot 2}, \qquad a_7 = -\frac{c^7 B}{7!}, \ldots$$

$$a_{2k+1} = (-1)^k \frac{c^{2k+1} B}{(2k+1)!}, \qquad k = 0, 1, 2, \ldots \tag{4.19}$$

We have

$$y = \sum_{n=0}^{\infty} a_n x^n = \sum_{n=0,2,4,\ldots}^{\infty} a_n x^n + \sum_{n=1,3,5,\ldots}^{\infty} a_n x^n$$

$$y = A \sum_{k=0}^{\infty} (-1)^k \frac{c^{2k} x^{2k}}{(2k)!} + B \sum_{k=0}^{\infty} (-1)^k \frac{c^{2k+1} x^{2k+1}}{(2k+1)!} \qquad (4.20)$$

The two series in (4.20) are the Taylor series for $\cos(cx)$ and $\sin(cx)$ (Problem 4.9); hence, in agreement with (4.2), we have

$$y = A \cos(cx) + B \sin(cx) \qquad (4.21)$$

4.2 The One-Dimensional Harmonic Oscillator

In this section we will increase our quantum-mechanical repertoire by solving the Schroedinger equation for the one-dimensional harmonic oscillator. This system is important as a model for molecular vibrations.

Before looking at the wave mechanics of the harmonic oscillator, we review the classical treatment. We have a single particle of mass m attracted toward the origin by a force proportional to its displacement from the origin:

$$F_x = -kx \qquad (4.22)$$

F_x is the x component of the force on the particle. This is also the total force in this one-dimensional problem. Newton's second law gives

$$-kx = m \frac{d^2 x}{dt^2} \qquad (4.23)$$

where t is the time. Equation (4.23) is the same as Eq. (4.1) with $c^2 = k/m$; hence the solution is [Eq. (4.3)]:

$$x = A \sin(2\pi vt + b) \qquad (4.24)$$

where A and b are the integration constants and the vibration frequency v is

$$v = \frac{1}{2\pi} \left(\frac{k}{m} \right)^{1/2} \qquad (4.25)$$

k is the *force constant*. Now consider the energy. The potential energy V is related to the components of force in the three-dimensional case by

$$F_x = -\frac{\partial V}{\partial x}, \qquad F_y = -\frac{\partial V}{\partial y}, \qquad F_z = -\frac{\partial V}{\partial z} \qquad (4.26)$$

Equation (4.26) is the definition of potential energy. Since we have a one-dimensional problem, we have

$$F_x = -\frac{dV}{dx} = -kx \qquad (4.27)$$

Integrating (4.27), we have

$$V = \tfrac{1}{2}kx^2 + C \qquad (4.28)$$

where C is the constant of integration. The potential energy always has an arbitrary additive constant. We choose $C = 0$; hence

$$V = \tfrac{1}{2}kx^2 = 2\pi^2\nu^2mx^2 \qquad (4.29)$$

The graph of $V(x)$ is a parabola—Fig. 4.2. The kinetic energy T is

$$T = \tfrac{1}{2}m\left(\frac{dx}{dt}\right)^2 \qquad (4.30)$$

and can be evaluated by differentiating (4.24) with respect to t. Adding T and V we find for the total energy:

$$E = T + V = \tfrac{1}{2}kA^2 = 2\pi^2\nu^2mA^2 \qquad (4.31)$$

where the identity $\sin^2\theta + \cos^2\theta = 1$ was used.

Now for the quantum-mechanical treatment. The Hamiltonian is

$$\hat{H} = -\frac{\hbar^2}{2m}\frac{d^2}{dx^2} + 2\pi^2\nu^2mx^2 = -\frac{\hbar^2}{2m}\left(\frac{d^2}{dx^2} - \alpha^2x^2\right) \qquad (4.32)$$

where to save time in writing, we defined α as

$$\alpha \equiv 2\pi\nu m/\hbar \qquad (4.33)$$

The Schroedinger equation $\hat{H}\psi = E\psi$ reads, after multiplication by $2m/\hbar^2$:

$$\frac{d^2\psi}{dx^2} + (2mE\hbar^{-2} - \alpha^2x^2)\psi = 0 \qquad (4.34)$$

We might now attempt a power-series solution of (4.34) using the methods of the last section. If we do now try a power series for ψ of the form (4.4), we will find that it leads to a three-term recursion relation, which is much more difficult to deal with than a two-term recursion relation like Eq. (4.15). We therefore attempt to modify the form of (4.34) so as to get a two-term recursion relation when we try a series solution. A substitution that will achieve this purpose is (see Problem 4.17):

$$\psi = e^{-\alpha x^2/2}f(x) \qquad (4.35)$$

This equation is simply the definition of a new function $f(x)$, which replaces $\psi(x)$ as the unknown function to be solved for. Differentiating (4.35) twice, we have

$$\psi'' = e^{-\alpha x^2/2}(f'' - 2\alpha xf' - \alpha f + \alpha^2x^2f) \qquad (4.36)$$

Substituting (4.35) and (4.36) into (4.34), we find:

$$f''(x) - 2\alpha xf'(x) + (2mE\hbar^{-2} - \alpha)f(x) = 0 \qquad (4.37)$$

Now we try a series solution for $f(x)$:

$$f(x) = \sum_{n=0}^{\infty} c_n x^n \qquad (4.38)$$

Assuming the validity of term-by-term differentiation of (4.38), we get

$$f'(x) = \sum_{n=1}^{\infty} nc_n x^{n-1} = \sum_{n=0}^{\infty} nc_n x^{n-1} \tag{4.39}$$

[The first term in the second sum in (4.39) is zero.] Also

$$f''(x) = \sum_{n=2}^{\infty} n(n-1) c_n x^{n-2} = \sum_{j=0}^{\infty} (j+2)(j+1) c_{j+2} x^j$$

$$= \sum_{n=0}^{\infty} (n+2)(n+1) c_{n+2} x^n \tag{4.40}$$

where we made the substitution $j = n-2$ and then changed the summation index from j to n. [Compare Eqs. (4.9) and (4.10).] Substitution into (4.37) gives

$$\sum_{n=0}^{\infty} (n+2)(n+1) c_{n+2} x^n - 2\alpha \sum_{n=0}^{\infty} nc_n x^n + (2mEh^{-2}-\alpha) \sum_{n=0}^{\infty} c_n x^n = 0$$

$$\sum_{n=0}^{\infty} [(n+2)(n+1) c_{n+2} - 2\alpha nc_n + (2mEh^{-2}-\alpha) c_n] x^n = 0 \tag{4.41}$$

Setting the coefficient of x^n equal to zero [for the same reason as in Eq. (4.13)], we have

$$c_{n+2} = \frac{(\alpha+2\alpha n-2mEh^{-2})}{(n+1)(n+2)} c_n \tag{4.42}$$

which is the desired two-term recursion relation. Equation (4.42) has the same form as (4.16), in that, knowing c_n we can calculate c_{n+2}; we thus have two arbitrary constants: c_0 and c_1. If we set c_1 equal to zero, then we will have as a solution a power series containing only even powers of x, multiplied by the exponential factor:

$$\psi = e^{-\alpha x^2/2} f(x) = e^{-\alpha x^2/2} \sum_{n=0,2,4,...}^{\infty} c_n x^n = e^{-\alpha x^2/2} \sum_{l=0}^{\infty} c_{2l} x^{2l} \tag{4.43}$$

If we set c_0 equal to zero, we get another independent solution:

$$\psi = e^{-\alpha x^2/2} \sum_{n=1,3,...}^{\infty} c_n x^n = e^{-\alpha x^2/2} \sum_{l=0}^{\infty} c_{2l+1} x^{2l+1} \tag{4.44}$$

The general solution of the Schroedinger equation is [recall Eq. (2.5)]:

$$\psi = Ae^{-\alpha x^2/2} \sum_{l=0}^{\infty} c_{2l+1} x^{2l+1} + Be^{-\alpha x^2/2} \sum_{l=0}^{\infty} c_{2l} x^{2l} \tag{4.45}$$

where A and B are arbitrary constants.

We now must see if the boundary conditions on the wave function lead to any restrictions on the solution. To see how the two infinite series behave for large x, we examine the ratio of successive coefficients in each series. The ratio of the coefficient of x^{2l+2} to that of x^{2l} in the second series is [set $n = 2l$ in Eq. (4.42)]:

$$\frac{c_{2l+2}}{c_{2l}} = \frac{\alpha+4\alpha l-2mEh^{-2}}{(2l+1)(2l+2)} \tag{4.46}$$

Assuming that for large values of x the later terms in the series are the dominant ones, we look at the ratio (4.46) for large values of l:

$$\frac{c_{2l+2}}{c_{2l}} \sim \frac{4\alpha l}{(2l)(2l)} = \frac{\alpha}{l} \qquad \text{for } l \text{ large} \tag{4.47}$$

Setting $n = 2l+1$ in (4.42), we find that for large l, the ratio of successive coefficients in the first series is also α/l. Now consider the power-series expansion for the function $e^{\alpha x^2}$. Using (Problem 4.10)

$$e^z = \sum_{n=0}^{\infty} \frac{z^n}{n!} = 1 + z + \frac{z^2}{2!} + \cdots \tag{4.48}$$

we get

$$e^{\alpha x^2} = 1 + \alpha x^2 + \cdots + \frac{\alpha^l x^{2l}}{l!} + \frac{\alpha^{l+1} x^{2l+2}}{(l+1)!} + \cdots \tag{4.49}$$

The ratio of the coefficients of x^{2l+2} and x^{2l} in this series is

$$\frac{\alpha^{l+1}}{(l+1)!} \div \frac{\alpha^l}{l!} = \frac{\alpha}{l+1} \sim \frac{\alpha}{l} \qquad \text{for large } l \tag{4.50}$$

Thus the ratio of successive coefficients in each of the infinite series in the solution (4.45) is the same as in the series for $e^{\alpha x^2}$ for large l. We conclude that for large x, each series goes as $e^{\alpha x^2}$. (This is not a rigorous proof.)

If each series goes as $e^{\alpha x^2}$, then (4.45) shows that ψ will behave as $e^{\alpha x^2/2}$ for large x. The wave function will become infinite as x goes to infinity and will not be quadratically integrable. If we could somehow break off the series after a finite number of terms, then the factor $e^{-\alpha x^2/2}$ would insure that ψ went to zero as x became infinite. (Using l'Hospital's rule it is easy to show that

$$\lim_{x \to \infty} x^p e^{-\alpha x^2/2} = 0$$

where p is any finite power.) In order to have one of the series break off after a finite number of terms, the coefficient of c_n in the recursion relation (4.42) must become zero for some value of n, say for $n = v$. This makes $c_{v+2}, c_{v+4}, \ldots$ all equal to zero, and one of the series in (4.45) will have a finite number of terms. In the recursion relation (4.42) there is one quantity whose value is not yet fixed, but can be adjusted to make the coefficient of c_v vanish; this quantity is the energy E. Setting the coefficient of c_v equal to zero in (4.42), we get

$$\alpha + 2\alpha v - 2mE\hbar^{-2} = 0$$

$$2mE\hbar^{-2} = (2v+1)\, 2\pi v m \hbar^{-1}$$

$$E = (v+\tfrac{1}{2})h\nu, \qquad v = 0, 1, 2, \ldots \tag{4.51}$$

and the recursion relation (4.42) becomes:

$$c_{n+2} = \frac{2\alpha(n-v)}{(n+1)(n+2)} c_n \tag{4.52}$$

By quantizing the energy according to (4.51), we have made one of the series break off after a finite number of terms. To get rid of the other infinite series in (4.45), we must set the arbitrary constant that multiplies it equal to zero. This leaves us with a wave function that is $e^{-\alpha x^2/2}$ times a finite power series containing only even or only odd powers of x, depending on whether v is even or odd, respectively.

The quantum number v must be a nonnegative integer, and we have a series of equally spaced energy levels. As in the particle in a box, *it is the boundary conditions that force us to quantize the energy.* A graph of a solution to (4.34) for any value of E that differs from the values in (4.51) would show ψ becoming infinite as x goes to infinity.

The state of lowest energy is called the *ground state* (or *normal state*). The harmonic-oscillator ground-state energy is nonzero; this energy, $\frac{1}{2}hv$, is called the *zero-point energy*. (This would be the vibrational energy of diatomic molecules at absolute zero.) The zero-point energy can be understood from the uncertainty principle. If the lowest state had an energy of zero, both its potential and kinetic energies (which are nonnegative) would have to be zero. Zero kinetic energy would mean that the momentum was exactly zero, so that Δp_x would be zero. Zero potential energy would mean that the particle was always located at the origin, so that Δx would be zero. But we cannot have both Δx and Δp_x equal to zero. Hence the necessity for a nonzero ground-state energy. Similar considerations apply for the particle in a box.

Before considering the wave functions, we define the concept of even and odd functions. If $f(x)$ satisfies

$$f(-x) = f(x) \qquad\qquad (4.53)$$

then f is an *even function* of x. Thus x^2 and e^{-bx^2} are each even functions of x since $(-x)^2 = x^2$ and $e^{-b(-x)^2} = e^{-bx^2}$. The graph of an even function is symmetric about the y axis (e.g., see Fig. 4.1a); hence

$$\int_{-a}^{+a} f(x)\,dx = 2\int_0^a f(x)\,dx \qquad \text{for } f(x) \text{ even} \qquad (4.54)$$

If $g(x)$ satisfies

$$g(-x) = -g(x) \qquad\qquad (4.55)$$

then g is an *odd function* of x. Examples are x, $1/x$, xe^{x^2}. Setting $x = 0$ in (4.55), we see that an odd function must be zero at $x = 0$, provided $g(0)$ is defined and single valued. The graph of an odd function has the general appearance of Fig. 4.1b. Because positive contributions on one side of the y axis are cancelled by corresponding negative contributions on the other side, we have

$$\int_{-a}^{+a} g(x)\,dx = 0 \qquad \text{for } g(x) \text{ odd} \qquad (4.56)$$

It is easy to show that the product of two even functions or of two odd functions is an even function, while the product of an even and an odd function is an odd function.

Coming back to the harmonic-oscillator eigenfunctions, we state that any eigenfunction is either an even or an odd function. The exponential factor is an even function of x. If v is even, then the polynomial factor contains only even powers of x, which makes ψ an even function. If v is odd, then the polynomial factor contains only odd powers of x, and ψ, being the product of an even and an odd function, is odd.

Let us find the wave functions for the lowest levels. For the ground state, $v = 0$, there are no odd powers of x in the polynomial factor, and the recursion relation (4.52) shows $c_2 = c_4 = \cdots = 0$. Hence, using the value of v as a subscript on ψ, we have

$$\psi_0 = c_0 e^{-\alpha x^2/2} \tag{4.57}$$

We fix c_0 by normalization:

$$1 = \int_{-\infty}^{\infty} |c_0|^2 e^{-\alpha x^2}\, dx = 2|c_0|^2 \int_0^{\infty} e^{-\alpha x^2}\, dx$$

where Eq. (4.54) has been used. Using the integral (A.5) in the Appendix, we find

$$|c_0| = (\alpha/\pi)^{1/4} \tag{4.58}$$

$$\psi_0 = \left(\frac{\alpha}{\pi}\right)^{1/4} e^{-\alpha x^2/2} \tag{4.59}$$

if we choose the phase of the normalization constant to be zero. The wave function (4.59) is a Gaussian function (Fig. 4.1a).

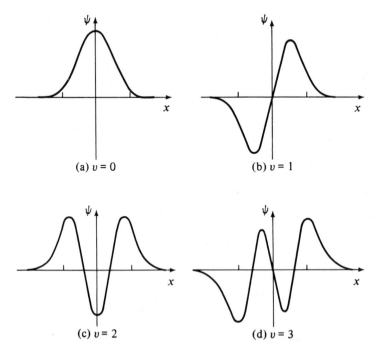

(a) $v = 0$

(b) $v = 1$

(c) $v = 2$

(d) $v = 3$

FIGURE 4.1 *Harmonic-oscillator wave functions. The same scale is used for all graphs; the points marked on the abscissas are for $\alpha^{1/2}x = \pm 2$.*

For $v = 1$ there are no even powers of x in the polynomial factor, and c_3, c_5, etc. all vanish; hence

$$\psi_1 = c_1 x e^{-\alpha x^2/2} \tag{4.60}$$

After normalization [the required integral is Eq. (A.6)] we have

$$\psi_1 = \left(\frac{4\alpha^3}{\pi}\right)^{1/4} x e^{-\alpha x^2/2} \tag{4.61}$$

This function is graphed in Fig. 4.1b.

For $v = 2$, there are no odd powers of x, and the even coefficients after c_2 all vanish; hence

$$\psi_2 = (c_0 + c_2 x^2) e^{-\alpha x^2/2} \tag{4.62}$$

From (4.52) we have for $v = 2$:

$$c_2 = \frac{2\alpha(-2) c_0}{1 \cdot 2} = -2\alpha c_0 \tag{4.63}$$

Hence

$$\psi_2 = c_0 (1 - 2\alpha x^2) e^{-\alpha x^2/2} \tag{4.64}$$

Evaluating c_0 by normalization, we find

$$\psi_2 = \left(\frac{\alpha}{4\pi}\right)^{1/4} (2\alpha x^2 - 1) e^{-\alpha x^2/2} \tag{4.65}$$

The number of nodes in the wave function equals the quantum number v. It can be proven (see *Pauling and Wilson*, p. 61) that in a one-dimensional problem the number of nodes interior to the boundary points is zero for the ground-state ψ and increases by one for each successive excited state. The boundary points for the harmonic oscillator are $\pm\infty$.

The polynomial factors in the harmonic-oscillator wave functions are well known in mathematics and are called *Hermite polynomials*, after a French mathematician. (See Problem 4.14.)

A state whose wave function is an even function is said to have *even parity*; if the wave function is odd, then the state is of *odd parity*. It can be shown (see Section 7.5) that if the potential energy $V(x)$ is an even function, then any wave function must either be an even function or an odd function.

According to the quantum-mechanical solution, there is some probability of finding the particle at any point on the x axis (except at the nodes). Classically, the particle is confined to the region where the potential energy does not exceed the total energy; this is the region from $-a$ to $+a$ in Fig. 4.2. It might seem that by saying the particle can be found outside the classically allowed region, we are allowing it to have negative kinetic energy. Actually there is no paradox in the quantum-mechanical view. To verify that the particle is in the classically forbidden region, we must measure its position. This measurement changes the state of the system (Sections 1.2 and 1.3); the interaction of the oscillator with the measuring apparatus

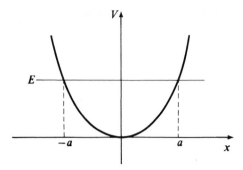

FIGURE 4.2 *The classically allowed ($|x| \le a$) and forbidden ($|x| > a$) regions for the harmonic oscillator.*

transfers sufficient energy to the oscillator for it to be in the classically forbidden region. An accurate measurement of x introduces a large uncertainty in the momentum, and hence in the kinetic energy.

The phenomenon of *tunneling* (Section 2.2) also involves the penetration by a particle into the classically forbidden region.

The vibrations of a diatomic molecule can be *approximated* by those of a harmonic oscillator. The vibration frequency is given by (4.25), except that m is replaced by the *reduced mass* $\mu = m_1 m_2/(m_1 + m_2)$, where m_1 and m_2 are the masses of the two atoms (see Section 6.2). The most probable transitions when the molecule is exposed to infrared radiation are those with a change of 1 in the quantum number v. (For the proof, see *Kauzmann*, p. 655.) Equations (1.2) and (4.51) show that a diatomic molecule with vibration frequency v_{vib} will most strongly absorb infrared light of frequency v_{light} given by

$$v_{light} = (E_2 - E_1)/h = [(v_2 + \tfrac{1}{2})hv_{vib} - (v_1 + \tfrac{1}{2})hv_{vib}]/h = v_{vib}$$

since $v_2 - v_1 = 1$.

PROBLEMS

4.1 For the ground state of the one-dimensional harmonic oscillator, find the average value of the kinetic energy and of the potential energy; verify that $\langle T \rangle = \langle V \rangle$ in this case.

4.2 Which of the following are even functions? are odd functions? (a) $\sin x$; (b) $\cos x$; (c) $\tan x$; (d) e^x; (e) 13; (f) $x \cosh x$; (g) $2 - 2x$.

4.3 Prove the statements made in this chapter about products of even and odd functions.

4.4 Draw rough graphs of ψ and of ψ^2 for the $v = 5$ state of the one-dimensional harmonic oscillator without finding the explicit formula for ψ.

4.5 The three-dimensional harmonic oscillator has the potential-energy function:

$$V = \tfrac{1}{2}k_x x^2 + \tfrac{1}{2}k_y y^2 + \tfrac{1}{2}k_z z^2$$

where the k's are three force constants. Find the energy eigenvalues by solving the Schroedinger equation.

4.6 Given that $f(x)$ is an even function that is differentiable at the origin. Find $f'(0)$.

4.7 Verify the normalization factors for the $v = 1$ and $v = 2$ harmonic-oscillator wave functions.

4.8 Provided certain conditions are met, we can expand the function $f(x)$ in an infinite power series about the point $x = a$:

$$f(x) = \sum_{n=0}^{\infty} c_n(x-a)^n \tag{4.66}$$

Differentiate (4.66) m times, and then set $x = a$ to show that $c_n = f^{(n)}(a)/n!$, thus giving the familiar *Taylor series*:

$$f(x) = \sum_{n=0}^{\infty} \frac{f^{(n)}(a)}{n!}(x-a)^n \tag{4.67}$$

4.9 (a) Use (4.67) to derive the first few terms in the Taylor-series expansion about $x = 0$ for the function $\sin x$, and infer the general formula. (b) Differentiate the Taylor series in (a) to obtain the Taylor series for $\cos x$.

4.10 (a) Obtain the Taylor-series expansion about $x = 0$ for e^x. (b) Use the Taylor series (about $x = 0$) of $\sin x$, $\cos x$, and e^x to verify Eq. (1.22).

4.11 Point out the similarities and differences between the particle-in-a-box and the harmonic-oscillator wave functions and energies.

4.12 For the $v = 1$ harmonic-oscillator state, find the most likely position(s) of the particle.

4.13 (a) The infrared absorption spectrum of H^1Cl^{35} has its strongest band at 8.65×10^{13} cycles/sec. Calculate the force constant of the bond in this molecule. (b) Predict the approximate frequencies of other H^1Cl^{35} infrared bands. (c) Predict the frequency of the strongest infrared band of H^1Cl^{37}.

4.14 The *Hermite polynomials* are defined by:

$$H_n(z) = (-1)^n e^{z^2} \frac{d^n e^{-z^2}}{dz^n} \tag{4.68}$$

(a) Verify that

$$H_0 = 1, \quad H_1 = 2z, \quad H_2 = 4z^2 - 2, \quad H_3 = 8z^3 - 12z$$

(b) The Hermite polynomials obey the relation (*Pauling and Wilson*, pp. 77–79):

$$zH_n(z) = nH_{n-1}(z) + \tfrac{1}{2}H_{n+1}(z) \tag{4.69}$$

Verify this identity for $n = 0$, 1, and 2. (c) The normalized harmonic-oscillator wave functions can be written as (*ibid.*, pp. 79–80):

$$\psi_v(x) = (2^v v!)^{-1/2}\left(\frac{\alpha}{\pi}\right)^{1/4} e^{-\alpha x^2/2} H_v(\alpha^{1/2}x) \tag{4.70}$$

Verify (4.70) for the three lowest states.

4.15 What single-valued function is both odd and even?

4.16 Find $\langle x \rangle$ for the harmonic-oscillator state with quantum number v.

4.17 When a second-order linear homogeneous differential equation is written in the form (2.4), any point at which $P(x)$ or $Q(x)$ become infinite is called a *singular point* (or *singularity*). In solving a differential equation by the power-series method, the proper substitution to give a two-term recursion relation can often be found by examining the differential equation near its singularities. For the harmonic-oscillator Schroedinger equation (4.34), the singularities are at $x = \pm \infty$. (To check whether $x = \infty$ is a singular point, one substitutes $z = 1/x$ and examines the coefficients at $z = 0$.) Verify that $\exp(-\alpha x^2/2)$ is an approximate solution of (4.34) for very large $|x|$.

4.18 Find the eigenvalues and eigenfunctions of $\hat{H}$ for a one-dimensional system with: $V(x) = \infty$ for $x < 0$, $V(x) = \frac{1}{2}kx^2$ for $x \geqslant 0$.

4.19 (a) A certain system in a certain stationary state has $\psi = Ne^{-ax^4}$. (N is the normalization constant.) Find the system's potential-energy function $V(x)$ and its energy E. [*Hint:* The zero level of energy is arbitrary, so choose $V(0) = 0$]. (b) Sketch $V(x)$. (c) Is this the ground-state ψ? Explain.

4.20 Show that adding a constant C to the potential energy leaves the stationary-state wave functions unchanged and simply adds C to the energy eigenvalues.

4.21 Explain why helium remains a liquid as its temperature goes to absolute zero, rather than solidifying.

CHAPTER

5

Angular Momentum

5.1 Simultaneous Measurement of Several Properties

In this chapter we will discuss angular momentum, and in the next chapter we will show that for the stationary states of the hydrogen atom the magnitude of the electron's angular momentum is constant. As a preliminary, we consider what criterion we can use to decide which properties of a system can be simultaneously assigned definite values.

In Section 3.3 we postulated that if the state function Ψ is an eigenfunction of the operator $\hat{A}$ with eigenvalue s, then a measurement of the physical property A is certain to yield the result s. If Ψ is simultaneously an eigenfunction of the two operators $\hat{A}$ and $\hat{B}$,

$$\hat{A}\Psi = s\Psi, \qquad \hat{B}\Psi = t\Psi \tag{5.1}$$

we can simultaneously assign definite values to the physical quantities A and B. When will it be possible for Ψ to be simultaneously an eigenfunction of two different operators? In Chapter 7 we will prove the following two theorems. First, a necessary condition for the existence of a complete set of simultaneous eigenfunctions of two operators is that the operators commute with each other. (The word "complete" is used here in a certain technical sense, which we won't worry about until Chapter 7.) Conversely, if $\hat{A}$ and $\hat{B}$ are two commuting operators that correspond to physical quantities, then there exists a complete set of functions that are eigenfunctions of both $\hat{A}$ and $\hat{B}$. Thus if $[\hat{A}, \hat{B}] = 0$, then Ψ can be an eigenfunction of both $\hat{A}$ and $\hat{B}$.

To facilitate the calculation of commutators, we list some identities; these are easily proved by writing out the commutators in detail.

$$[\hat{A}, \hat{B}] = -[\hat{B}, \hat{A}] \tag{5.2}$$

$$[\hat{A}, \hat{A}^n] = 0, \qquad n = 1, 2, 3, \ldots \tag{5.3}$$

$$[k\hat{A}, \hat{B}] = [\hat{A}, k\hat{B}] = k[\hat{A}, \hat{B}] \tag{5.4}$$

$$[\hat{A}, \hat{B} + \hat{C}] = [\hat{A}, \hat{B}] + [\hat{A}, \hat{C}] \tag{5.5}$$

$$[\hat{A} + \hat{B}, \hat{C}] = [\hat{A}, \hat{C}] + [\hat{B}, \hat{C}] \tag{5.6}$$

$$[\hat{A}, \hat{B}\hat{C}] = [\hat{A}, \hat{B}]\hat{C} + \hat{B}[\hat{A}, \hat{C}] \tag{5.7}$$

$$[\hat{A}\hat{B}, \hat{C}] = [\hat{A}, \hat{C}]\hat{B} + \hat{A}[\hat{B}, \hat{C}] \tag{5.8}$$

where k is a constant, and the operators are assumed to be linear.

Let us use these identities to work out some of the commutators in Problem 3.11. Our starting point is Eq. (3.9):

$$\left[\frac{\partial}{\partial x}, x\right] = 1 \tag{5.9}$$

We have

$$[\hat{x}, \hat{p}_x] = \left[x, \frac{\hbar}{i}\frac{\partial}{\partial x}\right] = \frac{\hbar}{i}\left[x, \frac{\partial}{\partial x}\right] = -\frac{\hbar}{i}\left[\frac{\partial}{\partial x}, x\right] = -\frac{\hbar}{i}$$

$$[\hat{x}, \hat{p}_x] = i\hbar \tag{5.10}$$

$$[\hat{x}, \hat{p}_x^2] = [\hat{x}, \hat{p}_x]\hat{p}_x + \hat{p}_x[\hat{x}, \hat{p}_x] = i\hbar \cdot \frac{\hbar}{i}\frac{\partial}{\partial x} + \frac{\hbar}{i}\frac{\partial}{\partial x} \cdot i\hbar$$

$$[\hat{x}, \hat{p}_x^2] = 2\hbar^2 \frac{\partial}{\partial x} \tag{5.11}$$

For a one-particle three-dimensional system, we have

$$[\hat{x}, \hat{H}] = [\hat{x}, \hat{T} + \hat{V}] = [\hat{x}, \hat{T}] + [\hat{x}, \hat{V}(x, y, z)] = [\hat{x}, \hat{T}]$$

$$= \left[\hat{x}, \frac{1}{2m}(\hat{p}_x^2 + \hat{p}_y^2 + \hat{p}_z^2)\right]$$

$$= \frac{1}{2m}[\hat{x}, \hat{p}_x^2] + \frac{1}{2m}[\hat{x}, \hat{p}_y^2] + \frac{1}{2m}[\hat{x}, \hat{p}_z^2]$$

$$= \frac{1}{2m} \cdot 2\hbar^2 \frac{\partial}{\partial x} + 0 + 0$$

$$[\hat{x}, \hat{H}] = \frac{\hbar^2}{m}\frac{\partial}{\partial x} = \frac{i\hbar}{m}\hat{p}_x \tag{5.12}$$

We leave it to you to show that

$$[\hat{p}_x, \hat{H}] = \frac{\hbar}{i}\frac{\partial V(x, y, z)}{\partial x} \tag{5.13}$$

The above commutators have important physical consequences. Since $[\hat{x}, \hat{p}_x] \neq 0$, we cannot expect the state function to be simultaneously an eigenfunction of $\hat{x}$ and of $\hat{p}_x$; hence, we cannot simultaneously assign definite values to x and p_x, in agreement with the uncertainty principle. Since $\hat{x}$ and $\hat{H}$ do not commute, we cannot expect to assign definite values to the energy and the x coordinate at the same time. A stationary state (which has a definite energy) shows a spread of possible values for x, the probabilities for observing various values of x being given by the Born postulate.

For a state function Ψ that is not an eigenfunction of $\hat{A}$, we get various possible outcomes when we measure A in identical systems. We want some measure of the spread or dispersion in the set of observed values A_i. If $\langle A \rangle$ is the average of these values, then the deviation of each measurement from the average is $A_i - \langle A \rangle$. If we averaged all the deviations, we would get zero, since positive and negative deviations would cancel. Hence, to make all deviations positive, we square them. The average of the squares of the deviations is called the *variance* of A, symbolized in statistics by σ_A^2 and in quantum mechanics by $(\Delta A)^2$:

$$(\Delta A)^2 \equiv \sigma_A^2 \equiv \langle (A - \langle A \rangle)^2 \rangle = \int \Psi^*(\hat{A} - \langle A \rangle)^2 \Psi \, d\tau \tag{5.14}$$

where (3.117) was used. The positive square root of the variance is called the *standard deviation*, σ_A or ΔA. The standard deviation is the most commonly used measure of spread, and we shall take it as the measure of the "uncertainty" in A. The definition (5.14) is equivalent to (Problem 5.1):

$$(\Delta A)^2 = \langle A^2 \rangle - \langle A \rangle^2 \tag{5.15}$$

For the product of the standard deviations of two properties, it can be shown (see Problem 7.35) that:

$$\Delta A \, \Delta B \geqslant \frac{1}{2} \left| \int \Psi^*[\hat{A}, \hat{B}] \Psi \, d\tau \right| \tag{5.16}$$

If $\hat{A}$ and $\hat{B}$ commute, then the integral in (5.16) is zero, and we have the possibility of having ΔA and ΔB both zero, in agreement with the previous discussion. As an example of (5.16), we find, using (5.10),

$$\Delta x \, \Delta p_x \geqslant \frac{1}{2} \left| \int \Psi^* i \hbar \Psi \, d\tau \right| = \tfrac{1}{2} \hbar |i| \left| \int \Psi^* \Psi \, d\tau \right| \tag{5.17}$$

$$\Delta x \, \Delta p_x \geqslant \tfrac{1}{2} \hbar \tag{5.18}$$

Equation (5.18) is the quantitative statement of the Heisenberg uncertainty principle. Consider, for example, the ground state of the particle in a three-dimensional box. Using the results of Problem 3.16 and Eqs. (3.124), (3.125), (3.120), and (3.47), we have

$$\langle x \rangle = \frac{a}{2} \qquad \langle x^2 \rangle = a^2 \left(\frac{1}{3} - \frac{1}{2\pi^2} \right) \tag{5.19}$$

$$\langle p_x \rangle = 0 \qquad \langle p_x^2 \rangle = h^2/4a^2 \tag{5.20}$$

From (5.15), we find

$$\Delta x = \frac{a}{2\pi}\left(\frac{\pi^2-6}{3}\right)^{1/2} \qquad \Delta p_x = \frac{h}{2a} \tag{5.21}$$

$$\Delta x\,\Delta p_x = \frac{\hbar}{2}\left(\frac{\pi^2-6}{3}\right)^{1/2} = 0.57\hbar > \frac{\hbar}{2}$$

There is also an uncertainty relation involving energy and time:

$$\Delta E\,\Delta t \geqslant \tfrac{1}{2}\hbar \tag{5.22}$$

Some texts state that (5.22) is derived from (5.16) by taking $i\hbar\,\partial/\partial t$ as the energy operator and multiplication by t as the time operator. However, the energy operator is the Hamiltonian $\hat{H}$, and not $i\hbar\,\partial/\partial t$. Moreover, time is not an observable but is a parameter in quantum mechanics; hence there is no quantum-mechanical time operator. (The noun *observable* in quantum mechanics means a physically measurable property of a system.) Equation (5.22) must be derived by a special treatment, which we omit. (See *Blokhintsev*, Sections 99 and 113.) The derivation of (5.22) shows that Δt is to be interpreted as the lifetime of the state whose energy is uncertain by ΔE. It is often stated that Δt in (5.22) is the duration of the energy measurement; however, Aharonov and Bohm have shown that "energy can be measured reproducibly in an arbitrarily short time." [See Y. Aharonov and D. Bohm, *Phys. Rev.*, **122**, 1649 (1961); **134**, B1417 (1964).]

Now consider the possibility of simultaneously assigning definite values to *three* physical quantities: A, B, and C. Suppose

$$[\hat{A},\hat{B}] = 0 \tag{5.23}$$

$$[\hat{A},\hat{C}] = 0 \tag{5.24}$$

Is this sufficient to insure that there exist simultaneous eigenfunctions of all three operators? Equation (5.23) insures that we can construct a common set of eigenfunctions for $\hat{A}$ and $\hat{B}$; Eq. (5.24) insures that we can construct a common set of eigenfunctions for $\hat{A}$ and $\hat{C}$. If these two sets of eigenfunctions are the same, then we will have a common set of eigenfunctions for all three operators. Hence we ask: Is the set of eigenfunctions of the linear operator $\hat{A}$ uniquely determined (apart from arbitrary multiplicative constants)? The answer is, in general, no. If there is more than one independent eigenfunction corresponding to each eigenvalue of $\hat{A}$ (i.e., degeneracy), then any linear combination of the eigenfunctions of the degenerate eigenvalue is an eigenfunction of $\hat{A}$ (Section 3.6). It might well be that the proper linear combinations needed to give eigenfunctions of $\hat{B}$ would differ from the linear combinations that give eigenfunctions of $\hat{C}$. It turns out that if we are to have a common complete set of eigenfunctions of all three operators, we require that

$$[\hat{B},\hat{C}] = 0 \tag{5.25}$$

in addition to (5.23) and (5.24). To have a complete set of functions that are simultaneous eigenfunctions of several operators, we must have each operator commute with every other operator.

5.2 Vectors

In the next section we will solve the eigenvalue problem for angular momentum, which is a vector property. We therefore first review vectors.

Physical properties (e.g., mass, length, energy) that are completely specified by their magnitude are called *scalars*. Physical properties (e.g., force, velocity, momentum) that require specification of both magnitude and direction are called *vectors*. A vector is represented by a directed line segment whose length and direction give the magnitude and direction of the property. We use boldface type for vectors.

We define the sum of two vectors **A** and **B** by the following procedure: Slide the first vector so that its tail touches the head of the second vector, keeping the direction of the first vector fixed. Then draw a new vector from the tail of the second vector to the head of the first vector. See Fig. 5.1. The product of a vector and a scalar, $c\mathbf{A}$, is defined as a vector of length $|c|$ times the length of **A**, and the same direction as **A** if c is positive, or the opposite direction as **A**, if c is negative.

To obtain an algebraic (as well as geometric) way of representing vectors, we set up Cartesian coordinates in space. We draw a vector of unit length directed along the positive x axis and call it **i**. (No connection with $i = \sqrt{-1}$.) Unit vectors

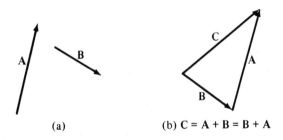

(a)　　　　　　(b) C = A + B = B + A

FIGURE 5.1　*Addition of vectors.*

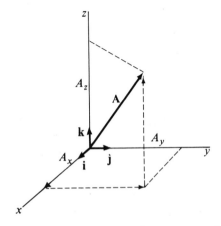

FIGURE 5.2　*Unit vectors and components of* **A**.

in the positive y and z directions are called $\mathbf{j}$ and $\mathbf{k}$ (Fig. 5.2). To represent any vector $\mathbf{A}$ in terms of the three unit vectors, we first slide $\mathbf{A}$ so that its tail is at the origin, preserving its direction during this process. We then find the projections of $\mathbf{A}$ on the x, y, and z axes: A_x, A_y, and A_z. From the definition of vector addition it follows that (Fig. 5.2):

$$\mathbf{A} = A_x \mathbf{i} + A_y \mathbf{j} + A_z \mathbf{k} \tag{5.26}$$

To specify $\mathbf{A}$, it is sufficient to specify its three components: (A_x, A_y, A_z). We can therefore define a vector in three-dimensional space as an ordered set of three numbers. The advantage of this definition is that it can be extended to more than three dimensions. Thus a vector in five-dimensional "space" is an ordered set of five numbers. Such abstract vector spaces (which can be of infinite dimension) are used in advanced formulations of quantum mechanics.

Two vectors $\mathbf{A}$ and $\mathbf{B}$ are equal if and only if all the corresponding components are equal: $A_x = B_x, A_y = B_y, A_z = B_z$. Hence a vector equation is equivalent to three scalar equations.

To add two vectors analytically, we add corresponding components:

$$\mathbf{A} + \mathbf{B} = A_x \mathbf{i} + A_y \mathbf{j} + A_z \mathbf{k} + B_x \mathbf{i} + B_y \mathbf{j} + B_z \mathbf{k}$$

$$\mathbf{A} + \mathbf{B} = (A_x + B_x)\mathbf{i} + (A_y + B_y)\mathbf{j} + (A_z + B_z)\mathbf{k} \tag{5.27}$$

Also, if c is a scalar, then

$$c\mathbf{A} = cA_x \mathbf{i} + cA_y \mathbf{j} + cA_z \mathbf{k} \tag{5.28}$$

The magnitude A of a vector $\mathbf{A}$ is its length, and is therefore a scalar. Often the notation $|\mathbf{A}|$ is used for the magnitude of $\mathbf{A}$.

The *dot product* (or *scalar product*) $\mathbf{A} \cdot \mathbf{B}$ of two vectors is defined by

$$\mathbf{A} \cdot \mathbf{B} = |\mathbf{A}| |\mathbf{B}| \cos \theta = \mathbf{B} \cdot \mathbf{A} \tag{5.29}$$

where θ is the angle between the vectors. The dot product, being the product of three scalars, is a scalar. Note that $|\mathbf{A}| \cos \theta$ is the projection of $\mathbf{A}$ on $\mathbf{B}$. From the definition of vector addition, it follows that the projection of the vector $(\mathbf{A} + \mathbf{B})$ on some vector $\mathbf{C}$ is the sum of the projections of $\mathbf{A}$ and of $\mathbf{B}$ on $\mathbf{C}$. Hence

$$(\mathbf{A} + \mathbf{B}) \cdot \mathbf{C} = \mathbf{A} \cdot \mathbf{C} + \mathbf{B} \cdot \mathbf{C} \tag{5.30}$$

Since the three unit vectors $\mathbf{i}$, $\mathbf{j}$, and $\mathbf{k}$ are each of unit length and are mutually perpendicular, we have

$$\mathbf{i} \cdot \mathbf{i} = \mathbf{j} \cdot \mathbf{j} = \mathbf{k} \cdot \mathbf{k} = \cos(0) = 1$$

$$\mathbf{i} \cdot \mathbf{j} = \mathbf{j} \cdot \mathbf{k} = \mathbf{k} \cdot \mathbf{i} = \cos\left(\frac{\pi}{2}\right) = 0 \tag{5.31}$$

We can use (5.31) and the distributive law (5.30) to get an important formula for the dot product of two vectors:

$$\mathbf{A} \cdot \mathbf{B} = (A_x \mathbf{i} + A_y \mathbf{j} + A_z \mathbf{k}) \cdot (B_x \mathbf{i} + B_y \mathbf{j} + B_z \mathbf{k}) \tag{5.32}$$

$$\mathbf{A} \cdot \mathbf{B} = A_x B_x + A_y B_y + A_z B_z \tag{5.33}$$

where six of the nine terms in the dot product are zero.

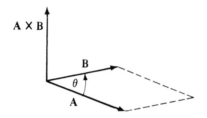

FIGURE 5.3   *Cross product of two vectors.*

Consider the dot product of a vector with itself.   From (5.29) we have

$$\mathbf{A} \cdot \mathbf{A} = |\mathbf{A}|^2 \tag{5.34}$$

Using (5.33) we therefore have:

$$|\mathbf{A}| = (A_x^2 + A_y^2 + A_z^2)^{1/2} \tag{5.35}$$

For three-dimensional vectors, there is another type of product.   The *vector product* or *cross product* $\mathbf{A} \times \mathbf{B}$ is a vector whose magnitude is

$$|\mathbf{A} \times \mathbf{B}| = |\mathbf{A}| \, |\mathbf{B}| \sin \theta \tag{5.36}$$

whose line segment is perpendicular to the plane defined by $\mathbf{A}$ and $\mathbf{B}$, and whose direction is such that $\mathbf{A}$, $\mathbf{B}$, and $\mathbf{A} \times \mathbf{B}$ form a right-handed system (just as the x, y, and z axes form a right-handed system).   (See Fig. 5.3.)   From the definition it follows that

$$\mathbf{B} \times \mathbf{A} = -\mathbf{A} \times \mathbf{B} \tag{5.37}$$

Also, it can be shown that (*Taylor and Mann*, pp. 281–282):

$$\mathbf{A} \times (\mathbf{B} + \mathbf{C}) = \mathbf{A} \times \mathbf{B} + \mathbf{A} \times \mathbf{C} \tag{5.38}$$

For the three unit vectors, we have

$$\mathbf{i} \times \mathbf{i} = \mathbf{j} \times \mathbf{j} = \mathbf{k} \times \mathbf{k} = \sin(0) = 0 \tag{5.39}$$

$$\mathbf{i} \times \mathbf{j} = \mathbf{k}, \qquad \mathbf{j} \times \mathbf{i} = -\mathbf{k}$$

$$\mathbf{j} \times \mathbf{k} = \mathbf{i}, \qquad \mathbf{k} \times \mathbf{j} = -\mathbf{i} \tag{5.40}$$

$$\mathbf{k} \times \mathbf{i} = \mathbf{j}, \qquad \mathbf{i} \times \mathbf{k} = -\mathbf{j}$$

Using these equations and the distributive property (5.38), we find

$$(\mathbf{A} \times \mathbf{B}) = (A_x \mathbf{i} + A_y \mathbf{j} + A_z \mathbf{k}) \times (B_x \mathbf{i} + B_y \mathbf{j} + B_z \mathbf{k}) \tag{5.41}$$

$$\mathbf{A} \times \mathbf{B} = (A_y B_z - A_z B_y)\mathbf{i} + (A_z B_x - A_x B_z)\mathbf{j} + (A_x B_y - A_y B_x)\mathbf{k}$$

As a mnemonic device, we can write (see Section 8.3)

$$\mathbf{A} \times \mathbf{B} = \begin{vmatrix} \mathbf{i} & \mathbf{j} & \mathbf{k} \\ A_x & A_y & A_z \\ B_x & B_y & B_z \end{vmatrix} = \mathbf{i} \begin{vmatrix} A_y & A_z \\ B_y & B_z \end{vmatrix} - \mathbf{j} \begin{vmatrix} A_x & A_z \\ B_x & B_z \end{vmatrix} + \mathbf{k} \begin{vmatrix} A_x & A_y \\ B_x & B_y \end{vmatrix} \tag{5.42}$$

We define the vector operator *del* as

$$\nabla \equiv \mathbf{i}\frac{\partial}{\partial x} + \mathbf{j}\frac{\partial}{\partial y} + \mathbf{k}\frac{\partial}{\partial z} \tag{5.43}$$

From Eq. (3.28) the operator for the linear-momentum vector is

$$\hat{\mathbf{p}} = -i\hbar\nabla \tag{5.44}$$

We define the *gradient* of a function $g(x, y, z)$ as the result of operating on the function with del:

$$\mathbf{grad}\, g(x, y, z) \equiv \nabla g(x, y, z) \equiv \mathbf{i}\frac{\partial g}{\partial x} + \mathbf{j}\frac{\partial g}{\partial y} + \mathbf{k}\frac{\partial g}{\partial z} \tag{5.45}$$

The gradient of a scalar function is a vector function. Physically, the vector $\nabla g(x, y, z)$ represents the spatial rate of change of the function g; the x component of ∇g is the rate of change of g with respect to x, etc. It can be shown that the vector ∇g points in the direction in which the rate of change of g is greatest. From Eq. (4.26), we have

$$\mathbf{F} = -\nabla V(x, y, z) = -\mathbf{i}\frac{\partial V}{\partial x} - \mathbf{j}\frac{\partial V}{\partial y} - \mathbf{k}\frac{\partial V}{\partial z} \tag{5.46}$$

For example, the force field of a point charge is radially directed, and the rate of change of potential energy of another charge in this field is greatest in the radial direction.

The *divergence* of a vector function is the scalar function found by taking the dot product of the vector operator del and the vector function:

$$\mathrm{div}\,\mathbf{A} \equiv \nabla\cdot\mathbf{A} = \left(\mathbf{i}\frac{\partial}{\partial x} + \mathbf{j}\frac{\partial}{\partial y} + \mathbf{k}\frac{\partial}{\partial z}\right)\cdot(A_x\mathbf{i} + A_y\mathbf{j} + A_z\mathbf{k})$$

$$\mathrm{div}\,\mathbf{A} \equiv \frac{\partial A_x}{\partial x} + \frac{\partial A_y}{\partial y} + \frac{\partial A_z}{\partial z} \tag{5.47}$$

For the divergence of the gradient of a function, we have:

$$\mathrm{div}\,[\mathbf{grad}\, g(x, y, z)] = \left(\mathbf{i}\frac{\partial}{\partial x} + \mathbf{j}\frac{\partial}{\partial y} + \mathbf{k}\frac{\partial}{\partial z}\right)\cdot\left(\mathbf{i}\frac{\partial g}{\partial x} + \mathbf{j}\frac{\partial g}{\partial y} + \mathbf{k}\frac{\partial g}{\partial z}\right)$$

$$\nabla\cdot\nabla g = \frac{\partial^2 g}{\partial x^2} + \frac{\partial^2 g}{\partial y^2} + \frac{\partial^2 g}{\partial z^2} = \nabla^2 g \tag{5.48}$$

which gives the Laplacian [Eq. (3.55)].

Finally, suppose that the components of a vector are each functions of some parameter t:

$$A_x = A_x(t), \qquad A_y = A_y(t), \qquad A_z = A_z(t) \tag{5.49}$$

We define the derivative of the vector with respect to t as:

$$\frac{d\mathbf{A}}{dt} = \mathbf{i}\frac{dA_x}{dt} + \mathbf{j}\frac{dA_y}{dt} + \mathbf{k}\frac{dA_z}{dt} \tag{5.50}$$

5.3 Angular Momentum of a One-Particle System

In Section 3.3 we found the eigenfunctions and eigenvalues for the linear-momentum operator $\hat{p}_x$. In this section, we consider the same problem for angular momentum. Angular momentum is extremely important in the quantum mechanics of atomic structure. We begin by reviewing the classical mechanics of angular momentum.

Consider a moving particle of mass m. We set up a Cartesian coordinate system that is fixed in space. Let $\mathbf{r}$ be the vector from the origin to the instantaneous position of the particle. We have

$$\mathbf{r} = \mathbf{i}x + \mathbf{j}y + \mathbf{k}z \tag{5.51}$$

where x, y, and z are the particle's coordinates at a given instant. These coordinates are functions of time, and defining the velocity vector $\mathbf{v}$ as the time derivative of the position vector, we have [Eq. (5.50)]:

$$\mathbf{v} = \frac{d\mathbf{r}}{dt} = \mathbf{i}\frac{dx}{dt} + \mathbf{j}\frac{dy}{dt} + \mathbf{k}\frac{dz}{dt} \tag{5.52}$$

$$v_x = \frac{dx}{dt}, \qquad v_y = \frac{dy}{dt}, \qquad v_z = \frac{dz}{dt} \tag{5.53}$$

We define the *linear momentum* vector $\mathbf{p}$ by

$$\mathbf{p} = m\mathbf{v} \tag{5.54}$$

$$p_x = mv_x, \qquad p_y = mv_y, \qquad p_z = mv_z \tag{5.55}$$

The particle's *angular momentum* $\mathbf{L}$ is defined as

$$\mathbf{L} = \mathbf{r} \times \mathbf{p} \tag{5.56}$$

$$\mathbf{L} = \begin{vmatrix} \mathbf{i} & \mathbf{j} & \mathbf{k} \\ x & y & z \\ p_x & p_y & p_z \end{vmatrix} \tag{5.57}$$

$$L_x = yp_z - zp_y, \qquad L_y = zp_x - xp_z, \qquad L_z = xp_y - yp_x \tag{5.58}$$

These are the components of the classical-mechanical angular momentum of a single particle.

The torque τ acting on a particle is defined as the cross product of $\mathbf{r}$ and the force acting on the particle:

$$\tau = \mathbf{r} \times \mathbf{F} \tag{5.59}$$

It is readily shown that (*Halliday and Resnick*, Section 12-3):

$$\tau = \frac{d\mathbf{L}}{dt} \tag{5.60}$$

When there is no torque acting on the particle, the rate of change of its angular momentum is zero; i.e., its angular momentum is constant (or conserved). For a planet orbiting the sun, the gravitational force is radially directed; since the cross product of two parallel vectors is zero, there is no torque on the planet and its angular momentum is conserved.

Now for the quantum-mechanical treatment. In quantum mechanics there are two kinds of angular momentum: *orbital* angular momentum results from the motion of a particle through space, and is the analog of the classical-mechanical quantity **L**; *spin* angular momentum (Chapter 10) is an intrinsic property of many microscopic particles, and has no classical-mechanical analog. We are now considering only orbital angular momentum. We get the quantum-mechanical operators for the components of orbital angular momentum of a particle by replacing the quantities in (5.58) by their corresponding operators [Eqs. (3.25)–(3.28)]. We find

$$\hat{L}_x = -i\hbar\left(y\frac{\partial}{\partial z} - z\frac{\partial}{\partial y}\right) \tag{5.61}$$

$$\hat{L}_y = -i\hbar\left(z\frac{\partial}{\partial x} - x\frac{\partial}{\partial z}\right) \tag{5.62}$$

$$\hat{L}_z = -i\hbar\left(x\frac{\partial}{\partial y} - y\frac{\partial}{\partial x}\right) \tag{5.63}$$

(Since $\hat{y}\hat{p}_z = \hat{p}_z\hat{y}$, etc., we don't run into any problems of noncommutativity in constructing these operators.) Using

$$\hat{L}^2 = |\hat{\mathbf{L}}|^2 = \hat{\mathbf{L}} \cdot \hat{\mathbf{L}} = \hat{L}_x^2 + \hat{L}_y^2 + \hat{L}_z^2 \tag{5.64}$$

we can construct the operator for the square of the angular-momentum magnitude from the operators in (5.61)–(5.63).

Since the commutation relations determine which observables can be assigned definite values, we investigate these relations for angular momentum. Operating on some function $f(x, y, z)$ with $\hat{L}_y$, we have

$$\hat{L}_y f = -i\hbar\left(z\frac{\partial f}{\partial x} - x\frac{\partial f}{\partial z}\right) \tag{5.65}$$

Operating on this last equation with $\hat{L}_x$, we have

$$\hat{L}_x\hat{L}_y f = -\hbar^2\left(y\frac{\partial f}{\partial x} + yz\frac{\partial^2 f}{\partial z\,\partial x} - yx\frac{\partial^2 f}{\partial z^2} - z^2\frac{\partial^2 f}{\partial y\,\partial x} + zx\frac{\partial^2 f}{\partial y\,\partial z}\right) \tag{5.66}$$

Similarly,

$$\hat{L}_x f = -i\hbar\left(y\frac{\partial f}{\partial z} - z\frac{\partial f}{\partial y}\right) \tag{5.67}$$

$$\hat{L}_y\hat{L}_x f = -\hbar^2\left(zy\frac{\partial^2 f}{\partial x\,\partial z} - z^2\frac{\partial^2 f}{\partial x\,\partial y} - xy\frac{\partial^2 f}{\partial z^2} + x\frac{\partial f}{\partial y} + xz\frac{\partial^2 f}{\partial z\,\partial y}\right) \tag{5.68}$$

Subtracting (5.68) from (5.66), we have

$$\hat{L}_x\hat{L}_y f - \hat{L}_y\hat{L}_x f = -\hbar^2\left(y\frac{\partial f}{\partial x} - x\frac{\partial f}{\partial y}\right) \tag{5.69}$$

$$[\hat{L}_x, \hat{L}_y] = i\hbar\hat{L}_z \tag{5.70}$$

where we have used relations such as

$$\frac{\partial^2 f}{\partial z\, \partial x} = \frac{\partial^2 f}{\partial x\, \partial z} \tag{5.71}$$

which are true for well-behaved functions. We could use the same procedure to find $[\hat{L}_y, \hat{L}_z]$ and $[\hat{L}_z, \hat{L}_x]$, but we can save time by noting a certain kind of symmetry in (5.61)–(5.63). By a *cyclic permutation* of x, y, and z we mean replace x by y, replace y by z, and replace z by x. If we carry out a cyclic permutation in $\hat{L}_x$, we get $\hat{L}_y$; a cyclic permutation in $\hat{L}_y$ gives $\hat{L}_z$; and $\hat{L}_z$ is transformed into $\hat{L}_x$ by a cyclic permutation. Hence, by carrying out two successive cyclic permutations on (5.70), we have:

$$[\hat{L}_y, \hat{L}_z] = i\hbar \hat{L}_x, \qquad [\hat{L}_z, \hat{L}_x] = i\hbar \hat{L}_y \tag{5.72}$$

Now we evaluate the commutators of $\hat{L}^2$ with each of its components, using commutator identities of Section 5.1.

$$\begin{aligned}
[\hat{L}^2, \hat{L}_x] &= [\hat{L}_x^2 + \hat{L}_y^2 + \hat{L}_z^2, \hat{L}_x] \\
&= [\hat{L}_x^2, \hat{L}_x] + [\hat{L}_y^2, \hat{L}_x] + [\hat{L}_z^2, \hat{L}_x] \\
&= [\hat{L}_y^2, \hat{L}_x] + [\hat{L}_z^2, \hat{L}_x] \\
&= [\hat{L}_y, \hat{L}_x]\hat{L}_y + \hat{L}_y[\hat{L}_y, \hat{L}_x] + [\hat{L}_z, \hat{L}_x]\hat{L}_z + \hat{L}_z[\hat{L}_z, \hat{L}_x] \\
&= -i\hbar \hat{L}_z \hat{L}_y - i\hbar \hat{L}_y \hat{L}_z + i\hbar \hat{L}_y \hat{L}_z + i\hbar \hat{L}_z \hat{L}_y
\end{aligned}$$

$$[\hat{L}^2, \hat{L}_x] = 0 \tag{5.73}$$

Since a cyclic permutation of x, y, and z leaves $\hat{L}^2 = \hat{L}_x^2 + \hat{L}_y^2 + \hat{L}_z^2$ unchanged, if we carry out two such permutations on (5.73), we get

$$[\hat{L}^2, \hat{L}_y] = 0, \qquad [\hat{L}^2, \hat{L}_z] = 0 \tag{5.74}$$

To which of the quantities L^2, L_x, L_y, L_z can we assign definite values simultaneously? Because $\hat{L}^2$ commutes with each of its components, we can specify an exact value for L^2 and any *one* component. However, because no two components of $\hat{L}$ commute with each other, we cannot specify more than one component simultaneously. (There is one exception to this statement which will be discussed shortly.) It is traditional to take L_z as the component of angular momentum that will be specified along with L^2. Note that in specifying $L^2 = |\mathbf{L}|^2$, we are not specifying the vector $\mathbf{L}$, only its magnitude. A complete specification of $\mathbf{L}$ requires simultaneous specification of each of its three components, which we usually cannot do. In classical mechanics when angular momentum is conserved, each of its three components has a definite value. In quantum mechanics when angular momentum is conserved, only its magnitude and one of its components are specifiable.

We could now attempt to find the eigenvalues and common eigenfunctions of $\hat{L}^2$ and $\hat{L}_z$ by using the forms for these operators in Cartesian coordinates. However, we would find that the partial differential equations obtained would not be separable. For this reason, we carry out a transformation to spherical polar

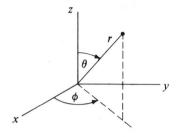

FIGURE 5.4 *Spherical polar coordinates.*

coordinates (Fig. 5.4). The coordinate r is the distance from the origin to the point (x, y, z). The angle θ is the angle the vector $\mathbf{r}$ makes with the positive z axis. The angle that the projection of $\mathbf{r}$ in the xy plane makes with the positive x axis is φ. (Mathematics texts often interchange θ and φ.) A little trigonometry gives:

$$x = r \sin\theta \cos\varphi, \qquad y = r \sin\theta \sin\varphi, \qquad z = r \cos\theta \tag{5.75}$$

$$r^2 = x^2 + y^2 + z^2 \tag{5.76}$$

$$\cos\theta = \frac{z}{(x^2 + y^2 + z^2)^{1/2}} \tag{5.77}$$

$$\tan\varphi = y/x \tag{5.78}$$

To transform the angular-momentum operators to spherical polar co-ordinates, we must transform $\partial/\partial x$, $\partial/\partial y$, and $\partial/\partial z$ into these coordinates. [This transformation may be skimmed if desired. Begin reading again after Eq. (5.93).]

To perform this transformation, we use the *chain rule*. Suppose we have a function of r, θ, and φ: $f(r, \theta, \varphi)$. If we carry out a change of independent variables by substituting

$$r = r(x, y, z), \qquad \theta = \theta(x, y, z), \qquad \varphi = \varphi(x, y, z) \tag{5.79}$$

into f, we transform it into a function of x, y, and z:

$$f[r(x, y, z), \theta(x, y, z), \varphi(x, y, z)] = g(x, y, z) \tag{5.80}$$

For example, suppose that

$$f(r, \theta, \varphi) = 3r \cos\theta + 2 \tan^2\varphi$$

Using (5.76), (5.77), and (5.78), we have

$$g(x, y, z) = 3z + 2y^2 x^{-2}$$

The chain rule tells us how the partial derivatives of $g(x, y, z)$ are related to those of $f(r, \theta, \varphi)$. In fact

$$\left(\frac{\partial g}{\partial x}\right)_{y, z} = \left(\frac{\partial f}{\partial r}\right)_{\theta, \varphi} \left(\frac{\partial r}{\partial x}\right)_{y, z} + \left(\frac{\partial f}{\partial \theta}\right)_{r, \varphi} \left(\frac{\partial \theta}{\partial x}\right)_{y, z} + \left(\frac{\partial f}{\partial \varphi}\right)_{r, \theta} \left(\frac{\partial \varphi}{\partial x}\right)_{y, z} \tag{5.81}$$

$$\left(\frac{\partial g}{\partial y}\right)_{x, z} = \left(\frac{\partial f}{\partial r}\right)_{\theta, \varphi} \left(\frac{\partial r}{\partial y}\right)_{x, z} + \left(\frac{\partial f}{\partial \theta}\right)_{r, \varphi} \left(\frac{\partial \theta}{\partial y}\right)_{x, z} + \left(\frac{\partial f}{\partial \varphi}\right)_{r, \theta} \left(\frac{\partial \varphi}{\partial y}\right)_{x, z} \tag{5.82}$$

$$\left(\frac{\partial g}{\partial z}\right)_{x, y} = \left(\frac{\partial f}{\partial r}\right)_{\theta, \varphi} \left(\frac{\partial r}{\partial z}\right)_{x, y} + \left(\frac{\partial f}{\partial \theta}\right)_{r, \varphi} \left(\frac{\partial \theta}{\partial z}\right)_{x, y} + \left(\frac{\partial f}{\partial \varphi}\right)_{r, \theta} \left(\frac{\partial \varphi}{\partial z}\right)_{x, y} \tag{5.83}$$

To convert these equations to operator equations, we delete f and g. However, it would not do to write, for example,

$$\frac{\partial}{\partial r}\left(\frac{\partial r}{\partial x}\right)_{y,z}$$

for the first term on the right side of the operator equation corresponding to (5.81), because this would imply that $\partial/\partial r$ was to operate on

$$\left[\left(\frac{\partial r}{\partial x}\right)_{y,z} f\right]$$

whereas, according to (5.81), it should operate only on f. For the operator equation corresponding to (5.81) we thus write

$$\frac{\partial}{\partial x} = \left(\frac{\partial r}{\partial x}\right)_{y,z}\frac{\partial}{\partial r} + \left(\frac{\partial\theta}{\partial x}\right)_{y,z}\frac{\partial}{\partial\theta} + \left(\frac{\partial\varphi}{\partial x}\right)_{y,z}\frac{\partial}{\partial\varphi} \tag{5.84}$$

with similar equations for $\partial/\partial y$ and $\partial/\partial z$. The task now is to evaluate the partial derivatives such as $(\partial r/\partial x)_{y,z}$. Taking the partial derivative of (5.76) with respect to x, at constant y and z, we have

$$2r\left(\frac{\partial r}{\partial x}\right)_{y,z} = 2x = 2r\sin\theta\cos\varphi$$

$$\left(\frac{\partial r}{\partial x}\right)_{y,z} = \sin\theta\cos\varphi \tag{5.85}$$

Differentiating (5.76) with respect to y and with respect to z, we find

$$\left(\frac{\partial r}{\partial y}\right)_{x,z} = \sin\theta\sin\varphi, \qquad \left(\frac{\partial r}{\partial z}\right)_{x,y} = \cos\theta \tag{5.86}$$

From (5.77) we find

$$-\sin\theta\left(\frac{\partial\theta}{\partial x}\right)_{y,z} = -\frac{xz}{r^3} \tag{5.87}$$

$$\left(\frac{\partial\theta}{\partial x}\right)_{y,z} = \frac{\cos\theta\cos\varphi}{r} \tag{5.88}$$

Also

$$\left(\frac{\partial\theta}{\partial y}\right)_{x,z} = \frac{\cos\theta\sin\varphi}{r}, \qquad \left(\frac{\partial\theta}{\partial z}\right)_{x,y} = -\frac{\sin\theta}{r} \tag{5.89}$$

From (5.78), we have

$$\left(\frac{\partial\varphi}{\partial x}\right)_{y,z} = -\frac{\sin\varphi}{r\sin\theta}, \qquad \left(\frac{\partial\varphi}{\partial y}\right)_{x,z} = \frac{\cos\varphi}{r\sin\theta}, \qquad \left(\frac{\partial\varphi}{\partial z}\right)_{x,y} = 0 \tag{5.90}$$

Substituting (5.85), (5.88), and (5.90) into (5.84), we find

$$\frac{\partial}{\partial x} = \sin\theta\cos\varphi\frac{\partial}{\partial r} + \frac{\cos\theta\cos\varphi}{r}\frac{\partial}{\partial\theta} - \frac{\sin\varphi}{r\sin\theta}\frac{\partial}{\partial\varphi} \tag{5.91}$$

Similarly

$$\frac{\partial}{\partial y} = \sin\theta\sin\varphi\frac{\partial}{\partial r} + \frac{\cos\theta\sin\varphi}{r}\frac{\partial}{\partial\theta} + \frac{\cos\varphi}{r\sin\theta}\frac{\partial}{\partial\varphi} \tag{5.92}$$

$$\frac{\partial}{\partial z} = \cos\theta\frac{\partial}{\partial r} - \frac{\sin\theta}{r}\frac{\partial}{\partial\theta} \tag{5.93}$$

At long last, we are ready to express the angular-momentum components in spherical polar coordinates. Substituting (5.75), (5.92), and (5.93) into (5.61), we have

$$\hat{L}_x = -i\hbar\left[r\sin\theta\sin\varphi\left(\cos\theta\frac{\partial}{\partial r} - \frac{\sin\theta}{r}\frac{\partial}{\partial\theta}\right)\right.$$
$$\left. - r\cos\theta\left(\sin\theta\sin\varphi\frac{\partial}{\partial r} + \frac{\cos\theta\sin\varphi}{r}\frac{\partial}{\partial\theta} + \frac{\cos\varphi}{r\sin\theta}\frac{\partial}{\partial\varphi}\right)\right]$$

$$\hat{L}_x = i\hbar\left(\sin\varphi\frac{\partial}{\partial\theta} + \cot\theta\cos\varphi\frac{\partial}{\partial\varphi}\right) \tag{5.94}$$

Also

$$\hat{L}_y = -i\hbar\left(\cos\varphi\frac{\partial}{\partial\theta} - \cot\theta\sin\varphi\frac{\partial}{\partial\varphi}\right) \tag{5.95}$$

$$\hat{L}_z = -i\hbar\frac{\partial}{\partial\varphi} \tag{5.96}$$

By squaring each of $\hat{L}_x$, $\hat{L}_y$, and $\hat{L}_z$, and then adding their squares, we can construct $\hat{L}^2$ [Eq. (5.64)]. The result is (Problem 5.10):

$$\hat{L}^2 = -\hbar^2\left(\frac{\partial^2}{\partial\theta^2} + \cot\theta\frac{\partial}{\partial\theta} + \frac{1}{\sin^2\theta}\frac{\partial^2}{\partial\varphi^2}\right) \tag{5.97}$$

Although the angular-momentum operators depend on all three Cartesian coordinates, x, y, and z, they involve only the two spherical polar coordinates θ and φ.

We now find the common eigenfunctions of $\hat{L}^2$ and $\hat{L}_z$, which we denote by Y. Since these operators involve θ and φ only, Y will be a function of these two coordinates: $Y = Y(\theta, \varphi)$. (Of course, since the operators are linear, we can multiply Y by an arbitrary function of r, and still have an eigenfunction of $\hat{L}^2$ and $\hat{L}_z$.) We must solve

$$\hat{L}_z Y(\theta, \varphi) = bY(\theta, \varphi) \tag{5.98}$$

$$\hat{L}^2 Y(\theta, \varphi) = cY(\theta, \varphi) \tag{5.99}$$

where b and c are the eigenvalues of $\hat{L}_z$ and $\hat{L}^2$.

Using the $\hat{L}_z$ operator, we have

$$-i\hbar\frac{\partial}{\partial\varphi}Y(\theta, \varphi) = bY(\theta, \varphi) \tag{5.100}$$

Since the operator in (5.100) does not involve θ, we try a separation of variables, writing

$$Y(\theta, \varphi) = S(\theta)T(\varphi) \tag{5.101}$$

Equation (5.100) becomes

$$-i\hbar \frac{\partial}{\partial \varphi}[S(\theta)T(\varphi)] = bS(\theta)T(\varphi)$$

$$-i\hbar S(\theta)\frac{dT(\varphi)}{d\varphi} = bS(\theta)T(\varphi)$$

$$\frac{dT(\varphi)}{T(\varphi)} = \frac{ib}{\hbar}d\varphi$$

$$T(\varphi) = Ae^{ib\varphi/\hbar} \qquad \textbf{(5.102)}$$

where A is an arbitrary constant. Is T suitable as an eigenfunction? The answer is no, since it is not, in general, a single-valued function. If we add 2π to φ, we will still be at the same point in space, and hence we want no change in T when this is done. For T to be single-valued, we have the restriction

$$T(\varphi+2\pi) = T(\varphi) \qquad \textbf{(5.103)}$$

$$Ae^{ib\varphi/\hbar}e^{ib2\pi/\hbar} = Ae^{ib\varphi/\hbar}$$

$$e^{ib2\pi/\hbar} = 1 \qquad \textbf{(5.104)}$$

To satisfy $e^{i\alpha} = \cos\alpha + i\sin\alpha = 1$, we must have $\alpha = 2\pi m$, where

$$m = 0, \pm 1, \pm 2, \pm \cdots$$

Therefore (5.104) gives

$$2\pi b/\hbar = 2\pi m$$

$$b = m\hbar, \qquad m = \cdots -2, -1, 0, 1, 2 \cdots \qquad \textbf{(5.105)}$$

and (5.102) becomes

$$T(\varphi) = Ae^{im\varphi}, \qquad m = 0, \pm 1, \pm 2, ... \qquad \textbf{(5.106)}$$

The eigenvalues for the z component of angular momentum are quantized.

We fix A by normalizing T. First let us consider normalizing some function F of r, θ, and φ. The ranges of the independent variables are (see Fig. 5.4):

$$0 \leqslant r \leqslant \infty, \qquad 0 \leqslant \theta \leqslant \pi, \qquad 0 \leqslant \varphi \leqslant 2\pi$$

The infinitesimal volume element in spherical polar coordinates corresponding to $dx\, dy\, dz$ in Cartesian coordinates is (*Taylor and Mann*, p. 417):

$$r^2 \sin\theta\, dr\, d\theta\, d\varphi \qquad \textbf{(5.107)}$$

Hence we have

$$\int_0^\infty \left[\int_0^\pi \left[\int_0^{2\pi} |F^2(r, \theta, \varphi)|\, d\varphi \right] \sin\theta\, d\theta \right] r^2\, dr = 1 \qquad \textbf{(5.108)}$$

If it happens that F has the form

$$F(r, \theta, \varphi) = R(r)S(\theta)T(\varphi) \qquad \textbf{(5.109)}$$

then (5.108) becomes

$$\int_0^\infty |R^2(r)| r^2 \, dr \int_0^\pi |S^2(\theta)| \sin\theta \, d\theta \int_0^{2\pi} |T^2(\varphi)| \, d\varphi = 1 \qquad \text{(5.110)}$$

and it is convenient to normalize each factor of F separately:

$$\int_0^\infty |R^2| r^2 \, dr = 1, \qquad \int_0^\pi |S^2| \sin\theta \, d\theta = 1, \qquad \int_0^{2\pi} |T^2| \, d\varphi = 1 \quad \text{(5.111)}$$

(We did the same sort of thing for the wave function of the particle in a three-dimensional box.) Therefore

$$\int_0^{2\pi} (Ae^{im\varphi})^* Ae^{im\varphi} \, d\varphi = 1 = |A|^2 \int_0^{2\pi} d\varphi \qquad \text{(5.112)}$$

$$|A| = (2\pi)^{-1/2} \qquad \text{(5.113)}$$

$$T(\varphi) = \frac{1}{\sqrt{2\pi}} e^{im\varphi}, \qquad m = 0, \pm 1, \pm 2, \ldots \qquad \text{(5.114)}$$

We now solve (5.99) for the eigenvalues of $\hat{L}^2$. Using (5.97), (5.101), and (5.114), we have

$$-\hbar^2 \left(\frac{\partial^2}{\partial\theta^2} + \cot\theta \frac{\partial}{\partial\theta} + \frac{1}{\sin^2\theta} \frac{\partial^2}{\partial\varphi^2} \right) \left(S(\theta) \frac{1}{\sqrt{2\pi}} e^{im\varphi} \right) = cS(\theta) \frac{1}{\sqrt{2\pi}} e^{im\varphi}$$

$$\frac{d^2 S}{d\theta^2} + \cot\theta \frac{dS}{d\theta} - \frac{m^2}{\sin^2\theta} S = -\frac{c}{\hbar^2} S \qquad \text{(5.115)}$$

To solve (5.115), we carry out some rather unexciting manipulations, which may be skimmed on a first reading. First, for convenience, we change the independent variable by making the substitution

$$w = \cos\theta \qquad \text{(5.116)}$$

This transforms S into some new function of w:

$$S(\theta) = G(w) \qquad \text{(5.117)}$$

The chain rule gives

$$\frac{dS}{d\theta} = \frac{dG}{dw} \frac{dw}{d\theta} = -\sin\theta \frac{dG}{dw} = -(1-w^2)^{1/2} \frac{dG}{dw} \qquad \text{(5.118)}$$

To calculate $d^2 S/d\theta^2$, we use some operator algebra:

$$\frac{d}{d\theta} = -(1-w^2)^{1/2} \frac{d}{dw}$$

$$\frac{d^2}{d\theta^2} = (1-w^2)^{1/2} \frac{d}{dw} (1-w^2)^{1/2} \frac{d}{dw}$$

$$\frac{d^2}{d\theta^2} = (1-w^2) \frac{d^2}{dw^2} + (1-w^2)^{1/2} (\tfrac{1}{2})(1-w^2)^{-1/2}(-2w) \frac{d}{dw}$$

$$\frac{d^2 S}{d\theta^2} = (1-w^2) \frac{d^2 G}{dw^2} - w \frac{dG}{dw} \qquad \text{(5.119)}$$

Using (5.119), (5.118), and

$$\cot \theta = \frac{\cos \theta}{\sin \theta} = \frac{w}{(1-w^2)^{1/2}}$$

we find that (5.115) becomes

$$(1-w^2)\frac{d^2 G}{dw^2} - 2w\frac{dG}{dw} + \left[\frac{c}{\hbar^2} - \frac{m^2}{(1-w^2)}\right]G(w) = 0 \qquad \textbf{(5.120)}$$

The range of w is $-1 \leqslant w \leqslant 1$.

To get a two-term recursion relation when we try a power-series solution, we make the following change of dependent variable:

$$G(w) = (1-w^2)^{|m|/2}H(w) \qquad \textbf{(5.121)}$$

Differentiating (5.121), we evaluate G' and G'', and (5.120) becomes, after we divide by $(1-w^2)^{|m|/2}$,

$$(1-w^2)H'' - 2(|m|+1)wH' + [c\hbar^{-2} - |m|(|m|+1)]H = 0 \qquad \textbf{(5.122)}$$

We now try a power series for H:

$$H(w) = \sum_{j=0}^{\infty} a_j w^j \qquad \textbf{(5.123)}$$

Differentiating [compare Eqs. (4.38)–(4.40)], we have

$$H'(w) = \sum_{j=0}^{\infty} ja_j w^{j-1}$$

$$H''(w) = \sum_{j=0}^{\infty} j(j-1)a_j w^{j-2} = \sum_{j=0}^{\infty} (j+2)(j+1)a_{j+2} w^j$$

Substitution of these power series into (5.122) yields (after combining sums):

$$\sum_{j=0}^{\infty}\left[(j+2)(j+1)a_{j+2} + \left(-j^2 - j - 2|m|j + \frac{c}{\hbar^2} - |m|^2 - |m|\right)a_j\right]w^j = 0$$

Setting the coefficient of w^j equal to zero, we have the recursion relation:

$$a_{j+2} = \frac{[(j+|m|)(j+|m|+1) - c/\hbar^2]}{(j+1)(j+2)}a_j \qquad \textbf{(5.124)}$$

Just as in the harmonic-oscillator case, the general solution of (5.122) is an arbitrary linear combination of a series of even powers (whose coefficients are determined by a_0) and a series of odd powers (whose coefficients are determined by a_1). It can be shown[1] that the infinite series defined by the recursion relation (5.124) does not give well-behaved eigenfunctions. Hence, as in the harmonic-oscillator case, we must cause one of the series to break off, its last term being $a_k w^k$. We eliminate the other series by setting a_0 or a_1 equal to zero, depending on

---

[1] Many texts point out that the infinite series diverges at $w = \pm1$. However, this is not sufficient cause to reject the infinite series, since the eigenfunctions might be quadratically integrable, even though infinite at two points. For a careful discussion see M. Whippen, *Am. J. Phys.*, **34**, 656 (1966).

whether k is odd or even. Setting the coefficient of a_k in (5.124) equal to zero, we have

$$c = \hbar^2 (k + |m|) (k + |m| + 1), \qquad k = 0, 1, 2, \ldots \qquad (5.125)$$

Since $|m|$ takes on the values $0, 1, 2, \ldots$, the quantity $k + |m|$ takes on the values $0, 1, 2, \ldots$. We therefore define the quantum number l as

$$l \equiv k + |m| \qquad (5.126)$$

and the allowed eigenvalues for the square of the magnitude of angular momentum are

$$c = l(l+1)\hbar^2, \qquad l = 0, 1, 2, \ldots \qquad (5.127)$$

From (5.126) it follows that $|m| \leqslant l$. The possible values for m are thus

$$m = -l, -l + 1, -l + 2, \ldots, -1, 0, 1, \ldots, l - 2, l - 1, l \qquad (5.128)$$

Taking the positive square root of (5.127), we have for the magnitude of the angular momentum:

$$[l(l+1)]^{1/2}\hbar \qquad (5.129)$$

Since $l \geqslant |m|$, Eq. (5.129) shows that the magnitude of the total angular momentum is greater than the magnitude of the z component $|m|\hbar$ (except for $l = 0$). If it were possible to have the total angular momentum equal to its z component, this would mean that the x and y components were zero, and we would have specified all three components of **L**. However, since the components of angular momentum do not commute with each other, we cannot do this. The one exception is when l is zero. In this case, $|\mathbf{L}|^2 = L_x^2 + L_y^2 + L_z^2$ has zero for its eigenvalue, and it must be true that all three components L_x, L_y, and L_z have zero eigenvalues. From Eq. (5.16), the uncertainties in angular-momentum components satisfy

$$\Delta L_x \, \Delta L_y \geqslant \frac{1}{2} \left| \int \Psi^*[\hat{L}_x, \hat{L}_y] \Psi \, dq \right| = \frac{\hbar}{2} \left| \int \Psi^* \hat{L}_z \Psi \, dq \right| \qquad (5.130)$$

and two similar equations obtained by cyclic permutation. When the eigenvalues of $\hat{L}_z$, $\hat{L}_x$, and $\hat{L}_y$ are zero, $\hat{L}_x \Psi = 0$, $\hat{L}_y \Psi = 0$, $\hat{L}_z \Psi = 0$, the right-hand sides of (5.130) and the two similar equations are zero, and having $\Delta L_x = \Delta L_y = \Delta L_z = 0$ is permitted. But what about the statement in Section 5.1 that to have simultaneous eigenfunctions of two operators, the operators must commute? The answer is that this theorem refers to the possibility of having the whole set of eigenfunctions of one operator being eigenfunctions of the other operator. Thus, even though $\hat{L}_x$ and $\hat{L}_z$ do not commute, it is possible to have *some* of the eigenfunctions of $\hat{L}_z$ (those with $l = 0 = m$) being eigenfunctions of $\hat{L}_x$. However, it is impossible to have *all* of the $\hat{L}_z$ eigenfunctions also be eigenfunctions of $\hat{L}_x$.

Let us find some of the angular-momentum eigenfunctions. From Eqs. (5.116), (5.117), (5.121), (5.123), (5.125), and (5.126), the theta factor in the eigenfunctions is:

$$S_{l,m}(\theta) = \sin^{|m|}(\theta) \sum_{\substack{j=1, 3, \cdots \\ \text{or } j=0, 2, \cdots}}^{l-|m|} a_j \cos^j \theta \qquad (5.131)$$

where the sum is over even or odd values of j, depending on whether $l - |m|$ is even or odd.

For $l = 0$, we have $m = 0$, and the theta factor is

$$S_{0,0}(\theta) = a_0 \tag{5.132}$$

Normalizing [Eq. (5.111)], we have

$$\int_0^\pi |a_0^2| \sin \theta \, d\theta = 1 = 2|a_0^2|$$

$$|a_0| = 2^{-1/2} \tag{5.133}$$

The eigenfunction is [Eqs. (5.101) and (5.114)]:

$$Y_l^m(\theta, \varphi) = S_{l,m}(\theta) T(\varphi) = \frac{1}{\sqrt{2\pi}} S_{l,m}(\theta) e^{im\varphi} \tag{5.134}$$

$$Y_0^0(\theta, \varphi) = \frac{1}{\sqrt{4\pi}} \tag{5.135}$$

[Obviously, (5.135) is an eigenfunction of the operators $\hat{L}^2$, $\hat{L}_x$, $\hat{L}_y$, and $\hat{L}_z$, Eqs. (5.94)–(5.97).] For $l = 0$, there is no angular dependence in the eigenfunction—we say that the eigenfunctions are *spherically symmetric* for $l = 0$.

For $l = 1$, the possible values for m are $-1, 0, 1$. For $|m| = 1$:

$$S_{1, \pm 1}(\theta) = a_0 \sin \theta \tag{5.136}$$

Note that a_0 in (5.136) is not necessarily the same as a_0 in (5.132). Normalization gives

$$1 = |a_0^2| \int_0^\pi \sin^2 \theta \sin \theta \, d\theta = |a_0^2| \int_{-1}^1 (1 - w^2) \, dw$$

$$|a_0| = \sqrt{3/2} \tag{5.137}$$

where the substitution $w = \cos \theta$ was made. For $m = 0$, we find

$$S_{1,0}(\theta) = (3/2)^{1/2} \cos \theta \tag{5.138}$$

To find further functions we may need the recursion relation (5.124), which, using (5.127), becomes

$$a_{j+2} = \frac{[(j + |m|)(j + |m| + 1) - l(l + 1)]}{(j + 1)(j + 2)} a_j \tag{5.139}$$

The functions $S_{l,m}(\theta)$ are well known in mathematics, and are *associated Legendre functions* multiplied by a normalization constant. The associated Legendre functions $P_l^{|m|}(w)$ are defined by

$$P_l^{|m|}(w) = \frac{1}{2^l l!} (1 - w^2)^{|m|/2} \frac{d^{l+|m|}}{dw^{l+|m|}} (w^2 - 1)^l, \qquad l = 0, 1, 2, \ldots \tag{5.140}$$

These functions are related to the *Legendre polynomials* $P_l(w)$, which are defined by

$$P_l(w) = \frac{1}{2^l l!} \frac{d^l}{dw^l} (w^2 - 1)^l, \qquad l = 0, 1, 2, \ldots \tag{5.141}$$

From the definitions, we have

$$P_l^{|m|}(w) = (1-w^2)^{|m|/2} \frac{d^{|m|}}{dw^{|m|}} P_l(w), \qquad P_l^0(w) = P_l(w) \qquad (5.142)$$

It can be shown that (*Pauling and Wilson*, p. 129):

$$S_{l,m}(\theta) = \left[\frac{(2l+1)}{2} \frac{(l-|m|)!}{(l+|m|)!}\right]^{1/2} P_l^{|m|}(\cos\theta) \qquad (5.143)$$

Equations (5.143) and (5.140) give the explicit formula for the normalized theta factor in the angular-momentum eigenfunctions. The first few Legendre polynomials are

$$\begin{array}{ll} P_0(w) = 1 & P_2(w) = \tfrac{1}{2}(3w^2-1) \\ P_1(w) = w & P_3(w) = \tfrac{1}{2}(5w^3-3w) \end{array} \qquad (5.144)$$

Some associated Legendre functions are

$$\begin{array}{ll} P_0^0(w) = 1 & P_2^0(w) = \tfrac{1}{2}(3w^2-1) \\ P_1^0(w) = w & P_2^1(w) = 3w(1-w^2)^{1/2} \\ P_1^1(w) = (1-w^2)^{1/2} & P_2^2(w) = 3 - 3w^2 \end{array} \qquad (5.145)$$

Using (5.143) we construct Table 5.1, which gives the theta factor in the angular-momentum eigenfunctions.

Table 5.1 $S_{l,m}(\theta)$

$l = 0$:	$S_{0,0}$	$= \tfrac{1}{2}\sqrt{2}$
$l = 1$:	$S_{1,0}$	$= \tfrac{1}{2}\sqrt{6}\cos\theta$
	$S_{1,\pm1}$	$= \tfrac{1}{2}\sqrt{3}\sin\theta$
$l = 2$:	$S_{2,0}$	$= \tfrac{1}{4}\sqrt{10}(3\cos^2\theta-1)$
	$S_{2,\pm1}$	$= \tfrac{1}{2}\sqrt{15}\sin\theta\cos\theta$
	$S_{2,\pm2}$	$= \tfrac{1}{4}\sqrt{15}\sin^2\theta$
$l = 3$:	$S_{3,0}$	$= \tfrac{3}{4}\sqrt{14}(\tfrac{5}{3}\cos^3\theta-\cos\theta)$
	$S_{3,\pm1}$	$= \tfrac{1}{8}\sqrt{42}\sin\theta(5\cos^2\theta-1)$
	$S_{3,\pm2}$	$= \tfrac{1}{4}\sqrt{105}\sin^2\theta\cos\theta$
	$S_{3,\pm3}$	$= \tfrac{1}{8}\sqrt{70}\sin^3\theta$

The eigenfunctions of $\hat{L}^2$ and $\hat{L}_z$ are called *spherical harmonics* (or surface harmonics), and are given by the formula:

$$Y_l^m(\theta, \varphi) = \left[\frac{2l+1}{4\pi} \frac{(l-|m|)!}{(l+|m|)!}\right]^{1/2} P_l^{|m|}(\cos\theta)\, e^{im\varphi} \qquad (5.146)$$

The phase of the normalization constant of the spherical harmonics is arbitrary

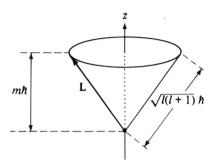

FIGURE 5.5   *Orientation of* **L**.

(see Section 1.6); many physics texts use a different phase convention than in (5.146). Thus Y_l^m differs from text to text by a minus sign.

Summarizing our results, the one-particle orbital-angular-momentum eigenfunctions and eigenvalues are:

$$\hat{L}^2 Y_l^m(\theta, \varphi) = l(l+1)\,\hbar^2\, Y_l^m(\theta, \varphi), \qquad l = 0, 1, 2, \ldots \qquad \textbf{(5.147)}$$

$$\hat{L}_z Y_l^m(\theta, \varphi) = m\hbar Y_l^m(\theta, \varphi), \qquad m = -l, -l+1, \ldots, l-1, l \qquad \textbf{(5.148)}$$

where the eigenfunctions are given by (5.146). (Often the symbol m_l is used instead of m for the L_z quantum number.)

Since we cannot specify L_x and L_y, the vector **L** can lie anywhere on the surface of a cone whose axis is the z axis, whose altitude is $m\hbar$, and whose slant height is $\sqrt{l(l+1)}\,\hbar$ (Fig. 5.5). The possible orientations of **L** with respect to the z axis for the case $l = 1$ are shown in Fig. 5.6. For each eigenvalue of $\hat{L}^2$ there are $2l+1$ different eigenfunctions Y_l^m, corresponding to the $2l+1$ values of m. We say that the $\hat{L}^2$ eigenvalues are $(2l+1)$-fold degenerate. (The term *degeneracy* is applicable to the eigenvalues of any operator, not just the Hamiltonian.)

Of course, there is nothing special about the z axis; all directions of space are equivalent. If we had chosen to specify L^2 and L_x (rather than L_z), we would have gotten the same eigenvalues for L_x as we found for L_z. However, it is easier to solve the $\hat{L}_z$ eigenvalue equation because $\hat{L}_z$ has a simple form in spherical polar coordinates (which involve the angle of rotation φ about the z axis).

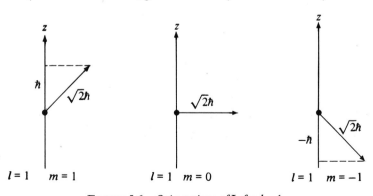

FIGURE 5.6   *Orientations of* **L** *for* $l = 1$.

5.4 The Ladder-Operator Method for Angular Momentum

We obtained the eigenvalues of $\hat{L}^2$ and $\hat{L}_z$ by expressing these orbital-angular-momentum operators as differential operators and solving the resulting differential equations. We now demonstrate that it is possible to solve for these eigenvalues using only the operator commutation relations. The work in this section is applicable to any operators that satisfy the angular-momentum commutation relations. In particular, it applies to spin angular momentum (Chapter 10), as well as orbital angular momentum. The operator manipulations that follow are abstract, and may be difficult to fully grasp at first reading. However, the process of finding the eigenvalues of operators without using their explicit forms has an elegance that will reward the persistent student.

We used the letter L for orbital angular momentum. Here we will use the letter M to indicate that we are dealing with any kind of angular momentum. We have three linear operators $\hat{M}_x$, $\hat{M}_y$, and $\hat{M}_z$, and all we know about them is that they obey the commutation relations:

$$[\hat{M}_x, \hat{M}_y] = i\hbar\hat{M}_z, \qquad [\hat{M}_y, \hat{M}_z] = i\hbar\hat{M}_x, \qquad [\hat{M}_z, \hat{M}_x] = i\hbar\hat{M}_y \quad \text{(5.149)}$$

We define the operator $\hat{M}^2$ as:

$$\hat{M}^2 = \hat{M}_x^2 + \hat{M}_y^2 + \hat{M}_z^2 \qquad \text{(5.150)}$$

Our problem is to find the eigenvalues of $\hat{M}^2$ and $\hat{M}_z$.

We begin by evaluating the commutators of $\hat{M}^2$ with its components, using Eqs. (5.149) and (5.150). The work is identical with that used to derive Eqs. (5.73)–(5.74), and we have

$$[\hat{M}^2, \hat{M}_x] = [\hat{M}^2, \hat{M}_y] = [\hat{M}^2, \hat{M}_z] = 0 \qquad \text{(5.151)}$$

Hence we can have simultaneous eigenfunctions of $\hat{M}^2$ and $\hat{M}_z$.

Next we define two new operators—the *raising operator* $\hat{M}_+$ and the *lowering operator* $\hat{M}_-$:

$$\hat{M}_+ \equiv \hat{M}_x + i\hat{M}_y \qquad \text{(5.152)}$$

$$\hat{M}_- \equiv \hat{M}_x - i\hat{M}_y \qquad \text{(5.153)}$$

These are examples of *ladder operators*. The reason for the terminology will become clear shortly. Let us investigate their properties. We have

$$\hat{M}_+\hat{M}_- = (\hat{M}_x + i\hat{M}_y)(\hat{M}_x - i\hat{M}_y) = \hat{M}_x(\hat{M}_x - i\hat{M}_y) + i\hat{M}_y(\hat{M}_x - i\hat{M}_y)$$

$$= \hat{M}_x^2 - i\hat{M}_x\hat{M}_y + i\hat{M}_y\hat{M}_x + \hat{M}_y^2 = \hat{M}^2 - \hat{M}_z^2 + i[\hat{M}_y, \hat{M}_x]$$

$$\hat{M}_+\hat{M}_- = \hat{M}^2 - \hat{M}_z^2 + \hbar\hat{M}_z \qquad \text{(5.154)}$$

Similarly we find

$$\hat{M}_-\hat{M}_+ = \hat{M}^2 - \hat{M}_z^2 - \hbar\hat{M}_z \qquad \text{(5.155)}$$

For the commutators of these operators with $\hat{M}_z$, we have

$$[\hat{M}_+, \hat{M}_z] = [\hat{M}_x + i\hat{M}_y, \hat{M}_z] = [\hat{M}_x, \hat{M}_z] + i[\hat{M}_y, \hat{M}_z]$$
$$= -i\hbar\hat{M}_y - \hbar\hat{M}_x$$

$$[\hat{M}_+, \hat{M}_z] = -\hbar\hat{M}_+ \tag{5.156}$$

$$\hat{M}_+\hat{M}_z = \hat{M}_z\hat{M}_+ - \hbar\hat{M}_+ \tag{5.157}$$

Similarly we find

$$\hat{M}_-\hat{M}_z = \hat{M}_z\hat{M}_- + \hbar\hat{M}_- \tag{5.158}$$

Using Y for the common eigenfunctions of $\hat{M}^2$ and $\hat{M}_z$, we have

$$\hat{M}^2 Y = cY \tag{5.159}$$

$$\hat{M}_z Y = bY \tag{5.160}$$

where c and b are the eigenvalues. Operating on Eq. (5.160) with the raising operator, we get

$$\hat{M}_+\hat{M}_z Y = \hat{M}_+ bY \tag{5.161}$$

Using Eq. (5.157) and the fact that $\hat{M}_+$ is linear, we have

$$(\hat{M}_z\hat{M}_+ - \hbar\hat{M}_+)Y = b\hat{M}_+ Y$$
$$\hat{M}_z(\hat{M}_+ Y) = (b+\hbar)(\hat{M}_+ Y) \tag{5.162}$$

This last equation says that the function $\hat{M}_+ Y$ is an eigenfunction of $\hat{M}_z$ with eigenvalue $b+\hbar$. In other words, operating on the eigenfunction Y with the raising operator converts Y into another eigenfunction of $\hat{M}_z$ with eigenvalue $\hbar$ higher than the eigenvalue of Y. If we now apply the raising operator to (5.162) and use (5.157) again, we find similarly

$$\hat{M}_z(\hat{M}_+^2 Y) = (b+2\hbar)(\hat{M}_+^2 Y)$$

Repeated application of the raising operator gives

$$\hat{M}_z(\hat{M}_+^k Y) = (b+k\hbar)(\hat{M}_+^k Y), \quad k = 0, 1, 2, \ldots \tag{5.163}$$

If we operate on (5.160) with the lowering operator and apply (5.158) we find in the same manner

$$\hat{M}_z(\hat{M}_- Y) = (b-\hbar)(\hat{M}_- Y) \tag{5.164}$$

$$\hat{M}_z(\hat{M}_-^k Y) = (b-k\hbar)(\hat{M}_-^k Y) \tag{5.165}$$

Thus by using the raising and lowering operators on the eigenfunction with eigenvalue b, we generate a ladder of eigenvalues, the difference from step to step being $\hbar$:

$$\vdots$$
$$\underline{\qquad} b + 2\hbar$$
$$\underline{\qquad} b + \hbar$$
$$\underline{\qquad} b$$
$$\underline{\qquad} b - \hbar$$
$$\underline{\qquad} b - 2\hbar$$
$$\vdots$$

The functions $\hat{M}_{\pm}^{k} Y$ are eigenfunctions of $\hat{M}_z$ with eigenvalues $b \pm k\hbar$. We now show that these functions are also eigenfunctions of $\hat{M}^2$, all with the *same* eigenvalue c:

$$\hat{M}_z \hat{M}_{\pm}^{k} Y = (b \pm k\hbar) \hat{M}_{\pm}^{k} Y \tag{5.166}$$

$$\hat{M}^2 \hat{M}_{\pm}^{k} Y = c \hat{M}_{\pm}^{k} Y, \qquad k = 0, 1, 2, \ldots \tag{5.167}$$

To prove (5.167) we first show that $\hat{M}^2$ commutes with $\hat{M}_+$ and $\hat{M}_-$:

$$[\hat{M}^2, \hat{M}_{\pm}] = [\hat{M}^2, \hat{M}_x \pm i\hat{M}_y] = [\hat{M}^2, \hat{M}_x] \pm i[\hat{M}^2, \hat{M}_y] = 0 \pm 0 = 0$$

We also have

$$[\hat{M}^2, \hat{M}_{\pm}^2] = [\hat{M}^2, \hat{M}_{\pm}] \hat{M}_{\pm} + \hat{M}_{\pm} [\hat{M}^2, \hat{M}_{\pm}] = 0 + 0 = 0 \tag{5.168}$$

and it follows by induction that

$$[\hat{M}^2, \hat{M}_{\pm}^{k}] = 0 \qquad \text{or} \qquad \hat{M}^2 \hat{M}_{\pm}^{k} = \hat{M}_{\pm}^{k} \hat{M}^2, \qquad k = 0, 1, 2, \ldots \tag{5.169}$$

If we operate on (5.159) with $\hat{M}_{\pm}^{k}$ and use (5.169), we get

$$\hat{M}_{\pm}^{k} \hat{M}^2 Y = \hat{M}_{\pm}^{k} cY$$

$$\hat{M}^2 (\hat{M}_{\pm}^{k} Y) = c (\hat{M}_{\pm}^{k} Y) \tag{5.170}$$

which is what we wanted to prove.

Next we show that the set of eigenvalues of $\hat{M}_z$ generated using the ladder operators must be bounded. For the particular eigenfunction Y with eigenvalue b, we have

$$\hat{M}_z Y = bY \tag{5.171}$$

and for the set of eigenfunctions and eigenvalues generated by the ladder operators we have

$$\hat{M}_z Y_k = b_k Y_k \tag{5.172}$$

where [2]

$$Y_k = M_{\pm}^{k} Y \tag{5.173}$$

$$b_k = b \pm k\hbar \tag{5.174}$$

Operating on (5.172) with $\hat{M}_z$, we have

$$\hat{M}_z^2 Y_k = b_k \hat{M}_z Y_k$$

$$\hat{M}_z^2 Y_k = b_k^2 Y_k \tag{5.175}$$

Now subtract (5.175) from (5.167), and use (5.173) and (5.150):

$$\hat{M}^2 Y_k - \hat{M}_z^2 Y_k = cY_k - b_k^2 Y_k$$

$$(\hat{M}_x^2 + \hat{M}_y^2) Y_k = (c - b_k^2) Y_k \tag{5.176}$$

---

[2] Application of $\hat{M}_+$ (or $\hat{M}_-$) destroys the normalization of Y, so that Y_k is not normalized. For the normalization constant, see Problem 10.13.

The operator $\hat{M}_x^2 + \hat{M}_y^2$ corresponds to a nonnegative physical quantity and hence has nonnegative eigenvalues. Therefore (5.176) implies that

$$c - b_k^2 \geqslant 0$$

$$\sqrt{c} \geqslant |b_k|$$

$$\sqrt{c} \geqslant b_k \geqslant -\sqrt{c}, \qquad k = 0, \pm 1, \pm 2, \ldots \tag{5.177}$$

Since c remains constant as k varies, (5.177) shows that the set of eigenvalues b_k is bounded above and below. Let b_{max} and b_{min} denote the maximum and minimum values of b_k. Y_{max} and Y_{min} will be the corresponding eigenfunctions:

$$\hat{M}_z Y_{max} = b_{max} Y_{max} \tag{5.178}$$

$$\hat{M}_z Y_{min} = b_{min} Y_{min} \tag{5.179}$$

Now operate on (5.178) with the raising operator, and use (5.157):

$$\hat{M}_+ \hat{M}_z Y_{max} = b_{max} \hat{M}_+ Y_{max}$$

$$\hat{M}_z (\hat{M}_+ Y_{max}) = (b_{max} + \hbar)(\hat{M}_+ Y_{max}) \tag{5.180}$$

This last equation seems to contradict the statement that b_{max} is the largest eigenvalue of $\hat{M}_z$, since it says that $\hat{M}_+ Y_{max}$ is an eigenfunction of $\hat{M}_z$ with eigenvalue $b_{max} + \hbar$. The only way out of this contradiction is to have the function $\hat{M}_+ Y_{max}$ vanish. (We always reject zero as an eigenfunction on physical grounds.) Thus:

$$\hat{M}_+ Y_{max} = 0 \tag{5.181}$$

Operating on (5.181) with the lowering operator, and using (5.155) and (5.178), we have

$$\hat{M}_- \hat{M}_+ Y_{max} = 0$$

$$(\hat{M}^2 - \hat{M}_z^2 - \hbar \hat{M}_z) Y_{max} = 0$$

$$(c - b_{max}^2 - \hbar b_{max}) Y_{max} = 0$$

$$c - b_{max}^2 - \hbar b_{max} = 0$$

$$c = b_{max}^2 + \hbar b_{max} \tag{5.182}$$

A similar argument shows that

$$\hat{M}_- Y_{min} = 0 \tag{5.183}$$

and by applying the raising operator to this equation and using (5.154), we find

$$c = b_{min}^2 - \hbar b_{min} \tag{5.184}$$

Subtracting this last equation from (5.182), we have

$$b_{max}^2 + \hbar b_{max} + (\hbar b_{min} - b_{min}^2) = 0 \tag{5.185}$$

This is a quadratic equation in the unknown b_{max}, and using the usual formula (it still works in quantum mechanics) we find

$$b_{max} = -b_{min}, \qquad b_{max} = b_{min} - \hbar \tag{5.186}$$

The second root is rejected since it says that b_{max} is less than b_{min}. So

$$b_{min} = -b_{max} \qquad (5.187)$$

Moreover, from (5.174) we know that b_{max} and b_{min} differ by an integral multiple of $\hbar$:

$$b_{max} - b_{min} = n\hbar, \qquad n = 0, 1, 2, \dots \qquad (5.188)$$

Substituting (5.187) in (5.188), we have

$$b_{max} = \tfrac{1}{2}n\hbar \qquad (5.189)$$

$$b_{max} = j\hbar, \qquad j = 0, \tfrac{1}{2}, 1, \tfrac{3}{2}, 2, \dots \qquad (5.190)$$

$$b_{min} = -j\hbar$$

$$b = -j\hbar, (-j+1)\hbar, (-j+2)\hbar, \dots, (j-2)\hbar, (j-1)\hbar, j\hbar \qquad (5.191)$$

and from (5.182) we find

$$c = j(j+1)\hbar^2, \qquad j = 0, \tfrac{1}{2}, 1, \tfrac{3}{2}, \dots \qquad (5.192)$$

We have found the eigenvalues of $\hat{M}^2$ and $\hat{M}_z$ using just the commutation relations. However, comparing (5.191)–(5.192) with Eqs. (5.147) and (5.148) shows that in addition to integral values for the angular-momentum quantum number ($l = 0, 1, 2, \dots$) we now also have the possibility for half-integral values ($j = 0, \tfrac{1}{2}, 1, \tfrac{3}{2}, \dots$). This perhaps suggests that there might be another kind of angular momentum besides orbital angular momentum. In Chapter 10 we will see that spin angular momentum can have half-integral, as well as integral, quantum numbers. The particular form of the orbital-angular-momentum differential operators rules out half-integral values.

The ladder-operator method can be used to solve other eigenvalue problems; see Problem 5.17.

PROBLEMS

5.1 Derive Eq. (5.15) for the standard deviation of an observable.

5.2 For the ground state of the one-dimensional harmonic oscillator, compute the standard deviations Δx and Δp_x, and check that the uncertainty principle is obeyed. Use the results of Problem 4.1 to save time.

5.3 Show that the standard deviation ΔA is zero when Ψ is an eigenfunction of $\hat{A}$.

5.4 Verify the commutator identities (5.2)–(5.8).

5.5 Let **A** have the components $(3, -2, 6)$; let **B** have the components $(-1, 4, 4)$. Find $|\mathbf{A}|$, $|\mathbf{B}|$, $\mathbf{A}+\mathbf{B}$, $\mathbf{A}-\mathbf{B}$, $\mathbf{A}\cdot\mathbf{B}$, $\mathbf{A}\times\mathbf{B}$. Find the angle between **A** and **B**.

5.6 Use the vector dot product to find the obtuse angle between two diagonals of a cube. What is the chemical significance of this angle?

5.7 Show that

$$\nabla^2[f(x, y, z)g(x, y, z)] = g\nabla^2 f + 2\nabla f \cdot \nabla g + f\nabla^2 g$$

5.8 Let $f = 2x^2 - 5xyz + z^2 - 1$. Find $\mathbf{grad}\, f$. Find $\nabla^2 f$.

5.9 Find $\nabla \cdot \mathbf{r}$ where $\mathbf{r}$ is given by (5.51).

5.10 Derive Eq. (5.97) for $\hat{L}^2$ from Eqs. (5.94)–(5.96).

5.11 Derive the formula for $S_{2,0}$ (Table 5.1) in two ways: (a) by using (5.143); (b) by using the recursion relation and normalization.

5.12 Calculate the possible angles between $\mathbf{L}$ and the z axis for $l = 2$.

5.13 Let w be the variable defined as the number of heads that show when two coins are tossed simultaneously. Find $\langle w \rangle$ and σ_w. [*Hint:* use (3.108) and (5.15).]

5.14 Show that the spherical harmonics are eigenfunctions of the operator $(\hat{L}_x^2 + \hat{L}_y^2)$. (The proof is short.) What are the eigenvalues?

5.15 Show that the three commutation relations (5.70) and (5.72) are equivalent to the single relation

$$\hat{\mathbf{L}} \times \hat{\mathbf{L}} = i\hbar\hat{\mathbf{L}}$$

5.16 Apply the lowering operator three times in succession to $Y_1^1(\theta, \varphi)$ and verify that we obtain functions that are proportional to Y_1^0, Y_1^{-1}, and zero.

5.17 The one-dimensional harmonic-oscillator Hamiltonian is

$$\hat{H} = \frac{\hat{p}_x^2}{2m} + 2\pi^2 v^2 m \hat{x}^2$$

The raising and lowering operators for this problem are defined as:

$$\hat{A}_+ \equiv \frac{1}{(2m)^{1/2}}[\hat{p}_x + 2\pi i v m \hat{x}], \qquad \hat{A}_- \equiv \frac{1}{(2m)^{1/2}}[\hat{p}_x - 2\pi i v m \hat{x}]$$

Show that

$$\hat{A}_+ \hat{A}_- = \hat{H} - \tfrac{1}{2}hv, \qquad \hat{A}_- \hat{A}_+ = \hat{H} + \tfrac{1}{2}hv$$

$$[\hat{A}_+, \hat{A}_-] = -hv$$

$$[\hat{H}, \hat{A}_+] = hv\hat{A}_+, \qquad [\hat{H}, \hat{A}_-] = -hv\hat{A}_-$$

Show that $\hat{A}_+$ and $\hat{A}_-$ are indeed ladder operators and that the eigenvalues are spaced at intervals of hv. Since both the kinetic energy and the potential energy are nonnegative, we expect the energy eigenvalues to be nonnegative. Hence, there must be a state of minimum energy. Operate on the wave function for this state first with $\hat{A}_-$ and then with $\hat{A}_+$ and show that the lowest energy eigenvalue is $\tfrac{1}{2}hv$. Finally, conclude that

$$E = (n + \tfrac{1}{2})hv, \qquad n = 0, 1, 2, \ldots$$

5.18 Consider the following objection to the conclusions of Section 5.4. It might be argued that although we proved that the quantities

$$-j\hbar, (-j+1)\hbar, \ldots, j\hbar$$

are eigenvalues of $\hat{M}_z$, there might be other eigenvalues spaced between the eigenvalues we found. How can this objection be answered?

5.19 The *curl* of a vector function $\mathbf{A}$ is defined by $\operatorname{curl} \mathbf{A} \equiv \nabla \times \mathbf{A}$. Prove that $\operatorname{curl} \operatorname{grad} g(x, y, z) = 0$ for all well-behaved functions g.

5.20 Consider the following incorrect derivation. Differentiation of x in (5.75) gives $\partial x / \partial r = \sin \theta \cos \varphi$. Then, since $\partial r / \partial x = 1/(\partial x / \partial r)$, we have $(\partial r / \partial x)_{y,z} = 1/(\sin \theta \cos \varphi)$ (?). But this result disagrees with (5.85). Find the error in this reasoning.

CHAPTER
6

The Hydrogen Atom

6.1 The Central-Force Problem

Before tackling the hydrogen atom, we shall consider the more general problem of a single particle moving under a central force. The results of this section will be applicable to any central-force problem, e.g., the hydrogen atom (Section 6.4), the isotropic three-dimensional harmonic oscillator (Problem 6.23).

A *central force* is one derived from a potential-energy function that is spherically symmetric, i.e., that is a function only of the distance of the particle from the origin: $V = V(r)$. The relation between force and potential energy is given by Eq. (5.46). The partial derivatives in (5.46) can be evaluated by the chain rule [Eqs. (5.81)–(5.83)]. Since, in this case, V is a function of r only, we have

$$\left(\frac{\partial V}{\partial \theta}\right)_{r,\varphi} = \left(\frac{\partial V}{\partial \varphi}\right)_{r,\theta} = 0 \qquad (6.1)$$

Hence:

$$\left(\frac{\partial V}{\partial x}\right)_{y,z} = \frac{dV}{dr}\left(\frac{\partial r}{\partial x}\right)_{y,z} = \frac{x}{r}\frac{dV}{dr} \qquad (6.2)$$

$$\left(\frac{\partial V}{\partial y}\right)_{x,z} = \frac{y}{r}\frac{dV}{dr}, \qquad \left(\frac{\partial V}{\partial z}\right)_{x,y} = \frac{z}{r}\frac{dV}{dr} \qquad (6.3)$$

where Eqs. (5.85) and (5.86) have been used. Equation (5.46) becomes

$$\mathbf{F} = -\frac{1}{r}\frac{dV}{dr}(x\mathbf{i} + y\mathbf{j} + z\mathbf{k}) = -\frac{dV(r)}{dr}\frac{\mathbf{r}}{r} \qquad (6.4)$$

A central force has only a radial component.

Now we consider the quantum mechanics of a single particle subject to a central force. The Hamiltonian operator is

$$\hat{H} = \hat{T} + \hat{V} = -(\hbar^2/2m)\nabla^2 + V(r) \tag{6.5}$$

where ∇^2 is given by Eq. (3.55). Since V is spherically symmetric, we will work in spherical polar coordinates. Hence, we want to transform the Laplacian operator to these coordinates. We already have the forms of the operators $\partial/\partial x$, $\partial/\partial y$, and $\partial/\partial z$ in these coordinates [Eqs. (5.91)–(5.93)], and by squaring each of these operators and then adding their squares, we get the Laplacian. This calculation is left as an exercise. The result is (Problem 6.12):

$$\nabla^2 = \frac{\partial^2}{\partial r^2} + \frac{2}{r}\frac{\partial}{\partial r} + \frac{1}{r^2}\frac{\partial^2}{\partial \theta^2} + \frac{1}{r^2}\cot\theta\,\frac{\partial}{\partial \theta} + \frac{1}{r^2\sin^2\theta}\frac{\partial^2}{\partial \varphi^2} \tag{6.6}$$

Looking back to (5.97), which gives the operator for the square of the magnitude of the orbital angular momentum of a single particle, $\hat{L}^2$, we see that

$$\nabla^2 = \frac{\partial^2}{\partial r^2} + \frac{2}{r}\frac{\partial}{\partial r} - \frac{1}{r^2\hbar^2}\hat{L}^2 \tag{6.7}$$

The Hamiltonian (6.5) becomes

$$\hat{H} = -\frac{\hbar^2}{2m}\left(\frac{\partial^2}{\partial r^2} + \frac{2}{r}\frac{\partial}{\partial r}\right) + \frac{1}{2mr^2}\hat{L}^2 + V(r) \tag{6.8}$$

In classical mechanics, a particle subject to a central force has its angular momentum conserved (Section 5.3). In quantum mechanics, we might ask whether we can have states with definite values for both the energy and the angular momentum. To have the set of eigenfunctions of $\hat{H}$ also be eigenfunctions of $\hat{L}^2$, the commutator $[\hat{H}, \hat{L}^2]$ must vanish. We have

$$[\hat{H}, \hat{L}^2] = [\hat{T}, \hat{L}^2] + [\hat{V}, \hat{L}^2] \tag{6.9}$$

$$[\hat{T}, \hat{L}^2] = \left[-\frac{\hbar^2}{2m}\left(\frac{\partial^2}{\partial r^2} + \frac{2}{r}\frac{\partial}{\partial r}\right) + \frac{1}{2mr^2}\hat{L}^2, \hat{L}^2\right] \tag{6.10}$$

$$[\hat{T}, \hat{L}^2] = -\frac{\hbar^2}{2m}\left[\frac{\partial^2}{\partial r^2} + \frac{2}{r}\frac{\partial}{\partial r}, \hat{L}^2\right] + \frac{1}{2m}\left[\frac{1}{r^2}\hat{L}^2, \hat{L}^2\right] \tag{6.11}$$

Recall that $\hat{L}^2$ involves only θ and φ and not r [Eq. (5.97)]. Hence, it commutes with any operator that involves only r. [To reach this conclusion we must use relations like (5.71) with x and z replaced by r and θ.] Thus the first commutator in (6.11) is zero. Moreover, since any operator commutes with itself, the second commutator in (6.11) is zero. Hence

$$[\hat{T}, \hat{L}^2] = 0 \tag{6.12}$$

Now, since $\hat{L}^2$ does not involve r, and V involves only r, we have

$$[\hat{V}(r), \hat{L}^2] = 0$$

Therefore

$$[\hat{H}, \hat{L}^2] = 0 \tag{6.13}$$

The Hamiltonian commutes with $\hat{L}^2$ when the potential-energy function is independent of θ and φ.

Consider now the $\hat{L}_z$ operator, Eq. (5.96). Since $\hat{L}_z$ doesn't involve r, and since it commutes with $\hat{L}^2$ [Eq. (5.74)], we see that $\hat{L}_z$ commutes with the Hamiltonian (6.8):

$$[\hat{H}, \hat{L}_z] = 0 \tag{6.14}$$

We can, therefore, have a set of simultaneous eigenfunctions of $\hat{H}$, $\hat{L}^2$, and $\hat{L}_z$ for the central-force problem. Using ψ to denote these common eigenfunctions, we have

$$\hat{H}\psi = E\psi \tag{6.15}$$

$$\hat{L}^2\psi = l(l+1)\hbar^2\psi, \qquad l = 0, 1, 2, ... \tag{6.16}$$

$$\hat{L}_z\psi = m\hbar\psi, \qquad m = -l, -l+1, ..., l \tag{6.17}$$

where Eqs. (5.147) and (5.148) have been used.

Using (6.8) and (6.16), we have for the Schroedinger equation (6.15):

$$\left[-\frac{\hbar^2}{2m}\left(\frac{\partial^2}{\partial r^2} + \frac{2}{r}\frac{\partial}{\partial r} \right) + \frac{1}{2mr^2}\hat{L}^2 + V(r) \right]\psi = E\psi \tag{6.18}$$

$$\left[-\frac{\hbar^2}{2m}\left(\frac{\partial^2}{\partial r^2} + \frac{2}{r}\frac{\partial}{\partial r} \right) + \frac{l(l+1)\hbar^2}{2mr^2} + V(r) \right]\psi = E\psi \tag{6.19}$$

The eigenfunctions of $\hat{L}^2$ are the spherical harmonics $Y_l^m(\theta, \varphi)$, and since $\hat{L}^2$ does not involve r, we can multiply Y_l^m by an arbitrary function of r and still have eigenfunctions of $\hat{L}^2$. Therefore

$$\psi = R(r)Y_l^m(\theta, \varphi) \tag{6.20}$$

Using (6.20) in (6.19), we then divide both sides by Y_l^m to obtain an ordinary differential equation for the unknown function $R(r)$:

$$-\frac{\hbar^2}{2m}\left(R'' + \frac{2}{r}R' \right) + \frac{l(l+1)\hbar^2}{2mr^2}R + V(r)R = ER(r) \tag{6.21}$$

We have shown that for *any* one-particle problem with a spherically symmetric potential-energy function $V(r)$, the wave function ψ is a product of a radial factor and a spherical harmonic. The radial factor $R(r)$ satisfies Eq. (6.21). By using some specific form for $V(r)$ in (6.21), we can solve it for some particular problem.

6.2 Reduction of the Two-Particle Problem to a One-Particle Problem

The hydrogen atom contains two particles, the proton and the electron. So far we have considered only one-particle problems. We now show how we can frequently reduce a two-particle problem to a one-particle problem.

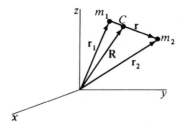

FIGURE 6.1   *A two-particle system.*

Consider the classical-mechanical treatment of two particles of masses m_1 and m_2. We specify their positions by the radius vectors $\mathbf{r}_1$ and $\mathbf{r}_2$ drawn from the origin of a Cartesian coordinate system (Fig. 6.1). Particles one and two have coordinates (x_1, y_1, z_1) and (x_2, y_2, z_2). We draw the vector $\mathbf{r} = \mathbf{r}_2 - \mathbf{r}_1$ from particle one to two, and denote the components of $\mathbf{r}$ by x, y, and z:

$$x = x_2 - x_1, \qquad y = y_2 - y_1, \qquad z = z_2 - z_1 \tag{6.22}$$

The coordinates x, y, and z are called the *relative* (or *internal*) coordinates. We now draw the vector $\mathbf{R}$ from the origin to the center of mass, point C, and denote the coordinates of C by X, Y, and Z:

$$\mathbf{R} = \mathbf{i}X + \mathbf{j}Y + \mathbf{k}Z \tag{6.23}$$

The definition of the center of mass of this two-particle system gives

$$X = \frac{m_1 x_1 + m_2 x_2}{m_1 + m_2}, \qquad Y = \frac{m_1 y_1 + m_2 y_2}{m_1 + m_2}, \qquad Z = \frac{m_1 z_1 + m_2 z_2}{m_1 + m_2} \tag{6.24}$$

These three equations are equivalent to the vector equation

$$\mathbf{R} = \frac{m_1 \mathbf{r}_1 + m_2 \mathbf{r}_2}{m_1 + m_2} \tag{6.25}$$

We also have

$$\mathbf{r} = \mathbf{r}_2 - \mathbf{r}_1 \tag{6.26}$$

We regard (6.25) and (6.26) as simultaneous linear equations in the two unknowns $\mathbf{r}_1$ and $\mathbf{r}_2$, and solve for them to get

$$\mathbf{r}_1 = \mathbf{R} - \frac{m_2}{m_1 + m_2}\mathbf{r}, \qquad \mathbf{r}_2 = \mathbf{R} + \frac{m_1}{m_1 + m_2}\mathbf{r} \tag{6.27}$$

Equations (6.25) and (6.26) represent a transformation of coordinates from $x_1, y_1, z_1, x_2, y_2, z_2$ to X, Y, Z, x, y, z. Consider what happens to the Hamiltonian under this transformation. Let an overhead dot indicate differentiation with respect to time; the velocity of particle one is [Eq. (5.52)]

$$\mathbf{v}_1 = \frac{d\mathbf{r}_1}{dt} = \dot{\mathbf{r}}_1 \tag{6.28}$$

The kinetic energy is the sum of the kinetic energies of the two particles:

$$T = \tfrac{1}{2}m_1\,|\dot{\mathbf{r}}_1|^2 + \tfrac{1}{2}m_2\,|\dot{\mathbf{r}}_2|^2 \tag{6.29}$$

Introducing the time derivatives of Eqs. (6.27) into (6.29), we have

$$T = \tfrac{1}{2}m_1\left(\dot{\mathbf{R}} - \frac{m_2}{m_1+m_2}\,\dot{\mathbf{r}}\right)\cdot\left(\dot{\mathbf{R}} - \frac{m_2}{m_1+m_2}\,\dot{\mathbf{r}}\right)$$

$$+ \tfrac{1}{2}m_2\left(\dot{\mathbf{R}} + \frac{m_1}{m_1+m_2}\,\dot{\mathbf{r}}\right)\cdot\left(\dot{\mathbf{R}} + \frac{m_1}{m_1+m_2}\,\dot{\mathbf{r}}\right)$$

where (5.34) has been used. Using the distributive law for the dot products, we find, after simplifying,

$$T = \tfrac{1}{2}(m_1+m_2)\,|\dot{\mathbf{R}}|^2 + \frac{1}{2}\frac{m_1 m_2}{(m_1+m_2)}\,|\dot{\mathbf{r}}|^2 \tag{6.30}$$

Let M be the total mass of the system:

$$M \equiv m_1 + m_2 \tag{6.31}$$

We define the *reduced mass* μ of the two-particle system as

$$\mu \equiv \frac{m_1 m_2}{m_1 + m_2} \tag{6.32}$$

Then

$$T = \tfrac{1}{2}M\,|\dot{\mathbf{R}}|^2 + \tfrac{1}{2}\mu\,|\dot{\mathbf{r}}|^2 \tag{6.33}$$

The first term in (6.33) is the kinetic energy due to translational motion of the whole system of mass M. The second term is kinetic energy of internal motion of the two particles. This internal motion is of two types. The distance r between the two particles can change (vibration), and the direction of the $\mathbf{r}$ vector can change (rotation). Note that

$$|\dot{\mathbf{r}}| = \left|\frac{d}{dt}\mathbf{r}\right| \neq \frac{d}{dt}|\mathbf{r}| \tag{6.34}$$

Corresponding to the original coordinates $x_1, y_1, z_1, x_2, y_2, z_2$, we had six linear momenta:

$$p_{x_1} = m_1\dot{x}_1, \ldots, p_{z_2} = m_2\dot{z}_2 \tag{6.35}$$

Comparing Eqs. (6.29) and (6.33), we define the six linear momenta for the new coordinates X, Y, Z, x, y, z as

$$p_X \equiv M\dot{X}, \qquad p_Y \equiv M\dot{Y}, \qquad p_Z \equiv M\dot{Z} \tag{6.36}$$

$$p_x \equiv \mu\dot{x}, \qquad p_y \equiv \mu\dot{y}, \qquad p_z \equiv \mu\dot{z} \tag{6.37}$$

We define two new momentum vectors as:

$$\mathbf{p}_M \equiv \mathbf{i}M\dot{X} + \mathbf{j}M\dot{Y} + \mathbf{k}M\dot{Z} \tag{6.38}$$

$$\mathbf{p}_\mu \equiv \mathbf{i}\mu\dot{x} + \mathbf{j}\mu\dot{y} + \mathbf{k}\mu\dot{z} \tag{6.39}$$

Introducing these momenta into (6.33), we have

$$T = \frac{|\mathbf{p}_M|^2}{2M} + \frac{|\mathbf{p}_\mu|^2}{2\mu} \tag{6.40}$$

Now consider the potential energy. We make the restriction that V is a function *only* of the relative coordinates x, y, and z of the two particles:

$$V = V(x, y, z) \tag{6.41}$$

An example of (6.41) is two charged particles interacting according to Coulomb's law [see Eq. (3.65)]. With this restriction on V, the Hamiltonian function is

$$H = \frac{p_M^2}{2M} + \left[\frac{p_\mu^2}{2\mu} + V(x, y, z) \right] \tag{6.42}$$

Now suppose we had a system composed of a particle of mass M subject to no forces and a particle of mass μ subject to the potential-energy function $V(x, y, z)$, and further suppose that there was no interaction between these particles. If (X, Y, Z) are the coordinates of the particle of mass M, and (x, y, z) are the coordinates of the particle of mass μ, what is the Hamiltonian of this hypothetical system? Clearly it is identical with (6.42). Since our hypothetical system has no interaction between the two particles, we could treat the motion of each separately. The particle of mass M, being subject to no forces, would simply undergo translational motion at constant velocity, and its contribution to the total energy of the system would be some constant. We could then treat separately the motion of the hypothetical particle of mass μ, using the potential-energy function in brackets in (6.42).

Thus, we have reduced our original two-body problem to two separate one-body problems: (1) The translational motion of the system as a whole, which simply adds a constant to the total energy. (2) The internal motion, which may be dealt with by considering a hypothetical particle of mass μ subject to the potential-energy function $V(x, y, z)$.

Up to now in this section, we have been working with classical mechanics. We now want to show that this same separation holds in quantum mechanics. To this end, we will prove an important theorem. Let us suppose that our system is composed of two particles that do not interact with each other. We use q_1 to symbolize the coordinates (x_1, y_1, z_1) of particle one, and q_2 to symbolize the coordinates (x_2, y_2, z_2) of particle two. Let $\hat{H}_1$ and $\hat{H}_2$ be the Hamiltonian operators for particles one and two, respectively. Since there is no interaction between the particles, the Hamiltonian for the whole system is

$$\hat{H} = \hat{H}_1 + \hat{H}_2$$

and the Schroedinger equation reads

$$(\hat{H}_1 + \hat{H}_2)\psi(q_1, q_2) = E\psi(q_1, q_2) \tag{6.43}$$

We attempt a solution of (6.43) by separation of variables, setting

$$\psi(q_1, q_2) = G_1(q_1) G_2(q_2) \tag{6.44}$$

We have

$$\hat{H}_1 G_1(q_1) G_2(q_2) + \hat{H}_2 G_1(q_1) G_2(q_2) = E G_1(q_1) G_2(q_2) \qquad (6.45)$$

Now $\hat{H}_1$ involves only the coordinate and momentum operators of particle one. Therefore

$$\hat{H}_1 [G_1(q_1) G_2(q_2)] = G_2(q_2) \hat{H}_1 G_1(q_1) \qquad (6.46)$$

since as far as $\hat{H}_1$ is concerned, G_2 is a constant. Using (6.46) and a similar equation for $\hat{H}_2$, Eq. (6.45) becomes

$$G_2(q_2) \hat{H}_1 G_1(q_1) + G_1(q_1) \hat{H}_2 G_2(q_2) = E G_1(q_1) G_2(q_2)$$

$$\frac{\hat{H}_1 G_1(q_1)}{G_1(q_1)} + \frac{\hat{H}_2 G_2(q_2)}{G_2(q_2)} = E \qquad (6.47)$$

Now, by the same arguments used in connection with Eq. (3.78), we conclude that each term on the left in (6.47) must be a constant. Using E_1 and E_2 to denote these constants, we have

$$\frac{\hat{H}_1 G_1(q_1)}{G_1(q_1)} = E_1, \qquad \frac{\hat{H}_2 G_2(q_2)}{G_2(q_2)} = E_2$$

$$E = E_1 + E_2 \qquad (6.48)$$

In other words, when our system is composed of two noninteracting particles, we can reduce the two-particle problem to two separate one-particle problems by solving

$$\hat{H}_1 G_1(q_1) = E_1 G_1(q_1), \qquad \hat{H}_2 G_2(q_2) = E_2 G_2(q_2) \qquad (6.49)$$

The total energy is the sum of the individual energies of each particle, according to (6.48).

This result is easily generalized to any number of noninteracting particles. For n such particles, we have

$$\hat{H} = \hat{H}_1 + \hat{H}_2 + \cdots + \hat{H}_n$$

$$\psi(q_1, q_2, \dots, q_n) = G_1(q_1) G_2(q_2) \cdots G_n(q_n)$$

$$E = E_1 + E_2 + \cdots + E_n \qquad (6.50)$$

$$\hat{H}_i G_i = E_i G_i, \qquad i = 1, 2, \dots, n$$

Our results are also applicable to a single particle whose Hamiltonian is the sum of separate terms for each coordinate:

$$\hat{H} = \hat{H}_x(\hat{x}, \hat{p}_x) + \hat{H}_y(\hat{y}, \hat{p}_y) + \hat{H}_z(\hat{z}, \hat{p}_z)$$

In this case, we conclude that the wave functions and energies are

$$\psi(x, y, z) = F(x) G(y) K(z), \qquad E = E_x + E_y + E_z$$

$$\hat{H}_x F(x) = E_x F(x), \qquad \hat{H}_y G(y) = E_y G(y), \qquad \hat{H}_z K(z) = E_z K(z)$$

Examples include the particle in a three-dimensional box (Section 3.5), the three-dimensional free particle (Problem 3.23), and the three-dimensional harmonic oscillator (Problem 4.5).

Now consider again the two-particle quantum-mechanical problem of masses m_1 and m_2 interacting so that the potential energy is a function of their relative coordinates only [Eqs. (6.41) and (6.22)]. By making the coordinate transformation of Eqs. (6.25) and (6.26), we can write the Hamiltonian as the sum of the Hamiltonians of two independent hypothetical particles [Eq. (6.42)]. Therefore the total energy of the system will be the sum of the energies of these two particles. One particle will have mass M and will move as a free particle ($V = 0$) with some nonnegative energy. The second hypothetical particle will have mass μ, and its Hamiltonian operator $\hat{H}_\mu$ is formed from the two terms in brackets in (6.42):

$$\hat{H}_\mu = \frac{\hat{p}_\mu^2}{2\mu} + \hat{V}(x, y, z) \tag{6.51}$$

6.3 The Two-Particle Rigid Rotor

Although we are now equipped to solve the Schroedinger equation for the hydrogen atom, we will first solve a simpler problem: the two-particle rigid rotor. By this, we mean a two-particle system with the particles held at a fixed distance from each other by a rigid massless rod of length d. For this problem, the vector $\mathbf{r}$ in Fig. 6.1 has the constant magnitude $|\mathbf{r}| = d$. Therefore (see Section 6.2) the kinetic energy of internal motion is wholly rotational energy. The energy of the rotor is wholly kinetic, and we have

$$V = 0 \tag{6.52}$$

Equation (6.52) is a special case of Eq. (6.41), and we may therefore use the results of the last section to separate off the translational motion of the system as a whole. We will concern ourselves only with the rotational energy. The Hamiltonian for the rotation is given by (6.51) as

$$\hat{H} = \frac{\hat{p}_\mu^2}{2\mu} = -\frac{\hbar^2}{2\mu}\nabla^2, \qquad \mu = \frac{m_1 m_2}{m_1 + m_2} \tag{6.53}$$

where m_1 and m_2 are the masses of the two particles. The coordinates of the fictitious particle are the relative coordinates of m_1 and m_2, as given by Eq. (6.22).

Instead of the relative Cartesian coordinates, x, y, z, it will prove more fruitful to use the relative spherical polar coordinates, r, θ, φ. The r coordinate is equal to the magnitude of the $\mathbf{r}$ vector in Fig. 6.1, and since m_1 and m_2 are constrained to remain a fixed distance apart, we have $r = d$. Thus, the problem is equivalent to a particle of mass μ constrained to move on the surface of a sphere of radius d. Because the radial coordinate is constant, the wave function will be a function of θ and φ only. Hence, the first two terms of the Laplacian operator in (6.8) will give zero when operating on the wave function and may be omitted. (Looking at things in a slightly different way, the operators in (6.8) that involve r

derivatives correspond to the kinetic energy of radial motion, and since there is no radial motion, the r derivatives are omitted from the Hamiltonian.)

Since $V = 0$ is a special case of $V = V(r)$, the results of Section 6.1 tell us that the eigenfunctions are given by (6.20), with the r factor omitted:

$$\psi = Y_l^m(\theta, \varphi) \tag{6.54}$$

The Hamiltonian operator is [Eq. (6.8)]

$$\hat{H} = -\frac{\hbar^2}{2\mu}\left[\frac{1}{d^2 \sin\theta}\frac{\partial}{\partial\theta}\left(\sin\theta\frac{\partial}{\partial\theta}\right) + \frac{1}{d^2 \sin^2\theta}\frac{\partial^2}{\partial\varphi^2}\right] \tag{6.55}$$

$$\hat{H} = \frac{1}{2\mu d^2}\hat{L}^2 \tag{6.56}$$

We have, using (6.16):

$$\hat{H}\psi = E\psi$$

$$\frac{1}{2\mu d^2}\hat{L}^2 Y_J^m(\theta, \varphi) = E Y_J^m(\theta, \varphi) \tag{6.57}$$

$$\frac{1}{2\mu d^2}J(J+1)\hbar^2 Y_J^m(\theta, \varphi) = E Y_J^m(\theta, \varphi)$$

$$E = \frac{J(J+1)\hbar^2}{2\mu d^2}, \qquad J = 0, 1, 2, \dots \tag{6.58}$$

where we use J rather than l for the rotational quantum number.

The *moment of inertia I* of a system of n particles about some particular axis in space is defined as

$$I \equiv \sum_{i=1}^{n} m_i \rho_i^2 \tag{6.59}$$

where m_i is the mass of the ith particle and ρ_i is the perpendicular distance from this particle to the axis. The value of I depends on the choice of axis. For the two-particle rigid rotor, we choose our axis to be a line that passes through the center of mass and is perpendicular to the line joining m_1 and m_2 (Fig. 6.2). If we place the

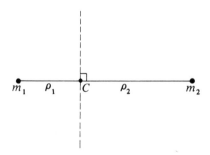

FIGURE 6.2   *Axis (dashed line) for calculating the moment of inertia of a two-particle rigid rotor.*

rotor so that the center of mass, point C, lies at the origin of a Cartesian coordinate system, and also have the line joining m_1 and m_2 lying on the x axis, then C will have the coordinates $(0,0,0)$, m_1 will have the coordinates $(-\rho_1,0,0)$, and m_2 will have the coordinates $(\rho_2,0,0)$. Using these coordinates in (6.24), we find

$$m_1\rho_1 = m_2\rho_2 \tag{6.60}$$

The moment of inertia of the rotor about the axis we have chosen is

$$I = m_1\rho_1^2 + m_2\rho_2^2 \tag{6.61}$$

Using (6.60), we transform Eq. (6.61) to

$$I = \frac{m_1 m_2}{m_1 + m_2}(\rho_1 + \rho_2)^2 = \mu d^2 \tag{6.62}$$

where μ is the reduced mass of the system and d is the distance between m_1 and m_2. The allowed energy levels of the rotor are

$$E = \frac{J(J+1)\hbar^2}{2I}, \qquad J = 0, 1, 2, \dots \tag{6.63}$$

The lowest level is $E = 0$, so we have no zero-point rotational energy. Having zero rotational energy and therefore zero angular momentum for the rotor does not violate the uncertainty principle—recall the discussion following Eq. (5.129).

Are the rigid-rotor energy levels degenerate? The energy depends only on J, but the wave function depends on J and m. For each value of J, we can have $2J+1$ values of m, ranging from $-J$ to J; hence, the levels are $(2J+1)$-fold degenerate. Physically, this corresponds to the different possible orientations of the angular-momentum vector of the rotor about a space-fixed axis.

The angles θ and φ which occur in the wave function are relative coordinates of the two point masses. If we set up a Cartesian coordinate system with the origin at the center of mass of the rotor, θ and φ will be as shown in Fig. 6.3. This coordinate system undergoes the same translational motion as the center of mass of the rotor, but does not rotate in space.

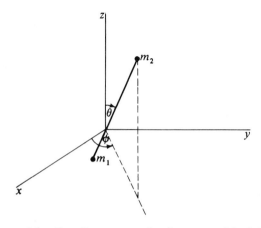

FIGURE 6.3   Coordinate system for the two-particle rigid rotor.

The rotational levels of a diatomic molecule can be *approximated* by the two-particle rigid-rotor energies (6.63). The rotational spectrum falls in the microwave (or far infrared) regions. It is found (*Kauzmann*, p. 658) that the allowed transitions involve a change of ± 1 in J. The frequencies of the microwave spectral lines of a diatomic molecule are then (approximately)

$$\nu = \frac{E(J+1)-E(J)}{h} = \frac{[(J+1)(J+2)-J(J+1)]h}{8\pi^2 I} = 2(J+1)B$$

where the *rotational constant B* is defined as $h/8\pi^2 I$.

6.4 The Hydrogen Atom

The hydrogen atom consists of a proton and an electron. If e represents the charge on the proton ($e = +4.8 \times 10^{-10}$ statcoul), then the electron's charge is $-e$. (From time to time, scientists have speculated that the proton and electron charges might not be exactly equal in magnitude. In 1959 Lyttleton and Bondi pointed out that if a difference of 10^{-27} statcoulombs existed between the magnitudes of these charges, then the observed rate of expansion of the universe could be accounted for by electrostatic repulsions between the charged galaxies. Subsequent experimental work[1] showed that if such a difference exists, it is much less than the amount required by the Lyttleton-Bondi hypothesis.) We will assume the electron and proton to be two point masses whose interaction is given by Coulomb's law. In our discussions of atoms and molecules, we will be considering isolated systems, ignoring interatomic or intermolecular interactions. The isolated hydrogen atom is a two-particle system, and we will use the results of Section 6.2 to treat it.

Instead of treating just the hydrogen atom, we consider a slightly more general problem: the *hydrogenlike atom*; by this, we mean a system consisting of one electron and a nucleus of charge Ze. For $Z = 1$, we have the hydrogen atom; for $Z = 2$, the He^+ ion; for $Z = 3$, the Li^{++} ion, etc. The hydrogenlike atom is the single most important system in quantum chemistry. An exact solution of the Schroedinger equation for atoms with more than one electron cannot be obtained, due to the interelectronic repulsions. If, as a first approximation, we ignore these repulsions, then the electrons can be treated independently. (See Section 6.2.) The atomic wave function will be approximated by a product of one-electron functions, which will be hydrogenlike wave functions. We call such one-electron functions *atomic orbitals*; we will use atomic orbitals to construct approximate molecular wave functions, as well as to discuss many-electron atoms. Let (x, y, z) be the coordinates of the electron relative to the nucleus, and let $\mathbf{r} = \mathbf{i}x + \mathbf{j}y + \mathbf{k}z$. The Coulomb's-law force on the electron in the hydrogenlike atom is

$$\mathbf{F} = -\frac{Ze^2}{r^2}\frac{\mathbf{r}}{r} \tag{6.64}$$

[1] J. G. King, *Phys. Rev. Letters*, **5**, 562 (1960); H. F. Dylla and J. G. King, *Phys. Rev. A*, **7**, 1224 (1973).

The minus sign indicates an attractive force. [The possibility of small deviations from Coulomb's law has been considered. If the Coulomb's-law force is written as being proportional to r^{-2+s}, then experiments have shown that $|s| < 10^{-15}$. Interestingly, it can be shown that a deviation from Coulomb's law would imply a nonzero rest mass for the photon. See A. S. Goldhaber and M. M. Nieto, *Rev. Mod. Phys.*, **43**, 277 (1971).]

We have a central force, and Eq. (6.4) gives

$$\frac{dV(r)}{dr} = \frac{Ze^2}{r^2}$$

$$V = Ze^2 \int \frac{dr}{r^2} = -\frac{Ze^2}{r} \tag{6.65}$$

where the integration constant has been taken as 0 to make $V = 0$ at infinite separation between the charges. For any two charges q_1 and q_2 separated by distance r_{12}, Eq. (6.65) becomes

$$V = q_1 q_2 / r_{12} \tag{6.66}$$

Since the potential energy of this two-particle system depends only on the relative coordinates of the particles, we can apply the results of Section 6.2 to reduce the problem to two one-particle problems. The translational motion of the atom as a whole simply adds some constant to the total energy, and we will not concern ourselves with it. To deal with the internal motion of the system, we introduce our fictitious particle of mass μ, where

$$\mu = \frac{m_e m_N}{m_e + m_N} \tag{6.67}$$

where m_e and m_N are the electronic and nuclear masses. The particle of reduced mass μ moves subject to the potential-energy function (6.65), and its coordinates (r, θ, φ) are the spherical polar coordinates of one particle relative to the other (Fig. 6.4).

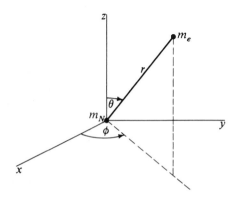

FIGURE 6.4   *Relative spherical polar coordinates.*

The Hamiltonian for the internal motion is [Eq. (6.51)]:

$$\hat{H} = -\frac{\hbar^2}{2\mu}\nabla^2 - \frac{Ze^2}{r} \tag{6.68}$$

Since V is a function of the r coordinate only, we have a one-particle central-force problem, and we may apply the results of Section 6.1. Using Eqs. (6.20) and (6.21), we have for the wave function:

$$\psi(r, \theta, \varphi) = R(r)Y_l^m(\theta, \varphi), \qquad l = 0, 1, 2, \ldots, \qquad |m| \leqslant l \tag{6.69}$$

where Y_l^m is a spherical harmonic, and the radial function $R(r)$ satisfies

$$-\frac{\hbar^2}{2\mu}\left(R'' + \frac{2}{r}R'\right) + \frac{l(l+1)\hbar^2}{2\mu r^2}R - \frac{Ze^2}{r}R = ER(r) \tag{6.70}$$

To save time in writing, we define the constant a as

$$a \equiv \hbar^2/\mu e^2 \tag{6.71}$$

and (6.70) becomes

$$R'' + \frac{2}{r}R' + \left[\frac{2E}{ae^2} + \frac{2Z}{ar} - \frac{l(l+1)}{r^2}\right]R = 0 \tag{6.72}$$

We could now try a power-series solution of (6.72), but we would get a three-term rather than a two-term recursion relation. We therefore seek a substitution that will lead to a two-term recursion relation. It turns out that the proper substitution can be found by examining the behavior of the solution for large values of r. For large r, (6.72) becomes

$$R'' + \frac{2E}{ae^2}R = 0, \qquad r \text{ large} \tag{6.73}$$

which may be solved using the auxiliary equation. The solutions are

$$\exp[\pm(-2E/ae^2)^{1/2}r] \tag{6.74}$$

Suppose that E is positive. The quantity under the square-root sign in (6.74) is negative and the factor multiplying r is imaginary:

$$R(r) \sim e^{\pm i\sqrt{2\mu E}\,r/\hbar}, \qquad E \geqslant 0 \tag{6.75}$$

where (6.71) has been used. The symbol $\sim$ in (6.75) indicates that we are giving the behavior of $R(r)$ for large values of r; this is called the *asymptotic* behavior of the function. Note the resemblance of (6.75) to Eq. (2.30), the free-particle wave function. Equation (6.75) does not give the complete radial factor in the wave function for positive energies. Further study[2] shows that the radial function for $E \geqslant 0$ remains finite for all values of r, no matter what the value of E. Thus, just as for the free particle, all nonnegative energies of the hydrogen atom are allowed. Physically, these eigenfunctions correspond to states in which the electron is not

---

[2] *Bethe and Salpeter*, pp. 21–24.

bound to the nucleus. (A classical-mechanical analogy is a comet moving in a hyperbolic orbit about the sun. The comet is not bound, and makes but one visit to the solar system.) Since we get continuous rather than discrete allowed values for $E \geqslant 0$, the positive-energy eigenfunctions are called *continuum* eigenfunctions. The angular part of a continuum wave function is, of course, a spherical harmonic. Like the free-particle wave functions, the continuum eigenfunctions are not normalizable in the usual sense.

We now consider the *bound* states of the hydrogen atom, with $E < 0$. In this case, the quantity under the square-root sign in (6.74) is positive. Since we want the wave functions to remain finite as r goes to infinity, we prefer the minus sign in (6.74), and in order to get a two-term recursion relation, we make the substitution

$$R(r) = e^{-cr} K(r) \tag{6.76}$$

$$c \equiv \left(-\frac{2E}{ae^2} \right)^{1/2} \tag{6.77}$$

[Note that e stands for two different things in (6.76) and (6.77): the base of natural logs, and the proton charge.] Use of the substitution (6.76) will guarantee nothing about the behavior of the wave function for large r. The differential equation we obtain from this substitution will still have two linearly independent solutions. We can make any substitution we please in a differential equation; in fact we could make the substitution $R(r) = e^{+cr} J(r)$ and still wind up with the correct eigenfunctions and eigenvalues. The relation between J and K would naturally be $J(r) = e^{-2cr} K(r)$.

Proceeding with (6.76), we evaluate R' and R'', substitute into (6.72), multiply through by $r^2 e^{cr}$, and use (6.77) to obtain the following differential equation for $K(r)$:

$$r^2 K'' + (2r - 2cr^2) K' + [(2Za^{-1} - 2c)r - l(l+1)] K = 0 \tag{6.78}$$

We could now substitute a power series of the form

$$K = \sum_{k=0}^{\infty} c_k r^k \tag{6.79}$$

for K; if we did, we would find that, in general, the first few coefficients in (6.79) are zero. If c_s is the first nonzero coefficient, (6.79) can be written as

$$K = \sum_{k=s}^{\infty} c_k r^k, \qquad c_s \neq 0 \tag{6.80}$$

Letting $j \equiv k - s$, and then defining b_j as $b_j \equiv c_{j+s}$, we have

$$K = \sum_{j=0}^{\infty} c_{j+s} r^{j+s} = r^s \sum_{j=0}^{\infty} b_j r^j, \qquad b_0 \neq 0 \tag{6.81}$$

(Although the various substitutions we are making might seem arbitrary, they are standard procedure in solving differential equations by power series.) In (6.81),

s is an integer whose value is to be determined by substitution into the differential equation. We thus set

$$K(r) = r^s M(r) \tag{6.82}$$

$$M(r) = \sum_{j=0}^{\infty} b_j r^j, \qquad b_0 \neq 0 \tag{6.83}$$

Evaluating K' and K'' from (6.82) and substituting into (6.78), we get

$$r^2 M'' + [(2s+2)r - 2cr^2] M' + [s^2 + s + (2Za^{-1} - 2c - 2cs)r - l(l+1)] M = 0 \tag{6.84}$$

Let us look at (6.84) for $r = 0$, to determine s. From (6.83) we have

$$M(0) = b_0, \qquad M'(0) = b_1, \qquad M''(0) = 2b_2 \tag{6.85}$$

Using (6.85) in (6.84), we find for $r = 0$:

$$b_0 [s^2 + s - l^2 - l] = 0 \tag{6.86}$$

Since b_0 is not zero, the terms in brackets must vanish:

$$s^2 + s - l^2 - l = 0 \tag{6.87}$$

This is a quadratic equation in the unknown s, with the roots

$$s = l, \qquad s = -l - 1 \tag{6.88}$$

These roots correspond to the two linearly independent solutions of the differential equation. Let us examine them from the standpoint of proper behavior of the wave function. From Eqs. (6.76), (6.82), and (6.83), we have

$$R(r) = e^{-cr} r^s \sum_{j=0}^{\infty} b_j r^j \tag{6.89}$$

Since $e^{-cr} = 1 - cr + \cdots$, the function $R(r)$ behaves for small r as $b_0 r^s$. For the root $s = l$, $R(r)$ behaves properly at the origin. However, for $s = -l-1$, $R(r)$ is proportional to

$$\frac{1}{r^{l+1}} \tag{6.90}$$

for small r. Since $l = 0, 1, 2, \ldots$, the root $s = -l-1$ makes the radial factor in the wave function infinite at the origin. Many texts take this as sufficient reason for rejecting this root. However, this is not a good argument, since for the *relativistic* hydrogen atom, the $l = 0$ eigenfunctions are infinite at $r = 0$. Let us therefore look at (6.90) from the standpoint of quadratic integrability, since we certainly require the bound-state eigenfunctions to be normalizable.

The normalization integral [Eq. (5.111)] for the radial functions that behave like (6.90) looks like

$$\int_0^{} |R|^2 r^2 \, dr \approx \int_0^{} \frac{1}{r^{2l}} \, dr \tag{6.91}$$

for small r. The behavior of the integral at the lower limit of integration is

$$\frac{1}{r^{2l-1}}\bigg|_{r=0} \qquad (6.92)$$

For $l = 1, 2, 3, \ldots$, (6.92) is infinite, and the normalization integral is infinite. Hence we must reject the root $s = -l-1$ for $l \geqslant 1$. However, for $l = 0$, (6.92) is finite, and there is no trouble with quadratic integrability. Thus there is a solution to the radial equation which behaves as r^{-1} for small r, and is quadratically integrable.

Further study of this solution shows that it corresponds to an energy value which the experimental hydrogen-atom spectrum shows does not exist. Thus the r^{-1} solution must be rejected, but there is some dispute over the reason for doing so. We will state the two reasons most often given, omitting the detailed arguments. One view[3] is that the $1/r$ solution satisfies the Schroedinger equation everywhere in space *except* at the origin, and hence must be rejected. A second view[4] is that the $1/r$ solution must be rejected because the Hamiltonian operator is not Hermitian with respect to it. (In Chapter 7, we will define Hermitian operators, and show that we require quantum-mechanical operators to be Hermitian.)

Taking the first root in (6.88), we have for the radial factor (6.89)

$$R(r) = e^{-cr}r^l M(r) \qquad (6.93)$$

With $s = l$, Eq. (6.84) becomes

$$rM'' + [2l+2-2cr]\,M' + [2Za^{-1}-2c-2cl]\,M = 0 \qquad (6.94)$$

From (6.83) we have

$$M(r) = \sum_{j=0}^{\infty} b_j r^j \qquad (6.95)$$

$$M' = \sum_{j=0}^{\infty} jb_j r^{j-1} = \sum_{j=1}^{\infty} jb_j r^{j-1} = \sum_{k=0}^{\infty} (k+1)b_{k+1}r^k = \sum_{j=0}^{\infty} (j+1)b_{j+1}r^j$$

$$M'' = \sum_{j=0}^{\infty} j(j-1)b_j r^{j-2} = \sum_{j=1}^{\infty} j(j-1)b_j r^{j-2} = \sum_{k=0}^{\infty} (k+1)kb_{k+1}r^{k-1}$$

$$= \sum_{j=0}^{\infty} (j+1)jb_{j+1}r^{j-1} \qquad (6.96)$$

Substituting these expressions in (6.94), we have after combining sums:

$$\sum_{j=0}^{\infty} \left[j(j+1)b_{j+1} + 2(l+1)(j+1)b_{j+1} + \left(\frac{2Z}{a} - 2c - 2cl - 2cj\right)b_j \right] r^j = 0$$

$$\qquad (6.97)$$

Setting the coefficient of r^j equal to zero, we get the recursion relation

$$b_{j+1} = \frac{(2c+2cl+2cj-2Za^{-1})}{j(j+1)+2(l+1)(j+1)}b_j \qquad (6.98)$$

---

[3] *Dirac*, p. 156.
[4] *Merzbacher*, Section 10.5; B. H. Armstrong and E. A. Power, *Am. J. Phys.*, **31**, 262 (1963).

We now must examine the behavior of the infinite series (6.95) for large r. Since for large r the behavior of the series is determined by the terms with large j, we examine the ratio b_{j+1}/b_j for large j:

$$\frac{b_{j+1}}{b_j} \sim \frac{2cj}{j^2} = \frac{2c}{j} \qquad \text{for } j \text{ large} \tag{6.99}$$

Now consider the power series for e^{2cr}:

$$e^{2cr} = 1 + 2cr + \cdots + \frac{(2c)^j r^j}{j!} + \frac{(2c)^{j+1} r^{j+1}}{(j+1)!} + \cdots \tag{6.100}$$

The ratio of successive powers of r in (6.100) is

$$\frac{(2c)^{j+1}}{(j+1)!} \cdot \frac{j!}{(2c)^j} = \frac{2c}{(j+1)} \sim \frac{2c}{j} \qquad \text{for } j \text{ large} \tag{6.101}$$

which is the same as (6.99) for large j. This indicates that for large r, the infinite series (6.95) behaves like e^{2cr}. For large r, the radial function (6.93) behaves like

$$R(r) \sim e^{-cr} r^l e^{2cr} = r^l e^{cr} \tag{6.102}$$

Therefore $R(r)$ will become infinite as r goes to infinity, and will not be quadratically integrable. The only way to avoid this "infinity catastrophe" (as in the harmonic-oscillator case) is to have the series terminate after a finite number of terms, in which case the e^{-cr} factor will insure that the wave function goes to zero as r goes to infinity. Let the last term in the series be $b_k r^k$. Then, to have $b_{k+1}, b_{k+2}, \ldots$ all vanish, the fraction multiplying b_j in the recursion relation (6.98) must vanish when $j = k$; we have

$$2c(k+l+1) = 2Za^{-1}, \qquad k = 0, 1, 2, \ldots \tag{6.103}$$

k and l are integers, and we now define a new integer n by

$$n \equiv k + l + 1, \qquad n = 1, 2, 3, \ldots \tag{6.104}$$

From (6.104), the quantum number l must satisfy

$$l \leqslant n - 1 \tag{6.105}$$

Hence, l ranges from 0 to $n-1$. Equation (6.103) reads

$$cn = Za^{-1} \tag{6.106}$$

Using (6.77) and (6.71) in (6.106), we find

$$E = -\frac{Z^2}{n^2}\left(\frac{e^2}{2a}\right) = -\frac{Z^2 \mu e^4}{2n^2 \hbar^2} \tag{6.107}$$

These are the bound-state energy levels of the hydrogenlike atom, and they are discrete. Figure 6.5 shows the potential-energy curve [Eq. (6.65)] and some of the allowed energy levels for the hydrogen atom ($Z = 1$). The crosshatching indicates that all positive energies are allowed.

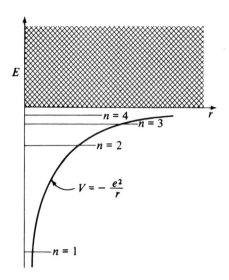

FIGURE 6.5   *Energy levels of the hydrogen atom.*

It turns out that all changes in n are allowed in light absorption and emission; the reciprocal wavelengths of hydrogen-atom spectral lines are then:

$$\frac{1}{\lambda} = \frac{\nu}{c} = \frac{E_2 - E_1}{hc} = \frac{e^2}{2ahc}\left(\frac{1}{n_1^2} - \frac{1}{n_2^2}\right) \equiv R_H\left(\frac{1}{n_1^2} - \frac{1}{n_2^2}\right)$$

where $R_H = 109{,}677.6 \text{ cm}^{-1}$ is the *Rydberg constant* for hydrogen.

Are the hydrogen-atom energy levels degenerate? For the bound states, the energy (6.107) depends only on n. However, the wave function (6.69) depends on all three quantum numbers n, l, and m, whose allowed values are [Eqs. (6.104), (6.105), (5.147), and (5.148)]:

$$n = 1, 2, 3, \ldots \tag{6.108}$$

$$l = 0, 1, 2, \ldots, n - 1 \tag{6.109}$$

$$m = -l, -l+1, \ldots, 0, \ldots, l-1, l \tag{6.110}$$

States with different values of l or m, but the same value of n, have the same energy; we have degeneracy, except for $n = 1$, where l and m must both be 0. For a given value of n, we can have n different values of l. For each of these values of l, we can have $2l+1$ values of m. The degree of degeneracy of a given bound-state level is then

$$\sum_{l=0}^{n-1} (2l+1) = \sum_{l=0}^{n-1} (2l) + \sum_{l=0}^{n-1} 1 \tag{6.111}$$

The second sum on the right side of (6.111) has n terms, each term having the value 1. Therefore it is equal to n. For the first sum, we have

$$\sum_{l=0}^{n-1} (2l) = 2\sum_{l=0}^{n-1} l = 2\sum_{l=1}^{n-1} l \tag{6.112}$$

The sum of the integers from 1 to k is (Problem 6.25) $\frac{1}{2}k(k+1)$; thus, the sum of the integers from 1 to $n-1$ is $\frac{1}{2}(n-1)n$. We have

$$\sum_{l=0}^{n-1} (2l+1) = 2 \cdot \tfrac{1}{2}(n-1)n + n = n^2 \tag{6.113}$$

and the degeneracy of the discrete levels for the hydrogenlike atom is n^2 (spin considerations being omitted). For the continuum levels, it turns out that for a given energy, there is no restriction on the maximum value of l; hence, these levels are infinity-fold degenerate.

The radial equation for the hydrogen atom can also be solved by the use of ladder operators (also known as *factorization*); see Z. W. Salsburg, *Am. J. Phys.*, **33**, 36 (1965).

6.5 The Bound-State Hydrogen-Atom Wave Functions

Using (6.106), we have for the recursion relation (6.98):

$$b_{j+1} = \frac{2Z}{na}\frac{(j+l+1-n)}{(j+1)(j+2l+2)}b_j \tag{6.114}$$

The discussion preceding Eq. (6.104) shows that the highest power of r in the polynomial $M(r)$ [Eq. (6.95)] is $k = n-l-1$; hence, using (6.106), the radial factor (6.93) is

$$R_{nl}(r) = r^l e^{-Zr/na} \sum_{j=0}^{n-l-1} b_j r^j \tag{6.115}$$

where a is given by (6.71). The complete wave function is [Eq. (6.69)]

$$\psi_{nlm} = R_{nl}(r)Y_l^m(\theta, \varphi) = R_{nl}(r)S_{lm}(\theta)\frac{1}{\sqrt{2\pi}}e^{im\varphi} \tag{6.116}$$

where the first few theta functions are given in Table 5.1.

How many nodes does $R(r)$ have? The radial function is zero at $r = \infty$, at $r = 0$ for $l \neq 0$, and at values of r that make $M(r)$ vanish. $M(r)$ is a polynomial of degree $(n-l-1)$, and it can be shown that the roots of $M(r) = 0$ are all real and positive. Thus, aside from the origin and infinity, there are $(n-l-1)$ nodes in $R(r)$. The nodes of the spherical harmonics are discussed in Problem 6.21.

For the ground state of the hydrogenlike atom we have $n = 1$, $l = 0$, $m = 0$. The radial factor is

$$R_{10}(r) = b_0 e^{-Zr/a} \tag{6.117}$$

The constant b_0 is determined by normalization [Eq. (5.111)]:

$$|b_0|^2 \int_0^\infty e^{-2Zr/a}r^2 \, dr = 1 \tag{6.118}$$

Using the Appendix integral (A.4), we find

$$R_{10}(r) = 2\left(\frac{Z}{a}\right)^{3/2} e^{-Zr/a} \tag{6.119}$$

Multiplying by Y_0^0, we have as the ground-state wave function

$$\psi_{100} = \frac{1}{\pi^{1/2}}\left(\frac{Z}{a}\right)^{3/2} e^{-Zr/a} \tag{6.120}$$

The energy of the ground state is given by (6.107) with $n = 1$. A convenient unit for electronic energies is the *electron volt* (eV), defined as the kinetic energy acquired by an electron accelerated through a potential difference of one volt. Potential difference is defined as energy per unit charge; since $e = 1.6022 \times 10^{-19}$ coul, and 1 volt coul $= 1$ joule $= 10^7$ ergs, we have

$$1 \text{ eV} = 1.6022 \times 10^{-12} \text{ erg} \tag{6.121}$$

Substituting the values of the physical constants into (6.107), we find for the hydrogen-atom ($Z = 1$) ground-state energy

$$E = -13.598 \text{ electron volts} \approx -13.60 \text{ eV} \tag{6.122}$$

a number worth remembering. This is the minimum energy needed to ionize a hydrogen atom in its ground state.

The energies and wave functions of the hydrogen atom involve the reduced mass μ_H, given by (6.67) with $m_N = m_p$, the proton mass. Since $m_p = 1836.1m_e$, we have:

$$\mu_H = \frac{1836.1}{1837.1} m_e = 0.99946 m_e \tag{6.123}$$

The reduced mass is quite close to the electron mass. In fact many texts do not bother to use the reduced mass, but simply use the electron mass in the Schroedinger equation for the hydrogen atom. Physically, this corresponds to assuming that the proton mass is infinite in comparison to the electron mass and that all the internal motion is motion of the electron—taking the limit of (6.67) as m_p goes to infinity, we find

$$\lim_{m_p \to \infty} \frac{m_p m_e}{m_p + m_e} \doteq \frac{m_p m_e}{m_p} = m_e \tag{6.124}$$

The error introduced by using the electron mass for the reduced mass is about one part in two thousand for the hydrogen atom. For heavier atoms, the error introduced by assuming an infinitely heavy nucleus is even less than this. Also, for many-electron atoms, the form of the correction for nuclear motion is quite complicated. For these reasons, we will in future assume an infinitely heavy nucleus, and simply use the electron mass in writing the Schroedinger equation for atoms.

If we replace the reduced mass of the hydrogen atom by the electron mass, the quantity a defined by (6.71) becomes

$$a_0 \equiv \frac{\hbar^2}{m_e e^2} = 0.5292 \text{ Å} \tag{6.125}$$

where the subscript zero indicates use of the electron mass instead of the reduced mass. For historical reasons, a_0 is called the *Bohr radius*; it was the radius of the circle in which the electron moved in the ground state of the hydrogen atom, according to the Bohr theory. Of course, since the ground-state wave function (6.120) is nonzero for all finite values of r, there is some probability of finding the electron at any distance from the nucleus. The electron is certainly not confined to a circle. (In a 1959 freshman chemistry text, there is the amusing statement that the electron is confined to the surface of a sphere.) Use of the electron mass instead of the reduced mass to calculate the ground-state energy of the hydrogen atom gives -13.606 eV, which is in error by 7 parts in 13,000.

Let's have a look at an interesting feature of the ground-state wave function, Eq. (6.120). For points on the x axis, where $y = 0$ and $z = 0$, the coordinate r in (5.76) equals $(x^2)^{1/2} = |x|$, and

$$\psi_{100}(x,0,0) = \frac{1}{\pi^{1/2}}\left(\frac{Z}{a}\right)^{3/2} e^{-Z|x|/a} \tag{6.126}$$

Figure 6.6 shows how (6.126) varies along the x axis. Although the wave function is continuous at the origin, the slope of the tangent to the curve is positive at the left of the origin, but negative at its right. Thus $\partial\psi/\partial x$ is discontinuous at the origin; we say that the wave function has a *cusp* at the origin. The cusp is present because the potential energy (6.65) becomes infinite at the origin. (Recall the discontinuous slope of the particle-in-a-box wave functions at the walls of the box.)

We denoted the hydrogen-atom bound-state wave functions by three subscripts which give the values of n, l, and m. We now introduce a slightly different notation, in which the value of l is indicated by a letter:

letter	s	p	d	f	g	h	i	k $\cdots$
l	0	1	2	3	4	5	6	7 $\cdots$

(6.127)

The letters s, p, d, f are of spectroscopic origin, standing for sharp, principal, diffuse, fundamental. After these, we go alphabetically, except that j is omitted. Preceding the code letter for l, we write the value of n. Thus the ground-state wave function ψ_{100} is called ψ_{1s}.

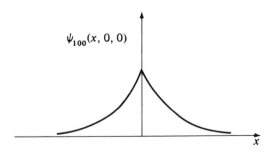

$\psi_{100}(x, 0, 0)$

FIGURE 6.6 *Cusp in the hydrogen atom ground-state wave function.*

For $n = 2$, we have the following states: $\psi_{200}, \psi_{21-1}, \psi_{210}, \psi_{211}$. We denote ψ_{200} as ψ_{2s}. To distinguish the three $2p$ functions, we use a subscript giving the value of m: $\psi_{2p-1}, \psi_{2p0}, \psi_{2p+1}$. The radial factor in the wave function depends on n and l, but not on m, as can be seen from (6.115). Each of the three $2p$ wave functions thus has the same radial factor. The $2s$ and $2p$ radial factors may be found in the usual manner from (6.115) and (6.114), followed by normalization. The results are given in Table 6.1. Note that the exponential factor in these radial functions is not the same as in the R_{1s} function, Eq. (6.119). The complete wave function is found by multiplying the radial factor by the appropriate spherical harmonic. Using (6.116), Table 6.1, and Table 5.1, we have

$$\psi_{2s} = \frac{1}{\pi^{1/2}} \left(\frac{Z}{2a}\right)^{3/2} \left(1 - \frac{Zr}{2a}\right) e^{-Zr/2a} \tag{6.128}$$

$$\psi_{2p-1} = \frac{1}{8\pi^{1/2}} \left(\frac{Z}{a}\right)^{5/2} r e^{-Zr/2a} \sin\theta \, e^{-i\varphi} \tag{6.129}$$

$$\psi_{2p0} = \frac{1}{\pi^{1/2}} \left(\frac{Z}{2a}\right)^{5/2} r e^{-Zr/2a} \cos\theta \tag{6.130}$$

$$\psi_{2p1} = \frac{1}{8\pi^{1/2}} \left(\frac{Z}{a}\right)^{5/2} r e^{-Zr/2a} \sin\theta \, e^{i\varphi} \tag{6.131}$$

Table 6.1 lists some of the normalized radial factors in the hydrogenlike wave functions. Figure 6.7 gives graphs of some of the radial functions. The r^l factor makes the radial functions zero at $r = 0$, except for s states.

Table 6.1 Radial Factors in the Hydrogenlike-Atom Wave Functions

$$R_{1s} = 2\left(\frac{Z}{a}\right)^{3/2} e^{-Zr/a}$$

$$R_{2s} = \frac{1}{\sqrt{2}} \left(\frac{Z}{a}\right)^{3/2} \left(1 - \frac{Zr}{2a}\right) e^{-Zr/2a}$$

$$R_{2p} = \frac{1}{2\sqrt{6}} \left(\frac{Z}{a}\right)^{5/2} r e^{-Zr/2a}$$

$$R_{3s} = \frac{2}{3\sqrt{3}} \left(\frac{Z}{a}\right)^{3/2} \left(1 - \frac{2Zr}{3a} + \frac{2Z^2 r^2}{27a^2}\right) e^{-Zr/3a}$$

$$R_{3p} = \frac{8}{27\sqrt{6}} \left(\frac{Z}{a}\right)^{3/2} \left(\frac{Zr}{a} - \frac{Z^2 r^2}{6a^2}\right) e^{-Zr/3a}$$

$$R_{3d} = \frac{4}{81\sqrt{30}} \left(\frac{Z}{a}\right)^{7/2} r^2 e^{-Zr/3a}$$

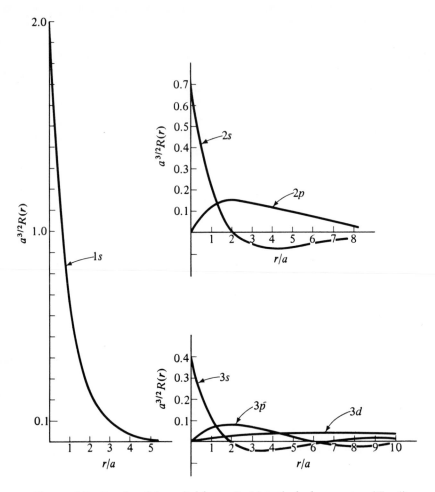

FIGURE 6.7 *Graphs of the radial factor $R_{nl}(r)$ in the hydrogen-atom $(Z = 1)$ wave functions. The same scale is used in all the graphs. (In some well-known texts, these functions are not properly drawn to scale.)*

The probability of finding the electron in the region of space where its r coordinate is between r and $r+dr$, its θ coordinate is between θ and $\theta+d\theta$, and its φ coordinate is between φ and $\varphi+d\varphi$, is [Eq. (5.107)]:

$$|\psi|^2 \, d\tau = [R_{nl}(r)]^2 \, |Y_l^m(\theta, \varphi)|^2 r^2 \sin\theta \, dr \, d\theta \, d\varphi \qquad (6.132)$$

We now ask, what is the probability of the electron having its r coordinate between r and $r+dr$ with no restriction on the values of θ and φ? We are asking for the probability of finding the electron in a thin spherical shell centered at the origin, of inner radius r and outer radius $r+dr$. We must thus add up the probabilities (6.132) for all possible values of θ and φ, keeping r fixed. This amounts to integrating (6.132) over θ and φ. Hence, the probability of finding the electron between

r and $r+dr$ is

$$[R_{nl}(r)]^2 r^2 \, dr \int_0^{2\pi} \int_0^{\pi} |Y_l^m(\theta, \varphi)|^2 \sin\theta \, d\theta \, d\varphi = [R_{nl}(r)]^2 r^2 \, dr \qquad (6.133)$$

since the spherical harmonics are normalized:

$$\int_0^{2\pi} \int_0^{\pi} |Y_l^m(\theta, \varphi)|^2 \sin\theta \, d\theta \, d\varphi = 1 \qquad (6.134)$$

as can be seen from (5.112), (5.111), and (5.101). The function $R^2(r)r^2$, which determines the probability of finding the electron at a distance r from the nucleus, is called the *radial distribution function*; see Fig. 6.8. Although $R_{1s}(r)$ is not zero

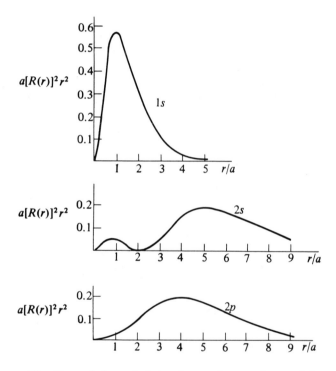

FIGURE 6.8 *Plots of the radial distribution function* $[R_{nl}(r)]^2 r^2$ *for the hydrogen atom.*

at the origin, the 1s radial distribution function is zero at $r = 0$ because of the r^2 factor; the volume of the thin spherical shell becomes zero as r goes to zero. The maximum in the radial distribution function for the 1s state of hydrogen is at $r = a$.

The factor $e^{im\varphi}$ makes the spherical harmonics imaginary, except when $m = 0$. Instead of working with imaginary wave functions such as (6.129) and (6.131), chemists often use real wave functions formed by taking certain linear combinations of the complex functions. The justification for this procedure is given by the theorem of Section 3.6: Any linear combination of eigenfunctions of a degenerate energy level is an eigenfunction of the Hamiltonian with the same eigenvalue. Since the energy of the hydrogen atom does not depend on m, the $2p_1$ and $2p_{-1}$ states belong to a degenerate energy level; any linear combination of them is an eigenfunction of the Hamiltonian with the same energy eigenvalue.

There are essentially two different ways to combine these two functions to obtain a real function. One way is

$$\psi_{2p_x} = \frac{1}{\sqrt{2}}(\psi_{2p_{-1}}+\psi_{2p_1}) = \frac{1}{4\sqrt{2\pi}}\left(\frac{Z}{a}\right)^{5/2} re^{-Zr/2a}\sin\theta\cos\varphi \qquad (6.135)$$

where we have used (6.129), (6.131), and $e^{\pm i\varphi} = \cos\varphi \pm i\sin\varphi$. The $1/\sqrt{2}$ factor normalizes ψ_{2p_x}:

$$\int |\psi_{2p_x}|^2\,d\tau = \frac{1}{2}\left(\int |\psi_{2p_{-1}}|^2\,d\tau + \int |\psi_{2p_1}|^2\,d\tau + \int \psi_{2p_{-1}}^*\psi_{2p_1}\,d\tau + \int \psi_{2p_1}^*\psi_{2p_{-1}}\,d\tau\right)$$

$$= \tfrac{1}{2}(1+1+0+0) = 1 \qquad (6.136)$$

Here we have used the fact that ψ_{2p_1} and $\psi_{2p_{-1}}$ are normalized, and are orthogonal to each other, since

$$\int_0^{2\pi}(e^{-i\varphi})^*e^{i\varphi}\,d\varphi = \int_0^{2\pi}e^{2i\varphi}\,d\varphi = 0 \qquad (6.137)$$

The designation ψ_{2p_x} for (6.135) becomes clearer if we note that (5.75) gives

$$\psi_{2p_x} = \frac{1}{4\sqrt{2\pi}}\left(\frac{Z}{a}\right)^{5/2} xe^{-Zr/2a} \qquad (6.138)$$

The second way of combining the functions is

$$\psi_{2p_y} \equiv \frac{1}{i\sqrt{2}}(\psi_{2p_1}-\psi_{2p_{-1}}) = \frac{1}{4\sqrt{2\pi}}\left(\frac{Z}{a}\right)^{5/2} r\sin\theta\sin\varphi\, e^{-Zr/2a} \qquad (6.139)$$

$$\psi_{2p_y} = \frac{1}{4\sqrt{2\pi}}\left(\frac{Z}{a}\right)^{5/2} ye^{-Zr/2a} \qquad (6.140)$$

The function ψ_{2p_0} is real and is often denoted by

$$\psi_{2p_0} = \psi_{2p_z} = \frac{1}{\sqrt{\pi}}\left(\frac{Z}{2a}\right)^{5/2} ze^{-Zr/2a} \qquad (6.141)$$

where capital Z stands for the number of protons in the nucleus, and small z is the z coordinate of the electron. We leave it to you to show that ψ_{2p_x}, ψ_{2p_y}, and ψ_{2p_z} are mutually orthogonal. Note that ψ_{2p_z} is zero in the xy plane, positive above this plane, and negative below it.

The functions $\psi_{2p_{-1}}$ and ψ_{2p_1} are eigenfunctions of $\hat{L}^2$ with the *same* eigenvalue: $2\hbar^2$. The reasoning of Section 3.6 shows that the linear combinations (6.135) and (6.139) are also eigenfunctions of $\hat{L}^2$ with eigenvalue $2\hbar^2$. However, $\psi_{2p_{-1}}$ and ψ_{2p_1} are eigenfunctions of $\hat{L}_z$ with *different* eigenvalues: $-\hbar$ and $+\hbar$. Therefore, ψ_{2p_x} and ψ_{2p_y} are not eigenfunctions of $\hat{L}_z$.

Table 6.2 Real Hydrogenlike Wave Functions

$$\psi_{1s} = \frac{1}{\pi^{1/2}} \left(\frac{Z}{a}\right)^{3/2} e^{-Zr/a}$$

$$\psi_{2s} = \frac{1}{4(2\pi)^{1/2}} \left(\frac{Z}{a}\right)^{3/2} \left(2 - \frac{Zr}{a}\right) e^{-Zr/2a}$$

$$\psi_{2p_z} = \frac{1}{4(2\pi)^{1/2}} \left(\frac{Z}{a}\right)^{5/2} r e^{-Zr/2a} \cos\theta$$

$$\psi_{2p_x} = \frac{1}{4(2\pi)^{1/2}} \left(\frac{Z}{a}\right)^{5/2} r e^{-Zr/2a} \sin\theta \cos\varphi$$

$$\psi_{2p_y} = \frac{1}{4(2\pi)^{1/2}} \left(\frac{Z}{a}\right)^{5/2} r e^{-Zr/2a} \sin\theta \sin\varphi$$

$$\psi_{3s} = \frac{1}{81(3\pi)^{1/2}} \left(\frac{Z}{a}\right)^{3/2} \left(27 - 18\frac{Zr}{a} + 2\frac{Z^2 r^2}{a^2}\right) e^{-Zr/3a}$$

$$\psi_{3p_z} = \frac{2^{1/2}}{81\pi^{1/2}} \left(\frac{Z}{a}\right)^{5/2} \left(6 - \frac{Zr}{a}\right) r e^{-Zr/3a} \cos\theta$$

$$\psi_{3p_x} = \frac{2^{1/2}}{81\pi^{1/2}} \left(\frac{Z}{a}\right)^{5/2} \left(6 - \frac{Zr}{a}\right) r e^{-Zr/3a} \sin\theta \cos\varphi$$

$$\psi_{3p_y} = \frac{2^{1/2}}{81\pi^{1/2}} \left(\frac{Z}{a}\right)^{5/2} \left(6 - \frac{Zr}{a}\right) r e^{-Zr/3a} \sin\theta \sin\varphi$$

$$\psi_{3d_{z^2}} = \frac{1}{81(6\pi)^{1/2}} \left(\frac{Z}{a}\right)^{7/2} r^2 e^{-Zr/3a}(3\cos^2\theta - 1)$$

$$\psi_{3d_{xz}} = \frac{2^{1/2}}{81\pi^{1/2}} \left(\frac{Z}{a}\right)^{7/2} r^2 e^{-Zr/3a} \sin\theta \cos\theta \cos\varphi$$

$$\psi_{3d_{yz}} = \frac{2^{1/2}}{81\pi^{1/2}} \left(\frac{Z}{a}\right)^{7/2} r^2 e^{-Zr/3a} \sin\theta \cos\theta \sin\varphi$$

$$\psi_{3d_{x^2-y^2}} = \frac{1}{81(2\pi)^{1/2}} \left(\frac{Z}{a}\right)^{7/2} r^2 e^{-Zr/3a} \sin^2\theta \cos 2\varphi$$

$$\psi_{3d_{xy}} = \frac{1}{81(2\pi)^{1/2}} \left(\frac{Z}{a}\right)^{7/2} r^2 e^{-Zr/3a} \sin^2\theta \sin 2\varphi$$

We can extend this procedure to construct real wave functions for higher states. Since m ranges from $-l$ to $+l$, for each imaginary function containing the factor $e^{-i|m|\varphi}$ there is a function with the same value of n and l, but having the factor $e^{+i|m|\varphi}$. Addition and subtraction of these functions gives two real functions, one with the factor $\cos(|m|\varphi)$, the other with the factor $\sin(|m|\varphi)$. Table 6.2 lists these real wave functions for the hydrogenlike atom. The subscripts on these functions come from similar considerations as for the $2p_x$, $2p_y$, and $2p_z$ functions. For example,

$$\psi_{3d_{x^2-y^2}} \equiv 2^{-1/2}(\psi_{3d_{+2}}+\psi_{3d_{-2}}) \tag{6.142}$$

$$= \frac{1}{81\sqrt{2\pi}}\left(\frac{Z}{a}\right)^{7/2} e^{-Zr/3a}r^2 \sin^2\theta (\cos^2\varphi - \sin^2\varphi)$$

$$= \frac{1}{81\sqrt{2\pi}}\left(\frac{Z}{a}\right)^{7/2} e^{-Zr/3a}(x^2-y^2) \tag{6.143}$$

where we have used Table 6.1 for the radial factor, Table 5.1 for the theta factor, and $e^{im\varphi}/\sqrt{2\pi}$ for the phi factor.

The real hydrogenlike functions are derived from the complex functions by replacing $e^{im\varphi}/(2\pi)^{1/2}$ with $\pi^{-1/2}\sin|m|\varphi$ or $\pi^{-1/2}\cos|m|\varphi$ for $m \neq 0$; for $m = 0$ the φ factor is $1/(2\pi)^{1/2}$ for both real and complex functions.

6.6 Hydrogenlike Orbitals

We shall refer to the hydrogenlike wave functions as hydrogenlike *orbitals*. These functions have been derived for a one-electron atom, and we cannot expect to use them to give a truly accurate representation of the wave function of a many-electron atom. We will consider the use of the orbital concept to approximate many-electron atomic wave functions in Chapter 11. For the present we restrict ourselves to one-electron atoms.

There are two fundamentally different ways of depicting orbitals: Method I is to draw graphs of the functions; Method II is to draw contour surfaces of constant probability density. There is considerable confusion between the two methods; many texts draw graphs of the angular part of the wave function and then say that these are orbital contour surfaces, which is wrong.

First consider drawing graphs (Method I). To graph the variation of ψ as a function of the three independent variables r, θ, and φ, we need four dimensions; the three-dimensional nature of our world prevents us from drawing such a graph. Instead, we draw graphs of the factors in ψ. Graphing $R(r)$ versus r, we get the curves of Fig. 6.7. Such graphs contain no information on the angular variation of ψ.

Now consider graphs of $S(\theta)$. We have (Table 5.1)

$$S_{0,0} = 1/\sqrt{2}, \qquad S_{1,0} = \tfrac{1}{2}\sqrt{6}\cos\theta$$

We can graph these functions using two-dimensional Cartesian coordinates, plotting S on the vertical axis and θ on the horizontal axis. $S_{0,0}$ gives a horizontal straight line, and $S_{1,0}$ gives a cosine curve. More commonly, S is graphed using plane polar coordinates. The variable θ is the angle with the positive z axis and $S(\theta)$ is the distance from the origin to the point on the graph. For $S_{0,0}$ we naturally get a circle; for $S_{1,0}$ we obtain two tangent circles (Fig. 6.9). The negative sign on the lower circle of the graph of $S_{1,0}$ indicates that for $\tfrac{1}{2}\pi < \theta \leqslant \pi$, $S_{1,0}$ is negative. Strictly speaking, in graphing $\cos\theta$ we only get the upper circle, which is traced out twice; to get two tangent circles we must graph $|\cos\theta|$.

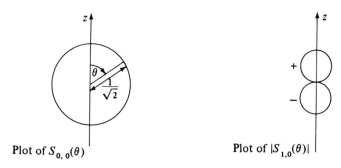

Plot of $S_{0,0}(\theta)$ Plot of $|S_{1,0}(\theta)|$

FIGURE 6.9   *Polar graphs of the θ factors in the hydrogen-atom wave functions.*

Instead of graphing the angular factors separately, we can draw a single graph that plots $|S(\theta)\,T(\varphi)|$ as a function of θ and φ; we will use spherical polar coordinates, and the distance from the origin to a point on the graph will be $|S(\theta)\,T(\varphi)|$. For an s state, ST is independent of the angles, and we get a sphere of radius $1/(4\pi)^{1/2}$ for our graph. For a p_z state, $ST = \frac{1}{2}\sqrt{3/\pi}\,\cos\theta$, and the graph of $|ST|$ consists of two spheres with centers on the z axis and tangent at the origin (Fig. 6.10). No doubt Fig. 6.10 is familiar. Many texts say this gives the shape of a p_z orbital, which is wrong; Fig. 6.10 is simply a *graph* of the *angular factor* in a p_z wave function. Graphs of the p_x and p_y angular factors give tangent spheres lying on the x and y axes, respectively. If we graph $S^2 T^2$ in spherical polar coordinates we get surfaces with the familiar figure-eight cross sections; again, these are graphs and not orbital shapes.

Now consider Method II, drawing contour surfaces of constant probability density. No doubt you are familiar with geographical contour maps, which show lines of constant altitude. We will draw surfaces in space, on each of which the value of $|\psi|^2$, the probability density, is constant. Naturally, if $|\psi|^2$ is constant on a given surface, $|\psi|$ is also constant on that surface; the contour surfaces for $|\psi|^2$ and for $|\psi|$ are identical.

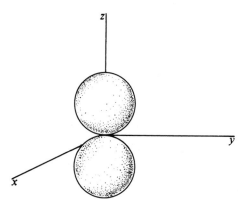

FIGURE 6.10   *Graph of $|Y_1^0(\theta, \varphi)|$, the angular factor for a p_z wave function.*

For an s orbital, the wave function depends only on r, so that a contour surface is a surface of constant r, i.e., a sphere centered at the origin. To pin down the size of an orbital, we take a contour surface within which it is, say, 90 per cent probable to find the electron; thus we want

$$\int_V |\psi|^2 \, d\tau = 0.90 \tag{6.144}$$

where V is the volume enclosed by the orbital contour surface.

Let us obtain the cross section of the $2p_y$ hydrogenlike orbital in the yz plane. In this plane, $\varphi = \pi/2$ (Fig. 6.4) and $\sin \varphi = 1$; hence Table 6.2 gives for this orbital in the yz plane:

$$|\psi_{2p_y}| = k^{5/2} \pi^{-1/2} r e^{-kr} |\sin \theta| \tag{6.145}$$

where $k = Z/2a$. To find the orbital cross section, we use plane polar coordinates to plot (6.145) for a fixed value of ψ; r is the distance from the origin, and θ the angle with the z axis. The result for a typical contour (Problem 6.18) is shown in Fig. 6.11. Since

$$y e^{-kr} = y \exp[-k(x^2 + y^2 + z^2)^{1/2}]$$

we see that ψ_{2p_y} is a function of y and $(x^2 + z^2)$; hence, on a circle centered on the y axis and parallel to the xz plane, ψ_{2p_y} is constant. Thus a three-dimensional contour surface may be developed by rotating the cross section in Fig. 6.11 about the y axis, giving a pair of distorted ellipsoids. The shape of a real $2p$ orbital is two separated, distorted ellipsoids, and not two tangent spheres. The two tangent spheres are a crude, simple (-minded) approximation to the true orbital shape, and will probably continue to be used by many chemists.

Now consider the shape of the complex orbitals $\psi_{2p_{\pm 1}}$. We have

$$\psi_{2p_{\pm 1}} = k^{5/2} \pi^{-1/2} r e^{-kr} \sin \theta e^{\pm i\varphi} \tag{6.146}$$

$$|\psi_{2p_{\pm 1}}| = k^{5/2} \pi^{-1/2} e^{-kr} r |\sin \theta| \tag{6.147}$$

and the two orbitals have the same shape. Since the right sides of (6.147) and (6.145)

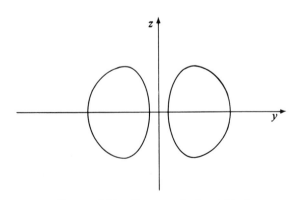

FIGURE 6.11   Contour of a $2p_y$ orbital.

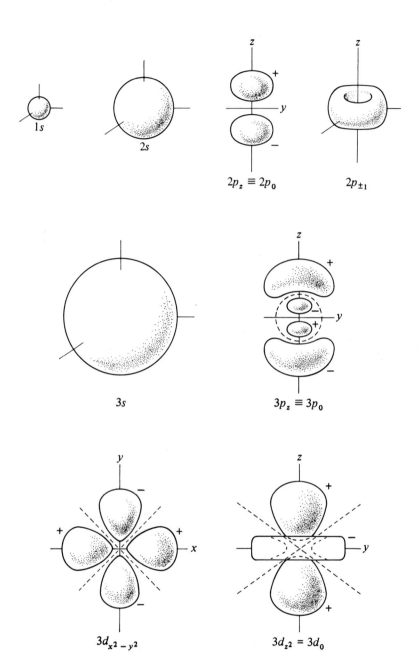

FIGURE 6.12 *Shapes of some hydrogen-atom orbitals. The 2s orbital has a spherical node, which is not visible; the 3s orbital has two such nodes. The $3p_z$ orbital has a spherical node (indicated by the dashed line) and a nodal plane (the xy plane). The $3d_{z^2}$ orbital has two nodal cones; the $3d_{x^2-y^2}$ orbital has two nodal planes. Note that the view shown is not the same for the various orbitals. The relative signs of the wave function are indicated. The three other real 3d orbitals of Table 6.2 have the same shape as the $3d_{x^2-y^2}$ orbital, but different spatial orientations. [For a set of orthonormal d orbitals all five of which have the same shape, see R. E. Powell, J. Chem. Educ., 45, 45 (1968).]*

are identical, we conclude that Fig. 6.11 also gives the cross section of the $2p_{\pm 1}$ orbitals in the yz plane. Since [Eq. (5.75)]

$$e^{-kr}r|\sin\theta| = \exp[-k(x^2+y^2+z^2)^{1/2}](x^2+y^2)^{1/2}$$

we see that $|\psi_{2p_{\pm 1}}|$ is a function of z and (x^2+y^2); so we get the three-dimensional orbital shape by rotating Fig. 6.11 about the z axis. This gives a doughnut-shaped surface. Various hydrogenlike orbital surfaces are shown in Fig. 6.12.

Schroedinger's original interpretation of $|\psi|^2$ was that the electron was "smeared out" into a charge cloud. If we consider an electron passing from one medium to another, we find that $|\psi|^2$ is nonzero in both mediums. According to the charge-cloud interpretation, this would mean that part of the electron was reflected and part transmitted. However, experimentally one never detects a fraction of an electron; electrons behave as indivisible entities. This difficulty is removed by the Born interpretation, according to which the values of $|\psi|^2$ in the two mediums give the *probabilities* for reflection and transmission. The orbital shapes we have drawn give the regions of space in which it is 90 per cent probable to find the electron.

Figure 6.13 represents the probability density in the yz plane for various orbitals; the number of dots in a given region is proportional to the value of $|\psi|^2$ in that region. Rotation of these diagrams about the vertical (z) axis gives the three-dimensional probability density. The $2s$ orbital has a constant for its angular factor, and hence has no angular nodes; for this orbital we have $n-l-1=1$, indicating one radial node. The sphere on which $\psi_{2s}=0$ is evident in Fig. 6.13.

1s

2s

$2p_z$

FIGURE 6.13 *Probability densities for some hydrogen-atom states.* [*For accurate stereo plots, see D. T. Cromer, J. Chem. Educ., 45, 626 (1968).*]

6.7 The Zeeman Effect

In 1896 Zeeman observed that application of an external magnetic field caused a splitting of atomic spectral lines. We will consider this *Zeeman effect* for the hydrogen atom; we begin by reviewing magnetism.

Magnetic fields arise from moving electric charges. A charge q with velocity $\mathbf{v}$ gives rise to a magnetic field $\mathbf{B}$ at point P in space, such that

$$\mathbf{B} = \frac{q\mathbf{v}\times\mathbf{r}}{cr^3} \tag{6.148}$$

where $\mathbf{r}$ is the vector from q to P. [Equation (6.148) is valid only for a nonaccelerated charge moving with a speed much smaller than the speed of light c.] The vector **B** is called the magnetic induction. (It was formerly believed that the vector **H** was the fundamental magnetic field vector, so that **H** was called the magnetic field strength. It is now known that **B** is the fundamental magnetic vector. In vacuum **B** = **H**; many quantum-mechanics texts write **H** instead of **B**.) Equation (6.148) is in Gaussian units, a mixed system of units in which electrical quantities are measured in cgs electrostatic units (esu), and magnetic quantities are measured in cgs electromagnetic units (emu). The conversion factor between esu and emu is c. In (6.148), q is in statcoulombs, and **B** is in gauss.

Two electric charges $\pm q$ separated by a small distance s constitute an electric dipole. The *electric dipole moment* is defined as a vector from $-q$ to $+q$, with magnitude qs. For a small planar loop of electric current, it turns out that the magnetic field generated by the moving charges of the current is given by the same mathematical expression as the electric field due to an electric dipole, except that the electric dipole moment is replaced by the *magnetic dipole moment* μ; μ is a vector of magnitude IA/c, where I is the current in esu flowing in a loop of area A; the direction of μ is perpendicular to the current loop. [An electric charge q is an electric monopole; one might wonder whether magnetic monopoles exist. All attempts to find them have failed. See R. L. Fleischer *et al.*, *J. Appl. Phys.*, **41**, 958 (1970).]

Consider the magnetic (dipole) moment associated with a charge q moving in a circle of radius r with speed v. The current is the charge flow per unit time. The circumference of the circle is $2\pi r$ and the time for one revolution is $2\pi r/v$. Hence

$$I = \frac{qv}{2\pi r} \tag{6.149}$$

The magnitude of μ is

$$|\mu| = \frac{IA}{c} = \frac{qv}{2\pi r}\frac{\pi r^2}{c} = \frac{qvr}{2c} = \frac{qrp}{2mc} \tag{6.150}$$

where m is the mass of the charged particle, and p is its linear momentum. Since the radius vector **r** is perpendicular to **p**, we have

$$\mu_L = \frac{q\mathbf{r} \times \mathbf{p}}{2mc} = \frac{q}{2mc}\mathbf{L} \tag{6.151}$$

where the definition of orbital angular momentum **L** was used, and where the subscript on μ indicates that it arises from the orbital motion of the particle. Although we derived (6.151) for the special case of circular motion, its validity is general. For an electron, $q = -e$, and the magnetic moment due to its orbital motion is

$$\mu_L = -\frac{e}{2mc}\mathbf{L} \tag{6.152}$$

The magnitude of **L** is given by (5.129), and the magnitude of the orbital magnetic moment of an electron with orbital-angular-momentum quantum number l is

$$|\mu_L| = \frac{e\hbar}{2mc}[l(l+1)]^{1/2} = \beta_e[l(l+1)]^{1/2} \tag{6.153}$$

The constant $e\hbar/2mc$ is called the *Bohr magneton* β_e:

$$\beta_e \equiv \frac{e\hbar}{2mc} = 9.27 \times 10^{-21} \text{ ergs/gauss} \tag{6.154}$$

Now consider applying an external magnetic field to the hydrogen atom. The energy of interaction between a magnetic dipole μ and an external magnetic field **B** is [*Halliday and Resnick*, Eq. (33–12)]:

$$E_B = -\mu \cdot \mathbf{B} \tag{6.155}$$

Using Eq. (6.152), we have

$$E_B = \frac{e}{2mc} \mathbf{L} \cdot \mathbf{B} \tag{6.156}$$

We take the z axis along the direction of the applied field: $\mathbf{B} = B\mathbf{k}$, where **k** is a unit vector in the z direction. We have

$$E_B = \frac{e}{2mc} B(L_x \mathbf{i} + L_y \mathbf{j} + L_z \mathbf{k}) \cdot \mathbf{k} = \frac{e}{2mc} BL_z = \frac{\beta_e}{\hbar} BL_z$$

where L_z is the z component of orbital angular momentum. We now replace L_z by the operator $\hat{L}_z$ to give the following additional term in the Hamiltonian, due to the external magnetic field

$$\hat{H}_B = \beta_e B\hbar^{-1}\hat{L}_z \tag{6.157}$$

The Schroedinger equation for the hydrogen atom in a magnetic field is

$$(\hat{H} + \hat{H}_B)\psi = E\psi \tag{6.158}$$

where $\hat{H}$ is the hydrogen-atom Hamiltonian in the absence of an external field. We readily verify that the solutions of Eq. (6.158) are the complex hydrogenlike wave functions (6.69):

$$(\hat{H} + \hat{H}_B) R(r) Y_l^m (\theta, \varphi) = \hat{H} R Y_l^m + \beta_e \hbar^{-1} B \hat{L}_z R Y_l^m$$

$$= \left(-\frac{Z^2}{n^2} \frac{e^2}{2a} + \beta_e Bm \right) R Y_l^m \tag{6.159}$$

where Eqs. (6.107) and (5.148) were used. Thus, there is an additional term $\beta_e Bm$ in the energy, and the external magnetic field removes the m degeneracy. For obvious reasons, m is often called the *magnetic quantum number*. Actually the observed energy shifts do *not* match the predictions of Eq. (6.159), due to the existence of electron spin magnetic moment (Chapter 10 and Section 11.7).

In Chapter 5 we found that in quantum mechanics **L** lies on the surface of a cone. A *classical*-mechanical treatment (*Halliday and Resnick*, Sections 13-2 and 37-6) of the motion of **L** in an applied magnetic field shows that the field exerts a torque on μ_L causing **L** to revolve about the direction of **B** at a constant frequency given by $|\mu_L| B/2\pi |\mathbf{L}|$, while maintaining a constant angle with **B**. This gyroscopic motion is called *precession*. In quantum mechanics, a complete specification of **L** is impossible; however, one finds that $\langle \mathbf{L} \rangle$ precesses about the field direction (*Dicke and Wittke*, Section 12-3; *Blokhintsev*, Section 62).

PROBLEMS

6.1 The lowest observed microwave absorption frequency of $C^{12}O^{16}$ is $115,271 \times 10^6$ cycles/sec. (a) Compute the bond distance in $C^{12}O^{16}$. (b) Predict the next two lowest microwave absorption frequencies of $C^{12}O^{16}$. (c) Predict the lowest microwave absorption frequency of $C^{13}O^{16}$.

6.2 (a) For the hydrogen-atom ground state, find the probability of finding the electron further than twice the Bohr radius from the nucleus. (b) For the hydrogen-atom ground state, find the probability of finding the electron in the classically forbidden region. (c) Find the radius of the sphere defining the $1s$ hydrogen orbital, using the 90 per cent probability definition.

6.3 What is the value of the angular-momentum quantum number l for a t orbital?

6.4 For the ground state of the hydrogenlike atom, find: (a) the average value of r; (b) the most probable value of r. (c) Find $\langle r \rangle$ for a $2p$ state.

6.5 Where is the probability density a maximum for the hydrogen-atom ground state?

6.6 A stationary-state wave function is an eigenfunction of the Hamiltonian operator $\hat{H} = \hat{T} + \hat{V}$. Students sometimes erroneously believe that ψ is an eigenfunction of $\hat{T}$ and of $\hat{V}$. For the ground state of the hydrogen atom, verify directly that ψ is not an eigenfunction of $\hat{T}$ or of $\hat{V}$, but is an eigenfunction of $(\hat{T} + \hat{V})$. (Can you think of a problem we solved where ψ *is* an eigenfunction of $\hat{T}$ and of $\hat{V}$?)

6.7 Show that $\langle T \rangle + \langle V \rangle = E$ for a stationary state.

6.8 Compute $\langle V \rangle$, $\langle T \rangle$, and $\langle T \rangle / \langle V \rangle$ for the hydrogen-atom ground state. (Use the result of Problem 6.7 to shorten the work.)

6.9 Calculate in electron volts the ground-state energy of positronium—an "atom" which consists of a positron and an electron. (The positron has charge $+e$ and mass equal to the electronic mass.)

6.10 On the x axis the ground-state hydrogen-atom wave function is given by (6.126). Calculate the limit which the derivative of (6.126) approaches (a) as $x \to 0$ from the left; (b) as $x \to 0$ from the right.

6.11 Assign each of the following observed vacuum wavelengths to a transition between two hydrogen-atom levels:

$$6564.7 \text{ Å}, \quad 4862.7 \text{ Å}, \quad 4341.7 \text{ Å}, \quad 4102.9 \text{ Å} \quad \text{(Balmer series)}.$$

Predict the wavelengths of the next two lines in this series, and the wavelength of the series limit. (Balmer was a Swiss mathematician who, in 1885, came up with an empirical formula which fitted lines of the hydrogen spectrum.)

6.12 Verify Eq. (6.6) for the Laplacian in spherical polar coordinates.

6.13 Verify Eq. (6.62).

6.14 Calculate the ratio of the electrical and gravitational forces between a proton and an electron. Is neglect of the gravitational force justified?

6.15 Derive the $2s$ and $2p$ radial hydrogenlike functions.

6.16 For the hydrogen-atom ground state, use the value of $\langle T \rangle$ from Problem 6.8 to calculate the root-mean-square speed of the electron; find the numerical value of $\langle v^2 \rangle^{1/2}/c$, where c is the speed of light.

6.17 For the particle in a box and the harmonic oscillator, there are no continuum eigenfunctions, while for the hydrogen atom we do have continuum functions. Explain this in terms of the nature of the potential-energy function for each problem. Would you expect any continuum eigenfunctions for a particle in a box with walls of finite height?

6.18 Show that the maximum value for ψ_{2p_y} [Eq. (6.145)] is $k^{3/2}\pi^{-1/2}e^{-1}$. Use Eq. (6.145) to plot the $2p_y$ contour for which $\psi = 0.316\psi_{max}$.

6.19 For which hydrogen-atom states is ψ nonzero at the nucleus?

6.20 If we were to ignore the interelectronic repulsion in helium, what would be its ground-state energy and wave function? (See the latter part of Section 6.2.) Compute the percent error in the energy; the experimental He ground-state energy is -79.0 eV. (Assume an infinitely heavy nucleus.)

6.21 For the *real* hydrogenlike functions: (a) What is the shape of the $n-l-1$ nodal surfaces for which the radial factor is zero? (b) The nodal surfaces for which the φ factor vanishes are of the form $\varphi = $ constant; thus, they are planes perpendicular to the xy plane. How many such planes are there? (Values of φ that differ by π are considered to be part of the same plane.) (c) It can be shown that there are $l-m$ surfaces on which the θ factor vanishes. What is the shape of these surfaces? (d) How many nodal surfaces are there for the real hydrogenlike wave functions?

6.22 (a) The *Laguerre polynomials* are defined as

$$L_q(z) \equiv e^z \frac{d^q}{dz^q}(e^{-z}z^q)$$

Verify that

$$L_0 = 1, \quad L_1 = -z + 1, \quad L_2 = z^2 - 4z + 2, \quad L_3 = -z^3 + 9z^2 - 18z + 6$$

(b) The *associated Laguerre polynomials* are usually defined as

$$L_q^s(z) = \frac{d^s}{dz^s}L_q(z)$$

Verify that

$$L_q^0(z) = L_q(z), \quad L_1^1(z) = -1, \quad L_2^1(z) = 2z - 4, \quad L_2^2(z) = 2$$

$$L_3^1(z) = -3z^2 + 18z - 18, \quad L_3^2(z) = -6z + 18, \quad L_3^3(z) = -6$$

(c) The radial factor in the hydrogenlike wave functions can be shown to be[5]

$$R_{nl}(r) = -\left[\frac{4Z^3}{n^4a^3}\frac{(n-l-1)!}{[(n+l)!]^3}\right]^{1/2}\left(\frac{2Zr}{na}\right)^l e^{-Zr/na}L_{n+l}^{2l+1}\left(\frac{2Zr}{na}\right)$$

Verify this equation for the $1s$, $2s$, and $2p$ states.

6.23 If the three force constants in Problem 4.5 each have the same value, we have a three-dimensional isotropic harmonic oscillator. (a) State why the wave functions for this case can be written in the form

$$F(r)G(\theta, \varphi) \tag{6.160}$$

(b) What is the function G? (c) Write down a differential equation for $F(r)$. (d) Use the results of Problem 4.5 to show that the ground-state wave function has the form (6.160) and verify that the ground-state $F(r)$ satisfies the differential equation in (c). (e) Give the expression for the energy eigenvalues. (f) Give the degeneracies of the lowest three energy levels.

---

[5] *Pauling and Wilson*, p. 132.

6.24 Sketch rough contours of constant $|\psi|$ for each of the following states of a particle in a two-dimensional square box: $n_x n_y = 11; 12; 21; 22$. What are you reminded of?

6.25 To find the degeneracy of the hydrogen-atom energy levels, we used

$$\sum_{k=1}^{n} k = \frac{n(n+1)}{2} \tag{6.161}$$

Prove this result by adding corresponding terms of the two series: $1, 2, 3, ..., n$ and $n, n-1, n-2, ..., 1$. [Legend has it that Gauss used (6.161) at age six to add up a sum given him by his arithmetic teacher.]

6.26 The hydrogenlike wave functions $2p_1$, $2p_0$, and $2p_{-1}$ can be characterized as those $2p$ functions that are eigenfunctions of $\hat{L}_z$. What operators can we use to characterize the functions $2p_x$, $2p_y$, and $2p_z$, and what are the corresponding eigenvalues?

6.27 Given that $\hat{A}f = af$ and $\hat{A}g = bg$, where f and g are functions and a and b are constants, under what condition(s) is the linear combination $c_1 f + c_2 g$ an eigenfunction of the linear operator $\hat{A}$?

6.28 State which of the three operators $\hat{H}$, $\hat{L}^2$, and $\hat{L}_z$ each of the following functions is an eigenfunction of: (a) $2p_z$; (b) $2p_x$; (c) $2p_1$.

6.29 Each hydrogen-atom line of Problem 6.11 shows a very weak nearby satellite line. Two of the satellites occur at the vacuum wavelengths 6562.9 Å and 4861.4 Å. (a) Explain their origin. (The person who first answered this question got a Nobel Prize.) (b) Calculate the other two satellite wavelengths.

CHAPTER
7

Theorems of Quantum Mechanics

7.1 Introduction

The Schroedinger equation for the one-electron atom (Chapter 6) is exactly soluble; however, because of the interelectronic repulsion terms in the Hamiltonian, the Schroedinger equation for many-electron atoms and molecules is not separable in any coordinate system, and cannot be solved exactly. Hence, we must seek approximate methods of solution. The two main approximation methods, the variation method and perturbation theory, will be developed in Chapters 8 and 9; to derive these methods, we must develop further the theory of quantum mechanics, which is what we will do in this chapter. Although much of the work will be of an abstract nature, and perhaps not so easy to master, the theorems involved are basic to an understanding of quantum mechanics.

We will conclude this chapter with a summary of the postulates of quantum mechanics.

Before getting started, we introduce some notations for the integrals with which we will be dealing. The definite integral over all space of an operator sandwiched between two functions is of frequent occurrence, and various abbreviations are used:

$$\int \varphi_m^* \hat{A} \varphi_n \, d\tau \equiv \langle \varphi_m | \hat{A} | \varphi_n \rangle \equiv (\varphi_m | \hat{A} | \varphi_n) \equiv \langle m | \hat{A} | n \rangle \tag{7.1}$$

where φ_m and φ_n are two functions. If it is clear what functions are meant, we can use just the indices, as indicated in (7.1). The above notation, introduced by

Dirac, is called *bracket notation*. Another notation is:

$$\int \varphi_m^* \hat{A} \varphi_n \, d\tau \equiv A_{mn} \tag{7.2}$$

The notations A_{mn} and $\langle m| \hat{A} |n \rangle$ imply that we use the complex conjugate of the function whose letter appears first. An integral like $\int \varphi_m^* \hat{A} \varphi_n \, d\tau$ is called a *matrix element* of the operator $\hat{A}$. Matrices are rectangular arrays of numbers, and obey certain rules of combination. We will not make explicit use of matrices.

For the integral over all space between two functions, we write

$$\int \varphi_m^* \varphi_n \, d\tau \equiv \langle \varphi_m | \varphi_n \rangle \equiv \langle m|n \rangle \tag{7.3}$$

Another notation for the integral (7.3) is (φ_m, φ_n). Since

$$\left[\int \varphi_m^* \varphi_n \, d\tau \right]^* = \int \varphi_n^* \varphi_m \, d\tau \tag{7.4}$$

we have the identity

$$\langle m|n \rangle^* = \langle n|m \rangle \tag{7.5}$$

In particular

$$\langle m|m \rangle^* = \langle m|m \rangle \tag{7.6}$$

7.2 Hermitian Operators

We stated in Section 3.1 that the operators representing physical quantities are linear. There is another requirement such operators must meet, which we now discuss.

Let $\hat{A}$ be the linear operator representing the physical property A. For the average value of A, Eq. (3.117) gives

$$\langle A \rangle = \int \Psi^* \hat{A} \Psi \, d\tau \tag{7.7}$$

where Ψ is the state function of the system. The average value of a physical quantity must be a real number; therefore we demand that

$$\langle A \rangle = \langle A \rangle^* \tag{7.8}$$

$$\int \Psi^* \hat{A} \Psi \, d\tau = \int \Psi (\hat{A} \Psi)^* \, d\tau \tag{7.9}$$

Equation (7.9) must hold for any function Ψ that can represent a possible state of the system; i.e., it must hold for all well-behaved functions Ψ. A linear operator that satisfies (7.9) for all well-behaved functions is called a *Hermitian* operator.

Many texts define a Hermitian operator as one that satisfies

$$\int f^* \hat{A} g \, d\tau = \int g (\hat{A} f)^* \, d\tau \tag{7.10}$$

for all well-behaved functions f and g. [Note especially that on the left side of (7.10) $\hat{A}$ operates on g, but on the right side $\hat{A}$ operates on f.] For the special case $f = g$, (7.10) reduces to (7.9). Equation (7.10) is apparently a more stringent requirement than (7.9), but we will prove that (7.10) is a consequence of (7.9), so that the two definitions of a Hermitian operator are equivalent.

We begin the proof by setting $\Psi = f + cg$ in (7.9), where c is an arbitrary parameter; this gives

$$\int (f+cg)^* \hat{A} (f+cg) \, d\tau = \int (f+cg) [\hat{A}(f+cg)]^* \, d\tau \tag{7.11}$$

$$\int (f^* + c^* g^*) \hat{A} f \, d\tau + \int (f^* + c^* g^*) \hat{A} cg \, d\tau$$

$$= \int (f+cg)(\hat{A}f)^* \, d\tau + \int (f+cg)(\hat{A}cg)^* \, d\tau$$

$$\int f^* \hat{A} f \, d\tau + c^* \int g^* \hat{A} f \, d\tau + c \int f^* \hat{A} g \, d\tau + cc^* \int g^* \hat{A} g \, d\tau$$

$$= \int f(\hat{A}f)^* \, d\tau + c \int g(\hat{A}f)^* \, d\tau + c^* \int f(\hat{A}g)^* \, d\tau + c^* c \int g(\hat{A}g)^* \, d\tau$$

By virtue of (7.9), the first terms on each side of this last equation are equal to each other; likewise the last terms on each side are equal. Hence

$$c^* \int g^* \hat{A} f \, d\tau + c \int f^* \hat{A} g \, d\tau = c \int g(\hat{A}f)^* \, d\tau + c^* \int f(\hat{A}g)^* \, d\tau \tag{7.12}$$

Setting $c = 1$ in (7.12), we have

$$\int g^* \hat{A} f \, d\tau + \int f^* \hat{A} g \, d\tau = \int g(\hat{A}f)^* \, d\tau + \int f(\hat{A}g)^* \, d\tau \tag{7.13}$$

Setting $c = i$ in (7.12), we have, after dividing by i,

$$-\int g^* \hat{A} f \, d\tau + \int f^* \hat{A} g \, d\tau = \int g(\hat{A}f)^* \, d\tau - \int f(\hat{A}g)^* \, d\tau \tag{7.14}$$

We now add (7.13) and (7.14) to get (7.10). Q.E.D.

Therefore, a Hermitian operator $\hat{A}$ possesses the property that

$$\int \varphi_i^* \hat{A} \varphi_j \, d\tau = \int \varphi_j (\hat{A} \varphi_i)^* \, d\tau \tag{7.15}$$

where φ_i and φ_j are arbitrary well-behaved functions. Using the bracket and matrix-element notations, we write

$$\langle \varphi_i | \hat{A} | \varphi_j \rangle = \langle \varphi_j | \hat{A} | \varphi_i \rangle^* \tag{7.16}$$

$$\langle i | \hat{A} | j \rangle = \langle j | \hat{A} | i \rangle^* \tag{7.17}$$

$$A_{ij} = (A_{ji})^* \tag{7.18}$$

Let us show that some of the operators we have been using are indeed

Hermitian. For simplicity we will work in one dimension. To prove that an operator is Hermitian, it suffices to show that it satisfies (7.9) for all well-behaved functions; however, we will make things a bit tougher on ourselves by proving that (7.15) is satisfied.

First consider the potential-energy operator. The right side of (7.15) is

$$\int_{-\infty}^{\infty} \varphi_j(x)[V(x)\varphi_i(x)]^* \, dx \tag{7.19}$$

We have $V^* = V$, since the potential energy is a real function. Moreover, the order of the factors in (7.19) is immaterial. Hence

$$\int \varphi_j[V\varphi_i]^* \, dx = \int \varphi_j V^* \varphi_i^* \, dx = \int \varphi_i^* V \varphi_j \, dx \tag{7.20}$$

which proves V is Hermitian.

The operator for the x component of linear momentum is given by Eq. (3.28). For this operator, the left side of (7.15) is

$$-i\hbar \int_{-\infty}^{\infty} \varphi_i^*(x) \frac{d\varphi_j(x)}{dx} \, dx \tag{7.21}$$

Now we use the formula for integration by parts:

$$\int_a^b f(x) \frac{dg(x)}{dx} \, dx = f(x)g(x)\Big|_a^b - \int_a^b g(x) \frac{df(x)}{dx} \, dx \tag{7.22}$$

$$f(x) = -i\hbar\varphi_i^*(x), \qquad g(x) = \varphi_j(x)$$

$$-i\hbar \int_{-\infty}^{\infty} \varphi_i^* \frac{d\varphi_j}{dx} \, dx = -i\hbar\varphi_i^*\varphi_j\Big|_{-\infty}^{\infty} + i\hbar \int_{-\infty}^{\infty} \varphi_j(x) \frac{d\varphi_i^*(x)}{dx} \, dx \tag{7.23}$$

Now φ_i and φ_j are well-behaved functions; hence they vanish at $x = \pm\infty$. Therefore, (7.23) becomes

$$\int_{-\infty}^{\infty} \varphi_i^*\left(-i\hbar \frac{d\varphi_j}{dx}\right) dx = \int_{-\infty}^{\infty} \varphi_j\left(-i\hbar \frac{d\varphi_i}{dx}\right)^* dx \tag{7.24}$$

which is the same as (7.15), and proves that $\hat{p}_x$ is Hermitian. The proof that the kinetic-energy operator is Hermitian is left to the reader. The sum of two Hermitian operators can be shown to be Hermitian; hence the Hamiltonian operator $\hat{H} = \hat{T} + \hat{V}$ is Hermitian.

We now prove some theorems about the eigenvalues and eigenfunctions of Hermitian operators.

Since the eigenvalues of the operator $\hat{A}$ corresponding to the physical quantity A are the possible results of a measurement of A, these eigenvalues should all be real numbers. We now prove this, using the Hermitian property of $\hat{A}$. We start by setting $\varphi_j = \varphi_i$ in (7.15):

$$\int \varphi_i^* \hat{A}\varphi_i \, d\tau = \int \varphi_i(\hat{A}\varphi_i)^* \, d\tau \tag{7.25}$$

Now let us suppose that φ_i is an eigenfunction of $\hat{A}$ with eigenvalue b:

$$\hat{A}\varphi_i = b\varphi_i \tag{7.26}$$

Equation (7.25) becomes

$$b\int \varphi_i^* \varphi_i \, d\tau = \int \varphi_i (b\varphi_i)^* \, d\tau = b^* \int \varphi_i \varphi_i^* \, d\tau \tag{7.27}$$

$$(b-b^*)\int |\varphi_i|^2 \, d\tau = 0 \tag{7.28}$$

Since the integrand $|\varphi_i|^2$ is never negative, the only way the integral in (7.28) could be zero would be if φ_i were zero for all values of the coordinates. However, we always reject zero as an eigenfunction on physical grounds; hence, the integral in (7.28) cannot be zero. Therefore, $(b-b^*) = 0$, or $b = b^*$, which completes the proof.

To develop a familiarity with bracket notation, we will repeat the proof that eigenvalues of Hermitian operators are real, using bracket notation. We begin by setting $i = j$ in (7.17):

$$\langle i|\hat{A}|i\rangle = \langle i|\hat{A}|i\rangle^* \tag{7.29}$$

Using (7.26), we have

$$\langle i|b|i\rangle = \langle i|b|i\rangle^* \tag{7.30}$$

$$b\langle i|i\rangle = b^*\langle i|i\rangle^* = b^*\langle i|i\rangle$$

$$(b-b^*)\langle i|i\rangle = 0$$

$$b = b^* \tag{7.31}$$

where (7.6) was used.

We showed that the particle-in-a-box wave functions are mutually orthogonal. We now prove the general theorem that *the eigenfunctions of a Hermitian operator are, or can be chosen to be, mutually orthogonal.* Given

$$\hat{B}F = sF, \qquad \hat{B}G = tG \tag{7.32}$$

where F and G are two independent eigenfunctions of $\hat{B}$, we want to prove

$$\int F^*G \, d\tau \equiv \langle F|G\rangle = 0 \tag{7.33}$$

We begin with Eq. (7.17), which expresses the Hermitian nature of $\hat{B}$:

$$\langle F|\hat{B}|G\rangle = \langle G|\hat{B}|F\rangle^* \tag{7.34}$$

Using (7.32), we have

$$\langle F|t|G\rangle = \langle G|s|F\rangle^*$$

$$t\langle F|G\rangle = s^*\langle G|F\rangle^* \tag{7.35}$$

Since eigenvalues of Hermitian operators are real, we have $s^* = s$. Using (7.5),

we have

$$t\langle F|G\rangle = s\langle F|G\rangle$$

$$(t-s)\langle F|G\rangle = 0 \tag{7.36}$$

If $s \neq t$, then

$$\langle F|G\rangle = 0 \tag{7.37}$$

We have proved that two eigenfunctions of a Hermitian operator that correspond to *different* eigenvalues are orthogonal. The question now is: Can we have two independent eigenfunctions that have the *same* eigenvalue? The answer is yes. In the case of *degeneracy*, we have the same eigenvalue for more than one independent eigenfunction. Therefore, we can only be certain that two independent eigenfunctions of a Hermitian operator are orthogonal to each other if they do not correspond to a degenerate eigenvalue. We now show that in the case of degeneracy, we may *construct* eigenfunctions that will be orthogonal to one another. We shall use the theorem proved in Section 3.6, that any linear combination of eigenfunctions corresponding to a degenerate eigenvalue is an eigenfunction with the same eigenvalue. Let us therefore suppose that F and G are independent eigenfunctions that have the same eigenvalue:

$$\hat{B}F = sF, \qquad \hat{B}G = sG \tag{7.38}$$

We take linear combinations of F and G, to form two new eigenfunctions φ_1 and φ_2 that will be orthogonal to each other. We choose φ_1 equal to F, and for φ_2 we write

$$\varphi_2 = G + cF, \qquad \varphi_1 = F \tag{7.39}$$

The constant c will be chosen to insure orthogonality. We want

$$\int \varphi_1^* \varphi_2 \, d\tau = 0 \tag{7.40}$$

$$\int F^*(G+cF) \, d\tau = \int F^*G \, d\tau + c \int F^*F \, d\tau = 0 \tag{7.41}$$

Hence, choosing

$$c = -\int F^*G \, d\tau \Big/ \int F^*F \, d\tau \tag{7.42}$$

we have two orthogonal eigenfunctions φ_1 and φ_2, corresponding to the degenerate eigenvalue. This procedure (called Schmidt orthogonalization) can be extended to the case of n-fold degeneracy, to give n linearly independent orthogonal eigenfunctions corresponding to the degenerate eigenvalue.

Thus, although there is no guarantee that the eigenfunctions of a degenerate eigenvalue are orthogonal, we can always *choose* them to be orthogonal, if we desire, by using the Schmidt (or some other) orthogonalization method. In fact, unless stated otherwise, we will always assume that we have chosen the eigenfunctions to be orthogonal:

$$\int \varphi_i^* \varphi_j \, d\tau = 0, \qquad i \neq j \tag{7.43}$$

where φ_i and φ_j are independent eigenfunctions of a Hermitian operator.

We can usually multiply an eigenfunction by a suitable constant to normalize it, and we shall assume, unless stated otherwise, that all eigenfunctions are normalized:

$$\int \varphi_i^* \varphi_i \, d\tau = 1 \tag{7.44}$$

The exception is where the eigenvalues form a continuum, rather than a discrete set of values; in this case, the eigenfunctions are not quadratically integrable. Examples are the linear-momentum eigenfunctions, the free-particle energy eigenfunctions, and the hydrogen-atom continuum energy eigenfunctions.

Using the Kronecker delta, we can combine (7.43) and (7.44) into one equation:

$$\int \varphi_i^* \varphi_j \, d\tau = \langle i | j \rangle = \delta_{ij} \tag{7.45}$$

where φ_i and φ_j are eigenfunctions of some Hermitian operator.

As an example, consider the spherical harmonics. We shall prove that

$$\int_0^{2\pi} \int_0^{\pi} [Y_l^m(\theta, \varphi)]^* Y_{l'}^{m'}(\theta, \varphi) \sin \theta \, d\theta \, d\varphi = \delta_{l,l'} \delta_{m,m'} \tag{7.46}$$

where the $\sin \theta$ factor comes from the volume element in spherical polar coordinates, (5.107). The spherical harmonics are eigenfunctions of the Hermitian operator $\hat{L}^2$ [Eq. (5.147)]. Since eigenfunctions of a Hermitian operator belonging to different eigenvalues are orthogonal, we conclude that the integral in (7.46) is zero unless $l = l'$. Similarly, Eq. (5.148) allows us to conclude that this integral is zero unless $m = m'$. Also, the multiplicative constant in (5.146) has been chosen so that the spherical harmonics are normalized [Eq. (6.134)]. Therefore (7.46) is valid.

7.3 Expansion in Terms of Eigenfunctions

In the previous section, we proved the orthogonality of the eigenfunctions of a Hermitian operator. We now discuss another important property of these functions; this property allows us to expand an arbitrary well-behaved function in terms of these eigenfunctions.

We have often used the Taylor-series expansion [Eq. (4.67)] of a function as a linear combination of the nonnegative integral powers of $(x-a)$. Can we expand a function as a linear combination of some other set of functions besides 1, $(x-a), (x-a)^2, \ldots$? The answer is yes, as was first shown by Fourier in 1807. A Fourier series is an expansion of a function as a linear combination of an infinite number of sine and cosine functions. We will not go into detail about Fourier series, but will simply look at one example. Let us consider expanding a function in terms of the particle-in-a-box wave functions, which, according to (2.23), are

$$\psi_n = \left(\frac{2}{l}\right)^{1/2} \sin\left(\frac{n\pi x}{l}\right), \qquad n = 1, 2, 3, \ldots \tag{7.47}$$

for x between 0 and l. What are our chances for representing an arbitrary function

$f(x)$, in the interval $0 \leqslant x \leqslant l$, by a series of the form

$$f(x) = \sum_{n=1}^{\infty} a_n \psi_n = \left(\frac{2}{l}\right)^{1/2} \sum_{n=1}^{\infty} a_n \sin\left(\frac{n\pi x}{l}\right), \qquad 0 \leqslant x \leqslant l \qquad (7.48)$$

Substituting $x = 0$ and $x = l$ in (7.48), we have the restriction that $f(0) = 0 = f(l)$. In other words, $f(x)$ must satisfy the same boundary conditions as the ψ_n. We will also assume that $f(x)$ is finite, single-valued, and continuous, but not necessarily differentiable. With these assumptions, it can be shown that the expansion (7.48) is valid. We will not prove (7.48), but will simply illustrate its use to represent a function.

Before we can apply (7.48) to a specific $f(x)$, we must derive an expression for the expansion coefficients a_n. We start by multiplying (7.48) by ψ_m^*:

$$\psi_m^* f(x) = \sum_{n=1}^{\infty} a_n \psi_m^* \psi_n = \left(\frac{2}{l}\right) \sum_{n=1}^{\infty} a_n \sin\left(\frac{n\pi x}{l}\right) \sin\left(\frac{m\pi x}{l}\right) \qquad (7.49)$$

Now we integrate (7.49) from 0 to l. Assuming the validity of interchanging the integration and the infinite summation, we have

$$\int_0^l \psi_m^* f(x)\, dx = \sum_{n=1}^{\infty} a_n \int_0^l \psi_m^* \psi_n\, dx \qquad (7.50)$$

$$= \sum_{n=1}^{\infty} a_n \left(\frac{2}{l}\right) \int_0^l \sin\left(\frac{n\pi x}{l}\right) \sin\left(\frac{m\pi x}{l}\right) dx \qquad (7.51)$$

Recall that we proved the orthonormality of the particle-in-a-box wave functions [Eq. (2.27)]. Therefore (7.50) becomes

$$\int_0^l \psi_m^* f(x)\, dx = \sum_{n=1}^{\infty} a_n \delta_{mn} \qquad (7.52)$$

The type of sum in (7.52) is of frequent occurrence. Writing it in detail, we have

$$\sum_{n=1}^{\infty} a_n \delta_{mn} = a_1 \delta_{m,1} + a_2 \delta_{m,2} + \cdots + a_m \delta_{m,m} + a_{m+1} \delta_{m,m+1} + \cdots$$

$$= 0 + 0 + \cdots + a_m + 0 + \cdots$$

$$\sum_{n=1}^{\infty} a_n \delta_{mn} = a_m \qquad (7.53)$$

Thus, since δ_{mn} is zero except when the summation index n is equal to m, all terms but one vanish, and (7.52) becomes

$$a_m = \int_0^l \psi_m^* f(x)\, dx \qquad (7.54)$$

which is the desired expression. Using (7.54) in (7.48), we have

$$f(x) = \sum_{n=1}^{\infty} \left[\int_0^l \psi_n^* f(x)\, dx\right] \psi_n(x) \qquad (7.55)$$

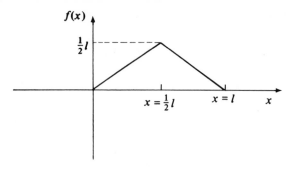

FIGURE 7.1   *Function to be expanded in terms of particle-in-a-box functions.*

We now use (7.48) to represent a specific function, the function of Fig. 7.1, which is defined by

$$f(x) = x \qquad \text{for } 0 \leqslant x \leqslant l/2$$
$$f(x) = l - x \qquad \text{for } \tfrac{1}{2}l \leqslant x \leqslant l \tag{7.56}$$

To evaluate the expansion coefficients, we use (7.54), (7.47), and (7.56):

$$a_n = \left(\frac{2}{l}\right)^{1/2} \int_0^l \sin\left(\frac{n\pi x}{l}\right) f(x)\, dx$$

$$= \left(\frac{2}{l}\right)^{1/2} \int_0^{l/2} x \sin\left(\frac{n\pi x}{l}\right) dx + \left(\frac{2}{l}\right)^{1/2} \int_{l/2}^l (l-x) \sin\left(\frac{n\pi x}{l}\right) dx$$

Using the Appendix integral (A.1), we find

$$a_n = \frac{(2l)^{3/2}}{n^2 \pi^2} \sin\left(\frac{n\pi}{2}\right) \tag{7.57}$$

Using (7.57) in the expansion (7.48), we have [note that $\sin(n\pi/2)$ vanishes for n even and equals $+1$ or -1 for n odd]:

$$f(x) = \frac{4l}{\pi^2}\left[\sin\left(\frac{\pi x}{l}\right) - \frac{1}{3^2}\sin\left(\frac{3\pi x}{l}\right) + \frac{1}{5^2}\sin\left(\frac{5\pi x}{l}\right) - \cdots\right] \tag{7.58}$$

$$f(x) = \frac{4l}{\pi^2}\sum_{n=1}^{\infty}(-1)^{n+1}\sin\left[(2n-1)\frac{\pi x}{l}\right]\frac{1}{(2n-1)^2}$$

where $f(x)$ is given by (7.56).   Let us check the accuracy of (7.58) at $x = \tfrac{1}{2}l$.   We have

$$f\left(\frac{l}{2}\right) = \frac{4l}{\pi^2}\left(1 + \frac{1}{3^2} + \frac{1}{5^2} + \frac{1}{7^2} + \cdots\right) \tag{7.59}$$

Let us tabulate the right side of (7.59) as a function of the number of terms we take in the infinite series:

Number of terms	1	2	3	4	5	6	20
Right side of (7.59)	0.405*l*	0.450*l*	0.467*l*	0.475*l*	0.480*l*	0.483*l*	0.495*l*

If we take an infinite number of terms, the series should sum to $\frac{1}{2}l$, which is the value of $f(\frac{1}{2}l)$. Assuming the validity of the series, we have the interesting result that the infinite sum in parentheses in (7.59) equals $\pi^2/8$.

We have seen an example of the expansion of a function in terms of a set of functions—the particle-in-a-box wave functions. There are many different sets of functions that can be used to expand an arbitrary function. Consider a set of functions $\varphi_1, \varphi_2, \ldots, \varphi_i, \ldots$. We say that the φ_i form a *complete set* if it is possible to expand any well-behaved function f that obeys the same boundary conditions as the φ_i, as a linear combination of the φ_i, according to

$$f = \sum_i a_i \varphi_i \qquad (7.60)$$

where the a_i are constants. By virtue of theorems of Fourier analysis (which we have not proved), it can be shown that the particle-in-a-box energy eigenfunctions form a complete set. Now let φ_i be the set of eigenfunctions of *any* linear Hermitian operator that represents a physical quantity. We *postulate* that these φ_i form a complete set. (Completeness of the eigenfunctions can usually be proved in the one-dimensional case but it must be postulated for multidimensional systems.) Thus, any well-behaved function that satisfies the same boundary conditions as the φ_i can be expanded using (7.60). Equation (7.48) is an example of (7.60).

Recall that the harmonic-oscillator wave functions are given by a Hermite polynomial times an exponential factor [Eq. (4.70)]. Therefore, by virtue of the expansion postulate, we can expand any well-behaved function $f(x)$, for which $f(\pm\infty) = 0$, as

$$f(x) = \left(\frac{\alpha}{\pi}\right)^{1/4} \sum_{n=0}^{\infty} \frac{a_n}{(2^n n!)^{1/2}} H_n(\alpha^{1/2}x) e^{-\alpha x^2/2} \qquad \text{for } -\infty \leqslant x \leqslant \infty \quad (7.61)$$

How about using the hydrogen-atom bound-state wave functions to expand an arbitrary function $f(r, \theta, \varphi)$? The answer is that these functions do *not* form a complete set, and we cannot expand f using them. To have a complete set, we must use *all* the eigenfunctions of a particular Hermitian operator. In addition to the bound-state eigenfunctions of the hydrogen-atom Hamiltonian, we have the continuum eigenfunctions, corresponding to ionized states. If we include the continuum eigenfunctions along with the bound-state eigenfunctions, then we have a complete set. (For the particle-in-a-box and the harmonic oscillator there are no continuum functions.) Equation (7.60) implies an integration over the continuum eigenfunctions, if there are any. Thus, if $\psi_{nlm}(r, \theta, \varphi)$ is a bound-state wave function of the hydrogen atom, and $\psi_{Elm}(r, \theta, \varphi)$ is a continuum eigenfunction, then (7.60) becomes

$$f(r, \theta, \varphi) = \sum_{n=1}^{\infty} \sum_{l=0}^{n-1} \sum_{m=-l}^{l} a_{nlm} \psi_{nlm}(r, \theta, \varphi) + \sum_{l=0}^{\infty} \sum_{m=-l}^{l} \int_0^{\infty} a_{lm}(E) \psi_{Elm}(r, \theta, \varphi) \, dE$$

As another example, consider the eigenfunctions of $\hat{p}_x$ [Eq. (3.43)]

$$\varphi_k = e^{ikx/\hbar}, \qquad -\infty < k < \infty \qquad (7.62)$$

Here the eigenvalues are all continuous, and the eigenfunction expansion (7.60) of an arbitrary function f becomes

$$f(x) = \int_{-\infty}^{\infty} a(k) e^{ikx/\hbar} dk \tag{7.63}$$

The reader with a good mathematical background may recognize the integral in (7.63) as very nearly the Fourier transform of $a(k)$.

Let us evaluate the expansion coefficients in (7.60). The work is identical to that involved in deriving (7.54). We multiply (7.60) by φ_j^* and integrate over all space to get

$$\int \varphi_j^* f \, d\tau = \sum_i a_i \int \varphi_j^* \varphi_i \, d\tau = \sum_i a_i \delta_{ij} \tag{7.64}$$

$$a_j = \int \varphi_j^* f \, d\tau \tag{7.65}$$

where the orthonormality of the eigenfunctions, Eq. (7.45), was used. The expansion (7.60) becomes

$$f = \sum_i \left[\int \varphi_i^* f \, d\tau \right] \varphi_i = \sum_i \langle \varphi_i | f \rangle \varphi_i \tag{7.66}$$

A useful theorem is as follows. Let φ_i be the complete set of eigenfunctions of the Hermitian operator $\hat{A}$. Let f be a function that is an eigenfunction of $\hat{A}$: $\hat{A}f = kf$. Then if f is expressed as a linear combination of the φ_i's according to (7.60), the only nonzero expansion coefficients a_i are those for which φ_i has the eigenvalue k. (There may be several φ_i's with eigenvalue k due to degeneracy.) Thus, in the expansion of f, we include only those eigenfunctions that have the same eigenvalue as f. The proof of this theorem follows at once from (7.65); if f and φ_j in (7.65) correspond to different eigenvalues of the Hermitian operator $\hat{A}$, they will be orthogonal [Eq. (7.37)] and a_j will vanish.

We shall occasionally use a notation (called *ket* notation) in which the function f is denoted by the symbol $|f\rangle$. There doesn't seem to be any point to this notation, but in advanced formulations of quantum mechanics it takes on a special significance. In ket notation, Eq. (7.66) reads

$$|f\rangle = \sum_i |\varphi_i\rangle \langle \varphi_i | f \rangle = \sum_i |i\rangle \langle i | f \rangle \tag{7.67}$$

Ket notation is conveniently used to specify eigenfunctions by listing their eigenvalues. For example, the hydrogen-atom wave function with quantum numbers n, l, m is denoted by $\psi_{nlm} = |nlm\rangle$.

The contents of Sections 7.2 and 7.3 can be summarized by the statement that *the eigenfunctions of a Hermitian operator form a complete, orthonormal set, and the eigenvalues are real.*

7.4 Eigenfunctions of Commuting Operators

In Section 5.1 we made some statements about simultaneous eigenfunctions of two different operators. We now prove these statements.

First we show that if there exists a common *complete set* of eigenfunctions for two linear operators, then the operators commute. Let $\hat{A}$ and $\hat{B}$ denote two linear operators that possess a common complete set of eigenfunctions, φ_i. We have

$$\hat{A}\varphi_i = s_i\varphi_i, \qquad \hat{B}\varphi_i = t_i\varphi_i \tag{7.68}$$

where s_i and t_i are the eigenvalues. We must prove that

$$[\hat{A}, \hat{B}] = \hat{0} \tag{7.69}$$

Equation (7.69) is an operator equation; for two operators to be equal, the result of operating with either of them on an arbitrary function f must be the same; we must therefore show that

$$(\hat{A}\hat{B} - \hat{B}\hat{A})f = \hat{0}f = 0 \tag{7.70}$$

where f is an arbitrary function. We begin the proof by expanding f (assuming that it obeys the proper boundary conditions) in terms of the complete set of eigenfunctions φ_i:

$$f = \sum_i c_i\varphi_i \tag{7.71}$$

Operating on each side of (7.71) with $\hat{A}\hat{B} - \hat{B}\hat{A}$, we have

$$(\hat{A}\hat{B} - \hat{B}\hat{A})f = (\hat{A}\hat{B} - \hat{B}\hat{A})\sum_i c_i\varphi_i \tag{7.72}$$

Since $\hat{A}\hat{B}$ and $\hat{B}\hat{A}$ are linear operators (Problem 3.7), we have

$$(\hat{A}\hat{B} - \hat{B}\hat{A})f = \sum_i c_i(\hat{A}\hat{B} - \hat{B}\hat{A})\varphi_i = \sum_i c_i[\hat{A}(\hat{B}\varphi_i) - \hat{B}(\hat{A}\varphi_i)]$$

where we have used the definitions of the sum and the product of operators. Use of (7.68) yields

$$(\hat{A}\hat{B} - \hat{B}\hat{A})f = \sum_i c_i[\hat{A}t_i\varphi_i - \hat{B}s_i\varphi_i] = \sum_i c_i(s_i t_i\varphi_i - t_i s_i\varphi_i) = 0$$

which completes the proof that $\hat{A}$ and $\hat{B}$ commute if they have a common complete set of eigenfunctions.

It is sometimes erroneously stated that if there exists a common eigenfunction of $\hat{A}$ and $\hat{B}$, then they commute. We have already seen an example that shows this statement to be false; in Section 5.3 we saw that the spherical harmonic Y_0^0 is an eigenfunction of both $\hat{L}_z$ and $\hat{L}_x$ even though these two operators do not commute. It is instructive to examine the "proof" that is often given of this erroneous statement. Let φ be the common eigenfunction:

$$\hat{A}\varphi = s\varphi, \qquad \hat{B}\varphi = t\varphi$$

We have

$$\hat{A}\hat{B}\varphi = \hat{A}t\varphi = st\varphi$$

$$\hat{B}\hat{A}\varphi = \hat{B}s\varphi = ts\varphi = st\varphi$$

$$\hat{A}\hat{B}\varphi = \hat{B}\hat{A}\varphi \tag{7.73}$$

The "proof" is completed by canceling φ from each side of (7.73) to get

$$\hat{A}\hat{B} = \hat{B}\hat{A} \; (?) \tag{7.74}$$

It is in going from (7.73) to (7.74) that the error lies. Just because the two operators $\hat{A}\hat{B}$ and $\hat{B}\hat{A}$ give the same result when acting on the single function φ is no reason to conclude that $\hat{A}\hat{B} = \hat{B}\hat{A}$. (For example, d/dx and d^2/dx^2 give the same result when operating on e^x, but d/dx is certainly not equal to d^2/dx^2.) The two operators must give the same result when acting on *every* (well-behaved) function in order to conclude that they are equal. Thus, even though $\hat{A}$ and $\hat{B}$ do not commute, there might exist one or more common eigenfunctions of $\hat{A}$ and $\hat{B}$. However, we cannot have a common *complete* set of eigenfunctions of two noncommuting operators, as we proved earlier in this section.

We have shown that *if there exists a common complete set of eigenfunctions of $\hat{A}$ and $\hat{B}$, then they commute.* We now prove the converse theorem: *if $\hat{A}$ and $\hat{B}$ commute, we can select a common complete set of eigenfunctions for them.* Let φ_i and t_i be the eigenfunctions and eigenvalues of $\hat{B}$:

$$\hat{B}\varphi_i = t_i\varphi_i \tag{7.75}$$

Operating on both sides of this equation with $\hat{A}$, we have

$$\hat{A}\hat{B}\varphi_i = \hat{A}t_i\varphi_i \tag{7.76}$$

Since $\hat{A}$ and $\hat{B}$ commute, and $\hat{A}$ is linear, we have

$$\hat{B}(\hat{A}\varphi_i) = t_i(\hat{A}\varphi_i) \tag{7.77}$$

This equation states that the function $\hat{A}\varphi_i$ is also an eigenfunction of the operator $\hat{B}$ with the same eigenvalue t_i as the eigenfunction φ_i. Let us for the moment assume that the eigenvalues of $\hat{B}$ are nondegenerate, i.e., that for any given eigenvalue t_i there corresponds one and only one linearly independent eigenfunction. If this is so, then the two eigenfunctions φ_i and $\hat{A}\varphi_i$, which correspond to the same eigenvalue t_i, must be linearly dependent, i.e., one must simply be a multiple of the other:

$$\hat{A}\varphi_i = c_i\varphi_i \tag{7.78}$$

where c_i is some constant. This equation states that the functions φ_i are eigenfunctions of $\hat{A}$, which is what we wanted to prove. In Section 7.3, we postulated that the eigenfunctions of any operator that represents a physical quantity form a complete set; hence, the φ_i form a complete set.

We have just proved the desired theorem for the nondegenerate case, but what about the degenerate case? Let the level with eigenvalue t_i be n-fold degenerate. We know from Eq. (7.77) that $\hat{A}\varphi_i$ is an eigenfunction of $\hat{B}$ with eigenvalue t_i. Hence, it must be some linear combination of the n linearly independent eigenfunctions corresponding to the eigenvalue t_i. From this statement, we cannot conclude that φ_i is an eigenfunction of $\hat{A}$. However, by taking suitable linear combinations of the n linearly independent eigenfunctions, we can construct a new set of n linearly independent eigenfunctions of $\hat{B}$ that will also be eigenfunctions of $\hat{A}$. For the proof that this can be done, see *Merzbacher*, Section 8.5.

Thus, when $\hat{A}$ and $\hat{B}$ commute it is always possible to *select* a common set of eigenfunctions for them. As an example, consider the hydrogen atom, where the operators $\hat{L}_z$ and $\hat{H}$ were shown to commute. If we desired, we could take the phi factor in the eigenfunctions of $\hat{H}$ as $\sin m\varphi$ and $\cos m\varphi$. In this case, we will not have eigenfunctions of $\hat{L}_z$, except for $m = 0$. However, the linear combinations

$$R(r)\,S(\theta)\,[\cos m\varphi + i\sin m\varphi] = RS e^{im\varphi}, \qquad m = -l, \ldots, +l$$

give us eigenfunctions of $\hat{L}_z$ that are still eigenfunctions of $\hat{H}$ by virtue of the theorem in Section 3.6.

Extension of the above proofs to the case of more than two operators shows that for a set of Hermitian operators $\hat{A}, \hat{B}, \hat{C}, \ldots$ there exists a common complete set of eigenfunctions if and only if every pair of operators commutes.

Let us prove a useful theorem about matrix elements. Let $\hat{A}$ be a Hermitian operator with eigenfunctions φ_i:

$$\hat{A}\varphi_i = s_i\varphi_i \tag{7.79}$$

Let $\hat{B}$ be an operator that commutes with $\hat{A}$. We assert that

$$B_{ij} = \int \varphi_i^* \hat{B}\varphi_j \, d\tau = 0 \qquad \text{for } s_i \neq s_j \tag{7.80}$$

We have

$$\int \varphi_i^* \hat{B}\varphi_j \, d\tau = \frac{1}{s_j} \int \varphi_i^* \hat{B}s_j\,\varphi_j \, d\tau$$

$$B_{ij} = \frac{1}{s_j} \int \varphi_i^* \hat{B}\hat{A}\varphi_j \, d\tau = \frac{1}{s_j} \int \varphi_i^* \hat{A}\hat{B}\varphi_j \, d\tau$$

$$s_j B_{ij} = \langle \varphi_i | \hat{A} | \hat{B}\varphi_j \rangle$$

Using the Hermitian property of $\hat{A}$ [Eq. (7.16)], we have

$$s_j B_{ij} = \langle \hat{B}\varphi_j | \hat{A} | \varphi_i \rangle^*$$

Using (7.79) and the fact that the eigenvalues of $\hat{A}$ are real, we have

$$s_j B_{ij} = s_i^* \langle \hat{B}\varphi_j | \varphi_i \rangle^*$$

$$s_j B_{ij} = s_i \langle \varphi_i | \hat{B}\varphi_j \rangle = s_i B_{ij}$$

$$B_{ij}(s_j - s_i) = 0 \tag{7.81}$$

We conclude that (7.80) holds.

A proof of the uncertainty principle is outlined in Problem 7.35.

7.5 Parity

There are certain quantum-mechanical operators that have no classical analog. One of these is the parity operator. Recall that the harmonic-oscillator wave functions are either even or odd; we will show how this property is related to the parity operator.

The parity operator $\hat{\Pi}$ is defined by giving its effect on an arbitrary function f:

$$\hat{\Pi}f(x, y, z) = f(-x, -y, -z) \tag{7.82}$$

The parity operator replaces each Cartesian coordinate with its negative. For example, $\hat{\Pi}(x^2 - ze^{ay}) = x^2 + ze^{-ay}$.

As with any quantum-mechanical operator, we are interested in the eigenvalues c_i and the eigenfunctions g_i of the parity operator:

$$\hat{\Pi}g_i = c_i g_i \qquad (7.83)$$

The key to the problem is to calculate the square of $\hat{\Pi}$:

$$\hat{\Pi}^2 f(x,y,z) = \hat{\Pi}[\hat{\Pi}f(x,y,z)]$$
$$\hat{\Pi}^2 f(x,y,z) = \hat{\Pi}[f(-x,-y,-z)]$$
$$\hat{\Pi}^2 f(x,y,z) = f(x,y,z)$$

Since f is arbitrary, we conclude that $\hat{\Pi}^2$ equals the unit operator:

$$\hat{\Pi}^2 = \hat{1} \qquad (7.84)$$

We now operate on (7.83) with $\hat{\Pi}$, to get

$$\hat{\Pi}\hat{\Pi}g_i = \hat{\Pi}c_i g_i$$

Since $\hat{\Pi}$ is linear (Problem 7.15), we have

$$\hat{\Pi}^2 g_i = c_i \hat{\Pi}g_i$$
$$\hat{\Pi}^2 g_i = c_i^2 g_i \qquad (7.85)$$

where the eigenvalue equation (7.83) has been used. Since $\hat{\Pi}^2$ is the unit operator, the left side of (7.85) is simply g_i, and we have

$$g_i = c_i^2 g_i \qquad (7.86)$$

The function g_i cannot be zero everywhere (zero is always rejected as an eigenfunction on physical grounds); hence, we can divide (7.86) by g_i to obtain $c_i^2 = 1$, and

$$c_i = \pm 1 \qquad (7.87)$$

The eigenvalues of $\hat{\Pi}$ are $+1$ and -1. (Note that this derivation is applicable to any operator whose square is the unit operator.)

What are the eigenfunctions g_i? The eigenvalue equation (7.83) reads

$$\hat{\Pi}g_i(x,y,z) = \pm g_i(x,y,z)$$
$$g_i(-x,-y,-z) = \pm g_i(x,y,z) \qquad (7.88)$$

If the eigenvalue is $+1$, then

$$g_i(-x,-y,-z) = g_i(x,y,z) \qquad (7.89)$$

so that g_i is an even function. If the eigenvalue is -1, then g_i is odd:

$$g_i(-x,-y,-z) = -g_i(x,y,z) \qquad (7.90)$$

Hence, the eigenfunctions are all possible well-behaved even and odd functions.

When the parity operator commutes with the Hamiltonian operator $\hat{H}$, we can select a common set of eigenfunctions for these operators, as proved in Section 7.4. The eigenfunctions of $\hat{H}$ are the stationary-state wave functions ψ_i. Hence, when

$$[\hat{\Pi}, \hat{H}] = 0 \qquad (7.91)$$

the wave functions ψ_i can be chosen to be eigenfunctions of $\hat{\Pi}$. We just proved that the eigenfunctions of $\hat{\Pi}$ are either even or odd; hence, when (7.91) holds, each wave function can be chosen to be either even or odd. Let us find out when the parity and Hamiltonian operators commute.

We have, for a one-particle system:

$$[\hat{H}, \hat{\Pi}] = [\hat{T}, \hat{\Pi}] + [\hat{V}, \hat{\Pi}] = -\frac{\hbar^2}{2m}\left[\frac{\partial^2}{\partial x^2}, \hat{\Pi}\right] - \frac{\hbar^2}{2m}\left[\frac{\partial^2}{\partial y^2}, \hat{\Pi}\right]$$
$$- \frac{\hbar^2}{2m}\left[\frac{\partial^2}{\partial z^2}, \hat{\Pi}\right] + [\hat{V}, \hat{\Pi}] \qquad (7.92)$$

Since

$$\hat{\Pi}\left[\frac{\partial^2}{\partial x^2}\varphi(x,y,z)\right] = \frac{\partial}{\partial(-x)}\frac{\partial}{\partial(-x)}\varphi(-x,-y,-z) = \frac{\partial^2}{\partial x^2}\varphi(-x,-y,-z)$$
$$= \frac{\partial^2}{\partial x^2}\hat{\Pi}\varphi(x,y,z)$$

where φ is any function, we conclude that

$$\left[\frac{\partial^2}{\partial x^2}, \hat{\Pi}\right] = 0$$

Similar equations hold for the y and z coordinates, and (7.92) becomes:

$$[\hat{H}, \hat{\Pi}] = [\hat{V}, \hat{\Pi}]$$

Now

$$\hat{\Pi}[V(x,y,z)\varphi(x,y,z)] = V(-x,-y,-z)\varphi(-x,-y,-z) \qquad (7.93)$$

If the potential energy is an even function, i.e., if $V(-x,-y,-z) = V(x,y,z)$, then (7.93) becomes

$$\hat{\Pi}[V(x,y,z)\varphi(x,y,z)] = V(x,y,z)\varphi(-x,-y,-z)$$
$$= V(x,y,z)\hat{\Pi}\varphi(x,y,z)$$

so that $[\hat{V}, \hat{\Pi}] = 0$. Hence, when the potential energy is an even function, the parity operator commutes with the Hamiltonian:

$$[\hat{H}, \hat{\Pi}] = 0 \qquad \text{if } V \text{ is even} \qquad (7.94)$$

These results are easily extended to the n-particle case. For an n-particle system, the parity operator is defined by

$$\hat{\Pi}f(x_1,y_1,z_1,...,x_n,y_n,z_n) = f(-x_1,-y_1,-z_1,...,-x_n,-y_n,-z_n)$$

It is easy to see that (7.91) holds when

$$V(x_1,y_1,z_1,...,x_n,y_n,z_n) = V(-x_1,-y_1,-z_1,...,-x_n,-y_n,-z_n)$$

If V satisfies this equation, we say that it is an even function of the $3n$ coordinates. In summary, when the potential energy V is an even function, we can choose the wave functions so that each ψ_i is either even or odd. A function that is either even or odd is said to have a definite parity.

If there is no degeneracy in the energy levels (as is usually true in one-dimensional problems), then there is only one independent wave function ψ_i corresponding to each energy E_i, and there is no element of choice (apart from an arbitrary multiplicative constant) in the wave functions. Thus, for the non-degenerate case, the stationary-state wave functions must be of definite parity when V is an even function. For example, the one-dimensional harmonic oscillator has $V = \frac{1}{2}kx^2$, which is an even function, and we found the wave functions to be of definite parity.

For the degenerate case, we have an element of choice in the wave functions, since an arbitrary linear combination of the functions corresponding to the degenerate level is an eigenfunction of $\hat{H}$. For a degenerate energy level, by taking appropriate linear combinations we can choose wave functions that are of definite parity, but there is no necessity that they be of definite parity.

Parity aids in evaluating integrals. In Chapter 4, we showed that

$$\int_{-\infty}^{\infty} f(x)\, dx = 0 \tag{7.95}$$

when $f(x)$ is an odd function. Let us extend this result to the $3n$-dimensional case. An odd function of $3n$ variables satisfies

$$g(-x_1, -y_1, -z_1, \ldots, -x_n, -y_n, -z_n) = -g(x_1, y_1, z_1, \ldots, x_n, y_n, z_n)$$

If g is an odd function of the $3n$ variables, then

$$\int_{-\infty}^{\infty} \cdots \int_{-\infty}^{\infty} g(x_1, \ldots, z_n)\, dx_1 \cdots dz_n = 0 \tag{7.96}$$

where the integration is over the $3n$ coordinates. This equation holds because the contribution to the integral from the value of g at $(x_1, y_1, z_1, \ldots, x_n, y_n, z_n)$ is cancelled by the contribution from $(-x_1, -y_1, -z_1, \ldots, -x_n, -y_n, -z_n)$.

A more general case is where the integrand is an odd function of some (but not necessarily all) of the variables. Let f be a function such that

$$f(-q_1, -q_2, \ldots, -q_k, q_{k+1}, q_{k+2}, \ldots, q_m) = -f(q_1, q_2, \ldots, q_k, q_{k+1}, q_{k+2}, \ldots, q_m) \tag{7.97}$$

where $1 \leqslant k \leqslant m$. We assert that if f obeys (7.97), then

$$\int_{-\infty}^{\infty} \cdots \int_{-\infty}^{\infty} f(q_1, \ldots, q_m)\, dq_1 \cdots dq_m = 0 \tag{7.98}$$

The proof of (7.98) is simple. The integral in (7.98) can be written as

$$\int_{-\infty}^{\infty} \cdots \int_{-\infty}^{\infty} \left[\int_{-\infty}^{\infty} \cdots \int_{-\infty}^{\infty} f(q_1, \ldots, q_k, q_{k+1}, \ldots, q_m)\, dq_1 \cdots dq_k \right] dq_{k+1} \cdots dq_m \tag{7.99}$$

As far as the multiple integral in brackets is concerned, q_{k+1} through q_m are constants. By virtue of (7.97), the contributions from

$$f(-q_1, \ldots, -q_k, q_{k+1}, \ldots, q_m) \quad \text{and} \quad f(q_1, \ldots, q_k, q_{k+1}, \ldots, q_m)$$

cancel, so that the bracketed integral in (7.99) vanishes and (7.98) follows.

7.6 Measurement and the Superposition of States

Quantum mechanics can be regarded as a scheme for calculating the probabilities of the various possible outcomes of a measurement. For example, if we know the state function $\Psi(x, t)$, then the probability that a measurement at time t of the particle's position yields a value between x and $x + dx$ is given by $|\Psi(x, t)|^2 dx$. We now consider measurement of the general property G; our aim is to find out how to use Ψ to calculate the probabilities for each possible result of a measurement of G. The results of this section lie at the very heart of quantum mechanics.

We will deal with an n-particle system, and will use q to symbolize the $3n$ coordinates. We have postulated that the eigenvalues g_i of the operator $\hat{G}$ are the only possible results of a measurement of the property G. Using φ_i for the eigenfunctions of $\hat{G}$, we have

$$\hat{G}\varphi_i(q) = g_i\varphi_i(q) \tag{7.100}$$

We postulated in Section 7.3 that the eigenfunctions of any linear Hermitian operator which represents a physical observable form a complete set. Since the φ_i form a complete set, we can expand any well-behaved function in terms of them; in particular, we can expand the state function Ψ in terms of the φ_i:

$$\Psi(q, t) = \sum_i c_i(t)\,\varphi_i(q) \tag{7.101}$$

To allow for the change of Ψ with time, the expansion coefficients c_i vary with time.

Now $|\Psi|^2$ is a probability density, so that we require

$$\int \Psi^*\Psi\,d\tau = 1 \tag{7.102}$$

Substituting (7.101) into the normalization condition, we get

$$1 = \int \sum_i c_i^*\varphi_i^* \sum_i c_i\varphi_i\,d\tau = \int \sum_i c_i^*\varphi_i^* \sum_j c_j\varphi_j\,d\tau$$

$$1 = \int \sum_i \sum_j c_i^* c_j \varphi_i^*\varphi_j\,d\tau \tag{7.103}$$

[It is important to use different symbols for the two dummy summation indices in (7.103). For example, consider the following product of two sums:

$$\sum_{i=1}^{2} a_i \sum_{i=1}^{2} b_i = (a_1 + a_2)(b_1 + b_2) = a_1 b_1 + a_1 b_2 + a_2 b_1 + a_2 b_2$$

If we carelessly write

$$\sum_{i=1}^{2} a_i \sum_{i=1}^{2} b_i \stackrel{\text{(wrong)}}{=} \sum_{i=1}^{2}\sum_{i=1}^{2} a_i b_i = \sum_{i=1}^{2} (a_1 b_1 + a_2 b_2) = 2(a_1 b_1 + a_2 b_2)$$

we get the wrong answer. The correct way to write the product is

$$\sum_{i=1}^{2} a_i \sum_{i=1}^{2} b_i = \sum_{i=1}^{2} a_i \sum_{j=1}^{2} b_j = \sum_{i=1}^{2}\sum_{j=1}^{2} a_i b_j$$

$$= \sum_{i=1}^{2} (a_i b_1 + a_i b_2) = a_1 b_1 + a_1 b_2 + a_2 b_1 + a_2 b_2$$

which gives the right answer.] Assuming the validity of interchanging the infinite summation and integration in (7.103), we have

$$\sum_i \sum_j c_i^* c_j \int \varphi_i^* \varphi_j \, d\tau = 1$$

Since $\hat{G}$ is Hermitian, the eigenfunctions φ_i are orthonormal [Eq. (7.45)]; hence

$$\sum_i \sum_j c_i^* c_j \delta_{ij} = 1$$

$$\sum_i |c_i|^2 = 1 \qquad (7.104)$$

We will point out the significance of (7.104) shortly.

Recall the postulate (Section 3.7) that if Ψ is the normalized state function of a system, then the average value of the property G is

$$\langle G \rangle = \int \Psi^*(q, t) \hat{G} \Psi(q, t) \, d\tau$$

Using the expansion (7.101) in the average-value expression, we have

$$\langle G \rangle = \int \sum_i c_i^* \varphi_i^* \hat{G} \sum_j c_j \varphi_j \, d\tau = \sum_i \sum_j c_i^* c_j \int \varphi_i^* \hat{G} \varphi_j \, d\tau \qquad (7.105)$$

Applying (7.100), we get

$$\langle G \rangle = \sum_i \sum_j c_i^* c_j g_j \int \varphi_i^* \varphi_j \, d\tau = \sum_i \sum_j c_i^* c_j g_j \delta_{ij}$$

$$\langle G \rangle = \sum_i |c_i|^2 g_i \qquad (7.106)$$

How do we interpret (7.106)? We postulated (Section 3.3) that the eigenvalues of an operator are the only possible numbers we can get when we measure the property that the operator represents. In any measurement of G we will get one of the values g_i. Now recall Eq. (3.108):

$$\langle G \rangle = \sum_i P_{g_i} g_i \qquad (7.107)$$

where P_{g_i} is the probability of getting g_i in a measurement of G. Comparing (7.106) and (7.107), we conclude that $|c_i|^2$ is the probability[1] of getting the value g_i in a measurement of the property G; the quantity c_i is the coefficient of the eigenfunction φ_i in the expansion (7.101). The $|c_i|^2$ sum to 1, as probabilities should [Eq. (7.104)].

When can we predict the result of a measurement of G with certainty? We can do this if all the coefficients c_i are zero, except one: $c_i = 0, i \neq k; c_k \neq 0$. For this case, Eq. (7.104) gives $|c_k|^2 = 1$, so that we are certain to find the result g_k. In this case, the state function (7.101) reduces to

$$\Psi = \varphi_k$$

---

[1] However, if g_i is a degenerate eigenvalue, we must add together the probabilities for all the states with eigenvalue g_i.

We may thus view the expansion (7.101) as expressing the general state Ψ as a *superposition* of the eigenstates φ_i of the operator $\hat{G}$; each eigenstate φ_i corresponds to the value g_i for the property G. The degree to which any function φ_i occurs in the expansion of Ψ, as measured by $|c_i|^2$, determines the probability of getting the value g_i in a measurement of G.

How do we calculate the expansion coefficients c_i, so that we can get the probabilities $|c_i|^2$? We multiply (7.101) by φ_j^* and integrate over all space to get

$$\int \varphi_j^* \Psi \, d\tau = \sum_i c_i \int \varphi_j^* \varphi_i \, d\tau = \sum_i c_i \delta_{ij}$$

$$c_j = \int \varphi_j^* \Psi \, d\tau = \langle \varphi_j | \Psi \rangle \qquad (7.108)$$

The probability of finding the value g_j in a measurement of G is

$$|c_j|^2 = \left| \int \varphi_j^* \Psi \, d\tau \right|^2 = |\langle \varphi_j | \Psi \rangle|^2 \qquad (7.109)$$

The quantity $\langle \varphi_j | \Psi \rangle$ is called a *probability amplitude*.

Thus, if we know the state of the system, as determined by the state function Ψ, we can use (7.109) to predict the probabilities for the various possible outcomes of a measurement of any property G. (Determination of the eigenfunctions φ_j and eigenvalues g_j is a mathematical problem.)

(To determine experimentally the probability of finding g_j on measurement, we take a large number of identical, noninteracting systems, each in the same state Ψ, and carry out a measurement of G on each system. 'If n_j of the measurements yield g_j, then

$$\frac{n_j}{n} = |\langle \varphi_j | \Psi \rangle|^2 \qquad (7.110)$$

where n is the total number of measurements made.)

We illustrate our conclusions with an example. Let the property G be the linear momentum p_x. The eigenfunctions and eigenvalues in (7.100) are [see Eqs. (3.43) and (3.44)]

$$\varphi_i = e^{ik_i x/\hbar}, \qquad g_i = k_i \qquad (7.111)$$

where k_i is any real number. Now consider a free particle moving in one dimension and having energy E; its state function is, according to (2.30) and (3.39),

$$\Psi = a_1 e^{-iEt/\hbar} e^{i(2mE)^{1/2}x/\hbar} + a_2 e^{-iEt/\hbar} e^{-i(2mE)^{1/2}x/\hbar} \qquad (7.112)$$

$$\Psi = c_1 e^{ik_1 x/\hbar} + c_2 e^{ik_2 x/\hbar} \qquad (7.113)$$

where

$$c_1 \equiv a_1 e^{-iEt/\hbar}, \qquad c_2 \equiv a_2 e^{-iEt/\hbar}$$

$$k_1 \equiv (2mE)^{1/2}, \qquad k_2 \equiv -(2mE)^{1/2}$$

Comparing this equation with (7.101), we see that the free-particle state function is a superposition of two of the eigenfunctions of $\hat{p}_x$; the probability that a measurement of p_x yields the value $k_1 = (2mE)^{1/2}$ is, according to the italicized statement following (7.107),

$$|c_1|^2 = |a_1 e^{-iEt/\hbar}|^2 = |a_1|^2$$

while the probability that a measurement of p_x yields $-(2mE)^{1/2}$ is

$$|c_2|^2 = |a_2|^2$$

The probability of getting any other value in a measurement of p_x is zero, since eigenfunctions corresponding to eigenvalues other than k_1 and k_2 do not occur in the expansion (7.113).

If G is a property that takes on a continuous range of eigenvalues (e.g., position), the summation in the expansion (7.101) is replaced by an integration over the values of g:

$$\Psi = \int c_g \, \varphi_g(q) \, dg \tag{7.114}$$

and the quantity

$$|\langle \varphi_g(q) | \Psi \rangle|^2$$

is interpreted as a probability density; i.e., the probability of finding a value of G between g and $g + dg$ for a system in the state Ψ is

$$|\langle \varphi_g(q) | \Psi(q, t) \rangle|^2 \, dg \tag{7.115}$$

We now consider the superposition of energy eigenstates. When the Hamiltonian is independent of time, we have shown that there are solutions of the time-dependent Schroedinger equation of the form

$$\Psi_n(q, t) = e^{-iE_n t/\hbar} \psi_n(q) \tag{7.116}$$

where the $\psi_n(q)$ are eigenfunctions of $\hat{H}$:

$$\hat{H} \psi_n(q) = E_n \psi_n(q) \tag{7.117}$$

Let the function Ψ be a superposition of the stationary states Ψ_n:

$$\Psi = \sum_n c_n \Psi_n = \sum_n c_n e^{-iE_n t/\hbar} \psi_n \tag{7.118}$$

The linear combination (7.118) is, of course, not an eigenfunction of $\hat{H}$ (unless all the stationary states in the sum belong to the same degenerate energy level), but it *is* a solution of the time-dependent Schroedinger equation. The time-dependent Schroedinger equation (3.51) is

$$\left[\frac{\hbar}{i} \frac{\partial}{\partial t} + \hat{H} \right] \Psi = 0 \tag{7.119}$$

Since the operator in brackets in (7.119) is linear, it follows that a linear combination [such as (7.118)] of solutions of (7.119) is a solution of (7.119). Also, a linear combination of well-behaved functions is a well-behaved function. Hence, the superposition (7.118) of energy eigenstates is a possible (nonstationary) state of the system. Because of the completeness of the eigenfunctions of $\hat{H}$, any state function can be written in the form (7.118). The state function (7.118) represents a state that does not have a definite energy; rather, when we make an energy measurement, the probability of getting E_n is, according to the results of this section,

$$\left| c_n e^{-iE_n t/\hbar} \right|^2 = |c_n|^2$$

What determines whether a system is in a stationary state such as (7.116) or a nonstationary state such as (7.118)? The answer is that the past history of the system determines its present state. For example, if we take a system that is in a stationary state and expose it to radiation, the time-dependent Schroedinger equation shows that the radiation causes the state to change to a nonstationary state; see *Gatz*, Chapter 17.

7.7 Position Eigenfunctions

We have derived the eigenfunctions of the linear-momentum and angular-momentum operators. We now ask: What are the eigenfunctions of the position operator?

We have

$$\hat{x} = x \cdot$$

Denoting the position eigenfunctions by $\varphi_a(x)$, we write

$$x\varphi_a(x) = a\varphi_a(x) \tag{7.120}$$

where a symbolizes the possible eigenvalues. It follows that

$$(x - a)\,\varphi_a(x) = 0 \tag{7.121}$$

We conclude from (7.121) that

$$\varphi_a(x) = 0 \quad \text{for } x \neq a \tag{7.122}$$

Moreover, since an eigenfunction that is zero everywhere is unacceptable, we have

$$\varphi_a(x) \neq 0 \quad \text{for } x = a \tag{7.123}$$

These conclusions make sense. If the state function is an eigenfunction of $\hat{x}$ with eigenvalue a, $\Psi = \varphi_a(x)$, we know (Section 7.6) that a measurement of x is certain to give the value a; this can only be true if the probability density $|\Psi|^2$ is zero for $x \neq a$, in agreement with (7.122).

Before considering further properties of $\varphi_a(x)$, we define the *Heaviside step function* $H(x)$ by (see Fig. 7.2):

$$H(x) = 1 \quad \text{for } x > 0$$

$$H(x) = 0 \quad \text{for } x < 0 \tag{7.124}$$

$$H(x) = \tfrac{1}{2} \quad \text{for } x = 0$$

We next define the *Dirac delta function* $\delta(x)$ as the derivative of the Heaviside step function:

$$\delta(x) \equiv \frac{dH(x)}{dx} \tag{7.125}$$

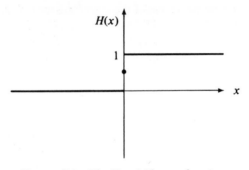

FIGURE 7.2   *The Heaviside step function.*

From (7.124) and (7.125) we have at once (see also Fig. 7.2):

$$\delta(x) = 0 \quad \text{for } x \neq 0 \tag{7.126}$$

Since $H(x)$ makes a sudden jump at $x = 0$, its derivative is infinite at the origin:

$$\delta(x) = \infty \quad \text{for } x = 0 \tag{7.127}$$

We can generalize these equations slightly by setting $x = t - a$, and then changing the symbol t to x; Eqs. (7.124)–(7.127) become

$$H(x-a) = 1, \quad x > a \tag{7.128}$$

$$H(x-a) = 0, \quad x < a \tag{7.129}$$

$$H(x-a) = \tfrac{1}{2}, \quad x = a \tag{7.130}$$

$$\delta(x-a) = \frac{d}{dx} H(x-a) \tag{7.131}$$

$$\delta(x-a) = 0, \quad x \neq a \tag{7.132}$$

$$\delta(x-a) = \infty, \quad x = a \tag{7.133}$$

Now consider the following integral:

$$\int_{-\infty}^{\infty} f(x)\, \delta(x-a)\, dx$$

We evaluate it using integration by parts:

$$\int u\, dv = uv - \int v\, du$$

$$u = f(x), \quad dv = \delta(x-a)\, dx$$

We have, using (7.131),

$$du = f'(x)\, dx, \quad v = H(x-a)$$

$$\int_{-\infty}^{\infty} f(x)\, \delta(x-a)\, dx = f(x)\, H(x-a) \Big|_{-\infty}^{\infty} - \int_{-\infty}^{\infty} H(x-a) f'(x)\, dx$$

$$\int_{-\infty}^{\infty} f(x)\, \delta(x-a)\, dx = f(\infty) - \int_{-\infty}^{\infty} H(x-a) f'(x)\, dx \tag{7.134}$$

where (7.128) and (7.129) have been used. Since $H(x-a)$ vanishes for $x < a$, Eq. (7.134) becomes

$$\int_{-\infty}^{\infty} f(x)\,\delta(x-a)\,dx = f(\infty) - \int_{a}^{\infty} H(x-a)\,f'(x)\,dx$$

$$= f(\infty) - \int_{a}^{\infty} f'(x)\,dx = f(\infty) - f(x)\Big|_{a}^{\infty}$$

$$\int_{-\infty}^{\infty} f(x)\,\delta(x-a)\,dx = f(a) \tag{7.135}$$

Comparing (7.135) with the equation

$$\sum_{j} c_j\,\delta_{ij} = c_i \tag{7.136}$$

we see that the Dirac delta function plays the same role in an integral that the Kronecker delta plays in a sum. The special case of (7.135) with $f(x) = 1$ is:

$$\int_{-\infty}^{\infty} \delta(x-a)\,dx = 1$$

The properties (7.132) and (7.133) of the Dirac delta function are in accord with the properties (7.122) and (7.123) for the position eigenfunctions. Let us therefore tentatively set

$$\varphi_a(x) = \delta(x-a) \tag{7.137}$$

To verify (7.137), we now show it to be in accord with the Born postulate that $|\Psi(a,t)|^2\,da$ is the probability of observing a value of x between a and $a+da$. According to (7.115), this probability is given by

$$|\langle\varphi_a(x)\,|\,\Psi(x,t)\rangle|^2\,da = \left|\int_{-\infty}^{\infty} \varphi_a^*(x)\,\Psi(x,t)\,dx\right|^2 da \tag{7.138}$$

Using (7.137) and then (7.135), we have for (7.138)

$$\left|\int_{-\infty}^{\infty} \delta(x-a)\,\Psi(x,t)\,dx\right|^2 da = |\Psi(a,t)|^2\,da \tag{7.139}$$

Q.E.D.

Since the quantity a in $\delta(x-a)$ can have any real value, the eigenvalues of $\hat{x}$ form a continuum: $-\infty < a < \infty$. As usual for continuum eigenfunctions, $\delta(x-a)$ is not quadratically integrable; we have, using (7.135),

$$\int_{-\infty}^{\infty} |\delta(x-a)|^2\,dx = \int_{-\infty}^{\infty} \delta(x-a)\,\delta(x-a)\,dx = \delta(a-a) = \delta(0) = \infty$$

Summarizing, the eigenfunctions and eigenvalues of position are

$$\hat{x}\,\delta(x-a) = a\,\delta(x-a) \tag{7.140}$$

where a is any real number.

(The delta function is rather badly behaved and, as a consequence, the various manipulations we performed are lacking in rigor, and would make a mathematician shudder. However, use of the delta function can be put on a rigorous basis by considering it to be the limiting case of a function that becomes successively more peaked at the origin; see Fig. 7.3.)

FIGURE 7.3 *Functions that approximate* $\delta(x)$ *with successively increasing accuracy. The area under each curve is* 1.

7.8 The Postulates of Quantum Mechanics

We have introduced the postulates of quantum mechanics as we went along. In this section we summarize them. There is no unique set of postulates; we will simply use a convenient set.

POSTULATE 1. *The state of a system is described by a function* Ψ *of the coordinates and the time. This function, called the state function (or wave function) contains all the information that can be determined about the system. We further postulate that* Ψ *is single-valued, continuous, and quadratically integrable. (For continuum states, the quadratic integrability requirement is omitted.)*

The designation "wave function" for Ψ is perhaps not the best choice. A physical wave moving in three-dimensional space is a function of the three spatial coordinates and the time; however, for an *n*-particle system, the function Ψ is a function of $3n$ spatial coordinates and the time. Hence, for a many-particle system, we cannot interpret Ψ as any sort of physical wave. The state function is best thought of as a function from which we can calculate various properties of the system; the nature of the information that Ψ contains is the subject of Postulate 5 and its consequences.

POSTULATE 2. *To every physical observable there corresponds a linear Hermitian operator. To find this operator, write down the classical-mechanical expression for the observable in terms of Cartesian coordinates*[2] *and corresponding linear-momentum components, and then replace each coordinate x by the operator* $x \cdot$ *and each momentum component* p_x *by the operator* $-i\hbar\partial/\partial x$.

---

[2] The process of finding the quantum-mechanical operators in coordinates other than Cartesian involves complications. See K. Simon, *Am. J. Phys.*, **33**, 60 (1965); G. R. Gruber, *Found. Phys.*, **1**, 227 (1971).

We saw in Section 7.2 that the restriction to Hermitian operators arises from the requirement that average values of physical quantities be real numbers. The requirement of linearity is closely connected to the superposition of states discussed in Section 7.6. In deriving (7.106) for the average value of a property G for a state that was expanded as a superposition of the eigenfunctions of $\hat{G}$, the linearity of $\hat{G}$ played a key role. In (7.105) we had to use the linearity condition:

$$\hat{G}(c_1\varphi_1 + c_2\varphi_2 + \cdots) = c_1\hat{G}\varphi_1 + c_2\hat{G}\varphi_2 + \cdots$$

When the classical quantity contains a product of a Cartesian coordinate and its conjugate momentum, we run into the problem of noncommutativity in constructing the correct quantum-mechanical operator. Several different rules have been proposed to handle this case. See J. R. Shewell, *Am. J. Phys.*, **27**, 16 (1959); E. H. Kerner and W. G. Sutcliffe, *J. Math. Phys.*, **11**, 391 (1970).

POSTULATE 3. *The only possible values that can result from measurements of the physical observable G are the eigenvalues g_i of the equation*

$$\hat{G}\varphi_i = g_i\varphi_i$$

where $\hat{G}$ is the operator corresponding to the property G. The eigenfunctions φ_i are required to be well-behaved.

Our main concern is with the energy levels of atoms and molecules. These are given by the eigenvalues of the energy operator, the Hamiltonian $\hat{H}$. The eigenvalue equation for $\hat{H}$, $\hat{H}\psi = E\psi$, is the time-independent Schroedinger equation. However, finding the possible values of any property involves solving an eigenvalue equation.

POSTULATE 4. *If $\hat{G}$ is any linear Hermitian operator that represents a physical observable, then the eigenfunctions φ_i of the eigenvalue equation*

$$\hat{G}\varphi_i = g_i\varphi_i$$

form a complete set.

This postulate is more a mathematical than a physical postulate. Since there is no mathematical proof (except in various special cases) of the completeness of the eigenfunctions of a linear Hermitian operator, we must assume completeness. Postulate 4 allows us to expand the wave function for any state as a superposition of the eigenfunctions of any quantum-mechanical operator:

$$\Psi = \sum_i c_i\varphi_i = \sum_i |\varphi_i\rangle\langle\varphi_i|\Psi\rangle \tag{7.141}$$

POSTULATE 5. *If $\Psi(q,t)$ is the normalized state function of a system at time t, then the average value of a physical observable G at time t is*

$$\langle G\rangle = \int \Psi^*\hat{G}\Psi \, d\tau \tag{7.142}$$

The definition of the quantum-mechanical average value is given in Section 3.7, and should not be confused with the time average used in classical mechanics.

From Postulates 4 and 5, we showed in Section 7.6 that the probability of observing the value g_i in a measurement of G at time t is given by

$$P_{g_i} = \left| \int \varphi_i^* \Psi \, d\tau \right|^2 = |\langle \varphi_i | \Psi \rangle|^2 \tag{7.143}$$

where $\hat{G}\varphi_i = g_i \varphi_i$. If the state function Ψ happens to be one of the eigenfunctions of $\hat{G}$, $\Psi = \varphi_k$, then (7.143) becomes

$$P_{g_i} = \left| \int \varphi_i^* \varphi_k \, d\tau \right|^2 = |\delta_{ik}|^2 = \delta_{ik} \tag{7.144}$$

where we have used the orthonormality of the eigenfunctions of a Hermitian operator. Equation (7.144) says that we are certain to observe the value g_k when $\Psi = \varphi_k$.

POSTULATE 6. *The time development of the state of an undisturbed system is given by the Schroedinger time-dependent equation*

$$-\frac{\hbar}{i} \frac{\partial \Psi}{\partial t} = \hat{H}\Psi \tag{7.145}$$

where $\hat{H}$ is the Hamiltonian (i.e., energy) operator of the system.

The time-dependent Schroedinger equation is a first-order differential equation in the time, so that, just as in classical mechanics, the present state of an undisturbed system determines the future state. However, unlike classical mechanics, knowledge of the state in quantum mechanics involves only a knowledge of the *probabilities* for various possible outcomes of a measurement. Thus, suppose we have several identical noninteracting systems, each having the same state function $\Psi(t_0)$ at time t_0. If we leave each system to itself, then the state function for each system will change in accord with (7.145); since each system has the same Hamiltonian, each system will have the same state function $\Psi(t_1)$ at any future time t_1. However, suppose that at time t_2 we make a measurement of property G in each system; although each system has the same state function $\Psi(t_2)$ at the instant the measurement begins, we will not get the same result for each system. Rather, we will get a spread of possible values g_i, where g_i are the eigenvalues of $\hat{G}$. The relative number of times we get each g_i can be calculated from the quantities $|c_i|^2$ where

$$\Psi(t_2) = \sum_i c_i \varphi_i$$

with φ_i being the eigenfunctions of $\hat{G}$.

In quantum mechanics, the state function of a system changes in two ways.[3] First, there is the continuous, causal change with time given by the time-dependent Schroedinger equation. Second, there is the sudden, discontinuous, probabilistic

---

[3] For a discussion, see E. P. Wigner, *Am. J. Phys.*, **31**, 6 (1963).

change that occurs when a measurement is made on the system; this kind of change cannot be predicted with certainty, since the result of a measurement cannot be predicted with certainty. The sudden change in Ψ caused by a measurement is called the *reduction of the wave function. A measurement of property G that yields the result g_k changes the state function to φ_k, the eigenfunction of $\hat{G}$ with eigenvalue g_k.* Let us give an example. Suppose that at time t we carry out a measurement of the particle's position. Let $\Psi(x, t_-)$ be the state function of the particle the instant before the measurement is made (Fig. 7.4a). We further suppose that the result of the measurement is that the particle is found to be in the small region of space:

$$a < x < a + da \qquad\qquad (7.146)$$

We ask, what is the state function $\Psi(x, t_+)$ the instant after the measurement? To answer this question, suppose we were to make a second measurement of position at time t_+. Since t_+ differs from the time t of the first measurement by an infinitesimal amount, we must still find that the particle is confined to the region (7.146). (If the particle moved a finite distance in an infinitesimal amount of time, it would have infinite velocity, which is unacceptable.) Since $|\Psi(x, t_+)|^2$ is the probability density for finding various values of x, we conclude that $\Psi(x, t_+)$ must be zero outside the region (7.146) and must look something like Fig. 7.4b. Thus, the position measurement at time t has reduced Ψ from a function that is spread out over all space to one that is localized in the region (7.146). The change from $\Psi(x, t_-)$ to $\Psi(x, t_+)$ is a probabilistic change.

The measurement process is one of the most controversial areas in quantum mechanics. Just how and at what stage in the measurement process reduction occurs is unclear. Some physicists take the reduction of Ψ as an additional quantum-mechanical postulate, while others claim it is a theorem derivable from the other postulates. (The physicist Margenau rejects the idea of reduction.)

The probabilistic nature of quantum mechanics has disturbed many eminent physicists, such as Einstein, de Broglie, and Schroedinger. These physicists

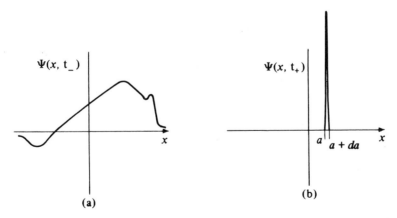

FIGURE 7.4 *Reduction of the wave function caused by a measurement of position.*

and others have suggested that quantum mechanics may not furnish a complete description of physical reality; rather, the probabilistic laws of quantum mechanics might simply be a reflection of deterministic laws that operate at a subquantum-mechanical level, and involve "hidden variables." An analogy given by the physicist Bohm is the Brownian motion of a dust particle in air. The particle undergoes random fluctuations of position, and its motion is not completely determined by its position and velocity. Of course, Brownian motion is a result of collisions with the gas molecules, and is determined by variables existing on the level of molecular motion. Analogously, the motions of electrons might be determined by hidden variables existing on a subquantum-mechanical level. The orthodox interpretation (often called the Copenhagen interpretation) of quantum mechanics, which was developed by Heisenberg and Bohr, denies the existence of hidden variables and asserts that the laws of quantum mechanics provide a complete description of physical reality.

It turns out that there are certain experimentally realizable situations where any possible local hidden-variable theory must make different predictions than quantum mechanics makes. (In a local theory, two systems very far from each other act independently of each other.) The result of such an experiment was in agreement with quantum-mechanical predictions, thus providing very strong evidence against all local hidden-variable theories. [S. J. Freedman and J. F. Clauser, *Phys. Rev. Letters*, **28**, 938 (1972).] There seems to be a fundamental randomness in nature, not explainable in any deterministic way.

Although the experimental predictions of quantum mechanics are not arguable, its conceptual interpretation is still the subject of heated debate, with several different viewpoints being advocated. An excellent bibliography with commentary on this subject is B. S. DeWitt and R. N. Graham, *Am. J. Phys.*, **39**, 724 (1971).

If the Hamiltonian is independent of time, we have the possibility of states of definite energy E. For such states, the state function must satisfy

$$\hat{H}\Psi = E\Psi \tag{7.147}$$

and the time-dependent Schroedinger equation becomes

$$-\frac{\hbar}{i}\frac{\partial\Psi}{\partial t} = E\Psi$$

which integrates to $\Psi = Be^{-iEt/\hbar}$, where B, the integration "constant," is independent of time. The function Ψ depends on the coordinates and the time, so that B is some function of the coordinates, which we designate as $\psi(q)$. We have

$$\Psi(q, t) = e^{-iEt/\hbar}\psi(q) \tag{7.148}$$

for a state of constant energy. The function $\psi(q)$ satisfies the time-independent Schroedinger equation

$$\hat{H}\psi(q) = E\psi(q) \tag{7.149}$$

which follows from (7.147) and (7.148). The factor $\exp(-iEt/\hbar)$ simply indicates a change in the phase of the wave function $\Psi(q, t)$ with time, and has no direct physical significance; hence, we generally refer to $\psi(q)$ as "the wave function." The Hamiltonian operator plays a unique role in quantum mechanics in that it occurs in the fundamental dynamical equation, the time-dependent Schroedinger equation; the eigenstates of $\hat{H}$ (known as stationary states) have the special property that the probability density $|\Psi|^2$ is independent of time.

You might be wondering about the absence from our list of the Born postulate that $|\Psi(x, t)|^2 \, dx$ is the probability at time t for finding the particle between x and $x+dx$; this postulate is actually a consequence of Postulate 5, as we now demonstrate. From the definition of average value in Section 3.7, we derived Eq. (3.108):

$$\langle G \rangle = \sum_g P_g g$$

where P_g is the probability of observing the value g in a measurement of the property G. This equation is for a variable that takes on discrete values; the corresponding equation for a continuous variable is

$$\langle G \rangle = \int P(g) g \, dg \qquad (7.150)$$

where $P(g)$ is the probability density for observing various values of G. For the average value of the x coordinate, Eq. (7.150) reads

$$\langle x \rangle = \int P(x) x \, dx$$

According to Postulate 5, we have

$$\langle x \rangle = \int \Psi^* \hat{x} \Psi \, dx = \int |\Psi|^2 x \, dx$$

Comparing these last two equations, we conclude that $|\Psi|^2$ is the probability density for the x coordinate of a one-dimensional system.

In Chapter 10, we will introduce two further postulates, dealing with spin and the Pauli principle.

PROBLEMS

7.1 True or false: (a) The state function is always equal to a function of time multiplied by a function of the coordinates. (b) In both classical and quantum mechanics, knowledge of the present state of an isolated system allows its future state to be calculated. (c) The state function is always an eigenfunction of the Hamiltonian. (d) Any linear combination of eigenfunctions of the Hamiltonian is an eigenfunction of the Hamiltonian. (e) If the state function is not an eigenfunction of the operator $\hat{A}$, then a measurement of the property A might give a value that is not one of the eigenvalues of $\hat{A}$. (f) The probability density is independent of time for a stationary state. (g) If two operators do not commute, then they cannot possess any common eigenfunctions. (h) If two operators commute, then every eigenfunction of one must be an eigenfunction of the other.

7.2 Let $\hat{A}$ and $\hat{B}$ be Hermitian operators and let c be a real constant. Show that $c\hat{A}$ and $\hat{A}+\hat{B}$ are Hermitian.

7.3 Show that (a) d^2/dx^2 is Hermitian; (b) $\langle T_x \rangle = (\hbar^2/2m) \int |\partial \Psi / \partial x|^2 \, d\tau$.

7.4 Which of the following operators are Hermitian: d/dx, $i(d/dx)$, $4d^2/dx^2$, $i(d^2/dx^2)$?

7.5 Let $\hat{A}$ be a Hermitian operator. Show that $\langle A^2 \rangle = \int |\hat{A}\psi|^2 \, d\tau$ and therefore $\langle A^2 \rangle \geqslant 0$. [This result can be used to derive Eq. (5.177) more rigorously than in the text. Thus, since $\hat{M}^2 - \hat{M}_z^2 = \hat{M}_x^2 + \hat{M}_y^2$, we have $\langle M^2 \rangle - \langle M_z^2 \rangle = \langle M_x^2 \rangle + \langle M_y^2 \rangle$. Now $\langle M^2 \rangle = c$, $\langle M_z^2 \rangle = b_k^2$ and by the theorem of this exercise $\langle M_x^2 \rangle \geqslant 0$, $\langle M_y^2 \rangle \geqslant 0$. Hence $c - b_k^2 \geqslant 0$.]

7.6 Verify that $\hat{L}_z$ is Hermitian using: (a) spherical polar coordinates; (b) Cartesian coordinates.

7.7 Extend the Schmidt orthogonalization procedure to the case of threefold degeneracy.

7.8 Evaluate the coefficients in the sine-series expansion (7.48) for the parabolic function $f(x) = x(l - x)$. What is the result at $x = \frac{1}{2}l$? Use the first five terms of the result to approximate π^3.

7.9 What operator is shown to be Hermitian by $\langle m | n \rangle = \langle n | m \rangle^*$?

7.10 For the hydrogenlike atom, we have $V = -Ze^2(x^2 + y^2 + z^2)^{-1/2}$ so that the potential energy is an even function of the coordinates. (a) What is the parity of ψ_{2s}? (b) What is the parity of ψ_{2p_x}? (c) Consider $\psi_{2s} + \psi_{2p_x}$. Is it an eigenfunction of $\hat{H}$? Does it have definite parity?

7.11 Let $\hat{\Pi}$ be the parity operator and m be a positive integer. What is $\hat{\Pi}^m$ if m is even? if m is odd?

7.12 Let $\hat{\Pi}$ be the parity operator and let $\psi_i(x)$ be a normalized harmonic-oscillator wave function. We define the matrix elements Π_{ij} as

$$\Pi_{ij} = \int_{-\infty}^{\infty} \psi_i^* \hat{\Pi} \psi_j \, dx$$

Show that $\Pi_{ij} = 0$ for $i \neq j$, and $\Pi_{ii} = \pm 1$.

7.13 Let $\hat{T}$ be a linear operator such that $\hat{T}^n = \hat{1}$, where n is a positive integer, and no lower power of $\hat{T}$ equals $\hat{1}$. Find the eigenvalues of $\hat{T}$.

7.14 On the basis of parity considerations, which of the following integrals must be zero:

(a) $\int \psi_{2s}^* x \psi_{2p_x} \, d\tau$ (b) $\int \psi_{2s}^* x^2 \psi_{2p_x} \, d\tau$ (c) $\int \psi_{2p_y}^* x \psi_{2p_x} \, d\tau$

where the wave functions are the hydrogenlike orbitals.

7.15 (a) Show that the parity operator is linear. (b) Show that the parity operator is Hermitian; a proof in one dimension is sufficient.

7.16 (a) In Cartesian coordinates the parity operator $\hat{\Pi}$ corresponds to the transformation of variables: $x \to -x$, $y \to -y$, $z \to -z$. Show that in spherical polar coordinates the parity operator corresponds to the transformation: $r \to r$, $\theta \to \pi - \theta$, $\varphi \to \varphi + \pi$. (b) Show that $\hat{\Pi} e^{im\varphi} = (-1)^m e^{im\varphi}$. (c) Use Eq. (5.131) to show that

$$\hat{\Pi} S_{l,m}(\theta) = (-1)^{l - |m|} S_{l,m}(\theta) = (-1)^{l-m} S_{l,m}(\theta)$$

(d) Combine the results of (b) and (c) to conclude that the spherical harmonic $Y_l^m(\theta, \varphi)$ is an even function if l is even, and is an odd function if l is odd.

7.17 Which of the following operators meet the requirements for a quantum-mechanical operator which is to represent a physical quantity: (a) $(\ )^{1/2}$; (b) d/dx; (c) d^2/dx^2; (d) $i(d/dx)$?

7.18 Consider an operator $\hat{A}$ that contains the time as a parameter. We are interested in how the average value of the property A changes with time, and we have

$$\frac{d\langle A \rangle}{dt} = \frac{d}{dt} \int \Psi^* \hat{A} \Psi \, d\tau$$

The definite integral on the right side of this equation is a function of the parameter t, and it is generally a valid mathematical operation to calculate its derivative with respect to t by differentiating the integrand with respect to t:

$$\frac{d\langle A \rangle}{dt} = \int \frac{\partial}{\partial t} [\Psi^* \hat{A} \Psi] \, d\tau = \int \frac{\partial \Psi^*}{\partial t} \hat{A} \Psi \, d\tau + \int \Psi^* \frac{\partial \hat{A}}{\partial t} \Psi \, d\tau$$

$$+ \int \Psi^* \hat{A} \frac{\partial \Psi}{\partial t} \, d\tau$$

Use the time-dependent Schroedinger equation and its complex conjugate, and the Hermitian property of $\hat{H}$ to show that

$$\frac{d\langle A \rangle}{dt} = \int \Psi^* \frac{\partial \hat{A}}{\partial t} \Psi \, d\tau + \frac{i}{\hbar} \int \Psi^* (\hat{H}\hat{A} - \hat{A}\hat{H}) \Psi \, d\tau$$

$$\frac{d\langle A \rangle}{dt} = \left\langle \frac{\partial \hat{A}}{\partial t} \right\rangle + \frac{i}{\hbar} \langle [\hat{H}, \hat{A}] \rangle \tag{7.151}$$

7.19 Use (7.151) and (5.12) to show that

$$\frac{d}{dt} \langle x \rangle = \frac{\langle p_x \rangle}{m} = \frac{1}{m} \int \Psi^* \frac{\hbar}{i} \frac{\partial \Psi}{\partial x} \, d\tau \tag{7.152}$$

From (7.152) it follows that

$$\frac{d^2\langle x \rangle}{dt^2} = \frac{1}{m} \frac{d}{dt} \langle p_x \rangle$$

Use (7.151), (5.13), and (4.26) to show that

$$\langle F_x \rangle = m \frac{d^2\langle x \rangle}{dt^2} \tag{7.153}$$

If we consider a classical-mechanical particle, its wave function will be large only in a very small region corresponding to its position, and we may then drop the averages in (7.153) to obtain Newton's second law. Thus, classical mechanics is a special case of quantum mechanics. Equation (7.153) is known as *Ehrenfest's theorem*, after the physicist who derived it in 1927.

7.20 In accord with the probability interpretation of $\Psi^*\Psi$, we have normalized the wave function: $\int \Psi^*\Psi \, d\tau = 1$. Assuming that particles are neither created nor destroyed, we expect this normalization to hold for all time, i.e.,

$$\frac{d}{dt} \int \Psi^*\Psi \, d\tau = 0 \tag{7.154}$$

Prove (7.154) as a special case of (7.151).

7.21 For a hydrogen atom in a p state, the possible outcomes of a measurement of L_z are $-\hbar$, 0, and $\hbar$. For each of the following wave functions, give the probabilities for each of these three results. (a) ψ_{2p_z}; (b) ψ_{2p_x}; (c) ψ_{2p_y}; (d) $\psi_{2p_{+1}}$.

7.22 Verify the following Kronecker-delta identities:

$$\delta_{ij} = \delta_{ji} \qquad [\delta_{ij}]^2 = \delta_{ij}$$

$$\delta_{ij}\,\delta_{ik} = \delta_{ij}\,\delta_{jk} \qquad \delta_{i+n,j} = \delta_{i,j-n}$$

7.23 Give the value of each of the following integrals:

(a) $\displaystyle\int_{-\infty}^{\infty} \delta(x)\,dx$ \qquad (b) $\displaystyle\int_{-\infty}^{-1} \delta(x)\,dx$

(c) $\displaystyle\int_{-1}^{1} \delta(x)\,dx$ \qquad (d) $\displaystyle\int_{1}^{2} f(x)\,\delta(x-3)\,dx$

7.24 What is the value of $\displaystyle\int_{0}^{\infty} f(x)\,\delta(x)\,dx$?

7.25 (a) If $\hat{A}$ and $\hat{B}$ are Hermitian operators, prove that their product $\hat{A}\hat{B}$ is Hermitian if and only if $\hat{A}$ and $\hat{B}$ commute. (b) If $\hat{A}$ and $\hat{B}$ are Hermitian, prove that $\frac{1}{2}(\hat{A}\hat{B}+\hat{B}\hat{A})$ is Hermitian. (c) Is $\hat{x}\hat{p}_x$ Hermitian? (d) Is $\frac{1}{2}(\hat{x}\hat{p}_x + \hat{p}_x\hat{x})$ Hermitian?

7.26 Since the parity operator is Hermitian (Problem 7.15), two eigenfunctions of $\hat{\Pi}$ that correspond to different eigenvalues must be orthogonal. Show directly that this is so.

7.27 Consider the integral $\langle v_2|x|v_1\rangle$, where the functions are one-dimensional harmonic-oscillator wave functions with quantum numbers v_2 and v_1. Under what conditions do parity considerations allow us to conclude that this integral must be zero? Might the integral be zero in other cases as well? (This integral is important in discussing radiative transitions.)

7.28 Consider a particle in a nonstationary state in a one-dimensional box of length l. Suppose that at time t_0, its state function is the parabolic function

$$\Psi(t_0) = Nx(l-x), \qquad 0 \leqslant x \leqslant l$$

where N is the normalization constant. If at time t_0 we were to make a measurement of the particle's energy, what would be the possible outcomes of the measurement, and what would be the probability for each such outcome?

7.29 Use the results of Problem 7.28 to evaluate

$$\sum_{m=0}^{\infty} \frac{1}{(2m+1)^6}$$

7.30 (a) Show that for a particle in a one-dimensional box of length l, the probability of observing a value of p_x between p and $p+dp$ is

$$\frac{4|N|^2 s^2}{l(s^2-b^2)^2}[1-(-1)^n \cos bl]\,dp \qquad (7.155)$$

where $s \equiv n\pi l^{-1}$ and $b \equiv p\hbar^{-1}$. The constant N is to be chosen so that the integral from minus infinity to infinity of (7.155) is unity. (b) Evaluate (7.155) for $p = \pm nh/2l$. [At these values of p_x, the denominator of (7.155) is zero and the probability reaches a large but finite value.]

7.31 A measurement yields $2^{1/2}\hbar$ for the magnitude of a particle's orbital angular momentum. If L_x is now measured, what are the possible outcomes?

7.32 The functions in Fig. 7.3 approximate the Dirac delta function. Draw graphs of the corresponding functions that approximate the Heaviside step function with successively increasing accuracy.

7.33 The energy of most stars results from the fusion of hydrogen nuclei to helium nuclei.[4] The interior of the sun (a typical star) is at 15×10^6 °C. At this temperature, virtually no nuclei have sufficient kinetic energy to allow them to overcome the electrostatic repulsion between nuclei and approach each other closely enough to undergo a fusion reaction. Therefore, when Eddington proposed in 1920 that nuclear fusion is the source of stellar energy, his idea was rejected. Explain why fusion does occur in stars, despite the above-mentioned apparent difficulty.

7.34 Quantum mechanics postulates that the present state of an undisturbed system determines its future state. Consider the special case of a system with a time-independent Hamiltonian $\hat{H}$. Suppose it is known that at time t_0 the state function is $\Psi(x, t_0)$. Use Eqs. (7.145) and (7.101) to show that

$$\Psi(x, t) = \sum_j \langle \psi_j(x) \, | \, \Psi(x, t_0) \rangle \exp\left[-iE_j(t - t_0)/\hbar\right] \psi_j(x)$$

where $\hat{H}\psi_j = E_j\psi_j$.

7.35 Prove the uncertainty principle (5.16) for any two Hermitian operators $\hat{A}$ and $\hat{B}$, as follows. (a) Define functions f and g as $f = (\hat{A} - \langle A \rangle)\Psi$ and $g = i(\hat{B} - \langle B \rangle)\Psi$. Prove that $\langle f | f \rangle = \langle f | f \rangle^* = (\Delta A)^2$ and $\langle g | g \rangle = (\Delta B)^2$. (b) Now let $I \equiv \langle f + sg | f + sg \rangle$, where s is defined as an arbitrary *real* parameter. The integrand $|f + sg|^2$ of I is everywhere nonnegative and I must therefore be positive, unless it happens that $f = -sg$. We have two possible cases: either (1) $f = -sg$, or (2) $f \neq -sg$. Show directly that for case (1), we have $4\langle f | f \rangle \langle g | g \rangle = [\langle f | g \rangle + \langle g | f \rangle]^2$. For case (2), we have $I = as^2 + bs + c > 0$, where a, b, and c are certain integrals. This inequality means that the equation $as^2 + bs + c = 0$ can have no real roots for s, which (using the quadratic formula) means that $4ac > b^2$. Show that this inequality leads to $4\langle f | f \rangle \langle g | g \rangle > [\langle f | g \rangle + \langle g | f \rangle]^2$. (c) Combining cases (1) and (2), we have shown that $4\langle f | f \rangle \langle g | g \rangle \geqslant [\langle g | f \rangle^* + \langle f | g \rangle^*]^2$. Show that this leads to the uncertainty principle (5.16).

---

[4] After a certain fraction of hydrogen has been used up, a star will fuse helium nuclei to form heavier nuclei, ultimately forming Fe^{56}, the most stable nuclide. Still heavier nuclei are formed by neutron capture by Fe^{56} followed by beta decay. It is believed that all elements heavier than helium were formed mainly by stars; except for hydrogen, most of the atomic nuclei in our bodies originated in the interiors of stars.

CHAPTER
8

The Variation Method

8.1 The Variation Principle

We now begin the study of the approximation methods needed to deal with the time-independent Schroedinger equation for systems of several interacting particles. This chapter deals with the *variation method*, which allows us to obtain an approximation to the ground-state energy of a system, without solving the Schroedinger equation.

The variation method is based on the following theorem: Given a system with Hamiltonian operator $\hat{H}$, then if φ is *any normalized well-behaved function that satisfies the boundary conditions of the problem*, it is true that

$$\int \varphi^* \hat{H} \varphi \, d\tau \geqslant E_0 \tag{8.1}$$

where E_0 is the true value of the lowest energy eigenvalue of $\hat{H}$. The significance of this theorem is that it allows us to calculate an upper bound for the ground-state energy.

We begin the proof of (8.1) by defining the integral I as

$$I = \int \varphi^* (\hat{H} - E_0) \varphi \, d\tau \tag{8.2}$$

$$I = \int \varphi^* \hat{H} \varphi \, d\tau - E_0 \int \varphi^* \varphi \, d\tau = \int \varphi^* \hat{H} \varphi \, d\tau - E_0 \tag{8.3}$$

since φ is normalized. If we prove that $I \geqslant 0$, we will have proved (8.1). Now let ψ_i and E_i be the true eigenfunctions and eigenvalues of $\hat{H}$:

$$\hat{H} \psi_i = E_i \psi_i \tag{8.4}$$

Since the eigenfunctions ψ_i form a complete set, we can expand φ in terms of the ψ_i. (Note that this requires that φ satisfy the same boundary conditions as the ψ_i.)

$$\varphi = \sum_k a_k \psi_k \tag{8.5}$$

We substitute this expansion into (8.2) to get

$$I = \int \sum_k a_k^* \psi_k^* (\hat{H} - E_0) \sum_j a_j \psi_j \, d\tau = \int \sum_k a_k^* \psi_k^* \sum_j (\hat{H} - E_0) a_j \psi_j \, d\tau \tag{8.6}$$

Applying (8.4), and assuming the validity of interchanging the integration and the infinite summations, we get

$$I = \int \sum_k a_k^* \psi_k^* \sum_j a_j (E_j - E_0) \psi_j \, d\tau = \sum_k \sum_j a_k^* a_j (E_j - E_0) \int \psi_k^* \psi_j \, d\tau \tag{8.7}$$

Use of the orthonormality of the eigenfunctions gives

$$I = \sum_k \sum_j a_k^* a_j (E_j - E_0) \delta_{kj} \tag{8.8}$$

We perform the sum over j and, as usual, the Kronecker delta factor makes all terms zero except the one with $j = k$, giving

$$I = \sum_k a_k^* a_k (E_k - E_0) = \sum_k |a_k|^2 (E_k - E_0) \tag{8.9}$$

By hypothesis, E_0 is the lowest eigenvalue; hence, $E_k - E_0 \geqslant 0$. Moreover, $|a_k|^2 \geqslant 0$. Thus, all the terms in the sum on the right of (8.9) are nonnegative, and we have the desired result that $I \geqslant 0$.

Suppose we have a function φ that is *not* normalized. To apply the variation theorem, we multiply φ by a normalization constant N, so that $N\varphi$ is normalized. Replacing φ by $N\varphi$ in (8.1), we have

$$|N|^2 \int \varphi^* \hat{H} \varphi \, d\tau \geqslant E_0 \tag{8.10}$$

The constant N is determined by

$$\int (N\varphi)^* N\varphi \, d\tau = |N|^2 \int \varphi^* \varphi \, d\tau = 1 \tag{8.11}$$

$$|N|^2 = 1 \Big/ \int \varphi^* \varphi \, d\tau \tag{8.12}$$

Hence

$$\frac{\int \varphi^* \hat{H} \varphi \, d\tau}{\int \varphi^* \varphi \, d\tau} \geqslant E_0 \tag{8.13}$$

where φ is any well-behaved function (not necessarily normalized) that satisfies the boundary conditions of the problem.

The function φ is called a *trial variation function*, and the integral in (8.1) is called the *variational integral*. To arrive at a good approximation to the ground-state energy E_0, we try many trial variation functions and look for the one that gives the lowest value of the variational integral. From (8.1), the lower the value of the variational integral, the better the approximation we have to E_0. (One way to disprove quantum mechanics would be to find a trial variation function that made the variational integral less than E_0 for some system where E_0 was known either experimentally, or from the exact solution of the Schroedinger equation.)

Let ψ_0 be the true ground-state wave function:

$$\hat{H}\psi_0 = E_0\psi_0 \tag{8.14}$$

If we happened to be lucky enough to hit upon a trial variation function that was equal to ψ_0, then, using (8.14) in (8.1), we see that the variational integral will be equal to E_0. Thus, the ground-state wave function gives the minimum value of the variational integral. We therefore expect that the lower the value of the variational integral, the closer the trial variational function will approach to the true ground-state wave function. However, it turns out that the variational integral approaches E_0 a lot faster than the trial variation function approaches ψ_0, and it is possible to get a rather good approximation to E_0 using a rather poor φ.

In practice, what is usually done is to put several parameters into the trial function φ, and then vary these parameters so as to minimize the variational integral. Successful use of the variation method depends on our ability to make a shrewd choice (or guess) for the trial function.

Let us look at some examples of the variation method. Although the real utility of the method is for problems to which we do not know the true solutions, we will here consider problems that are exactly soluble, so that we can judge the accuracy of our results.

We will use the variation method to get an upper bound to the ground-state energy of the particle in a one-dimensional box of length l (Section 2.2). The wave function is zero outside the box, and the boundary conditions require that $\psi = 0$ at $x = 0$ and at $x = l$. The trial variation function must satisfy these boundary conditions. A simple function satisfying these conditions is the parabolic function

$$\varphi = x(l-x) \tag{8.15}$$

for $0 \leqslant x \leqslant l$, and $\varphi = 0$ outside the box. Since we have not normalized φ, we use (8.13). Inside the box, the Hamiltonian is $-(\hbar^2/2m)\,d^2/dx^2$. For the numerator and denominator of (8.13), we have

$$\int \varphi^*\hat{H}\varphi\,d\tau = -\frac{\hbar^2}{2m}\int_0^l (lx-x^2)\frac{d^2}{dx^2}(lx-x^2)\,dx = -\frac{\hbar^2}{m}\int_0^l (x^2-lx)\,dx$$

$$\int \varphi^*\hat{H}\varphi\,d\tau = \frac{\hbar^2 l^3}{6m}$$

$$\int \varphi^*\varphi\,d\tau = \int_0^l x^2(l-x)^2\,dx = \frac{l^5}{30}$$

Substituting in (8.13), we get

$$\frac{5h^2}{4\pi^2 l^2 m} \geqslant E_0 \tag{8.16}$$

From Eq. (2.20), E_0 is $h^2/8ml^2$ and the percent error is

$$\frac{(5/4\pi^2)-(1/8)}{1/8} \times 100\% = 1.3\%$$

The preceding example did not have a parameter in the trial function. We now give an example involving the one-dimensional harmonic oscillator to illustrate this method. We expect the wave function to go to zero as x goes to $\pm\infty$. The function e^{-x} has the proper behavior at $+\infty$ but becomes infinite at $-\infty$. The function e^{-x^2} has the proper behavior at $\pm\infty$. However, it is not satisfactory from a dimensional standpoint, since the power to which we raise e must be dimensionless. This can be seen from the Taylor-series expansion (4.48). All the terms on the right of (4.48) must have the same dimensions. Therefore z must have the same dimensions as 1, i.e., z is dimensionless. The quantity α, defined in Eq. (4.33), has the dimensions $1/(\text{length})^2$; hence, αx^2 is dimensionless. This suggests a trial function of the form $e^{-\alpha x^2}$. Note that α is a constant, not a variable parameter. We now introduce some flexibility into the trial function by use of a parameter. Perhaps we might multiply the exponential function by terms involving powers of x. We might try $(1+bx)e^{-\alpha x^2}$, where b is a parameter. This function is, however, neither even nor odd, whereas we know that when $V(x)$ is an even function, the wave functions must be either even or odd. We therefore try

$$\varphi = (1+c\alpha x^2)e^{-\alpha x^2} \tag{8.17}$$

where c is a parameter. The factor α multiplying cx^2 was thrown in to simplify things by making c dimensionless. The Hamiltonian is given by Eq. (4.32). We have, using (4.54):

$$\int \varphi^* \varphi \, dx = 2\int_0^\infty (1+2c\alpha x^2 + c^2\alpha^2 x^4)e^{-2\alpha x^2}\, dx \tag{8.18}$$

Using the Appendix integrals (A.5) and (A.6), we find

$$\int \varphi^* \varphi \, dx = \left(\frac{\pi}{2\alpha}\right)^{1/2}\left(1 + \frac{c}{2} + \frac{3}{16}c^2\right) \tag{8.19}$$

$$\int \varphi^* \hat{H} \varphi \, dx = \frac{\hbar^2}{2m}\int_{-\infty}^\infty (1+c\alpha x^2)e^{-\alpha x^2}$$

$$\times \left(-\frac{d^2}{dx^2} + \alpha^2 x^2\right)(e^{-\alpha x^2} + x^2 c\alpha e^{-\alpha x^2})\, dx \tag{8.20}$$

$$\int \varphi^* \hat{H} \varphi \, dx = \frac{\hbar^2}{m}\left(\frac{\pi\alpha}{2}\right)^{1/2}\left(\frac{43}{128}c^2 - \frac{1}{16}c + \frac{5}{8}\right) \tag{8.21}$$

$$\frac{\int \varphi^* \hat{H} \varphi \, dx}{\int \varphi^* \varphi \, dx} = h v\frac{(43c^2 - 8c + 80)}{(24c^2 + 64c + 128)} \tag{8.22}$$

Now we vary c to minimize (8.22). A necessary condition that (8.22) be minimized is that

$$\frac{\partial}{\partial c}\left[\frac{\int \varphi^* \hat{H} \varphi \, dx}{\int \varphi^* \varphi \, dx}\right] = 0 \tag{8.23}$$

Differentiation of (8.22) with respect to c gives

$$\frac{(24c^2+64c+128)(86c-8)-(43c^2-8c+80)(48c+64)}{(24c^2+64c+128)^2} = 0$$

$$23c^2 + 56c - 48 = 0 \qquad (8.24)$$

$$c = -3.107, +0.6718 \qquad (8.25)$$

Substituting these roots in (8.22), we find that 0.6718 gives the smaller value, and using it we have

$$E_0 \leqslant 0.517\, hv \qquad (8.26)$$

The (true) value of E_0 is $\frac{1}{2}hv$, and our error is 3.4 percent.

Instead of using a polynomial containing a parameter to multiply $e^{-\alpha x^2}$, as in (8.17), we might put the parameter in the exponent, taking

$$\varphi = e^{-b\alpha x^2} \qquad (8.27)$$

If we used (8.27) as a trial function, we would find (Problem 8.1) that minimization of the variational integral leads to $b = \frac{1}{2}$, and an energy

$$E_0 \leqslant \frac{1}{2}hv \qquad (8.28)$$

Recall [Eq. (4.59)] that with $b = \frac{1}{2}$, (8.27) is the true ground-state wave function.

8.2 Extension of the Variation Method

The variation method as presented in the last section has two major limitations. First, it provides information about only the *ground*-state energy and wave function. Second, it provides only an upper bound to the ground-state energy. We now discuss some extensions of the variation method. (See also Section 8.5.)

Consider how we might extend the variation method to obtain an estimate for the energy of the first excited state. We number the stationary states of the system $0, 1, 2, \ldots$ in order of increasing energy, i.e., so that

$$E_0 \leqslant E_1 \leqslant E_2 \leqslant \cdots \qquad (8.29)$$

We define I_1 as [*cf.* Eq. (8.2)]:

$$I_1 = \int \varphi^*(\hat{H} - E_1)\varphi\, d\tau \qquad (8.30)$$

where φ is a normalized function satisfying the boundary conditions of the problem. We expand φ as

$$\varphi = \sum_k a_k \psi_k \qquad (8.31)$$

where the ψ_k are the true wave functions. Carrying out the same steps as we did following Eq. (8.5), we are led to an equation that is the same as (8.9), except that E_0 is replaced by E_1, so that

$$I_1 = \sum_k |a_k|^2(E_k - E_1) = |a_0|^2(E_0 - E_1) + |a_2|^2(E_2 - E_1) + |a_3|^2(E_3 - E_1) + \cdots \qquad (8.32)$$

All the terms in (8.32) are nonnegative *except* the first term. From Eq. (7.65), the coefficients in the expansion (8.31) are given by

$$a_k = \int \psi_k^* \varphi \, d\tau \qquad (8.33)$$

If we restrict ourselves to variational functions φ that are *orthogonal* to the true ground-state wave function ψ_0, Eq. (8.33) gives

$$a_0 = \int \psi_0^* \varphi \, d\tau = 0 \qquad (8.34)$$

For normalized trial functions orthogonal to ψ_0, the first term in the sum (8.32) vanishes, and we conclude that $I_1 \geqslant 0$, or

$$\int \varphi^* \hat{H} \varphi \, d\tau \geqslant E_1 \qquad \text{if} \quad \int \psi_0^* \varphi \, d\tau = 0 \qquad (8.35)$$

Thus (8.35) provides a method for obtaining an upper bound for the energy of the first excited state, E_1. However, the restriction (8.34) makes the method troublesome to apply.

For certain problems it is possible to rigorously guarantee that (8.34) holds even though we do not know the true ground-state wave function. One example is a one-dimensional problem for which V is an even function of x. In this case the ground-state wave function is always an even function, while the first excited-state wave function is odd. (All the wave functions must be of definite parity. The ground-state wave function is nodeless, and, since an odd function vanishes at the origin, the ground-state wave function must be even. The first excited-state wave function has one node, and must be odd.) Therefore, for odd trial functions, it must be true that

$$\int_{-\infty}^{\infty} \psi_0^* \varphi \, dx = 0 \qquad (8.36)$$

(The function ψ_0^* times the odd function φ gives an odd integrand, and the integral of an odd function from $-\infty$ to ∞ is zero.)

Another example is a particle moving in a central field (Section 6.1). The form of the potential energy might be such that we could not solve for the radial factor $R(r)$ in the eigenfunction. However, we know that the angular factor is a spherical harmonic [Eq. (6.20)] and that spherical harmonics with different values of l are orthogonal. Thus, we can get an upper bound to the energy of the lowest state with any given angular momentum l, by using the factor $Y_l^m(\theta, \varphi)$ in the trial function. This result depends on the extension of (8.35) to higher excited states, namely

$$\frac{\int \varphi^* \hat{H} \varphi \, d\tau}{\int \varphi^* \varphi \, d\tau} \geqslant E_{k+1} \qquad \text{if} \quad \int \psi_0^* \varphi \, d\tau = \int \psi_1^* \varphi \, d\tau = \cdots = \int \psi_k^* \varphi \, d\tau = 0 \quad (8.37)$$

Several procedures have been devised that yield *lower* bounds for energy levels, but these procedures are not so easy to apply and have not been used very often. (For a survey, see the article by F. Weinhold in *Advances in Quantum Chemistry*, Vol. 6, P.-O. Löwdin, ed., Academic Press, 1972, p. 299.)

8.3 Determinants

We will shortly consider a kind of variational function that gives rise to an equation involving a determinant. Therefore, we now review the properties of determinants.

A determinant is a square array of n^2 quantities (called elements); the value of the determinant is calculated from its elements in a manner to be given shortly. The number n is the *order* of the determinant. Using a_{ij} to represent a typical element, we write the nth-order determinant as

$$\det(a_{ij}) = \begin{vmatrix} a_{11} & a_{12} & a_{13} & \cdots & a_{1n} \\ a_{21} & a_{22} & a_{23} & \cdots & a_{2n} \\ a_{31} & a_{32} & a_{33} & \cdots & a_{3n} \\ \vdots & \vdots & \vdots & \vdots & \vdots \\ a_{n1} & a_{n2} & a_{n3} & \cdots & a_{nn} \end{vmatrix} \tag{8.38}$$

The vertical lines in (8.38) have nothing to do with absolute value. Before considering how the value of the nth-order determinant is defined, we consider determinants of first, second, and third orders.

A first-order determinant has one element and its value is simply the value of that element. Thus

$$|a_{11}| = a_{11} \tag{8.39}$$

where the vertical lines indicate a determinant, and not absolute value.

A second-order determinant has 4 elements and its value is defined by

$$\begin{vmatrix} a_{11} & a_{12} \\ a_{21} & a_{22} \end{vmatrix} = a_{11}a_{22} - a_{12}a_{21} \tag{8.40}$$

The value of a third-order determinant is defined by

$$\begin{vmatrix} a_{11} & a_{12} & a_{13} \\ a_{21} & a_{22} & a_{23} \\ a_{31} & a_{32} & a_{33} \end{vmatrix} = a_{11} \begin{vmatrix} a_{22} & a_{23} \\ a_{32} & a_{33} \end{vmatrix} - a_{12} \begin{vmatrix} a_{21} & a_{23} \\ a_{31} & a_{33} \end{vmatrix} + a_{13} \begin{vmatrix} a_{21} & a_{22} \\ a_{31} & a_{32} \end{vmatrix} \tag{8.41}$$

$$= a_{11}a_{22}a_{33} - a_{11}a_{32}a_{23} - a_{12}a_{21}a_{33} + a_{12}a_{31}a_{23}$$

$$+ a_{13}a_{21}a_{32} - a_{13}a_{31}a_{22} \tag{8.42}$$

A third-order determinant is evaluated by writing down the elements of the top row with alternating plus and minus signs, and multiplying each element by a certain second-order determinant; the second-order determinant that multiplies a given element is found by crossing out the row and column (of the third-order determinant) in which that element appears. The $(n-1)$-order determinant obtained by striking out the ith row and the jth column (of the nth-order determinant) is called the *minor* of the element a_{ij}. We define the *cofactor* of a_{ij} as the minor of a_{ij} times the factor $(-1)^{i+j}$. Thus (8.41) states that the third-order determinant is evaluated by multiplying each element of the top row by its cofactor and adding up the three products. [Note that (8.40) conforms to this evaluation by means of cofactors, since the cofactor of a_{11} in (8.40) is a_{22}, and the cofactor of a_{12} is $-a_{21}$.] A numerical example is

$$\begin{vmatrix} 5 & 10 & 2 \\ 0.1 & 3 & 1 \\ 0 & 4 & 4 \end{vmatrix} = 5 \begin{vmatrix} 3 & 1 \\ 4 & 4 \end{vmatrix} - 10 \begin{vmatrix} 0.1 & 1 \\ 0 & 4 \end{vmatrix} + 2 \begin{vmatrix} 0.1 & 3 \\ 0 & 4 \end{vmatrix}$$

$$= 5(8) - 10(0.4) + 2(0.4) = 36.8$$

We denote the minor of a_{ij} by M_{ij} and the cofactor of a_{ij} by C_{ij}. We have

$$C_{ij} = (-1)^{i+j} M_{ij} \tag{8.43}$$

The expansion (8.41) of the third-order determinant can be written as

$$\det(a_{ij}) = \begin{vmatrix} a_{11} & a_{12} & a_{13} \\ a_{21} & a_{22} & a_{23} \\ a_{31} & a_{32} & a_{33} \end{vmatrix} = a_{11}C_{11} + a_{12}C_{12} + a_{13}C_{13} \tag{8.44}$$

Let us note that we may expand the third-order determinant by using the elements of any row and the corresponding cofactors. For example, using the second row to expand the third-order determinant, we have

$$\det(a_{ij}) = a_{21}C_{21} + a_{22}C_{22} + a_{23}C_{23} \tag{8.45}$$

$$\det(a_{ij}) = -a_{21} \begin{vmatrix} a_{12} & a_{13} \\ a_{32} & a_{33} \end{vmatrix} + a_{22} \begin{vmatrix} a_{11} & a_{13} \\ a_{31} & a_{33} \end{vmatrix} - a_{23} \begin{vmatrix} a_{11} & a_{12} \\ a_{31} & a_{32} \end{vmatrix} \tag{8.46}$$

and expansion of the second-order determinants shows that (8.46) is equal to (8.42). We may also use the elements of any column and the corresponding cofactors to expand the determinant, as can be readily verified. Thus, for the third-order determinant, we can write

$$\det(a_{ij}) = a_{k1}C_{k1} + a_{k2}C_{k2} + a_{k3}C_{k3} = \sum_{l=1}^{3} a_{kl}C_{kl}, \quad k = 1 \text{ or } 2 \text{ or } 3$$

$$\det(a_{ij}) = a_{1k}C_{1k} + a_{2k}C_{2k} + a_{3k}C_{3k} = \sum_{l=1}^{3} a_{lk}C_{lk}, \quad k = 1 \text{ or } 2 \text{ or } 3$$

The first expansion uses one of the rows, while the second uses one of the columns.

We now define determinants of higher order by an analogous row (or column) expansion. Thus the fourth-order determinant is defined by

$$\det(a_{ij}) = \sum_{l=1}^{4} a_{kl}C_{kl}, \quad k = 1 \text{ or } 2 \text{ or } 3 \text{ or } 4 \tag{8.47}$$

$$\det(a_{ij}) = \sum_{l=1}^{4} a_{lk}C_{lk}, \quad k = 1 \text{ or } 2 \text{ or } 3 \text{ or } 4 \tag{8.48}$$

Extending the definition to the nth-order determinant, we have

$$\det(a_{ij}) = \sum_{l=1}^{n} a_{kl} C_{kl} = \sum_{l=1}^{n} a_{lk} C_{lk}, \qquad k = 1 \text{ or } 2 \text{ or } \cdots \text{ or } n \qquad \textbf{(8.49)}$$

We now state some theorems.[1]

I. If every element of a row (or column) of a determinant is zero, the value of the determinant is zero.

II. Interchanging any two rows (or columns) multiplies the value of a determinant by -1.

III. If any two rows (or columns) of a determinant are identical, the determinant has the value zero.

IV. Multiplication of each element of any one row (or any one column) by some constant k, multiplies the value of the determinant by k.

V. Addition to each element of one row, of the same constant multiple of the corresponding element of another row, leaves the value of the determinant unchanged. (This theorem also applies to the addition of a multiple of one column to another column.)

VI. The interchange of all corresponding rows and columns leaves the value of the determinant unchanged.

These theorems are useful in evaluating higher-order determinants. An example is the evaluation of

$$B = \begin{vmatrix} 1 & 2 & 3 & 4 \\ 4 & 1 & 2 & 3 \\ 3 & 4 & 1 & 2 \\ 2 & 3 & 4 & 1 \end{vmatrix} \qquad \textbf{(8.50)}$$

Addition of -2 times the elements of row one to the corresponding elements of row four, changes row four to $0, -1, -2, -7$. Then, addition of -3 times row one to row three, and -4 times row one to row two gives

$$B = \begin{vmatrix} 1 & 2 & 3 & 4 \\ 0 & -7 & -10 & -13 \\ 0 & -2 & -8 & -10 \\ 0 & -1 & -2 & -7 \end{vmatrix} = 1 \begin{vmatrix} -7 & -10 & -13 \\ -2 & -8 & -10 \\ -1 & -2 & -7 \end{vmatrix}$$

where we expanded B in terms of elements of the first column. Subtracting twice row three from row two and seven times row three from row one, we have

$$B = \begin{vmatrix} 0 & 4 & 36 \\ 0 & -4 & 4 \\ -1 & -2 & -7 \end{vmatrix} = (-1) \begin{vmatrix} 4 & 36 \\ -4 & 4 \end{vmatrix} = -(16 + 144) = -160 \qquad \textbf{(8.51)}$$

The determinant (8.50) is a special kind, called a *circulant*. A *circulant* (or *cyclic determinant*) has only n independent elements—they appear in the first row,

---

[1] For proofs, see *Sokolnikoff and Redheffer*, pp. 702–707.

and succeeding rows are formed by successive cyclic permutations of these elements. The nth-order circulant $C(a_1, a_2, ..., a_n)$ is

$$C(a_1, a_2, a_3, ..., a_n) = \begin{vmatrix} a_1 & a_2 & a_3 & \cdots & a_n \\ a_n & a_1 & a_2 & \cdots & a_{n-1} \\ a_{n-1} & a_n & a_1 & \cdots & a_{n-2} \\ \cdot & \cdot & \cdot & \cdots & \cdot \\ a_2 & a_3 & a_4 & \cdots & a_1 \end{vmatrix} \quad (8.52)$$

It can be shown[2] that

$$C(a_1, a_2, a_3, ..., a_n) = \prod_{k=1}^{n} (a_1 + \omega_k a_2 + \omega_k^2 a_3 + \cdots + \omega_k^{n-1} a_n) \quad (8.53)$$

where $\omega_1, \omega_2, ..., \omega_n$ are the n different nth roots of unity [Eq. (1.32)]:

$$\omega_k = e^{2\pi i k/n}, \quad k = 1, 2, ..., n, \quad i = \sqrt{-1} \quad (8.54)$$

The definition of the product notation used in (8.53) is

$$\prod_{k=1}^{n} b_k = b_1 b_2 b_3 \cdots b_n$$

As an illustration of (8.53), let us use it to evaluate the determinant (8.50). This is a fourth-order determinant and the 4 fourth roots of unity are $1, -1, i, -i$. We have

$$C(1, 2, 3, 4) = (1 + 1 \cdot 2 + 1 \cdot 3 + 1 \cdot 4)(1 - 1 \cdot 2 + 1 \cdot 3 - 1 \cdot 4)$$

$$\times (1 + i \cdot 2 - 1 \cdot 3 - i \cdot 4)(1 - i \cdot 2 - 1 \cdot 3 + i \cdot 4)$$

$$= -160$$

which checks with (8.51). Circulants occur in the quantum chemistry of molecules like benzene.

The diagonal of a determinant that runs from the top left to the lower right is the *principal diagonal*. For a determinant all of whose elements are zero except those on the principal diagonal, we have

$$\begin{vmatrix} a_{11} & 0 & 0 & \cdots & 0 \\ 0 & a_{22} & 0 & \cdots & 0 \\ 0 & 0 & a_{33} & \cdots & 0 \\ \cdot & \cdot & \cdot & \cdots & \cdot \\ 0 & 0 & 0 & \cdots & a_{nn} \end{vmatrix} = a_{11} \begin{vmatrix} a_{22} & 0 & \cdots & 0 \\ 0 & a_{33} & \cdots & 0 \\ \cdot & \cdot & \cdots & \cdot \\ 0 & 0 & \cdots & a_{nn} \end{vmatrix}$$

$$= a_{11} a_{22} \begin{vmatrix} a_{33} & 0 & \cdots & 0 \\ 0 & a_{44} & \cdots & 0 \\ \cdot & \cdot & \cdots & \cdot \\ 0 & 0 & \cdots & a_{nn} \end{vmatrix}$$

$$= \cdots = a_{11} a_{22} a_{33} \cdots a_{nn} \quad (8.55)$$

and this determinant equals the product of the diagonal elements.

---

[2] T. Muir, *A Treatise on the Theory of Determinants*, Dover, New York, 1960, pp. 442–445.

A determinant in which all elements are zero except the elements of the principal diagonal and the elements immediately above and below this diagonal is called a *continuant*. (The name arises from a relation between this type of determinant and continued fractions.) There is a special kind of continuant, whose value we will need, in which the elements immediately above the principal diagonal are all equal, those on the principal diagonal are all equal, and those immediately below the principal diagonal are all equal. It can be shown [3] that the nth-order continuant of this form has the value

$$\begin{vmatrix} a & b & 0 & 0 & \cdot & \cdot & \cdot & \cdot & 0 \\ c & a & b & 0 & \cdot & \cdot & \cdot & \cdot & 0 \\ 0 & c & a & b & \cdot & \cdot & \cdot & \cdot & 0 \\ \cdot & \cdot & \cdot & \cdot & \cdot & \cdot & \cdot & \cdot & \cdot \\ 0 & \cdot & \cdot & \cdot & \cdot & 0 & c & a & b \\ 0 & \cdot & \cdot & \cdot & \cdot & 0 & 0 & c & a \end{vmatrix}_n = \prod_{j=1}^{n}\left[a - 2(bc)^{1/2}\cos\left(\frac{j\pi}{n+1}\right)\right] \quad (8.56)$$

The subscript on the determinant denotes its order.

We say that a determinant is in *diagonal form* when the only nonzero elements are those on the principal diagonal. We showed that a determinant in diagonal form is equal to the product of the diagonal elements. We now consider a determinant whose only nonzero elements occur in square blocks centered about the principal diagonal. Such a determinant is in *block-diagonal form*. We assert that if we regard each square block as a determinant, then a block-diagonal determinant is equal to the product of all the blocks. For example

$$\begin{vmatrix} a & b & 0 & 0 & 0 & 0 \\ c & d & 0 & 0 & 0 & 0 \\ 0 & 0 & e & 0 & 0 & 0 \\ 0 & 0 & 0 & f & g & h \\ 0 & 0 & 0 & i & j & k \\ 0 & 0 & 0 & l & m & n \end{vmatrix} = \begin{vmatrix} a & b \\ c & d \end{vmatrix} (e) \begin{vmatrix} f & g & h \\ i & j & k \\ l & m & n \end{vmatrix} \quad (8.57)$$

(The dashed lines outline the blocks.) The proof of (8.57) is simple. Expanding in terms of elements of the top row, we have

$$\begin{vmatrix} a & b & 0 & \cdots & 0 \\ c & d & 0 & \cdots & 0 \\ 0 & 0 & e & \cdots & \cdot \\ \vdots & \vdots & \vdots & \vdots & \vdots \\ 0 & 0 & \cdot & \cdots & \cdot \end{vmatrix} = a \begin{vmatrix} d & 0 & \cdots & 0 \\ 0 & e & \cdots & \cdot \\ \vdots & \vdots & \vdots & \vdots \\ 0 & \cdot & \cdots & \cdot \end{vmatrix} - b \begin{vmatrix} c & 0 & \cdots & 0 \\ 0 & e & \cdots & \cdot \\ \vdots & \vdots & \vdots & \vdots \\ 0 & \cdot & \cdots & \cdot \end{vmatrix}$$

and expanding the two determinants on the right side of this equation in terms of

---

[3] T. Muir, *The Theory of Determinants in the Historical Order of Development*, Dover, New York, 1960, vol. 4, p. 401.

elements of the top rows, we get

$$
ad \begin{vmatrix} e & \cdot & \cdot & \cdot \\ \cdot & \cdot & \cdot & \cdot \\ \cdot & \cdot & \cdot & \cdot \\ \cdot & \cdot & \cdot & \cdot \end{vmatrix} - bc \begin{vmatrix} e & \cdot & \cdot & \cdot \\ \cdot & \cdot & \cdot & \cdot \\ \cdot & \cdot & \cdot & \cdot \\ \cdot & \cdot & \cdot & \cdot \end{vmatrix} = \begin{vmatrix} a & b \\ c & d \end{vmatrix} \begin{vmatrix} e & \cdot & \cdot & \cdot \\ \cdot & \cdot & \cdot & \cdot \\ \cdot & \cdot & \cdot & \cdot \\ \cdot & \cdot & \cdot & \cdot \end{vmatrix}
\tag{8.58}
$$

A similar expansion of the second determinant on the right side of (8.58) completes the proof.

8.4 Simultaneous Linear Equations

Determinants find application in solving systems of linear equations. Consider a system of n linear equations in n unknowns:

$$
\begin{aligned}
a_{11}x_1 + a_{12}x_2 + \cdots + a_{1n}x_n &= b_1 \\
a_{21}x_1 + a_{22}x_2 + \cdots + a_{2n}x_n &= b_2 \\
\cdot \quad \cdot \quad \cdot \quad \cdot \quad &\cdots \quad \cdot \quad \cdot \quad \cdot \\
a_{n1}x_1 + a_{n2}x_2 + \cdots + a_{nn}x_n &= b_n
\end{aligned}
\tag{8.59}
$$

where the a's and b's are known constants, and $x_1, x_2, ..., x_n$ are the unknowns.

If at least one of the b's in (8.59) is not zero, we have a system of *inhomogeneous* linear equations. Such a system can be solved by Cramer's rule.[4] Let $\det(a_{ij})$ be the determinant of the coefficients of the unknowns in (8.59). Cramer's rule states that x_k ($k = 1, 2, ..., n$) is equal to the determinant obtained by replacing the kth column of $\det(a_{ij})$ with the elements $b_1, b_2, ..., b_n$, divided by $\det(a_{ij})$:

$$
x_k = \frac{\begin{vmatrix} a_{11} & a_{12} & \cdots & a_{1,k-1} & b_1 & a_{1,k+1} & \cdots & a_{1n} \\ a_{21} & a_{22} & \cdots & a_{2,k-1} & b_2 & a_{2,k+1} & \cdots & a_{2n} \\ \cdot & \cdot & \cdots & \cdot & & \cdot & \cdots & \cdot \\ a_{n1} & a_{n2} & \cdots & a_{n,k-1} & b_k & a_{n,k+1} & \cdots & a_{nn} \end{vmatrix}}{\begin{vmatrix} a_{11} & a_{12} & \cdots & a_{1n} \\ a_{21} & a_{22} & \cdots & a_{2n} \\ \cdot & \cdot & \cdots & \cdot \\ a_{n1} & a_{n2} & \cdots & a_{nn} \end{vmatrix}}, \qquad k = 1, 2, ..., n
\tag{8.60}
$$

For example, application of Cramer's rule to the system

$$
2x + 10y = 9
$$

$$
1.5x - 6y = 0
$$

---

[4] For a proof, see *Sokolnikoff and Redheffer*, p. 708.

gives

$$x = \frac{\begin{vmatrix} 9 & 10 \\ 0 & -6 \end{vmatrix}}{\begin{vmatrix} 2 & 10 \\ 1.5 & -6 \end{vmatrix}} = 2, \qquad y = \frac{\begin{vmatrix} 2 & 9 \\ 1.5 & 0 \end{vmatrix}}{\begin{vmatrix} 2 & 10 \\ 1.5 & -6 \end{vmatrix}} = 0.5$$

Cramer's rule is of considerable theoretical significance, but for actually solving a given set of simultaneous equations, successive elimination of unknowns is much more efficient. One systematic procedure (Gauss reduction) is: Divide each equation in (8.59) by the coefficient of x_1 in that equation; then subtract the first equation from every other equation; this eliminates x_1 from all equations but the first. Now divide each of equations 2, ..., n by the coefficient of x_2 in that equation and then subtract equation 2 from each of equations 3, ..., n, thereby eliminating x_2 from all equations but the first and second. Continue in this manner. Ultimately equation n will contain only x_n, equation $n-1$ only x_{n-1} and x_n, etc. The value of x_n from equation n is substituted into equation $n-1$ to give x_{n-1}, etc.

Now we consider the case where all the b's in (8.59) are zero. We have a system of linear *homogeneous* equations:

$$a_{11}x_1 + a_{12}x_2 + \cdots + a_{1n}x_n = 0$$
$$a_{21}x_1 + a_{22}x_2 + \cdots + a_{2n}x_n = 0$$
$$\cdot \quad \cdot \quad \cdot \quad \cdot \quad \cdot \cdots \cdot \quad \cdot \quad \cdot \quad \quad \cdot \tag{8.61}$$
$$a_{n1}x_1 + a_{n2}x_2 + \cdots + a_{nn}x_n = 0$$

One obvious solution of (8.61) is $x_1 = x_2 = \cdots = x_n = 0$, which is called the *trivial solution*. If the determinant of the coefficients in (8.61) is not equal to zero, $\det(a_{ij}) \neq 0$, then we can use Cramer's rule (8.60) to solve for the unknowns, and we find $x_k = 0$, $k = 1, 2, ..., n$, since the determinant in the numerator of (8.60) has a column all of whose elements are zero. Thus when $\det(a_{ij}) \neq 0$, the only solution is the trivial solution (which is of no interest). To have a nontrivial solution of a system of n linear homogeneous equations in n unknowns, the determinant of the coefficients must be zero. It can also be shown [5] that this condition is sufficient to insure the existence of a nontrivial solution. We therefore have the extremely important theorem: *A system of n linear homogeneous equations in n unknowns has a nontrivial solution if and only if the determinant of the coefficients is zero.*

Suppose that $\det(a_{ij}) = 0$, so that (8.61) has a nontrivial solution. How do we go about finding it? With $\det(a_{ij}) = 0$, Cramer's rule (8.60) gives $x_k = 0/0$, $k = 1, ..., n$, which is indeterminate. Thus Cramer's rule is of no immediate help. We also observe that if $x_1 = d_1$, $x_2 = d_2$, ..., $x_n = d_n$ is a solution of (8.61), then so is $x_1 = cd_1$, $x_2 = cd_2$, ..., $x_n = cd_n$, where c is an arbitrary constant. This is easily seen since

$$a_{11}cd_1 + a_{12}cd_2 + \cdots + a_{1n}cd_n = c(a_{11}d_1 + a_{12}d_2 + \cdots + a_{1n}d_n)$$
$$= c \cdot 0 = 0$$

---

[5] T. L. Wade, *The Algebra of Vectors and Matrices*, Addison-Wesley, 1951, p. 146.

etc. Therefore, the solution to the linear homogeneous system of equations will contain an arbitrary constant, and we cannot determine a unique value for each unknown. To solve (8.61), we therefore assign an arbitrary value to any one of the unknowns, say x_n; we set $x_n = c$, where c is an arbitrary constant. Having assigned a value to x_n, we transfer the last term in each of the equations of (8.61) to the right-hand side to get

$$
\begin{aligned}
a_{11}x_1 &+ a_{12}x_2 + \cdots + a_{1,n-1}x_{n-1} &= -a_{1,n}c \\
a_{21}x_1 &+ a_{22}x_2 + \cdots + a_{2,n-1}x_{n-1} &= -a_{2,n}c \\
&\quad\cdot\quad\cdot\qquad\qquad\cdot\quad\cdot\qquad\qquad\cdot\quad\cdot \\
a_{n-1,1}x_1 &+ a_{n-1,2}x_2 + \cdots + a_{n-1,n-1}x_{n-1} &= -a_{n-1,n}c \\
a_{n1}x_1 &+ a_{n2}x_2 + \cdots + a_{n,n-1}x_{n-1} &= -a_{nn}c
\end{aligned}
\tag{8.62}
$$

We now have n equations in $n-1$ unknowns, which is one more equation than we need. We therefore discard any one of the equations of (8.62), say the last one. This gives a system of $n-1$ linear *inhomogeneous* equations in $n-1$ unknowns. We can then apply Cramer's rule (8.60) to solve for $x_1, x_2, \ldots, x_{n-1}$. Since the constants on the right side of the equations in (8.62) all contain the factor c, Theorem IV in Section 8.3 shows that all the unknowns contain this arbitrary constant as a factor. The form of the solution is therefore

$$
x_1 = ce_1, \; x_2 = ce_2, \ldots, x_{n-1} = ce_{n-1}, \; x_n = c
\tag{8.63}
$$

where $e_1, \ldots, e_{n-1}$ are numbers, and c is an arbitrary constant.

There is one possible hitch to the procedure just outlined. It might happen that the determinant of the coefficients of the inhomogeneous system of $n-1$ equations in $n-1$ unknowns [(8.62) with the last equation omitted] is zero. In this case, Cramer's rule would have a zero in the denominator and would be of no use. We could attempt to get around this difficulty by initially assigning the arbitrary value to another of the unknowns rather than to x_n. We could also try discarding some other equation of (8.62), rather than the last one. What we are looking for, really, is a nonvanishing determinant of order $n-1$, formed from the determinant of the coefficients of the system (8.61) by striking out a row and a column. If such a determinant exists, then by the procedure given, with the right choice of the equation to be discarded and the right choice of the unknown to be assigned an arbitrary value, we can solve the system and will obtain solutions of the form (8.63). If no such determinant exists, we must assign arbitrary values to two of the unknowns and attempt to proceed from there. Thus, it might happen that the solution to (8.61) would contain two (or even more) arbitrary constants.

8.5 Linear Variation Functions

A special kind of variation function widely used in the study of molecules is the linear variation function. A *linear variation function* is a linear combination of n linearly independent functions $f_1, f_2, \ldots, f_n$:

$$
\varphi = c_1 f_1 + c_2 f_2 + \cdots + c_n f_n = \sum_{j=1}^{n} c_j f_j
\tag{8.64}
$$

where φ is the trial variation function and the coefficients c_j are parameters to be determined by minimizing the variational integral. The functions f_j must satisfy the boundary conditions of the problem. We will restrict ourselves to *real* φ so that the c_j's and f_j's are all real.

We now apply the variation theorem (8.13). For the real linear variation function we have

$$\int \varphi^* \varphi \, d\tau = \int \sum_{j=1}^{n} c_j f_j \sum_{k=1}^{n} c_k f_k \, d\tau = \sum_{j=1}^{n} \sum_{k=1}^{n} c_j c_k \int f_j f_k \, d\tau \qquad (8.65)$$

We define the *overlap integral* S_{jk} as

$$S_{jk} \equiv \int f_j^* f_k \, d\tau \qquad (8.66)$$

We have

$$\int \varphi^* \varphi \, d\tau = \sum_{j=1}^{n} \sum_{k=1}^{n} c_j c_k S_{jk} \qquad (8.67)$$

Note that S_{jk} is not necessarily equal to δ_{jk}, since there is no reason to suppose that the functions f_j are mutually orthogonal. They are not necessarily the eigenfunctions of any operator. For the numerator of (8.13), we have

$$\int \varphi^* \hat{H} \varphi \, d\tau = \int \sum_{j=1}^{n} c_j f_j \hat{H} \sum_{k=1}^{n} c_k f_k \, d\tau = \sum_{j=1}^{n} \sum_{k=1}^{n} c_j c_k \int f_j \hat{H} f_k \, d\tau \qquad (8.68)$$

and using the abbreviation

$$H_{jk} \equiv \int f_j^* \hat{H} f_k \, d\tau \qquad (8.69)$$

we write

$$\int \varphi^* \hat{H} \varphi \, d\tau = \sum_{j=1}^{n} \sum_{k=1}^{n} c_j c_k H_{jk} \qquad (8.70)$$

The variational integral W is

$$W \equiv \frac{\int \varphi^* \hat{H} \varphi \, d\tau}{\int \varphi^* \varphi \, d\tau} = \frac{\sum_{j=1}^{n} \sum_{k=1}^{n} c_j c_k H_{jk}}{\sum_{j=1}^{n} \sum_{k=1}^{n} c_j c_k S_{jk}} \qquad (8.71)$$

$$W \sum_{j=1}^{n} \sum_{k=1}^{n} c_j c_k S_{jk} = \sum_{j=1}^{n} \sum_{k=1}^{n} c_j c_k H_{jk} \qquad (8.72)$$

We now minimize W, so as to approach as closely as we can to E_0 ($W \geqslant E_0$). The variational integral W is a function of the n independent variables $c_1, c_2, ..., c_n$:

$$W = W(c_1, c_2, ..., c_n) \qquad (8.73)$$

A necessary condition for a minimum in W is that its partial derivatives with respect to each of the variables must be zero.

$$\frac{\partial W}{\partial c_i} = 0, \qquad i = 1, 2, ..., n \qquad (8.74)$$

We now differentiate (8.72) partially with respect to each c_i to obtain n equations:

$$\frac{\partial W}{\partial c_i} \sum_{j=1}^n \sum_{k=1}^n c_j c_k S_{jk} + W \frac{\partial}{\partial c_i} \sum_{j=1}^n \sum_{k=1}^n c_j c_k S_{jk} = \frac{\partial}{\partial c_i} \sum_{j=1}^n \sum_{k=1}^n c_j c_k H_{jk}, \qquad i = 1, 2, ..., n$$

(8.75)

Now

$$\frac{\partial}{\partial c_i} \sum_{j=1}^n \sum_{k=1}^n c_j c_k S_{jk} = \sum_{j=1}^n \sum_{k=1}^n \left[\frac{\partial}{\partial c_i} (c_j c_k) \right] S_{jk}$$

$$= \sum_{j=1}^n \sum_{k=1}^n \left(c_k \frac{\partial c_j}{\partial c_i} + c_j \frac{\partial c_k}{\partial c_i} \right) S_{jk}$$

(8.76)

The c_j's are independent variables, and therefore

$$\frac{\partial c_j}{\partial c_i} = 0 \;\; \text{if } j \neq i, \qquad \frac{\partial c_j}{\partial c_i} = 1 \;\; \text{if } j = i$$

(8.77)

$$\frac{\partial c_j}{\partial c_i} = \delta_{ij}$$

(8.78)

We then have

$$\frac{\partial}{\partial c_i} \sum_{j=1}^n \sum_{k=1}^n c_j c_k S_{jk} = \sum_{k=1}^n \sum_{j=1}^n c_k \delta_{ij} S_{jk} + \sum_{j=1}^n \sum_{k=1}^n c_j \delta_{ik} S_{jk}$$

$$= \sum_{k=1}^n c_k S_{ik} + \sum_{j=1}^n c_j S_{ji}$$

(8.79)

where we have evaluated one of the sums in each double summation using Eq. (7.53). Now, according to Eq. (7.5), we have

$$S_{ji} = S_{ij}^* = S_{ij}$$

(8.80)

where the last equality follows because we are dealing with real functions. Hence,

$$\frac{\partial}{\partial c_i} \sum_{j=1}^n \sum_{k=1}^n c_j c_k S_{jk} = \sum_{k=1}^n c_k S_{ik} + \sum_{j=1}^n c_j S_{ij} = \sum_{k=1}^n c_k S_{ik} + \sum_{k=1}^n c_k S_{ik}$$

$$\frac{\partial}{\partial c_i} \sum_{j=1}^n \sum_{k=1}^n c_j c_k S_{jk} = 2 \sum_{k=1}^n c_k S_{ik}$$

(8.81)

By replacing S_{jk} by H_{jk} in each of these manipulations, we get

$$\frac{\partial}{\partial c_i} \sum_{j=1}^n \sum_{k=1}^n c_j c_k H_{jk} = 2 \sum_{k=1}^n c_k H_{ik}$$

(8.82)

This result depends on the fact that

$$H_{ji} = H_{ij}^* = H_{ij}$$

(8.83)

which is true because $\hat{H}$ is a Hermitian operator, and we are dealing with real functions and a real Hamiltonian.

Substituting Eqs. (8.74), (8.81), and (8.82) in (8.75), we have

$$2W \sum_{k=1}^{n} c_k S_{ik} = 2 \sum_{k=1}^{n} c_k H_{ik}, \qquad i = 1, 2, ..., n \qquad (8.84)$$

$$\sum_{k=1}^{n} [(H_{ik} - S_{ik} W) c_k] = 0, \qquad i = 1, 2, ..., n \qquad (8.85)$$

We have n simultaneous linear homogeneous equations in the n unknowns $c_1, c_2, ..., c_n$. Thus, for $n = 2$:

$$(H_{11} - S_{11} W) c_1 + (H_{12} - S_{12} W) c_2 = 0$$
$$(H_{21} - S_{21} W) c_1 + (H_{22} - S_{22} W) c_2 = 0 \qquad (8.86)$$

From the theorem of the last section, to have a solution of the system of linear homogeneous equations besides $0 = c_1 = c_2 = \cdots = c_n$ (which would make the variation function φ zero), the determinant of the coefficients must vanish. For $n = 2$, we have

$$\begin{vmatrix} H_{11} - S_{11} W & H_{12} - S_{12} W \\ H_{21} - S_{21} W & H_{22} - S_{22} W \end{vmatrix} = 0 \qquad (8.87)$$

and for the general case $\det (H_{ij} - S_{ij} W) = 0$, or

$$\begin{vmatrix} H_{11} - S_{11} W & H_{12} - S_{12} W & \cdots & H_{1n} - S_{1n} W \\ H_{21} - S_{21} W & H_{22} - S_{22} W & \cdots & H_{2n} - S_{2n} W \\ \vdots & \vdots & \ddots & \vdots \\ H_{n1} - S_{n1} W & H_{n2} - S_{n2} W & \cdots & H_{nn} - S_{nn} W \end{vmatrix} = 0 \qquad (8.88)$$

Expansion of the determinant in (8.88) gives an algebraic equation of degree n in the unknown W, with n roots (which may be shown to be real). Arranging these roots in order of increasing value, we denote them as

$$W_0 \leqslant W_1 \leqslant W_2 \leqslant \cdots \leqslant W_{n-1} \qquad (8.89)$$

If we number the states of the system in order of increasing energy we have

$$E_0 \leqslant E_1 \leqslant E_2 \leqslant \cdots \leqslant E_{n-1} \leqslant E_n \leqslant E_{n+1} \leqslant \cdots$$

where the E's denote the true energies of various states. From the variation theorem we know that

$$E_0 \leqslant W_0 \qquad (8.90)$$

Moreover it can be proved that[6]

$$E_1 \leqslant W_1, E_2 \leqslant W_2, ..., E_{n-1} \leqslant W_{n-1} \qquad (8.91)$$

In other words, the linear variation method provides upper bounds to the energies of the first n states of the system; we use the roots $W_0, W_1, ..., W_{n-1}$ as approximations to the energies of the n lowest states. If we want approximations to the energies of

---

[6] J. K. L. MacDonald, *Phys. Rev.*, **43**, 830 (1933); R. H. Young, *Int. J. Quantum Chem.*, **6**, 596 (1972).

more states, we increase the number of functions f_k in the trial function φ. It can also be shown that increasing the number of functions f_k will increase (or cause no change in) the accuracy of the previously obtained energies. A major difficulty in this method is in solving Eq. (8.88) for W. For example, we might want to include as many as 100 terms in the variation function. Solving a 100th-degree equation by hand is out of the question. The advent of the electronic computer after World War II has been a godsend for the quantum chemist.

If we want an approximation to the wave function of, say, the ground state, we take the value of W_0 we have found and substitute it in the set of equations (8.85), which we then solve for the coefficients $c_1, c_2, ..., c_n$. As stated in the previous section, all we can determine is the ratio of coefficients. We solve for $c_2, ..., c_n$ in terms of c_1, and then determine c_1 by normalization. Use of higher roots of (8.88) in (8.85) gives approximations to excited state wave functions. We can prove (Problem 8.15) that the approximate wave functions obtained form an orthogonal set.

Solution of (8.88) (which is called the *secular equation*) is facilitated by having as many of the determinant's elements equal to zero as possible. If the functions f_j are orthogonal, the off-diagonal S_{ij}'s vanish. Some of the off-diagonal H_{ij}'s can frequently be made to vanish by choosing the functions f_j as eigenfunctions of some operator $\hat{A}$ that commutes with $\hat{H}$; if f_i and f_j correspond to different eigenvalues of $\hat{A}$, then H_{ij} vanishes (Section 7.4). We shall use this method in Chapter 15 to simplify molecular variational calculations. (See also Section 9.6.)

Equations (8.85) and (8.88) are also valid when the restriction that the variation function be real is removed (Problem 8.12).

PROBLEMS

8.1 For the ground state of the harmonic oscillator, use the trial variation function (8.27) and show that minimization of the variational integral gives $b = \frac{1}{2}$, and that Eq. (8.28) holds.

8.2 Consider an integral whose integrand is a function of a parameter p. The integral itself is a function of this parameter and we have

$$\int_a^b f(x, p)\, dx = G(p)$$

Provided the integrand is reasonably well-behaved, we may differentiate under the integral sign to evaluate $G'(p)$, and we have (*Taylor and Mann*, p. 582):

$$G'(p) = \int_a^b \frac{\partial f(x, p)}{\partial p}\, dx$$

where a and b are constants. Use this theorem to derive Eq. (A.6) from (A.5).

8.3 Apply the function of Eq. (7.56) as a trial variation function for the ground state of the particle in a box. Note that $f''(x)$ is infinite at $x = \frac{1}{2}l$, because of the discontinuity in $f'(x)$ at this point. Therefore in evaluating $\int f^* \hat{H} f\, dx$ we run into difficulty in evaluating the integral of ff''. One way around this problem is to first show that

$$\int_0^l ff'' \, dx = -\int_0^l (f')^2 \, dx = -\int_0^{l/2} (f')^2 \, dx - \int_{l/2}^l (f')^2 \, dx \qquad \text{(8.92)}$$

for any function obeying the boundary conditions. Then using the expression on the right of (8.92) we can calculate the variational integral. Prove (8.92) and then calculate the percent error in the ground-state energy, using this triangular function. Note that there is no parameter in this trial function. [If you are ambitious, try this alternative procedure: Note that $f'(x)$ involves the Heaviside step function (Section 7.7) and therefore $f''(x)$ involves the Dirac delta function. Use the properties of the delta function to evaluate $\int_0^l ff'' \, dx$ and find the percent error using this triangular function.]

Functions with discontinuities in their first derivatives have been used as trial variation functions in atomic and molecular quantum mechanics.[7]

8.4 If we use the normalized trial variation function

$$\varphi = \left(\frac{3}{l^3}\right)^{1/2} x, \qquad 0 \leqslant x \leqslant l$$

for the particle in a one-dimensional box, we find that the variational integral has the value zero, which is *less* than the true ground-state energy. What is wrong?

8.5 (a) For the ground state of the hydrogen atom, use the Gaussian trial function

$$\varphi = e^{-cr^2/a_0^2} \qquad \text{(8.93)}$$

Find the optimum value of c, and the percent error in the energy. (Gaussian variational functions are often used in molecular quantum mechanics; see Section 15.3.) (b) Multiply the function (8.93) by the spherical harmonic Y_2^0 and then minimize the variational integral. This yields an upper bound to the energy of which hydrogen-atom state?

8.6 Prove that the value of a determinant all of whose elements below the principal diagonal are zero is equal to the product of the diagonal elements.

8.7 Evaluate

$$\begin{vmatrix} 2 & 5 & 1 & 3 \\ 8 & 0 & 4 & -1 \\ 6 & 6 & 6 & 1 \\ 5 & -2 & -2 & 2 \end{vmatrix}$$

8.8 (a) Consider some permutation of the integers $1, 2, 3, \ldots, n$. The permutation is an *even permutation* if an even number of interchanges of pairs of integers restores the permutation to the natural order $1, 2, 3, \ldots, n$. An *odd permutation* requires an odd number of interchanges of pairs to reach the natural order. For example, the permutation 3124 is even, since two interchanges restore it to the natural order: $3124 \rightarrow 1324 \rightarrow 1234$. Write down and classify (even or odd) all permutations of 123. (b) Verify that the definition (8.42) of the third-order determinant is equivalent to

$$\begin{vmatrix} a_{11} & a_{12} & a_{13} \\ a_{21} & a_{22} & a_{23} \\ a_{31} & a_{32} & a_{33} \end{vmatrix} = \sum (\pm 1) a_{1i} a_{2j} a_{3k}$$

---

[7] H. M. James and A. S. Coolidge, *Phys. Rev.*, **49**, 688 (1936); M. J. S. Dewar and C. Wulfman, *J. Chem. Phys.*, **29**, 158 (1958); L. C. Snyder and R. G. Parr, *ibid.*, **34**, 1661 (1961); C. A. Coulson and C. S. Sharma, *Proc. Roy. Soc.*, **272A**, 1 (1963).

where ijk is one of the permutations of the integers 123, the sum is over the 3! different permutations of these integers, and the sign of each term is plus or minus, depending on whether the permutation is even or odd. (c) How would we define the nth-order determinant using this type of definition?

8.9 Solve each set of simultaneous equations:

(a)
$$x + 2y + 3z = 0$$
$$3x + y + 2z = 0$$
$$2x + 3y + z = 0$$

(b)
$$x + 2y + 3z = 0$$
$$x - y + z = 0$$
$$7x - y + 11z = 0$$

8.10 How many terms are there in the expansion of an nth-order determinant?

8.11 Solve the second-order determinantal equation (8.87) for the special case where $H_{11} = H_{22}$ and $S_{11} = S_{22}$. Then solve for c_1/c_2 for each of the two roots.

8.12 Let the variation function of (8.64) be complex. Then $c_j = a_j + ib_j$, where a_j and b_j are real numbers. There are $2n$ parameters to be varied, namely the a_j's and b_j's. (a) Use the chain rule to show that the minimization conditions $\partial W/\partial a_i = 0$, $\partial W/\partial b_i = 0$ are equivalent to the conditions $\partial W/\partial c_i = 0$, $\partial W/\partial c_i^* = 0$. (b) Show that minimization of W leads to Eq. (8.85) and its complex conjugate, which may be discarded. Hence Eqs. (8.85) and (8.88) are valid for complex variation functions.

8.13 Apply the linear trial variation function

$$\varphi = c_1 x^2 (l - x) + c_2 x(l - x)^2, \qquad 0 \leqslant x \leqslant l$$

to the particle in a one-dimensional box. Calculate the percent errors for the $n = 1$ and 2 states. Sketch $x^2(l-x)$, $x(l-x)^2$, and the two approximate wave functions you find.

8.14 In 1971, a paper was published that applied the normalized variation function $N \exp(-br^2/a_0^2 - cr/a_0)$ to the hydrogen atom and stated that minimization of the variational integral with respect to the parameters b and c yielded an energy 0.7% above the true ground-state energy (for infinite nuclear mass). Without doing any calculations, state why this result must be in error.

8.15 We wish to prove that the approximate wave functions obtained in the linear variation method are orthogonal. Let the approximate function φ_α have the value W_α for the variational integral and the coefficients $c_j^{(\alpha)}$ in (8.64). [We add α to distinguish the n different φ's.] We rewrite (8.85) as

$$\sum_k [(\langle f_i| \hat{H} |f_k\rangle - \langle f_i|f_k\rangle W_\alpha) c_k^{(\alpha)}] = 0, \qquad i = 1, ..., n \qquad (8.94)$$

(a) Show that $\langle f_i| \hat{H} - W_\alpha|\varphi_\alpha\rangle = 0$ by showing this integral to equal the left side of (8.94). (b) Use the result of (a) to show

$$\langle \varphi_\beta| \hat{H} - W_\alpha |\varphi_\alpha\rangle = 0 \qquad \text{and} \qquad \langle \varphi_\alpha| \hat{H} - W_\beta |\varphi_\beta\rangle^* = 0$$

for all α and β. (c) Equate the two integrals in (b) and use the Hermitian property of $\hat{H}$ to show that

$$\langle \varphi_\beta|\varphi_\alpha\rangle (W_\beta - W_\alpha) = 0$$

We conclude that for $W_\alpha \neq W_\beta$, φ_α and φ_β are orthogonal. (For $W_\alpha = W_\beta$ we can form orthogonal linear combinations of φ_α and φ_β that will have the same value for the variational integral.)

CHAPTER
9

Perturbation Theory

9.1 Introduction

We now discuss the second major quantum-mechanical approximation method, perturbation theory.

Suppose we have a system with a time-independent Hamiltonian $\hat{H}$ and that we are unable to solve the Schroedinger equation

$$\hat{H}\psi_n = E_n\psi_n \tag{9.1}$$

for the eigenfunctions and eigenvalues of the bound stationary states. Suppose also that the Hamiltonian $\hat{H}$ is only slightly different from the Hamiltonian $\hat{H}^0$ of a system whose Schroedinger equation

$$\hat{H}^0\psi_n^{(0)} = E_n^{(0)}\psi_n^{(0)} \tag{9.2}$$

we are able to solve. An example is the one-dimensional anharmonic oscillator with Hamiltonian

$$\hat{H} = -\frac{\hbar^2}{2m}\frac{d^2}{dx^2} + \tfrac{1}{2}kx^2 + cx^3 + dx^4 \tag{9.3}$$

The Hamiltonian (9.3) is closely related to the Hamiltonian of the harmonic oscillator, which is

$$\hat{H}^0 = -\frac{\hbar^2}{2m}\frac{d^2}{dx^2} + \tfrac{1}{2}kx^2 \tag{9.4}$$

If the constants c and d in (9.3) are small, it is natural to suppose that the eigenfunctions and eigenvalues of the anharmonic oscillator are closely related to the eigenfunctions and eigenvalues of the harmonic oscillator.

We will call the system with Hamiltonian $\hat{H}^0$ the *unperturbed* system; the system with Hamiltonian $\hat{H}$ is the *perturbed* system. The difference between the two Hamiltonians is the *perturbation*, $\hat{H}'$:

$$\hat{H}' \equiv \hat{H} - \hat{H}^0$$

$$\hat{H} = \hat{H}^0 + \hat{H}' \tag{9.5}$$

(Of course the prime does not refer to differentiation.) For the anharmonic oscillator with Hamiltonian (9.3), the perturbation on the related harmonic oscillator is

$$\hat{H}' = cx^3 + dx^4 \tag{9.6}$$

Our task is to relate the unknown eigenvalues and eigenfunctions of the perturbed system to the known eigenvalues and eigenfunctions of the unperturbed system. To aid in doing so, we will imagine that the perturbation is applied in small steps, giving a continuous change from the unperturbed to the perturbed system. Mathematically, this corresponds to introducing a parameter λ into the Hamiltonian, so that

$$\hat{H} = \hat{H}^0 + \lambda \hat{H}' \tag{9.7}$$

When λ is zero, we have the unperturbed system. As λ increases toward one, the perturbation grows larger, and at $\lambda = 1$ the perturbation is fully "turned on." We have introduced λ as a convenience in relating the perturbed and unperturbed eigenfunctions, and ultimately we will set $\lambda = 1$, thereby eliminating it.

Throughout this chapter, we will be considering only time-independent Hamiltonians and stationary states.

9.2 Nondegenerate Perturbation Theory

The perturbation treatments of degenerate and nondegenerate energy levels differ. In this section we examine the effect of a perturbation on a nondegenerate level. If some of the energy levels of the unperturbed system are degenerate while others are nondegenerate, the treatment in this section will be applicable to the nondegenerate levels only.

Let $\psi_n^{(0)}$ be the wave function of some particular unperturbed nondegenerate level with energy $E_n^{(0)}$. Let ψ_n be the perturbed wave function into which $\psi_n^{(0)}$ is converted when the perturbation is applied. From (9.1) and (9.7), the Schroedinger equation for the perturbed state is

$$(\hat{H}^0 + \lambda \hat{H}') \psi_n = E_n \psi_n \tag{9.8}$$

Since the Hamiltonian in (9.8) depends on the parameter λ, both the eigenfunction ψ_n and the eigenvalue E_n depend on λ:

$$\psi_n = \psi_n(\lambda, q) \tag{9.9}$$

$$E_n = E_n(\lambda) \tag{9.10}$$

where q indicates the system's spatial coordinates. We now expand ψ_n and E_n as Taylor series in powers of λ:

$$\psi_n = \psi_n|_{\lambda=0} + \frac{\partial \psi_n}{\partial \lambda}\bigg|_{\lambda=0} \lambda + \frac{\partial^2 \psi_n}{\partial \lambda^2}\bigg|_{\lambda=0} \frac{\lambda^2}{2!} + \cdots \qquad (9.11)$$

$$E_n = E_n|_{\lambda=0} + \frac{dE_n}{d\lambda}\bigg|_{\lambda=0} \lambda + \frac{d^2 E_n}{d\lambda^2}\bigg|_{\lambda=0} \frac{\lambda^2}{2!} + \cdots \qquad (9.12)$$

By hypothesis, when λ goes to zero, ψ_n and E_n go to $\psi_n^{(0)}$ and $E_n^{(0)}$:

$$\psi_n|_{\lambda=0} = \psi_n^{(0)} \qquad (9.13)$$

$$E_n|_{\lambda=0} = E_n^{(0)} \qquad (9.14)$$

We introduce the following abbreviations:

$$\psi_n^{(k)} = \frac{1}{k!} \frac{\partial^k \psi_n}{\partial \lambda^k}\bigg|_{\lambda=0}, \qquad k = 1, 2, \ldots \qquad (9.15)$$

$$E_n^{(k)} = \frac{1}{k!} \frac{d^k E_n}{d\lambda^k}\bigg|_{\lambda=0}, \qquad k = 1, 2, \ldots \qquad (9.16)$$

Equations (9.11) and (9.12) become

$$\psi_n = \psi_n^{(0)} + \lambda \psi_n^{(1)} + \lambda^2 \psi_n^{(2)} + \cdots + \lambda^k \psi_n^{(k)} + \cdots \qquad (9.17)$$

$$E_n = E_n^{(0)} + \lambda E_n^{(1)} + \lambda^2 E_n^{(2)} + \cdots + \lambda^k E_n^{(k)} + \cdots \qquad (9.18)$$

We call $\psi_n^{(k)}$ and $E_n^{(k)}$ the kth-order corrections to the wave function and energy. We will assume that the series (9.17) and (9.18) converge for $\lambda = 1$, and we hope that for a small perturbation, taking just the first few terms of the series will provide a good approximation to the true energy and wave function.

Substituting (9.17) and (9.18) into (9.8), we have

$$(\hat{H}^0 + \lambda \hat{H}')(\psi_n^{(0)} + \lambda \psi_n^{(1)} + \lambda^2 \psi_n^{(2)} + \cdots)$$
$$= (E_n^{(0)} + \lambda E_n^{(1)} + \lambda^2 E_n^{(2)} + \cdots)(\psi_n^{(0)} + \lambda \psi_n^{(1)} + \lambda^2 \psi_n^{(2)} + \cdots) \qquad (9.19)$$

Collecting like powers of λ, we have

$$\hat{H}^0 \psi_n^{(0)} + \lambda(\hat{H}' \psi_n^{(0)} + \hat{H}^0 \psi_n^{(1)}) + \lambda^2 (\hat{H}^0 \psi_n^{(2)} + \hat{H}' \psi_n^{(1)}) + \cdots$$
$$= E_n^{(0)} \psi_n^{(0)} + \lambda(E_n^{(1)} \psi_n^{(0)} + E_n^{(0)} \psi_n^{(1)}) + \lambda^2 (E_n^{(2)} \psi_n^{(0)} + E_n^{(1)} \psi_n^{(1)} + E_n^{(0)} \psi_n^{(2)}) + \cdots$$
$$\qquad (9.20)$$

Now (assuming suitable convergence), for the two series on each side of (9.20) to be equal to each other for all values of λ, the coefficients of like powers of λ in the two series must be equal. [For the proof, see the argument following Eq. (4.13).]

Equating the coefficients of the λ^0 terms, we have

$$\hat{H}^0 \psi_n^{(0)} = E_n^{(0)} \psi_n^{(0)} \qquad (9.21)$$

which is the Schroedinger equation for the unperturbed problem, Eq. (9.2), and gives us no new information.

Equating the coefficients of the λ^1 terms, we have

$$\hat{H}'\psi_n^{(0)} + \hat{H}^0\psi_n^{(1)} = E_n^{(1)}\psi_n^{(0)} + E_n^{(0)}\psi_n^{(1)} \tag{9.22}$$

$$(\hat{H}^0 - E_n^{(0)})\psi_n^{(1)} = (E_n^{(1)} - \hat{H}')\psi_n^{(0)} \tag{9.23}$$

This equation contains $\psi_n^{(1)}$, which is something we do not know. Since $\hat{H}^0$ is Hermitian, the set of eigenfunctions of the unperturbed system is a complete set of known functions; hence, we expand $\psi_n^{(1)}$ using the unperturbed wave functions:

$$\psi_n^{(1)} = \sum_j a_j \psi_j^{(0)} \tag{9.24}$$

Equation (9.23) becomes

$$\sum_j a_j (\hat{H}^0\psi_j^{(0)} - E_n^{(0)}\psi_j^{(0)}) = (E_n^{(1)} - \hat{H}')\psi_n^{(0)} \tag{9.25}$$

$$\sum_j a_j (E_j^{(0)} - E_n^{(0)})\psi_j^{(0)} = (E_n^{(1)} - \hat{H}')\psi_n^{(0)} \tag{9.26}$$

where we used (9.2). We now multiply (9.26) by $\psi_m^{(0)*}$, and then integrate over all space, obtaining:

$$\int \psi_m^{(0)*} \sum_j a_j (E_j^{(0)} - E_n^{(0)})\psi_j^{(0)}\, d\tau = \int \psi_m^{(0)*}(E_n^{(1)} - \hat{H}')\psi_n^{(0)}\, d\tau$$

$$\sum_j a_j (E_j^{(0)} - E_n^{(0)}) \int \psi_m^{(0)*}\psi_j^{(0)}\, d\tau = E_n^{(1)} \int \psi_m^{(0)*}\psi_n^{(0)}\, d\tau - \int \psi_m^{(0)*}\hat{H}'\psi_n^{(0)}\, d\tau$$

$$\sum_j a_j (E_j^{(0)} - E_n^{(0)})\delta_{mj} = E_n^{(1)}\delta_{mn} - \int \psi_m^{(0)*}\hat{H}'\psi_n^{(0)}\, d\tau \tag{9.27}$$

since the unperturbed eigenfunctions are orthonormal:

$$\langle \psi_m^{(0)}|\psi_j^{(0)}\rangle = \delta_{mj} \tag{9.28}$$

Performing the sum, only the term with $j = m$ survives, and we have

$$a_m(E_m^{(0)} - E_n^{(0)}) = E_n^{(1)}\delta_{mn} - \int \psi_m^{(0)*}\hat{H}'\psi_n^{(0)}\, d\tau \tag{9.29}$$

We have two cases to consider: either $m = n$ or $m \neq n$. For $m = n$, the left side of (9.29) vanishes, and we have

$$E_n^{(1)} = \int \psi_n^{(0)*}\hat{H}'\psi_n^{(0)}\, d\tau = \langle \psi_n^{(0)}|\hat{H}'|\psi_n^{(0)}\rangle = H'_{nn} \tag{9.30}$$

Thus we have the not unreasonable result that the first-order correction to the energy is found by averaging the perturbation $\hat{H}'$ over the appropriate unperturbed wave function. Equation (9.30) is extremely important.

Setting $\lambda = 1$ in (9.18), we have

$$E_n \approx E_n^{(0)} + E_n^{(1)} = E_n^{(0)} + \int \psi_n^{(0)*}\hat{H}'\psi_n^{(0)}\, d\tau \tag{9.31}$$

Let us find the first-order correction to the wave function. For $m \neq n$, Eq. (9.29) becomes

$$a_m (E_m^{(0)} - E_n^{(0)}) = - \int \psi_m^{(0)*} \hat{H}' \psi_n^{(0)} \, d\tau, \qquad m \neq n \quad (9.32)$$

By hypothesis, the level $E_n^{(0)}$ is nondegenerate, so that $E_m^{(0)} \neq E_n^{(0)}$ for $m \neq n$, and we may divide by $(E_m^{(0)} - E_n^{(0)})$ to obtain

$$a_m = \frac{\int \psi_m^{(0)*} \hat{H}' \psi_n^{(0)} \, d\tau}{E_n^{(0)} - E_m^{(0)}} = \frac{H'_{mn}}{E_n^{(0)} - E_m^{(0)}}, \qquad m \neq n \quad (9.33)$$

The first-order correction to the wave function is, according to (9.24):

$$\psi_n^{(1)} = \sum_m a_m \psi_m^{(0)} \quad (9.34)$$

where we changed the dummy summation index. The $\psi_m^{(0)}$ are the known unperturbed wave functions. The coefficients a_m are given by (9.33), except for a_n, the coefficient of $\psi_n^{(0)}$. We might determine a_n by normalizing the perturbed wave function $\psi_n^{(0)} + \psi_n^{(1)}$, but this will not fully specify a_n since we can always multiply a wave function by an arbitrary phase factor $e^{i\alpha}$. A detailed investigation (which we omit) shows that the choice of a_n will not affect the expressions for any of the energy corrections. The conventional procedure is to set a_n (and similar constants which arise in calculating higher-order corrections to the wave function) equal to zero. If desired, the perturbed wave function may be normalized at the end of the calculation. With $a_n = 0$, Eqs. (9.33) and (9.34) give the first-order correction to the wave function as

$$\psi_n^{(1)} = \sum_{m \neq n} \frac{\int \psi_m^{(0)*} \hat{H}' \psi_n^{(0)} \, d\tau}{E_n^{(0)} - E_m^{(0)}} \psi_m^{(0)} \quad (9.35)$$

Setting $\lambda = 1$ in (9.17), and using just the first-order correction, we have as our approximation to the perturbed wave function

$$\psi_n \approx \psi_n^{(0)} + \sum_{m \neq n} \frac{H'_{mn}}{E_n^{(0)} - E_m^{(0)}} \psi_m^{(0)} \quad (9.36)$$

The symbol $\sum_{m \neq n}$ in (9.36) means that we sum over all the unperturbed states except state n.

We now consider the second-order correction to the energy. Equating coefficients of the λ^2 terms in (9.20), we have

$$(\hat{H}^0 - E_n^{(0)}) \psi_n^{(2)} = E_n^{(2)} \psi_n^{(0)} + (E_n^{(1)} - \hat{H}') \psi_n^{(1)} \quad (9.37)$$

We expand the second-order correction to the wave function as

$$\psi_n^{(2)} = \sum_j b_j \psi_j^{(0)} \quad (9.38)$$

and (9.37) becomes [after (9.2) is used]:

$$\sum_j b_j (E_j^{(0)} - E_n^{(0)}) \psi_j^{(0)} = E_n^{(2)} \psi_n^{(0)} + (E_n^{(1)} - \hat{H}') \psi_n^{(1)} \quad (9.39)$$

Multiplying by $\psi_m^{(0)*}$ and integrating, we get

$$\sum_j b_j (E_j^{(0)} - E_n^{(0)}) \delta_{mj} = E_n^{(2)} \delta_{mn} + E_n^{(1)} \int \psi_m^{(0)*} \psi_n^{(1)} \, d\tau - \int \psi_m^{(0)*} \hat{H}' \psi_n^{(1)} \, d\tau$$

where (9.28) has been used. Performing the sum, we find

$$b_m (E_m^{(0)} - E_n^{(0)}) = E_n^{(2)} \delta_{mn} + E_n^{(1)} \int \psi_m^{(0)*} \psi_n^{(1)} \, d\tau - \int \psi_m^{(0)*} \hat{H}' \psi_n^{(1)} \, d\tau \quad (9.40)$$

To determine $\psi_n^{(2)}$, we would consider the case $m \neq n$. We omit doing so, and only consider $m = n$. With $m = n$, Eq. (9.40) becomes

$$0 = E_n^{(2)} + E_n^{(1)} \int \psi_n^{(0)*} \psi_n^{(1)} \, d\tau - \int \psi_n^{(0)*} \hat{H}' \psi_n^{(1)} \, d\tau \quad (9.41)$$

Note from this last equation that to determine the *second*-order correction to the energy, we only have to know the *first*-order correction to the wave function. In fact it can be shown that knowledge of $\psi_n^{(1)}$ suffices to determine $E_n^{(3)}$ also; in general, it can be shown that if we know the corrections to the wave function through the kth order, then we can compute the corrections to the energy through order $2k+1$ (see *Bates*, Vol. I, p. 184).

Resuming consideration of (9.41), we have two integrals to do. From (9.35) we have

$$\psi_n^{(1)} = \sum_{k \neq n} \frac{H'_{kn}}{E_n^{(0)} - E_k^{(0)}} \psi_k^{(0)} \quad (9.42)$$

so that the first integral in (9.41) becomes

$$\int \psi_n^{(0)*} \psi_n^{(1)} \, d\tau = \sum_{k \neq n} \int \psi_n^{(0)*} \frac{H'_{kn}}{E_n^{(0)} - E_k^{(0)}} \psi_k^{(0)} \, d\tau \quad (9.43)$$

The quantities H'_{kn} are constants, since they are the values of certain definite integrals:

$$H'_{kn} \equiv \int \psi_k^{(0)*} \hat{H}' \psi_n^{(0)} \, d\tau$$

We have

$$\int \psi_n^{(0)*} \psi_n^{(1)} \, d\tau = \sum_{k \neq n} \frac{H'_{kn}}{E_n^{(0)} - E_k^{(0)}} \int \psi_n^{(0)*} \psi_k^{(0)} \, d\tau = \sum_{k \neq n} \frac{H'_{kn}}{E_n^{(0)} - E_k^{(0)}} \delta_{nk}$$

Because the sum does not include the term with $k = n$, the Kronecker delta causes all the terms to vanish, and we have

$$\int \psi_n^{(0)*} \psi_n^{(1)} \, d\tau = 0 \quad (9.44)$$

Equation (9.44) is a consequence of our choosing $a_n = 0$.

Equation (9.41) becomes

$$E_n^{(2)} = \int \psi_n^{(0)*} \hat{H}' \psi_n^{(1)} \, d\tau \quad (9.45)$$

Using (9.42) in (9.45), we have

$$E_n^{(2)} = \sum_{k \neq n} \frac{H'_{kn}}{E_n^{(0)} - E_k^{(0)}} \int \psi_n^{(0)*} \hat{H}' \psi_k^{(0)} \, d\tau = \sum_{k \neq n} \frac{H'_{kn} H'_{nk}}{E_n^{(0)} - E_k^{(0)}}$$

Since $\hat{H}'$ is Hermitian, we have $H'_{nk} = (H'_{kn})^*$, and

$$E_n^{(2)} = \sum_{k \neq n} \frac{|H'_{kn}|^2}{E_n^{(0)} - E_k^{(0)}} = \sum_{k \neq n} \frac{|\langle \psi_k^{(0)} | \hat{H}' | \psi_n^{(0)} \rangle|^2}{E_n^{(0)} - E_k^{(0)}} \qquad (9.46)$$

It might be thought that the result (9.46) depended on the choice of $a_n = 0$, since with $a_n \neq 0$, Eq. (9.44) is no longer true. However, if instead of (9.42) we had written

$$\psi_n^{(1)} = a_n \psi_n^{(0)} + \sum_{k \neq n} \frac{H'_{kn}}{E_n^{(0)} - E_k^{(0)}} \psi_k^{(0)} \qquad (9.47)$$

where a_n is left completely unspecified, and used (9.47) in (9.41), we would still get Eq. (9.46) for $E_n^{(2)}$. (See Problem 9.1.)

Using (9.46), our approximation to the energy of the perturbed state becomes [Eq. (9.18) with $\lambda = 1$]:

$$E_n \approx E_n^{(0)} + H'_{nn} + \sum_{k \neq n} \frac{|H'_{nk}|^2}{E_n^{(0)} - E_k^{(0)}} \qquad (9.48)$$

For formulas for higher-order corrections to the energy, see *Bates*, Vol. I, pp. 181–185. (The form of perturbation theory developed in this section is known as Rayleigh–Schroedinger perturbation theory; other approaches exist.)

Let us discuss our results, Eqs. (9.48) and (9.36). From (9.36) we see that the effect of the perturbation on the wave function $\psi_n^{(0)}$ is to "mix in" contributions from other states $\psi_m^{(0)}$, $m \neq n$. Because of the factor $1/(E_n^{(0)} - E_m^{(0)})$, the most important contributions (aside from $\psi_n^{(0)}$) to the perturbed wave function come from states nearest in energy to state n.

To evaluate the first-order correction to the energy, we only have to evaluate the single integral H'_{nn}, whereas to evaluate the second-order energy correction, we must evaluate the matrix elements of $\hat{H}'$ between the nth state and all other states k, and then perform the infinite sum in (9.46). In many cases it is impossible to evaluate exactly the second-order energy correction. Third-order and higher-order energy corrections are even more difficult to deal with.

The sums in (9.36) and (9.48) are sums over different states rather than sums over different energy values. If some of the energy levels (other than the nth) are degenerate, we must include a term in the sums for each linearly independent wave function corresponding to the degenerate levels.

The reason we have a sum over states in (9.36) and (9.48) is that we require a complete set of functions for the expansion (9.38), and therefore must include all linearly independent wave functions in the sum. If the unperturbed problem has continuum wave functions (e.g., the hydrogen atom) we must also include an integration over the continuum functions, if we are to have a complete set. If $\psi_E^{(0)}$

denotes an unperturbed continuum wave function of energy $E^{(0)}$, then (9.42) and (9.46) become

$$\psi_n^{(1)} = \sum_{k \neq n} \frac{H'_{kn}}{E_n^{(0)} - E_k^{(0)}} \psi_k^{(0)} + \int \frac{H'_{E,n}}{E_n^{(0)} - E^{(0)}} \psi_E^{(0)} \, dE^{(0)} \qquad \textbf{(9.42a)}$$

$$E_n^{(2)} = \sum_{k \neq n} \frac{|H'_{kn}|^2}{E_n^{(0)} - E_k^{(0)}} + \int \frac{|H'_{E,n}|^2}{E_n^{(0)} - E^{(0)}} \, dE^{(0)} \qquad \textbf{(9.46a)}$$

$$H'_{E,n} = \int \psi_E^{(0)*} \hat{H}' \psi_n^{(0)} \, d\tau$$

(Sometimes the symbol **S** is used to indicate summation over the discrete states and integration over the continuum states.) The integrals in (9.42a) and (9.46a) are over the range of continuum-state energies, e.g., from zero to infinity for the hydrogen atom. The existence of continuum states in the unperturbed problem makes evaluation of the second-order energy correction even more difficult.

Note that the unperturbed wave functions are normalized [Eq. (9.28)]. Hence, in using (9.30) and (9.46) we must use *normalized* unperturbed wave functions.

9.3 Perturbation Treatment of the Ground State of the Helium Atom

The helium atom has two electrons and a nucleus of charge $+2e$. We will consider the nucleus to be at rest (Section 6.5) and will place the origin of the co-ordinate system at the nucleus. The coordinates of electrons 1 and 2 are (x_1, y_1, z_1) and (x_2, y_2, z_2); see Fig. 9.1.

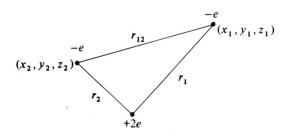

FIGURE 9.1 *The helium atom.*

If we take the nuclear charge to be $+Ze$ instead of $+2e$, we can treat helium-like ions such as H^-, Li^+, Be^{++}. The Hamiltonian operator is

$$\hat{H} = -\frac{\hbar^2}{2m} \nabla_1^2 - \frac{\hbar^2}{2m} \nabla_2^2 - \frac{Ze^2}{r_1} - \frac{Ze^2}{r_2} + \frac{e^2}{r_{12}} \qquad \textbf{(9.49)}$$

where m is the mass of the electron, r_1 and r_2 are the distances of electrons 1 and 2 from the nucleus, and r_{12} is the distance from electron 1 to 2. The first two terms are the operators for the electrons' kinetic energy; the third and fourth terms are the potential energies of attraction between the electrons and the nucleus; the final term is the potential energy of interelectronic repulsion [Eq. (6.66)]. (Note that the potential energy of a system of interacting particles cannot be written as the sum of potential energies of the individual particles; the potential energy is a property of the system as a whole.)

The Schroedinger equation involves six independent variables, three co-ordinates for each electron. In spherical polar coordinates

$$\psi = \psi(r_1, \theta_1, \varphi_1, r_2, \theta_2, \varphi_2) \tag{9.50}$$

The operator ∇_1^2 is given by Eq. (6.6) with r_1, θ_1, φ_1 replacing r, θ, φ. The variable r_{12} in Cartesian coordinates is $r_{12} = [(x_1 - x_2)^2 + (y_1 - y_2)^2 + (z_1 - z_2)^2]^{1/2}$, and by using the relations between Cartesian and spherical polar coordinates we can express r_{12} in terms of the coordinates of (9.50).

Because of the $1/r_{12}$ term, the Schroedinger equation for helium cannot be separated in any coordinate system, and we must use approximation methods. To use the perturbation method, we must separate the Hamiltonian (9.49) into two parts, $\hat{H}^0$ and $\hat{H}'$, where $\hat{H}^0$ is the Hamiltonian of an exactly soluble problem. If we choose

$$\hat{H}^0 = -\frac{\hbar^2}{2m}\nabla_1^2 - \frac{Ze^2}{r_1} - \frac{\hbar^2}{2m}\nabla_2^2 - \frac{Ze^2}{r_2} \tag{9.51}$$

$$\hat{H}' = \frac{e^2}{r_{12}} \tag{9.52}$$

our unperturbed Hamiltonian is the sum of two hydrogenlike Hamiltonians, one for each electron:

$$\hat{H}^0 = \hat{H}_1^0 + \hat{H}_2^0 \tag{9.53}$$

$$\hat{H}_1^0 \equiv -\frac{\hbar^2}{2m}\nabla_1^2 - \frac{Ze^2}{r_1}, \qquad \hat{H}_2^0 \equiv -\frac{\hbar^2}{2m}\nabla_2^2 - \frac{Ze^2}{r_2} \tag{9.54}$$

The unperturbed system is a helium atom in which the two electrons exert no forces on each other. Although there is no physical reality to such a system, this does not prevent us from applying the mathematics of perturbation theory to this system to obtain an approximation to the actual helium atom.

Since the unperturbed Hamiltonian (9.53) is the sum of the Hamiltonians for two independent particles, we can use the results of Eqs. (6.43)–(6.49) to conclude that the unperturbed wave functions have the form

$$\psi^{(0)}(r_1, \theta_1, \varphi_1, r_2, \theta_2, \varphi_2) = F_1(r_1, \theta_1, \varphi_1) F_2(r_2, \theta_2, \varphi_2) \tag{9.55}$$

and the unperturbed energies are

$$E^{(0)} = E_1 + E_2 \tag{9.56}$$

$$\hat{H}_1^0 F_1 = E_1 F_1, \qquad \hat{H}_2^0 F_2 = E_2 F_2 \tag{9.57}$$

Since the Hamiltonians $\hat{H}_1^0$ and $\hat{H}_2^0$ are hydrogenlike Hamiltonians, the solutions of (9.57) are the hydrogenlike eigenfunctions and eigenvalues. From Eq. (6.107), we have

$$E_1 = -\frac{Z^2}{n_1^2}\frac{e^2}{2a_0}, \qquad E_2 = -\frac{Z^2}{n_2^2}\frac{e^2}{2a_0} \tag{9.58}$$

$$E^{(0)} = -Z^2\left(\frac{1}{n_1^2} + \frac{1}{n_2^2}\right)\frac{e^2}{2a_0}, \qquad \begin{aligned} n_1 &= 1,2,3,\ldots \\ n_2 &= 1,2,3,\ldots \end{aligned} \tag{9.59}$$

where a_0 is the Bohr radius. Equation (9.59) gives the zeroth-order energies of states with both electrons bound to the nucleus; we also have continuum states.

The lowest level has $n_1 = 1$, $n_2 = 1$, and its zeroth-order wave function is [Eq. (6.120)]

$$\psi_{1s^2}^{(0)} = \frac{1}{\pi^{1/2}}\left(\frac{Z}{a_0}\right)^{3/2} e^{-Zr_1/a_0} \cdot \frac{1}{\pi^{1/2}}\left(\frac{Z}{a_0}\right)^{3/2} e^{-Zr_2/a_0} \tag{9.60}$$

where the subscript indicates that both electrons are in hydrogenlike $1s$ orbitals. (Note that the procedure of assigning electrons to orbitals and writing the atomic wave function as the product of one-electron orbital functions is an *approximation*.) The energy of this unperturbed ground state is

$$E_{1s^2}^{(0)} = -Z^2(2)\frac{e^2}{2a_0} \tag{9.61}$$

The quantity $-\tfrac{1}{2}e^2/a_0$ is the ground-state energy of the hydrogen atom (taking the nucleus to be infinitely heavy), and equals -13.606 eV (Section 6.5). For helium, $Z = 2$, and

$$E_{1s^2}^{(0)} = -108.8 \text{ eV} \tag{9.62}$$

How does this zeroth-order energy compare with the true ground-state energy of helium? The experimental first ionization potential of He is 24.6 volts. The second ionization potential of He is easily calculated theoretically, since it is the ionization potential of the hydrogenlike ion He$^+$ and is equal to $2^2(13.606$ volts$) = 54.4$ volts. If we choose the zero of energy as the completely ionized atom [this choice is implicit in (9.49)], then the ground-state energy of the helium atom is $-(24.6 + 54.4)$ electron volts $= -79.0$ eV. Thus the zeroth-order energy is in error by 38 percent. We should have expected such a large error, since the perturbation term e^2/r_{12} is not particularly small.

The next step is to evaluate the first-order perturbation correction to the energy. The unperturbed ground state is nondegenerate, and we have

$$E^{(1)} = \int \psi^{(0)*}\hat{H}'\psi^{(0)}\, d\tau$$

$$E^{(1)} = \frac{Z^6 e^2}{\pi^2 a_0^6} \int_0^{2\pi} \int_0^{2\pi} \int_0^{\pi} \int_0^{\pi} \int_0^{\infty} \int_0^{\infty} e^{-2Zr_1/a_0} e^{-2Zr_2/a_0} \frac{1}{r_{12}} r_1^2 \sin\theta_1$$

$$\times\, r_2^2 \sin\theta_2\, dr_1\, dr_2\, d\theta_1\, d\theta_2\, d\varphi_1\, d\varphi_2 \tag{9.63}$$

The volume element for this two-electron problem contains the coordinates of both electrons, $d\tau = d\tau_1 \, d\tau_2$. [The evaluation of the integral may be skimmed, if desired; begin reading again at Eq. (9.67).]

We must now express $1/r_{12}$ in terms of the spherical polar coordinates of the two electrons. If we try using

$$1/r_{12} = [(x_1-x_2)^2 + (y_1-y_2)^2 + (z_1-z_2)^2]^{-1/2}$$

together with the relations between Cartesian and spherical polar coordinates, we will find that we will be unable to do the integration. Instead, we use an expansion of $1/r_{12}$ in terms of spherical harmonics. We will not derive this expansion,[1] but will simply write it down and use it:

$$
\frac{1}{r_{12}} =
\begin{cases}
\dfrac{1}{r_1} \displaystyle\sum_{l=0}^{\infty} \sum_{m=-l}^{l} \frac{4\pi}{2l+1} \left(\frac{r_2}{r_1}\right)^l [Y_l^m(\theta_1,\varphi_1)]^* \, Y_l^m(\theta_2,\varphi_2) & \text{if } r_1 \geqslant r_2 \\[4mm]
\dfrac{1}{r_2} \displaystyle\sum_{l=0}^{\infty} \sum_{m=-l}^{l} \frac{4\pi}{2l+1} \left(\frac{r_1}{r_2}\right)^l [Y_l^m(\theta_1,\varphi_1)]^* \, Y_l^m(\theta_2,\varphi_2) & \text{if } r_2 \geqslant r_1
\end{cases}
\tag{9.64}
$$

Although the expansion looks formidable, it makes evaluation of the integral relatively simple. Using (9.64) and $Y_0^0 = 1/(4\pi)^{1/2}$, we have

$$
E^{(1)} = \frac{16Z^6 e^2}{a_0^6} \sum_{l=0}^{\infty} \sum_{m=-l}^{l} \frac{1}{2l+1} \int_0^\infty \int_0^\infty e^{-2Zr_1/a_0} e^{-2Zr_2/a_0} \frac{r_<^l}{r_>^{l+1}} r_1^2 r_2^2 \, dr_1 \, dr_2
$$

$$
\times \int_0^{2\pi} \int_0^{\pi} [Y_l^m(\theta_1,\varphi_1)]^* \, Y_0^0(\theta_1,\varphi_1) \sin\theta_1 \, d\theta_1 \, d\varphi_1
$$

$$
\times \int_0^{2\pi} \int_0^{\pi} [Y_0^0(\theta_2,\varphi_2)]^* \, Y_l^m(\theta_2,\varphi_2) \sin\theta_2 \, d\theta_2 \, d\varphi_2
\tag{9.65}
$$

where $r_<$ means the smaller of r_1 and r_2, and $r_>$ means the larger of r_1 and r_2. Recalling the orthonormality of the spherical harmonics [Eq. (7.46)], we have

$$
E^{(1)} = \frac{16Z^6 e^2}{a_0^6} \sum_{l=0}^{\infty} \sum_{m=-l}^{l} \frac{1}{2l+1} \int_0^\infty \int_0^\infty (\cdots) \, dr_1 \, dr_2 \, \delta_{l,0} \, \delta_{m,0} \, \delta_{l,0} \, \delta_{m,0}
$$

The Kronecker deltas cause all terms to vanish except the single term with $m = 0 = l$, so that

$$
E^{(1)} = \frac{16Z^6 e^2}{a_0^6} \int_0^\infty \int_0^\infty e^{-2Zr_1/a_0} e^{-2Zr_2/a_0} \frac{1}{r_>} r_1^2 r_2^2 \, dr_1 \, dr_2
$$

If we integrate first over r_1, then in the range $0 \leqslant r_1 \leqslant r_2$, we have $r_> = r_2$; in the range $r_2 \leqslant r_1 \leqslant \infty$, we have $r_> = r_1$. Thus

$$
E^{(1)} = \frac{16Z^6 e^2}{a_0^6} \int_0^\infty e^{-2Zr_2/a_0} r_2^2 \left[\int_0^{r_2} e^{-2Zr_1/a_0} \frac{r_1^2}{r_2} \, dr_1 + \int_{r_2}^\infty e^{-2Zr_1/a_0} \frac{r_1^2}{r_1} \, dr_1 \right] dr_2
$$

$$
E^{(1)} = \frac{16Z^6 e^2}{a_0^6} \int_0^\infty e^{-2Zr_2/a_0} r_2 \left(\int_0^{r_2} e^{-2Zr_1/a_0} r_1^2 \, dr_1 \right) dr_2
$$

$$
+ \frac{16Z^6 e^2}{a_0^6} \int_0^\infty e^{-2Zr_2/a_0} r_2^2 \left(\int_{r_2}^\infty e^{-2Zr_1/a_0} r_1 \, dr_1 \right) dr_2
\tag{9.66}
$$

---

[1] *Eyring, Walter, and Kimball*, p. 369.

Using the indefinite integrals (A.2) and (A.3) in the Appendix, we can do the r_1 integrals to obtain r_2 integrals, which are evaluated using (A.4). The result is

$$E^{(1)} = \frac{5Z}{8}\left(\frac{e^2}{a_0}\right)$$ (9.67)

Recalling that $\frac{1}{2}e^2/a_0 = 13.606$ eV and putting $Z = 2$, we find for the first-order perturbation energy correction for the helium ground state

$$E^{(1)} = \frac{10}{4}(13.606 \text{ eV}) = 34.0 \text{ eV}$$ (9.68)

Our approximation to the energy is now

$$E^{(0)} + E^{(1)} = -108.8 \text{ eV} + 34.0 \text{ eV} = -74.8 \text{ eV}$$ (9.69)

which, comparing with the experimental value -79.0 eV, is in error by 5.3 percent.

To evaluate the first-order correction to the wave function and higher-order corrections to the energy requires evaluating the matrix elements of $1/r_{12}$ between the ground unperturbed state and all excited states (including the continuum) and performing the appropriate summations and integrations. No one has yet figured out how to evaluate directly all of the contributions to $E^{(2)}$. Note that the effect of $\psi^{(1)}$ is to mix into the wave function contributions from other configurations besides $1s^2$; we call this *configuration interaction*. The largest contribution to the true ground-state wave function of He will naturally come from the $1s^2$ configuration, which is the unperturbed (zeroth-order) wave function.

It is possible to obtain very accurate estimates of $E^{(2)}$ and higher-order energies by an indirect method which is a combination of the variation and perturbation methods. We will outline this method, which was developed and applied to helium by Hylleraas. Consider the integral

$$\int \left[\varphi^{(1)*}(\hat{H}^0 - E^{(0)})\varphi^{(1)} + \varphi^{(1)*}(\hat{H}' - E^{(1)})\psi^{(0)} + \psi^{(0)*}(\hat{H}' - E^{(1)})\varphi^{(1)}\right] d\tau$$ (9.70)

where $\varphi^{(1)}$ is any well-behaved function satisfying the appropriate boundary conditions, and the other symbols have their usual meanings. Suppose we are lucky enough to guess a function $\varphi^{(1)}$ that is the true first-order correction to the wave function; setting $\varphi^{(1)} = \psi^{(1)}$, and using Eq. (9.23), we see that (9.70) becomes

$$\int \psi^{(0)*}[\hat{H}' - E^{(1)}]\psi^{(1)} d\tau$$ (9.71)

which [Eq. (9.41)] is $E^{(2)}$, the second-order energy correction. Moreover, it is possible to prove (see *Hameka*, p. 223) that for any function $\varphi^{(1)}$ satisfying the boundary conditions, the integral (9.70) is equal to or greater than the second-order correction to the ground-state energy. We can therefore carry out a variational procedure to obtain an upper bound to $E^{(2)}$ for the ground state. We take $\varphi^{(1)}$ to be a trial function containing several parameters, and we vary the parameters so as to minimize the integral (9.70). This integral is then an approximation to $E^{(2)}$, and $\varphi^{(1)}$ is an approximation to $\psi^{(1)}$. We can then use $\varphi^{(1)}$ to obtain an approximation to $E^{(3)}$ also. Similar variational integrals may be used to find approximations to higher-order corrections to the ground-state wave function and energy.

Hylleraas's work on helium using this *variation–perturbation* method has been extended by Scherr and Knight[2] who used 100-term trial functions to obtain extremely accurate approximations to the wave-function corrections through sixth order and thus to the energy corrections through 13th order! The second-order correction $E^{(2)}$ turns out to be -4.3 eV, and $E^{(3)}$ is $+0.1$ eV. Through third order, we have for the ground-state energy

$$E \approx -108.8 \text{ eV} + 34.0 \text{ eV} - 4.3 \text{ eV} + 0.1 \text{ eV} = -79.0 \text{ eV} \qquad (9.72)$$

which agrees (within 0.1 eV) with the experimental value -79.0 eV. Including corrections through 13th order, Scherr and Knight obtained a ground-state energy of helium of $-2.90372433\,(e^2/a_0)$ which is nearly as good as the value $-2.90372438\,(e^2/a_0)$ obtained from the purely variational calculations described in the next section.

9.4 Variation Treatments of the Ground State of Helium

Although it might seem that the variation and perturbation methods represent quite different approaches, they are actually related in several ways. As one example, suppose we are interested in the ground-state energy of a system with Hamiltonian $\hat{H}$. The perturbation approach would first split $\hat{H}$ into two parts, $\hat{H} = \hat{H}^0 + \hat{H}'$, and then solve the unperturbed problem

$$\hat{H}^0 \psi_g^{(0)} = E_g^{(0)} \psi_g^{(0)} \qquad (9.73)$$

where the subscript g indicates the ground state. Including only the first-order energy correction, the perturbation-theory approximation to the true ground-state energy is

$$E_g \approx E_g^{(0)} + \int \psi_g^{(0)*} \hat{H}' \psi_g^{(0)} \, d\tau \qquad (9.74)$$

The variation method would try various normalized functions φ to minimize the variational integral

$$\int \varphi^* \hat{H} \varphi \, d\tau \geqslant E_g \qquad (9.75)$$

Suppose we used a variation function which was the zeroth-order ground-state wave function of the perturbation treatment: $\varphi = \psi_g^{(0)}$. The variational integral would then be

$$\int \varphi^* \hat{H} \varphi \, d\tau = \int \psi_g^{(0)*} (\hat{H}^0 + \hat{H}') \psi_g^{(0)} \, d\tau = \int \psi_g^{(0)*} (E_g^{(0)} + \hat{H}') \psi_g^{(0)} \, d\tau$$

$$\int \varphi^* \hat{H} \varphi \, d\tau = E_g^{(0)} + \int \psi_g^{(0)*} \hat{H}' \psi_g^{(0)} \, d\tau \qquad (9.76)$$

---

[2] C. W. Scherr and R. E. Knight, *Rev. Mod. Phys.*, **35**, 436 (1963). For calculations of the energy corrections through 21st order, see J. Midtdal, *Phys. Rev.*, **138**, A1010 (1965).

since $\psi_g^{(0)}$ is normalized. Comparison with the perturbation-theory expression (9.74) shows that the variation method gives the same result if we use $\psi_g^{(0)}$ as the trial function.

With this discussion as background, we consider variation functions for the helium ground state. If we used $\psi_g^{(0)}$ [Eq. (9.60)] for the trial function, we would get the first-order perturbation result -74.8 eV. To improve on this result, we use a trial function of the form of (9.60) but having a variational parameter. We try the normalized function

$$\varphi = \frac{1}{\pi}\left(\frac{\zeta}{a_0}\right)^3 e^{-\zeta r_1/a_0}e^{-\zeta r_2/a_0} \tag{9.77}$$

which is obtained from (9.60) by replacing the true atomic number Z by a variational parameter ζ (zeta). ζ has a simple physical interpretation. Since one electron tends to screen the other from the nucleus, each electron is subject to an effective nuclear charge somewhat less than the full nuclear charge Z. If one electron fully shielded the other from the nucleus, we would have an effective nuclear charge of $Z-1$; since both electrons are in the same orbital, they will be only partly effective in shielding each other. We thus expect ζ to lie between $Z-1$ and Z.

We now evaluate the variational integral. To expedite things, we rewrite the Hamiltonian (9.49) as

$$\hat{H} = \left[-\frac{\hbar^2}{2m}\nabla_1^2 - \frac{\zeta e^2}{r_1} - \frac{\hbar^2}{2m}\nabla_2^2 - \frac{\zeta e^2}{r_2}\right] + (\zeta - Z)\frac{e^2}{r_1} + (\zeta - Z)\frac{e^2}{r_2} + \frac{e^2}{r_{12}} \tag{9.78}$$

where we have added and subtracted the terms involving zeta. The terms in brackets in (9.78) are the sum of two hydrogenlike Hamiltonians for nuclear charge ζ; moreover, the trial function (9.77) is the product of two hydrogenlike $1s$ functions for nuclear charge ζ. Therefore, when these terms operate on φ, we will have an eigenvalue equation, the eigenvalue being the sum of two hydrogenlike $1s$ energies for nuclear charge ζ:

$$\left[-\frac{\hbar^2}{2m}\nabla_1^2 - \frac{\zeta e^2}{r_1} - \frac{\hbar^2}{2m}\nabla_2^2 - \frac{\zeta e^2}{r_2}\right]\varphi = -\zeta^2(2)\frac{e^2}{2a_0}\varphi \tag{9.79}$$

Using (9.78) and (9.79), we have

$$\int \varphi^*\hat{H}\varphi\,d\tau = -\zeta^2\frac{e^2}{a_0}\int\varphi^*\varphi\,d\tau + (\zeta - Z)e^2\int\frac{\varphi^*\varphi}{r_1}\,d\tau$$

$$+ (\zeta - Z)e^2\int\frac{\varphi^*\varphi}{r_2}\,d\tau + e^2\int\frac{\varphi^*\varphi}{r_{12}}\,d\tau \tag{9.80}$$

Let f_1 be a normalized $1s$ hydrogenlike orbital for nuclear charge ζ, occupied by electron 1; let f_2 be the same function for electron 2:

$$f_1 = \frac{1}{\pi^{1/2}}\left(\frac{\zeta}{a_0}\right)^{3/2}e^{-\zeta r_1/a_0}, \quad f_2 = \frac{1}{\pi^{1/2}}\left(\frac{\zeta}{a_0}\right)^{3/2}e^{-\zeta r_2/a_0} \tag{9.81}$$

Noting that $\varphi = f_1 f_2$, we now evaluate the integrals in (9.80):

$$\int \varphi^* \varphi \, d\tau = \int \int f_1^* f_2^* f_1 f_2 \, d\tau_1 \, d\tau_2 = \int f_1^* f_1 \, d\tau_1 \int f_2^* f_2 \, d\tau_2 = 1$$

$$\int \frac{\varphi^* \varphi}{r_1} \, d\tau = \int \frac{f_1^* f_1}{r_1} \, d\tau_1 \int f_2^* f_2 \, d\tau_2 = \int \frac{f_1^* f_1}{r_1} \, d\tau_1$$

$$\int \frac{\varphi^* \varphi}{r_1} \, d\tau = \frac{1}{\pi} \frac{\zeta^3}{a_0^3} \int_0^\infty e^{-2\zeta r_1/a_0} \frac{r_1^2}{r_1} \, dr_1 \int_0^\pi \sin\theta_1 \, d\theta_1 \int_0^{2\pi} d\varphi_1 = \frac{\zeta}{a_0}$$

where the Appendix integral (A.4) was used. Also

$$\int \frac{\varphi^* \varphi}{r_2} \, d\tau = \int \frac{f_2^* f_2}{r_2} \, d\tau_2 = \int \frac{f_1^* f_1}{r_1} \, d\tau_1 = \frac{\zeta}{a_0} \tag{9.82}$$

since it doesn't matter whether we use the label 1 or 2 on the dummy variables in the definite integral. Finally we must evaluate

$$e^2 \int \frac{\varphi^* \varphi}{r_{12}} \, d\tau \tag{9.83}$$

We recognize (9.83) as the same integral (9.63) that occurred in the perturbation treatment, except that Z is replaced by ζ; hence from (9.67):

$$e^2 \int \frac{\varphi^* \varphi}{r_{12}} \, d\tau = \frac{5\zeta e^2}{8a_0} \tag{9.84}$$

The variational integral (9.80) thus has the value

$$\int \varphi^* \hat{H} \varphi \, d\tau = (\zeta^2 - 2Z\zeta + \tfrac{5}{8}\zeta) \frac{e^2}{a_0} \tag{9.85}$$

As a check, if we set $\zeta = Z$ in (9.85), we get the first-order-perturbation-theory result, (9.61) plus (9.67).

We now vary ζ to minimize the variational integral:

$$\frac{\partial}{\partial \zeta} \int \varphi^* \hat{H} \varphi \, d\tau = (2\zeta - 2Z + \tfrac{5}{8}) \frac{e^2}{a_0} = 0$$

$$\zeta = Z - \tfrac{5}{16} \tag{9.86}$$

As anticipated, the effective nuclear charge lies between Z and $Z-1$. Using (9.86) and (9.85), we get

$$\int \varphi^* \hat{H} \varphi \, d\tau = (-Z^2 + \tfrac{5}{8}Z - \tfrac{25}{256}) \frac{e^2}{a_0} = -(Z - \tfrac{5}{16})^2 \frac{e^2}{a_0} \tag{9.87}$$

Putting $Z = 2$, our approximation to the ground-state energy is $-(27/16)^2 e^2/a_0 = -(729/256)\, 27.21$ eV $= -77.5$ eV, as compared to the true value -79.0 eV. Use of ζ instead of Z has reduced the error from 5.3 percent to 1.9 percent. In accord with the variation theorem, the true ground-state energy is less than the variational integral.

How can we improve our variational result? We might try a function that had the general form of (9.77), i.e., a product of two functions, one for each electron:

$$\varphi = g(1)g(2) \tag{9.88}$$

However, we could try a variety of functions g in (9.88), instead of the single exponential used in (9.77). A systematic procedure for finding the function g that gives the lowest value of the variational integral will be discussed in Section 11.1. This procedure shows that for the best possible choice of g in (9.88), the variational integral equals -77.9 eV, which is still in error by 1.4 percent. We might ask why (9.88) does not cause the variational integral to converge to the true ground-state energy, no matter what form we try for g. The answer is that when we write the trial function as the product of separate functions for each electron, we are making an approximation. Because of the e^2/r_{12} term in the Hamiltonian, the Schroedinger equation for helium is not separable, and the true ground-state wave function cannot be written as the product of separate functions for each electron. To reach the true ground-state energy, we must go beyond a function of the form (9.88).

The Bohr model gave the correct energies for the hydrogen atom, but failed when applied to helium. Hence, in the early days of quantum mechanics it was important to show that the new theory could give an accurate treatment of helium. The pioneering work on the helium ground state was done by Hylleraas in the years 1928–1930. He used variational functions that contained the interelectronic distance r_{12} explicitly. This provides an effective way of taking into account the effects of one electron on the motion of the other. One function Hylleraas used is

$$\varphi = N[e^{-\zeta r_1/a_0}e^{-\zeta r_2/a_0}(1 + br_{12})] \tag{9.89}$$

where N is the normalization constant and ζ and b are the variational parameters. Since

$$r_{12} = [(x_2 - x_1)^2 + (y_2 - y_1)^2 + (z_2 - z_1)^2]^{1/2} \tag{9.90}$$

the function (9.89) goes beyond the simple product form (9.88). Minimization of the variational integral with respect to the parameters gives $\zeta = 1.849$, $b = 0.364$, and a ground-state energy of -78.7 eV, in error by 0.3 eV. The $1 + br_{12}$ term makes the wave function larger for large values of r_{12}; this is as it should be, because the repulsion between the electrons makes it energetically more favorable for the electrons to avoid each other. A more complicated function used by Hylleraas is

$$\varphi = e^{-\zeta r_1/a_0}e^{-\zeta r_2/a_0} \sum_{i,j,k} c_{ijk}(r_1 + r_2)^i(r_1 - r_2)^j r_{12}^k \tag{9.91}$$

where the summation is over nonnegative integral values of i, j, and k. Using a function containing six terms in the sum, Hylleraas obtained an energy only 0.01 eV above the true ground-state energy.

Hylleraas's work has been extended by others. Pekeris[3] used a function of the form (9.91) containing 1078 (!!) terms. The calculations involved a determinant of order 1078 and were carried out on an electronic computer. Pekeris found a

---

[3] C. L. Pekeris, *Phys. Rev.*, **115**, 1216 (1959).

ground-state energy of $-2.903724375\,(e^2/a_0)$. With relativistic corrections and corrections for nuclear motion, this gave an ionization energy of $198{,}310.69\ \text{cm}^{-1}$ compared to the experimental value $198{,}310.82\pm0.15\ \text{cm}^{-1}$. Schwartz[4] used half-integral as well as integral values for i in (9.91); with a 189-term function he bettered Pekeris's result by obtaining $-2.903724376\,(e^2/a_0)$. Schwartz estimates his result to be within $0.000000001\,(e^2/a_0)$ of the true nonrelativistic ground-state energy.

A variational calculation on the Li ground state using a 60-term function and including r_{12}, r_{13}, and r_{23} explicitly in the trial function gave[5] an energy of $-7.47802\,(e^2/a_0)$ as compared to the experimental value $-7.47807\,(e^2/a_0)$. Variational calculations with functions involving r_{ij} become quite difficult for many-electron atoms, because of the large number of terms and difficult integrals that must be dealt with.

Approximation of the helium ground-state wave function as a product of hydrogenlike $1s$ orbitals with effective nuclear charge ζ [Eq. (9.77)] provides a simple physical picture which is in accord with the usual chemical concepts; however, this function does not give a very accurate value for the energy. When we use a function like (9.91) with a hundred or so terms, we get an extremely accurate wave function and energy, but we lose the simple physical interpretation. This is a general occurrence in quantum chemistry; "the more accurate the calculations become the more the concepts tend to vanish into thin air."[6]

9.5 Perturbation Theory for a Degenerate Energy Level

We now consider the perturbation treatment of an energy level that is n-fold degenerate. We have n linearly independent unperturbed wave functions corresponding to the degenerate level. We shall use the labels $1, 2, \ldots, n$ for the states of the degenerate level; we do not mean to imply that these are necessarily the lowest lying states.

The unperturbed Schroedinger equation is

$$\hat{H}^0\psi_j^{(0)} = E_j^{(0)}\psi_j^{(0)} \tag{9.92}$$

and we have

$$E_1^{(0)} = E_2^{(0)} = \cdots = E_n^{(0)} \tag{9.93}$$

For the perturbed problem we have

$$\hat{H}\psi_j = E_j\psi_j \tag{9.94}$$

$$\hat{H} = \hat{H}^0 + \lambda\hat{H}' \tag{9.95}$$

As λ goes to zero, the eigenvalues of (9.94) go to the eigenvalues of (9.92). Figure 9.2 illustrates this for a hypothetical system with six states and a threefold-degenerate

[4] C. Schwartz, *Phys. Rev.*, **128**, 1146 (1962). See also K. Frankowski and C. L. Pekeris, *Phys. Rev.*, **146**, 46 (1966).
[5] S. Larsson, *Phys. Rev.*, **169**, 49 (1968).
[6] R. S. Mulliken, *J. Chem. Phys.*, **43**, S2 (1965).

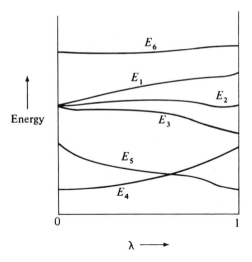

FIGURE 9.2 *Effect of a perturbation on energy levels.*

unperturbed level. Note that the effect of the perturbation is generally to split the degenerate energies. In some cases, the perturbation may have no effect on the degeneracy or may only partly remove the degeneracy. Figure 9.2 is a *correlation diagram*; it shows the correspondence between states of the perturbed and unperturbed problems. Later on, we will consider correlation diagrams relating the states of molecules to the states of the atoms from which they are formed. (The word *correlation* is also used to refer to the effects of one electron on the motion of another; do not confuse the two different usages.)

We express the correspondence between the perturbed and unperturbed energies by writing

$$\lim_{\lambda \to 0} E_j = E_j^{(0)} \qquad (9.96)$$

As λ goes to zero, the eigenfunctions satisfying (9.94) approach eigenfunctions satisfying (9.92). Does this mean that $\lim_{\lambda \to 0} \psi_j = \psi_j^{(0)}$? In general, the answer is no. If $E_j^{(0)}$ is nondegenerate, there is a unique normalized eigenfunction $\psi_j^{(0)}$ of $\hat{H}^0$ with eigenvalue $E_j^{(0)}$, and we can be sure that $\lim_{\lambda \to 0} \psi_j = \psi_j^{(0)}$. However, if $E_j^{(0)}$ is the eigenvalue of the n-fold degenerate level, then (Section 3.6) any function of the form

$$c_1 \psi_1^{(0)} + c_2 \psi_2^{(0)} + \cdots + c_n \psi_n^{(0)} \qquad (9.97)$$

will be a solution of (9.92) with eigenvalue $E_j^{(0)}$. The set of linearly independent normalized functions $\psi_1^{(0)}, \psi_2^{(0)}, \ldots, \psi_n^{(0)}$ which we use as eigenfunctions corresponding to the states of the degenerate level, is not unique; using (9.97), we can construct an infinite number of sets of n linearly independent normalized eigenfunctions for the degenerate level. As far as the unperturbed problem is concerned, one such set is as good as another. For example, for the three degenerate $2p$ states of the hydrogen atom we can use the $2p_1, 2p_0,$ and $2p_{-1}$ functions or the $2p_x, 2p_y,$ and $2p_z$ functions, or some other set of three linearly independent functions constructed as linear combinations of the members of one of the preceding sets. For the perturbed eigenfunctions that correspond to the n-fold degenerate unperturbed level, all we can say is that

$$\lim_{\lambda \to 0} \psi_j = \sum_{i=1}^{n} c_i \psi_i^{(0)}, \qquad 1 \leqslant j \leqslant n \tag{9.98}$$

Our first task is thus to determine the *correct* zeroth-order wave functions for the perturbation $\hat{H}'$. Calling these correct zeroth-order functions $\varphi_j^{(0)}$, we have

$$\varphi_j^{(0)} = \sum_{i=1}^{n} c_i \psi_i^{(0)}, \qquad 1 \leqslant j \leqslant n \tag{9.99}$$

For each particular $\varphi_j^{(0)}$, we have a different set of coefficients c_i in (9.99); we could indicate this by using a pair of subscripts on the coefficients, calling them c_{ij}, but to keep the notation uncluttered we have not done so. The right set of zeroth-order functions will depend on what the perturbation $\hat{H}'$ is.

The treatment of the n-fold degenerate level proceeds like the nondegenerate treatment of Section 9.2, except that instead of $\psi_j^{(0)}$ we use $\varphi_j^{(0)}$. Instead of Eqs. (9.17) and (9.18), we have

$$\psi_j = \varphi_j^{(0)} + \lambda \psi_j^{(1)} + \lambda^2 \psi_j^{(2)} + \cdots, \qquad j = 1, 2, \dots, n \tag{9.100}$$

$$E_j = E_n^{(0)} + \lambda E_j^{(1)} + \lambda^2 E_j^{(2)} + \cdots, \qquad j = 1, 2, \dots, n \tag{9.101}$$

where Eq. (9.93) has been used. Substituting these expansions into the Schroedinger equation (9.94), we obtain

$$(\hat{H}^0 + \lambda \hat{H}')(\varphi_j^{(0)} + \lambda \psi_j^{(1)} + \lambda^2 \psi_j^{(2)} + \cdots)$$
$$= (E_n^{(0)} + \lambda E_j^{(1)} + \lambda^2 E_j^{(2)} + \cdots)(\varphi_j^{(0)} + \lambda \psi_j^{(1)} + \lambda^2 \psi_j^{(2)} + \cdots) \tag{9.102}$$

Equating the coefficients of λ^0 in (9.102), we have

$$\hat{H}^0 \varphi_j^{(0)} = E_n^{(0)} \varphi_j^{(0)}$$

$$\hat{H}^0 \sum_{i=1}^{n} c_i \psi_i^{(0)} = E_n^{(0)} \sum_{i=1}^{n} c_i \psi_i^{(0)} \tag{9.103}$$

In view of (9.92) and (9.93), Eq. (9.103) is satisfied and gives no new information.

Equating the coefficients of λ^1, we have

$$\hat{H}' \varphi_j^{(0)} + \hat{H}^0 \psi_j^{(1)} = E_n^{(0)} \psi_j^{(1)} + E_j^{(1)} \varphi_j^{(0)}$$

$$(E_n^{(0)} - \hat{H}^0) \psi_j^{(1)} = \sum_{i=1}^{n} c_i (\hat{H}' - E_j^{(1)}) \psi_i^{(0)} \tag{9.104}$$

Expanding and substituting into (9.104), we have

$$\psi_j^{(1)} = \sum_{k=1}^{\infty} a_k \psi_k^{(0)} \tag{9.105}$$

$$\sum_{k=1}^{\infty} a_k (E_n^{(0)} - \hat{H}^0) \psi_k^{(0)} = \sum_{i=1}^{n} c_i (\hat{H}' - E_j^{(1)}) \psi_i^{(0)} \tag{9.106}$$

The sum on the left side is over all the unperturbed states, while the sum on the right side is over the n unperturbed states that correspond to the n-fold degenerate energy level we are treating. Applying (9.92), we have

$$\sum_{k=1}^{\infty} a_k(E_n^{(0)} - E_k^{(0)})\psi_k^{(0)} = \sum_{i=1}^{n} c_i(\hat{H}' - E_j^{(1)})\psi_i^{(0)} \tag{9.107}$$

As we did with Eq. (9.26), we multiply by $\psi_m^{(0)*}$ and integrate:

$$\sum_{k=1}^{\infty} a_k(E_n^{(0)} - E_k^{(0)})\int \psi_m^{(0)*}\psi_k^{(0)}\,d\tau = \sum_{i=1}^{n} c_i\left(\int \psi_m^{(0)*}\hat{H}'\psi_i^{(0)}\,d\tau - E_j^{(1)}\int \psi_m^{(0)*}\psi_i^{(0)}\,d\tau\right) \tag{9.108}$$

Consider (9.108) when m is one of the states corresponding to the n-fold degenerate level under consideration, i.e., $1 \leqslant m \leqslant n$. The sum on the left side can be split into two sums, as follows:

$$\sum_{k=1}^{n} a_k(E_n^{(0)} - E_k^{(0)})\int \psi_m^{(0)*}\psi_k^{(0)}\,d\tau + \sum_{k=n+1}^{\infty} a_k(E_n^{(0)} - E_k^{(0)})\int \psi_m^{(0)*}\psi_k^{(0)}\,d\tau$$

For $1 \leqslant k \leqslant n$, we have $E_k^{(0)} = E_n^{(0)}$, so that each term of the first sum is zero. In the second sum we have $k > n$, while by hypothesis $1 \leqslant m \leqslant n$, so that $\psi_k^{(0)}$ and $\psi_m^{(0)}$ are eigenfunctions of a Hermitian operator (the unperturbed Hamiltonian) corresponding to different eigenvalues. Hence, for all terms in the second sum, $\psi_k^{(0)}$ and $\psi_m^{(0)}$ are orthogonal, and every term in this sum vanishes. We have shown that when m is one of the states of the n-fold degenerate level, the sum on the left side of (9.108) is zero; hence

$$\sum_{i=1}^{n}\left[\int \psi_m^{(0)*}\hat{H}'\psi_i^{(0)}\,d\tau - E_j^{(1)}\int \psi_m^{(0)*}\psi_i^{(0)}\,d\tau\right]c_i = 0, \qquad m = 1, 2, \ldots, n \tag{9.109}$$

This is a set of linear homogeneous equations in the n unknowns $c_1, c_2, \ldots, c_n$. To have a nontrivial solution, the determinant of the coefficients must vanish (Section 8.4):

$$\det\left[\int \psi_m^{(0)*}\hat{H}'\psi_i^{(0)}\,d\tau - E_j^{(1)}\int \psi_m^{(0)*}\psi_i^{(0)}\,d\tau\right] = 0 \tag{9.110}$$

$$\det(H_{mi}' - S_{mi}E_j^{(1)}) = 0 \tag{9.111}$$

$$H_{mi}' \equiv \int \psi_m^{(0)*}\hat{H}'\psi_i^{(0)}\,d\tau, \qquad S_{mi} \equiv \int \psi_m^{(0)*}\psi_i^{(0)}\,d\tau \tag{9.112}$$

The determinant is of order n, the degeneracy of the unperturbed level we are considering.

Consider the overlap integrals S_{mi}, $1 \leqslant m \leqslant n$, $1 \leqslant i \leqslant n$. We can always choose the eigenfunctions corresponding to a degenerate eigenvalue to be orthogonal (Section 7.2):

$$S_{mi} = \delta_{mi} \tag{9.113}$$

and (9.111) becomes

$$\det(H'_{mi} - \delta_{mi} E_j^{(1)}) = 0 \tag{9.114}$$

[As a check, note that for $n = 1$, Eq. (9.114) reduces to (9.30).]

Equation (9.114) is known as the *secular equation*. Writing out the *secular determinant* in detail, we have

$$\begin{vmatrix} H'_{11} - E_j^{(1)} & H'_{12} & H'_{13} & \cdots & H'_{1n} \\ H'_{21} & H'_{22} - E_j^{(1)} & H'_{23} & \cdots & H'_{2n} \\ H'_{31} & H'_{32} & H'_{33} - E_j^{(1)} & \cdots & H'_{3n} \\ \cdot & \cdot & \cdot & \cdots & \cdot \\ H'_{n1} & H'_{n2} & H'_{n3} & \cdots & H'_{nn} - E_j^{(1)} \end{vmatrix} = 0 \tag{9.115}$$

The secular equation is an algebraic equation of nth degree in $E_j^{(1)}$. It has n roots, $E_1^{(1)}, E_2^{(1)}, ..., E_n^{(1)}$ which are the first-order corrections to the energy of the n-fold degenerate unperturbed level. If the roots are all different, then the first-order perturbation correction has split the n-fold degenerate unperturbed level into n different perturbed levels of energies (correct through first-order)

$$E_n^{(0)} + E_1^{(1)}, \quad E_n^{(0)} + E_2^{(1)}, \quad ..., \quad E_n^{(0)} + E_n^{(1)} \tag{9.116}$$

It may happen that two or more roots of the secular equation are equal, so that the degeneracy is not completely removed in first order. In the rest of this section we assume that all the roots of (9.115) are different.

Having determined the n first-order energy corrections, we go back to the set of equations (9.109) to determine the unknowns c_i, which are the coefficients determining the correct zeroth-order wave functions. Writing (9.109) out, we have

$$(H'_{11} - E_j^{(1)}) c_1 + H'_{12} c_2 + \cdots + H'_{1n} c_n = 0$$
$$H'_{21} c_1 + (H'_{22} - E_j^{(1)}) c_2 + \cdots + H'_{2n} c_n = 0$$
$$\cdots \cdots \cdots \cdots \cdots \cdots \cdots \cdots \cdots \cdots \cdots \tag{9.117}$$
$$H'_{n1} c_1 + H'_{n2} c_2 + \cdots + (H'_{nn} - E_j^{(1)}) c_n = 0$$

where we have assumed orthonormality, Eq. (9.113).

To determine the zeroth-order wave function

$$\varphi_j^{(0)} = c_1 \psi_1^{(0)} + c_2 \psi_2^{(0)} + \cdots + c_n \psi_n^{(0)}$$

corresponding to the root $E_j^{(1)}$, we solve (9.117) for $c_2, c_3, ..., c_n$ in terms of c_1, and then determine c_1 by the normalization requirement:

$$\int \varphi_j^{(0)*} \varphi_j^{(0)} d\tau = 1 = \sum_{k=1}^{n} \sum_{l=1}^{n} c_k^* c_l \int \psi_k^{(0)*} \psi_l^{(0)} d\tau = \sum_{k=1}^{n} \sum_{l=1}^{n} c_k^* c_l \delta_{kl}$$

$$\sum_{k=1}^{n} |c_k|^2 = 1 \tag{9.118}$$

For each root $E_j^{(1)}$, $j = 1, 2, ..., n$, we have a different set of coefficients $c_1, c_2, ..., c_n$ giving a different correct zeroth-order wave function.

Using procedures similar to the nondegenerate case, we can now find the first-order corrections to the correct zeroth-order wave functions, and the second-order energy corrections. We omit the details [7] and simply give the results. The coefficients in (9.105) determining the first-order wave-function correction are

$$a_k = \frac{\langle \psi_k^{(0)} | \hat{H}' | \varphi_j^{(0)} \rangle}{E_n^{(0)} - E_k^{(0)}}, \qquad k > n, \qquad 1 \leqslant j \leqslant n \qquad \text{(9.119)}$$

Equation (9.119) is the same as the corresponding equation (9.33) for the non-degenerate case, except that we must use the correct zeroth-order wave function $\varphi_j^{(0)}$ in the integral. Equation (9.119) gives only the correction due to mixing in of wave functions from states other than those belonging to the degenerate unperturbed level; we omit the formula for a_k with $k \leqslant n$. The second-order energy correction is

$$E_j^{(2)} = \sum_{k > n} \frac{|\langle \psi_k^{(0)} | \hat{H}' | \varphi_j^{(0)} \rangle|^2}{E_n^{(0)} - E_k^{(0)}}, \qquad 1 \leqslant j \leqslant n \qquad \text{(9.120)}$$

which is the same as (9.46) in the nondegenerate case, except that we must use the correct zeroth-order wave function in the integrals. In Section 9.6, we will show that Eq. (9.30) for the first-order energy correction in the nondegenerate case holds also for the degenerate case, if we use the correct zeroth-order wave function:

$$E_j^{(1)} = \langle \varphi_j^{(0)} | \hat{H}' | \varphi_j^{(0)} \rangle, \qquad 1 \leqslant j \leqslant n \qquad \text{(9.121)}$$

Thus, the equations for the degenerate case are essentially the same as for the non-degenerate case, provided we use the correct zeroth-order wave functions.

As an example, consider the effect of a perturbation $\hat{H}'$ on the lowest degenerate energy level of a particle in a cubic box. We have three states corresponding to this level: $\psi_{211}^{(0)}$, $\psi_{121}^{(0)}$, and $\psi_{112}^{(0)}$. These unperturbed wave functions are orthonormal, and the secular equation (9.114) is

$$\begin{vmatrix} \langle 211|\hat{H}'|211\rangle - E_j^{(1)} & \langle 211|\hat{H}'|121\rangle & \langle 211|\hat{H}'|112\rangle \\ \langle 121|\hat{H}'|211\rangle & \langle 121|\hat{H}'|121\rangle - E_j^{(1)} & \langle 121|\hat{H}'|112\rangle \\ \langle 112|\hat{H}'|211\rangle & \langle 112|\hat{H}'|121\rangle & \langle 112|\hat{H}'|112\rangle - E_j^{(1)} \end{vmatrix} = 0$$

Solving this equation, we find the first-order energy corrections:

$$E_1^{(1)}, \qquad E_2^{(1)}, \qquad E_3^{(1)} \qquad \text{(9.122)}$$

The triply degenerate unperturbed level is split into three levels of energies (through first order)

$$(6h^2/8ma^2) + E_1^{(1)}, \qquad (6h^2/8ma^2) + E_2^{(1)}, \qquad (6h^2/8ma^2) + E_3^{(1)}$$

Using each of the roots (9.122), we get a different set of simultaneous equations (9.117). Solving each set, we find three sets of coefficients, which determine the three correct zeroth-order wave functions.

The secular determinant (9.111) has the same general form as the determinant (8.88) occurring in the linear variation method. Hence, the determinant in (8.88) is often called a secular determinant.

---

[7] *Bates*, Vol. I, pp. 197–198; *Hameka*, pp. 208–209; Problem 9.5.

9.6 Simplification of the Secular Equation

For an unperturbed level with a high degree of degeneracy, the secular equation (9.115) becomes troublesome to solve. Things are simplified if some of the off-diagonal elements of the secular determinant are zero. In the most favorable case, all off-diagonal elements are zero, so that

$$
\begin{vmatrix}
H'_{11} - E_j^{(1)} & 0 & 0 & \cdots & 0 \\
0 & H'_{22} - E_j^{(1)} & 0 & \cdots & 0 \\
0 & 0 & H'_{33} - E_j^{(1)} & \cdots & 0 \\
\cdot & \cdot & \cdot & \cdots & \cdot \\
0 & 0 & 0 & \cdots & H'_{nn} - E_j^{(1)}
\end{vmatrix} = 0 \quad \text{(9.123)}
$$

$$
(H'_{11} - E_j^{(1)})(H'_{22} - E_j^{(1)})(H'_{33} - E_j^{(1)}) \cdots (H'_{nn} - E_j^{(1)}) = 0
$$

$$
E_1^{(1)} = H'_{11}, \quad E_2^{(1)} = H'_{22}, \quad E_3^{(1)} = H'_{33}, \quad \ldots, \quad E_n^{(1)} = H'_{nn} \quad \text{(9.124)}
$$

Now we want to determine the correct zeroth-order wave functions. We will assume that the roots (9.124) are all different. For the root $E_j^{(1)} = H'_{11}$, the system of equations (9.117) is

$$
0 = 0
$$

$$
(H'_{22} - H'_{11})c_2 = 0
$$

$$
\cdots \cdots \cdots \cdots \cdots \cdots \quad \text{(9.125)}
$$

$$
(H'_{nn} - H'_{11})c_n = 0
$$

Since we are assuming unequal roots, the factors of $c_2, c_3, \ldots, c_n$ in these equations are all nonzero; hence

$$
c_2 = 0, \quad c_3 = 0, \quad \ldots, \quad c_n = 0 \quad \text{(9.126)}
$$

The normalization condition (9.118) gives $c_1 = 1$. The correct zeroth-order wave function corresponding to the first-order perturbation energy correction H'_{11} is then [Eq. (9.99)]

$$
\varphi_1^{(0)} = \psi_1^{(0)} \quad \text{(9.127)}
$$

For the root H'_{22}, the same reasoning that led to (9.127) gives for the correct zeroth-order wave function corresponding to the root H'_{22}:

$$
\varphi_2^{(0)} = \psi_2^{(0)} \quad \text{(9.128)}
$$

Using each of the remaining roots, we find similarly,

$$
\varphi_3^{(0)} = \psi_3^{(0)}, \quad \ldots, \quad \varphi_n^{(0)} = \psi_n^{(0)} \quad \text{(9.129)}
$$

In other words, when the secular determinant is in diagonal form, the initially assumed functions $\psi_1^{(0)}, \psi_2^{(0)}, \ldots, \psi_n^{(0)}$ are the correct zeroth-order wave functions for the particular perturbation $\hat{H}'$.

The converse is also true; if the initially assumed functions are the correct zeroth-order functions, then the secular determinant is in diagonal form. This is seen as follows: from $\varphi_1^{(0)} = \psi_1^{(0)}$ we know that the coefficients in the expansion

$$\varphi_1^{(0)} = \sum_{i=1}^{n} c_i \psi_i^{(0)}$$

are $c_1 = 1, c_2 = c_3 = \cdots = c_n = 0$, so that for $j = 1$, the set of simultaneous equations (9.117) becomes

$$H'_{11} - E_1^{(1)} = 0$$

$$H'_{21} = 0$$

$$\cdots\cdots\cdots$$

$$H'_{n1} = 0$$

(9.130)

Applying the same reasoning to the remaining functions $\varphi_j^{(0)}$, we conclude that $H'_{im} = 0$ for $i \neq m$. Hence, use of the correct zeroth-order functions makes the secular determinant diagonal. Note also that the first-order corrections to the energy can be found by averaging the perturbation over the correct zeroth-order wave functions,

$$E_j^{(1)} = \int \varphi_j^{(0)*} \hat{H}' \varphi_j^{(0)} \, d\tau$$

(9.131)

a result mentioned in Eq. (9.121).

Often, instead of the secular determinant being in diagonal form, it is in block-diagonal form. For example, we might have

$$
\begin{vmatrix}
H'_{11} - E_j^{(1)} & H'_{12} & 0 & 0 \\
H'_{21} & H'_{22} - E_j^{(1)} & 0 & 0 \\
0 & 0 & H'_{33} - E_j^{(1)} & H'_{34} \\
0 & 0 & H'_{43} & H'_{44} - E_j^{(1)}
\end{vmatrix} = 0
$$

(9.132)

The secular equation (9.132) becomes (see Section 8.3)

$$
\begin{vmatrix}
H'_{11} - E_j^{(1)} & H'_{12} \\
H'_{21} & H'_{22} - E_j^{(1)}
\end{vmatrix}
\cdot
\begin{vmatrix}
H'_{33} - E_j^{(1)} & H'_{34} \\
H'_{43} & H'_{44} - E_j^{(1)}
\end{vmatrix} = 0
$$

(9.133)

and its roots are found from

$$
\begin{vmatrix}
H'_{11} - E_j^{(1)} & H'_{12} \\
H'_{21} & H'_{22} - E_j^{(1)}
\end{vmatrix} = 0
$$

(9.134)

$$
\begin{vmatrix}
H'_{33} - E_j^{(1)} & H'_{34} \\
H'_{43} & H'_{44} - E_j^{(1)}
\end{vmatrix} = 0
$$

(9.135)

Let the roots of (9.134) be $E_1^{(1)}$ and $E_2^{(1)}$ and the roots of (9.135) be $E_3^{(1)}$ and $E_4^{(1)}$. For $E_1^{(1)}$, the set of equations (9.117) becomes

$$\left.\begin{array}{l}(H'_{11} - E_1^{(1)})c_1 + H'_{12}c_2 = 0 \\ H'_{21}c_1 + (H'_{22} - E_1^{(1)})c_2 = 0\end{array}\right\}$$

(9.136)

$$\left.\begin{array}{l}(H'_{33} - E_1^{(1)})c_3 + H'_{34}c_4 = 0 \\ H'_{43}c_3 + (H'_{44} - E_1^{(1)})c_4 = 0\end{array}\right\}$$

(9.137)

Because $E_1^{(1)}$ is a root of (9.134), the set of equations (9.136) has the determinant of its coefficients equal to zero, and therefore possesses a nontrivial solution. However (assuming there are no equal roots of the secular equation), $E_1^{(1)}$ is not a root of (9.135), so that the determinant of the coefficients of the set of equations (9.137) is nonzero. Therefore (9.137) has only the trivial solution $c_3 = c_4 = 0$. The correct zeroth-order wave function $\varphi_1^{(0)}$ is then

$$\varphi_1^{(0)} = c_1 \psi_1^{(0)} + c_2 \psi_2^{(0)}$$

Similar reasoning shows that $\varphi_2^{(0)}$ is a linear combination of $\psi_1^{(0)}$ and $\psi_2^{(0)}$, while $\varphi_3^{(0)}$ and $\varphi_4^{(0)}$ are each linear combinations of $\psi_3^{(0)}$ and $\psi_4^{(0)}$. When the secular equation is in block-diagonal form, it factors into two or more smaller secular equations, and the set of simultaneous equations (9.117) breaks up into two or more smaller sets of simultaneous equations.

Conversely, if we have, say, a fourfold-degenerate unperturbed level, and we happen to know that $\varphi_1^{(0)}$ and $\varphi_2^{(0)}$ are each linear combinations of $\psi_1^{(0)}$ and $\psi_2^{(0)}$ only, while $\varphi_3^{(0)}$ and $\varphi_4^{(0)}$ are each linear combinations of $\psi_3^{(0)}$ and $\psi_4^{(0)}$ only, we are led to two 2×2 secular determinants rather than a 4×4 secular determinant. This is true because instead of (9.99) we have the two sets of equations

$$\varphi_j^{(0)} = \sum_{i=1}^{2} c_i \psi_i^{(0)}, \qquad j = 1, 2$$

$$\varphi_j^{(0)} = \sum_{i=3}^{4} c_i \psi_i^{(0)}, \qquad j = 3, 4$$

How can we choose the right zeroth-order wave functions in advance, and thereby simplify the secular equation? Suppose there is an operator $\hat{A}$ that commutes with both $\hat{H}^0$ and $\hat{H}'$. Then we can choose the unperturbed functions to be eigenfunctions of $\hat{A}$. Because $\hat{A}$ commutes with $\hat{H}'$, this choice of unperturbed functions will make the integrals H_{ij}' vanish if $\psi_i^{(0)}$ and $\psi_j^{(0)}$ belong to different eigenvalues of $\hat{A}$ [see Eq. (7.80)]. Thus, if the eigenvalues of $\hat{A}$ for $\psi_1^{(0)}, \psi_2^{(0)}, \ldots, \psi_n^{(0)}$ are all different, the secular determinant will be in diagonal form and we will have the right zeroth-order wave functions. If some of the eigenvalues of $\hat{A}$ are the same, we will get block-diagonal rather than diagonal form. In general, the correct zeroth-order functions will be linear combinations of those unperturbed functions that have the same eigenvalue of $\hat{A}$. (This is to be expected since $\hat{A}$ commutes with $\hat{H} = \hat{H}^0 + \hat{H}'$, so the perturbed eigenfunctions of $\hat{H}$ can be chosen to be eigenfunctions of $\hat{A}$.) For an application of these ideas, see Problem 9.11, dealing with the Stark effect in the hydrogen atom.

9.7 Perturbation Treatment of the First Excited States of Helium

In Section 9.3 we considered the ground state of the helium atom according to perturbation theory. In this section we treat the lowest excited states. The unperturbed energy is given by Eq. (9.59). The lowest excited unperturbed states have $n_1 = 1$, $n_2 = 2$ or $n_1 = 2$, $n_2 = 1$ with an energy

$$E^{(0)} = -\frac{5Z^2}{8}\left(\frac{e^2}{a_0}\right) \tag{9.138}$$

Recall that the $n = 2$ level of a hydrogenlike atom is fourfold degenerate, the $2s$ and three $2p$ states all having the same energy. The first excited unperturbed energy level is eightfold degenerate; the eight unperturbed wave functions are [Eq. (9.55)]

$$\begin{aligned}
\psi_1^{(0)} &= 1s(1)\,2s(2) & \psi_5^{(0)} &= 1s(1)\,2p_y(2) \\
\psi_2^{(0)} &= 2s(1)\,1s(2) & \psi_6^{(0)} &= 2p_y(1)\,1s(2) \\
\psi_3^{(0)} &= 1s(1)\,2p_x(2) & \psi_7^{(0)} &= 1s(1)\,2p_z(2) \\
\psi_4^{(0)} &= 2p_x(1)\,1s(2) & \psi_8^{(0)} &= 2p_z(1)\,1s(2)
\end{aligned} \tag{9.139}$$

where $1s(1)\,2s(2)$ signifies the product of a hydrogenlike $1s$ function for electron one and a hydrogenlike $2s$ function for electron two. The explicit form of, for example, $\psi_8^{(0)}$, is (Table 6.2)

$$\psi_8^{(0)} = \frac{1}{4(2\pi)^{1/2}}\left(\frac{Z}{a_0}\right)^{5/2} r_1 e^{-Zr_1/2a_0}\cos\theta_1 \cdot \frac{1}{\pi^{1/2}}\left(\frac{Z}{a_0}\right)^{3/2} e^{-Zr_2/a_0}$$

We have chosen to use the real $2p$ hydrogenlike orbitals, rather than the complex ones.

Since we have a degenerate unperturbed level, we must deal with a secular equation. To use (9.115), the functions $\psi_1^{(0)}, \psi_2^{(0)}, \ldots, \psi_8^{(0)}$ must be orthonormal. This condition is met. For example

$$\int \psi_1^{(0)*}\psi_1^{(0)}\,d\tau = \int\int 1s(1)^*2s(2)^*1s(1)\,2s(2)\,d\tau_1\,d\tau_2$$

$$= \int |1s(1)|^2\,d\tau_1 \int |2s(2)|^2\,d\tau_2 = 1\cdot 1 = 1$$

$$\int \psi_3^{(0)*}\psi_5^{(0)}\,d\tau = \int |1s(1)|^2\,d\tau_1 \int 2p_x(2)^*2p_y(2)\,d\tau_2 = 1\cdot 0 = 0$$

where the orthonormality of the hydrogenlike orbitals has been used.

The secular determinant contains $8^2 = 64$ elements. The operator $\hat{H}'$ is Hermitian, so that $H_{ij}' = (H_{ji}')^*$. Also, since $\hat{H}'$ and $\psi_1^{(0)}, \ldots, \psi_8^{(0)}$ are all real, we have $(H_{ji}')^* = H_{ji}'$, so that $H_{ij}' = H_{ji}'$. The secular determinant is symmetric about the principal diagonal. This cuts the labor of evaluating integrals almost in half.

By using parity considerations we can show that most of the integrals H_{ij}' are zero. First consider H_{13}':

$$H_{13}' = \int_{-\infty}^{\infty}\int_{-\infty}^{\infty}\int_{-\infty}^{\infty}\int_{-\infty}^{\infty}\int_{-\infty}^{\infty}\int_{-\infty}^{\infty} 1s(1)\,2s(2)\frac{e^2}{r_{12}}$$

$$\times\, 1s(1)\,2p_x(2)\,dx_1\,dy_1\,dz_1\,dx_2\,dy_2\,dz_2$$

An s hydrogenlike function depends only on $r = (x^2+y^2+z^2)^{1/2}$ and is therefore an even function. The $2p_x(2)$ function is an odd function of x_2 [Eq. (6.138)]. r_{12} is given by (9.90), and if we invert all six coordinates, r_{12} is unchanged:

$$r_{12} \rightarrow [(-x_1+x_2)^2 + (-y_1+y_2)^2 + (-z_1+z_2)^2]^{1/2} = r_{12}$$

Hence on inverting all six coordinates, the integrand of H'_{13} goes into minus itself. We conclude [Eq. (7.96)] that $H'_{13} = 0$. The same reasoning yields $H'_{14} = H'_{15} = H'_{16} = H'_{17} = H'_{18} = 0$ and $H'_{23} = H'_{24} = H'_{25} = H'_{26} = H'_{27} = H'_{28} = 0$. Now consider H'_{35}:

$$H'_{35} = \int_{-\infty}^{\infty} \cdots \int_{-\infty}^{\infty} 1s(1)\, 2p_x(2) \frac{e^2}{r_{12}} 1s(1)\, 2p_y(2)\, dx_1 \cdots dz_2 \qquad \textbf{(9.140)}$$

Consider the effect of inverting the coordinates x_1 and x_2: $x_1 \rightarrow -x_1$, $x_2 \rightarrow -x_2$. This transformation will leave r_{12} unchanged. The functions $1s(1)$ and $2p_y(2)$ will be unaffected. However, $2p_x(2)$ will go over to minus itself, so that the net effect will be to change the integrand of H'_{35} into minus itself. Therefore [Eq. (7.98)] $H'_{35} = 0$. Likewise $H'_{36} = H'_{37} = H'_{38} = 0$ and $H'_{45} = H'_{46} = H'_{47} = H'_{48} = 0$. By considering the transformation $y_1 \rightarrow -y_1$ $y_2 \rightarrow -y_2$, we see that $H'_{57} = H'_{58} = H'_{67} = H'_{68} = 0$. The secular equation is therefore

$$\begin{vmatrix} b_{11} & H'_{12} & 0 & 0 & 0 & 0 & 0 & 0 \\ H'_{12} & b_{22} & 0 & 0 & 0 & 0 & 0 & 0 \\ 0 & 0 & b_{33} & H'_{34} & 0 & 0 & 0 & 0 \\ 0 & 0 & H'_{34} & b_{44} & 0 & 0 & 0 & 0 \\ 0 & 0 & 0 & 0 & b_{55} & H'_{56} & 0 & 0 \\ 0 & 0 & 0 & 0 & H'_{56} & b_{66} & 0 & 0 \\ 0 & 0 & 0 & 0 & 0 & 0 & b_{77} & H'_{78} \\ 0 & 0 & 0 & 0 & 0 & 0 & H'_{78} & b_{88} \end{vmatrix} = 0$$

$$b_{ii} \equiv H'_{ii} - E^{(1)}, \qquad i = 1, 2, \ldots, 8$$

The secular determinant is in block-diagonal form and factors into four determinants, each of second order. We conclude that the correct zeroth-order functions have the form

$$\varphi_1^{(0)} = c_1 \psi_1^{(0)} + c_2 \psi_2^{(0)}, \qquad \varphi_2^{(0)} = \bar{c}_1 \psi_1^{(0)} + \bar{c}_2 \psi_2^{(0)}$$

$$\varphi_3^{(0)} = c_3 \psi_3^{(0)} + c_4 \psi_4^{(0)}, \qquad \varphi_4^{(0)} = \bar{c}_3 \psi_3^{(0)} + \bar{c}_4 \psi_4^{(0)}$$

$$\varphi_5^{(0)} = c_5 \psi_5^{(0)} + c_6 \psi_6^{(0)}, \qquad \varphi_6^{(0)} = \bar{c}_5 \psi_5^{(0)} + \bar{c}_6 \psi_6^{(0)}$$

$$\varphi_7^{(0)} = c_7 \psi_7^{(0)} + c_8 \psi_8^{(0)}, \qquad \varphi_8^{(0)} = \bar{c}_7 \psi_7^{(0)} + \bar{c}_8 \psi_8^{(0)}$$

$$\textbf{(9.141)}$$

where the unbarred coefficients correspond to one root of each second-order determinant and the barred coefficients correspond to the second root.

The first determinant is

$$\begin{vmatrix} H'_{11} - E^{(1)} & H'_{12} \\ H'_{12} & H'_{22} - E^{(1)} \end{vmatrix} = 0 \qquad \textbf{(9.142)}$$

We have

$$H'_{11} = \int_{-\infty}^{\infty} \cdots \int_{-\infty}^{\infty} 1s(1)\,2s(2)\frac{e^2}{r_{12}}\,1s(1)\,2s(2)\,dx_1 \cdots dz_2$$

$$H'_{11} = \int\int [1s(1)]^2\,[2s(2)]^2\,\frac{e^2}{r_{12}}\,d\tau_1\,d\tau_2$$

$$H'_{22} = \int\int [1s(2)]^2\,[2s(1)]^2\,\frac{e^2}{r_{12}}\,d\tau_1\,d\tau_2$$

The integration variables are dummy variables and may be given any symbols whatever. Let us relabel the integration variables in H'_{22} as follows: we interchange x_1 and x_2, interchange y_1 and y_2, and interchange z_1 and z_2. This relabeling leaves r_{12} [Eq. (9.90)] unchanged, so that

$$H'_{22} = \int\int [1s(1)]^2\,[2s(2)]^2\,\frac{e^2}{r_{12}}\,d\tau_2\,d\tau_1 = H'_{11} \tag{9.143}$$

(The same argument shows $H'_{33} = H'_{44}$, $H'_{55} = H'_{66}$, $H'_{77} = H'_{88}$.)

We denote H'_{11} by the symbol J_{1s2s}:

$$H'_{11} = J_{1s2s} = \int\int [1s(1)]^2\,[2s(2)]^2\,\frac{e^2}{r_{12}}\,d\tau_1\,d\tau_2 \tag{9.144}$$

This is an example of a *Coulomb integral*, the name arising from the fact that J_{1s2s} is equal to the electrostatic energy of repulsion between an electron with the probability density function $[1s]^2$ and an electron with probability density function $[2s]^2$. The integral H'_{12} is denoted by K_{1s2s}:

$$H'_{12} = K_{1s2s} = \int\int 1s(1)\,2s(2)\frac{e^2}{r_{12}}\,2s(1)\,1s(2)\,d\tau_1\,d\tau_2 \tag{9.145}$$

This is an *exchange integral*—the functions on the left and right of e^2/r_{12} differ from each other by an exchange of electrons one and two.

With this notation (9.142) becomes

$$\begin{vmatrix} J_{1s2s}-E^{(1)} & K_{1s2s} \\ K_{1s2s} & J_{1s2s}-E^{(1)} \end{vmatrix} = 0 \tag{9.146}$$

$$[J_{1s2s}-E^{(1)}]^2 = [K_{1s2s}]^2$$

$$E_1^{(1)} = J_{1s2s} + K_{1s2s}, \qquad E_2^{(1)} = J_{1s2s} - K_{1s2s} \tag{9.147}$$

We now find the coefficients of the correct zeroth-order wave functions corresponding to these two roots of the secular equation. Using $E_1^{(1)}$, we have for (9.117):

$$-K_{1s2s}c_1 + K_{1s2s}c_2 = 0$$

$$K_{1s2s}c_1 - K_{1s2s}c_2 = 0$$

so that $c_1 = c_2$. Normalizing, we have

$$\int |\varphi_1^{(0)}|^2 \, d\tau = \int [c_1 \psi_1^{(0)} + c_1 \psi_2^{(0)}]^2 \, d\tau = c_1^2 + c_1^2 = 1$$

$$c_1 = 1/\sqrt{2}$$

where the orthonormality of $\psi_1^{(0)}$ and $\psi_2^{(0)}$ has been used. The zeroth-order wave function corresponding to $E_1^{(1)}$ is then

$$\varphi_1^{(0)} = 2^{-1/2} (\psi_1^{(0)} + \psi_2^{(0)}) = 2^{-1/2} [1s(1) 2s(2) + 2s(1) 1s(2)] \qquad \text{(9.148)}$$

In like manner, we find as the function corresponding to $E_2^{(1)}$,

$$\varphi_2^{(0)} = 2^{-1/2} (\psi_1^{(0)} - \psi_2^{(0)}) = 2^{-1/2} [1s(1) 2s(2) - 2s(1) 1s(2)] \qquad \text{(9.149)}$$

We have three more second-order determinants to deal with:

$$\begin{vmatrix} H'_{33} - E^{(1)} & H'_{34} \\ H'_{34} & H'_{33} - E^{(1)} \end{vmatrix} = 0 \qquad \text{(9.150)}$$

$$\begin{vmatrix} H'_{55} - E^{(1)} & H'_{56} \\ H'_{56} & H'_{55} - E^{(1)} \end{vmatrix} = 0 \qquad \text{(9.151)}$$

$$\begin{vmatrix} H'_{77} - E^{(1)} & H'_{78} \\ H'_{78} & H'_{77} - E^{(1)} \end{vmatrix} = 0 \qquad \text{(9.152)}$$

Consider H'_{33} and H'_{55}:

$$H'_{33} = \int_{-\infty}^{\infty} \cdots \int_{-\infty}^{\infty} 1s(1) 2p_x(2) \frac{e^2}{r_{12}} 1s(1) 2p_x(2) \, dx_1 \cdots dz_2$$

$$H'_{55} = \int_{-\infty}^{\infty} \cdots \int_{-\infty}^{\infty} 1s(1) 2p_y(2) \frac{e^2}{r_{12}} 1s(1) 2p_y(2) \, dx_1 \cdots dz_2$$

These two integrals are equal; the only difference between them involves replacing $2p_x(2)$ by $2p_y(2)$, and these two orbitals differ only in their orientation in space. More formally, if we relabel the dummy integration variables in H'_{33} according to the scheme $x_2 \to y_2$, $y_2 \to x_2$, $x_1 \to y_1$, $y_1 \to x_1$, then r_{12} is unaffected and H'_{33} is transformed to H'_{55}. Similar reasoning shows H'_{77} is equal to these two integrals. Introducing the symbol J_{1s2p} for these Coulomb integrals, we have

$$H'_{33} = H'_{55} = H'_{77} = J_{1s2p} = \int\int 1s(1) 2p_z(2) \frac{e^2}{r_{12}} 1s(1) 2p_z(2) \, d\tau_1 \, d\tau_2$$

Also, the exchange integrals involving the $2p$ orbitals are equal:

$$H'_{34} = H'_{56} = H'_{78} = K_{1s2p} = \int\int 1s(1) 2p_z(2) \frac{e^2}{r_{12}} 2p_z(1) 1s(2) \, d\tau_1 \, d\tau_2$$

The three determinants (9.150)–(9.152) are thus identical and have the form

$$\begin{vmatrix} J_{1s2p} - E^{(1)} & K_{1s2p} \\ K_{1s2p} & J_{1s2p} - E^{(1)} \end{vmatrix} = 0 \qquad \text{(9.153)}$$

The determinant is similar to (9.146), and by analogy with (9.147)–(9.149), we have

$$E_3^{(1)} = E_5^{(1)} = E_7^{(1)} = J_{1s2p} + K_{1s2p} \tag{9.154}$$

$$E_4^{(1)} = E_6^{(1)} = E_8^{(1)} = J_{1s2p} - K_{1s2p} \tag{9.155}$$

$$\varphi_3^{(0)} = 2^{-1/2}[1s(1)\,2p_x(2) + 1s(2)\,2p_x(1)]$$
$$\varphi_4^{(0)} = 2^{-1/2}[1s(1)\,2p_x(2) - 1s(2)\,2p_x(1)]$$
$$\varphi_5^{(0)} = 2^{-1/2}[1s(1)\,2p_y(2) + 1s(2)\,2p_y(1)]$$
$$\varphi_6^{(0)} = 2^{-1/2}[1s(1)\,2p_y(2) - 1s(2)\,2p_y(1)] \tag{9.156}$$
$$\varphi_7^{(0)} = 2^{-1/2}[1s(1)\,2p_z(2) + 1s(2)\,2p_z(1)]$$
$$\varphi_8^{(0)} = 2^{-1/2}[1s(1)\,2p_z(2) - 1s(2)\,2p_z(1)]$$

The electrostatic repulsion e^2/r_{12} between the electrons has partly removed the degeneracy; the hypothetical eightfold-degenerate unperturbed level has been split into two nondegenerate levels associated with the configuration $1s2s$, and two triply degenerate levels associated with the configuration $1s2p$. (It might be thought that higher-order energy corrections would further resolve the degeneracy; actually it requires application of an external magnetic field to completely remove the degeneracy.)

We must now evaluate the integrals in (9.147) and (9.154). As might be expected, we employ the expansion (9.64). [Note that (9.63) is a Coulomb integral, J_{1s1s}.] We find (Problem 9.8)

$$J_{1s2s} = \frac{17}{81}\frac{Ze^2}{a_0}, \qquad J_{1s2p} = \frac{59}{243}\frac{Ze^2}{a_0}$$

$$K_{1s2s} = \frac{16}{729}\frac{Ze^2}{a_0}, \qquad K_{1s2p} = \frac{112}{6561}\frac{Ze^2}{a_0} \tag{9.157}$$

Figure 9.3 is a correlation diagram for the first group of helium excited states. For $Z = 2$, we have

$$E^{(0)} = -\frac{20}{8}\left(\frac{e^2}{a_0}\right) = -68.0 \text{ eV} \tag{9.158}$$

$$J_{1s2s} = 11.4 \text{ eV}, \qquad K_{1s2s} = 1.2 \text{ eV} \tag{9.159}$$

$$J_{1s2p} = 13.2 \text{ eV}, \qquad K_{1s2p} = 0.9 \text{ eV} \tag{9.160}$$

The results of the first-order energy corrections seem to indicate that the lower of the two levels of the $1s2p$ configuration lies below the higher of the two levels of the $1s2s$ configuration. Experimental study of the helium spectrum reveals that this is not so. The error is due, of course, to neglect of the higher-order perturbation energy corrections.

Knight and Scherr have calculated the second-order and third-order energy corrections, $E^{(2)}$ and $E^{(3)}$, for these four excited levels.[8] In Fig. 9.4 we give their

---

[8] R. E. Knight and C. W. Scherr, *Rev. Mod. Phys.*, **35**, 431 (1963); for energy corrections through 17th order, see F. C. Sanders and C. W. Scherr, *Phys. Rev.*, **181**, 84 (1969).

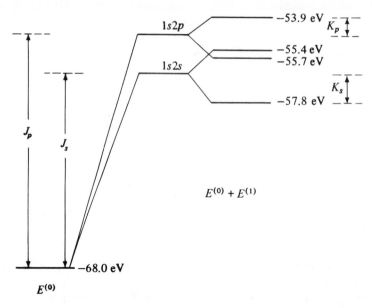

FIGURE 9.3 *Correlation diagram for the first excited levels of the helium atom.*

results, rounded off to the nearest 0.1 eV. They used the variational perturbation method outlined in Section 9.3. Comparison with experiment shows the Knight and Scherr values to differ from the true values by 0.01 to 0.09 eV. Figure 9.4 shows that Fig. 9.3 is quite inaccurate. Since the perturbation e^2/r_{12} is not really very small, we cannot expect great accuracy from a perturbation treatment that includes only the $E^{(1)}$ correction to the energy.

Note that the first-order correction to the wave function, $\psi^{(1)}$, will include contributions from other configurations (configuration interaction). When we say that a level belongs to the configuration $1s2s$, we are indicating the configuration that makes the largest contribution to the true wave function.

The perturbation treatment of the first excited states of helium illustrates several important points, which we now discuss. We started with the eight degenerate zeroth-order functions (9.139). These functions have three kinds of degeneracy. There is the degeneracy between hydrogenlike functions with the

$$
1s2p \left\{ \begin{array}{l} \rule{3cm}{0.4pt}\ -57.8\ \mathrm{eV} \\ \rule{3cm}{0.4pt}\ -58.1 \end{array} \right.
$$

$$
1s2s \left\{ \begin{array}{l} \rule{3cm}{0.4pt}\ -58.4 \\ \rule{3cm}{0.4pt}\ -59.2 \end{array} \right.
$$

FIGURE 9.4 $E^{(0)} + E^{(1)} + E^{(2)} + E^{(3)}$ *for the first excited levels of helium.*

same n, but different l; the $2s$ and the $2p$ functions have the same energy. There is the degeneracy between hydrogenlike functions with the same n and l, but different m; the $2p_1$, $2p_0$, and $2p_{-1}$ functions have the same energy. (For convenience we used the real functions $2p_{x,y,z}$, but we could have started with the functions $2p_{1,0,-1}$.) Finally, there is the degeneracy between functions that differ only in the interchange of the two electrons between the orbitals; the functions $\psi_1^{(0)} = 1s(1)2s(2)$ and $\psi_2^{(0)} = 1s(2)2s(1)$ have the same energy. We refer to this last kind of degeneracy as *exchange degeneracy*. When the interelectronic repulsion e^2/r_{12} was introduced as a perturbation, the degeneracy associated with the quantum number l, and the exchange degeneracy were removed. The degeneracy associated with m remained, however; each $1s2p$ helium level is triply degenerate, and we could just as well have used the $2p_1$, $2p_0$, and $2p_{-1}$ orbitals instead of the real orbitals in constructing the correct zeroth-order wave functions. Let us consider the reasons for the removal of the l and the exchange degeneracy.

The interelectronic repulsion in helium causes the $2s$ orbital energy to be less than the $2p$ energy. We can give a simple physical explanation for this fact. Figures 6.7 and 6.8 show that a $2s$ electron has a greater probability than a $2p$ electron of being closer to the nucleus than the $1s$ electron(s). A $2s$ electron will not be as effectively shielded from the nucleus by the $1s$ electron(s), and will therefore have a lower energy than a $2p$ electron. [According to Eq. (6.107), the greater the nuclear charge, the lower the energy.] Mathematically, the difference between the $1s2s$ and the $1s2p$ energies results from the Coulomb integral J_{1s2s} being smaller than J_{1s2p}. These Coulomb integrals represent the electrostatic repulsion between the appropriate charge distributions. When the $2s$ electron penetrates the charge distribution of the $1s$ electron, it feels a repulsion from only the unpenetrated part of the $1s$ charge distribution (recall that this point came up in the discussion of Rutherford scattering in Section 1.1); hence, the $1s$–$2s$ electrostatic repulsion is less than the $1s$–$2p$ repulsion, and the $1s2s$ levels lie below the $1s2p$ levels. The interelectronic repulsion in many-electron atoms lifts the l degeneracy, and the orbital energies for the same value of n increase with increasing l.

Now consider the removal of the exchange degeneracy. The functions (9.139) with which we began the perturbation treatment have each electron assigned to a definite orbital. For example, the function $\psi_1^{(0)} = 1s(1)2s(2)$ has electron 1 in the $1s$ orbital and electron 2 in the $2s$ orbital; for $\psi_2^{(0)}$ the opposite is true. The secular determinant was not diagonal, so that the initial functions were not the correct zeroth-order wave functions. The correct zeroth-order functions do not assign each electron to a definite orbital. Thus, the first two correct zeroth-order functions are

$$\varphi_1^{(0)} = 2^{-1/2}[1s(1)2s(2)+1s(2)2s(1)] \qquad (9.161)$$

$$\varphi_2^{(0)} = 2^{-1/2}[1s(1)2s(2)-1s(2)2s(1)] \qquad (9.162)$$

so that we cannot say which orbital electron 1 is in, for either $\varphi_1^{(0)}$ or $\varphi_2^{(0)}$. This feature of the wave functions of systems containing more than one electron is a result of the indistinguishability of identical particles in quantum mechanics, and will be discussed further in the next chapter. The functions (9.161) and (9.162) have different energies, so that the exchange degeneracy is removed when we use the correct zeroth-order functions. Note that the function (9.162) becomes zero when the two electrons are at the same point in space, since if $r_1 = r_2$, then $1s(r_1)2s(r_2) = 1s(r_2)2s(r_1)$. This means that the probability of having the two electrons close together is smaller for the state (9.162) than for (9.161). Thus $\langle e^2/r_{12} \rangle$, the average interelectronic repulsion, is less for (9.162) and hence it lies lower in energy.

Sometimes one speaks of an "exchange phenomenon." If we *know* that at a given instant of time electron 1 is in the $1s$ orbital and electron 2 is in the $2s$ orbital, then it is possible to show[9] that after a time interval $h/4K_{1s2s}$ has elapsed, the two electrons have exchanged states so that electron 1 is in the 2s orbital and electron 2 is in the $1s$ orbital. After another such interval, the electrons are back in their original orbitals, etc.

The exchange "phenomenon" should *not* be thought of as a real physical process, because the assumption that it is possible to *know* which electron at a given instant of time is in which orbital, is a violation of the principle of indistinguishability of identical particles. (To consider the exchange of electrons between atomic orbitals as a real phenomenon would be akin to speaking of benzene as existing part of the time as one Kekulé structure, and part of the time as the other Kekulé structure, a viewpoint roundly condemned by all chemists.)

The perturbation treatment of the helium excited states was given by Heisenberg in 1926 and his name is closely associated with the subject of exchange. Other excited states of helium can be treated by perturbation theory along the lines of the treatment of the $1s2s$ and $1s2p$ configurations.

9.8 Comparison of the Variation and Perturbation Methods

The perturbation method is applicable to all the states of an atom or molecule, whereas the variation method is restricted to the ground state (which is the state of greatest chemical interest) and possibly the first few excited states. However, it is usually extremely difficult to evaluate the infinite sums over discrete states and integrals over continuum states that are necessary to evaluate the second-order and higher-order perturbation energy corrections.

In the perturbation method one can calculate the energy much more accurately (to order $2k + 1$) than the wave function (to order k). The same situation holds in the variation method, where one can get a rather good energy with a rather inaccurate wave function; if one attempts to calculate properties other than the energy, the results will generally not be as reliable as the calculated energy. To avoid this problem, the use of the *constrained variational method* has been suggested.[10] In this approach, the trial function is constrained to give the known experimental value of some property such as the molecular dipole moment. The constrained variational function should then give more accurate values of molecular properties (other than the energy) than an unconstrained trial function.

---

[9] *Bethe and Salpeter*, p. 132.
[10] A. Mukherji and M. J. Karplus, *J. Chem. Phys.*, **38**, 44 (1963).

Although most calculations of molecular wave functions have been done using the variation method, there has been a revival of interest in applying the perturbation method to such problems.[11]

9.9 Techniques of Perturbation Theory

In this section we will discuss some methods used to deal with the higher-order energy corrections in perturbation theory. The reader who is not especially interested in perturbation theory can omit this section.

As a preliminary, we prove the following important sum rule:

$$\sum_i \langle R| \hat{A} |\varphi_i\rangle\langle\varphi_i| \hat{B} |S\rangle = \langle R| \hat{A}\hat{B} |S\rangle \tag{9.163}$$

In this equation, the functions φ_i form a complete orthonormal set, the functions R and S are any two well-behaved functions, the operators $\hat{A}$ and $\hat{B}$ are linear, and the sum is over all members of the complete set. We start with the expression (7.66) for the expansion of a function f in terms of a complete orthonormal set:

$$f = \sum_i \langle\varphi_i|f\rangle\varphi_i$$

Setting $f = \hat{B}S$, and then operating with $\hat{A}$, we get

$$\hat{A}\hat{B}S = \sum_i \langle\varphi_i|\hat{B}S\rangle \hat{A}\varphi_i$$

We now multiply by R^* and integrate over all space, to get

$$\langle R|\hat{A}\hat{B}S\rangle = \sum_i \langle\varphi_i|\hat{B}S\rangle\langle R|\hat{A}\varphi_i\rangle$$

which is the desired result (9.163).

Now consider Eq. (9.46) for the second-order energy correction:

$$E_n^{(2)} = \sum_{k \neq n} \frac{\langle n| \hat{H}' |k\rangle\langle k| \hat{H}' |n\rangle}{E_n^{(0)} - E_k^{(0)}} \tag{9.164}$$

If we are unable to evaluate $E_n^{(2)}$ explicitly, we can estimate it by the following procedure. We replace $[E_n^{(0)} - E_k^{(0)}]$ by the constant ΔE, where ΔE is some sort of average excitation energy for the particular problem. Although we don't know the exact value of ΔE to use, we should be able to estimate its magnitude from the spacings of the unperturbed levels. We have

$$E_n^{(2)} \approx \frac{1}{\Delta E} \sum_{k \neq n} \langle n| \hat{H}' |k\rangle\langle k| \hat{H}' |n\rangle$$

Changing the summation to include all states, we have

$$E_n^{(2)} \approx \frac{1}{\Delta E}\left[\sum_k \langle n| \hat{H}' |k\rangle\langle k| \hat{H}' |n\rangle - \langle n| \hat{H}' |n\rangle\langle n| \hat{H}' |n\rangle \right]$$

---

[11] For a discussion of developments in perturbation theory, see J. O. Hirschfelder, W. Byers Brown, and S. T. Epstein, *Advances in Quantum Chemistry*, vol. 1, p. 255, Academic Press Inc., New York, 1964.

Applying the sum rule (9.163), we find

$$E_n^{(2)} \approx \frac{1}{\Delta E} [\langle n| (\hat{H}')^2 |n\rangle - (\langle n| \hat{H}' |n\rangle)^2]$$

where n stands for $\psi_n^{(0)}$.

Let us consider another approach to finding $E_n^{(2)}$. We start with Eq. (9.23):

$$(\hat{H}^0 - E_n^{(0)}) \psi_n^{(1)} = (E_n^{(1)} - \hat{H}') \psi_n^{(0)} \tag{9.165}$$

Previously we expanded $\psi_n^{(1)}$ in terms of the unperturbed wave functions, according to (9.24). Here we use a different procedure. Since $\hat{H}^0$ is a differential operator, Eq. (9.165) is a differential equation, which we can attempt to solve directly for $\psi_n^{(1)}$. Rather than deal with (9.165), we simplify it by defining the function F, according to

$$F \equiv \frac{\psi_n^{(1)}}{\psi_n^{(0)}} \tag{9.166}$$

Then (9.165) becomes

$$(\hat{H}^0 - E_n^{(0)}) F\psi_n^{(0)} = (E_n^{(1)} - \hat{H}') \psi_n^{(0)} \tag{9.167}$$

The left side of (9.167) is equal to

$$(\hat{H}^0 F - F\hat{H}^0) \psi_n^{(0)} \tag{9.168}$$

The function F commutes with the potential-energy part of $\hat{H}^0$, so that

$$\hat{H}^0 F - F\hat{H}^0 = \hat{T}F - F\hat{T} \tag{9.169}$$

where $\hat{T}$ is the kinetic-energy operator for the unperturbed system. With the use of (9.169) and (3.59), the expression (9.168) becomes

$$-\frac{\hbar^2}{2} \sum_i \frac{1}{m_i} \nabla_i^2 (F\psi_n^{(0)}) + \frac{\hbar^2}{2} F \sum_i \frac{1}{m_i} \nabla_i^2 \psi_n^{(0)} \tag{9.170}$$

Using the identity of Problem 5.7, we have for (9.170):

$$-\frac{\hbar^2}{2} \psi_n^{(0)} \sum_i \frac{1}{m_i} \nabla_i^2 F - \hbar^2 \sum_i \frac{1}{m_i} \nabla_i F \cdot \nabla_i \psi_n^{(0)} \tag{9.171}$$

and Eq. (9.167) becomes

$$-\frac{\hbar^2}{2} \psi_n^{(0)} \sum_i \frac{1}{m_i} \nabla_i^2 F - \hbar^2 \sum_i \frac{1}{m_i} \nabla_i F \cdot \nabla_i \psi_n^{(0)} = (E_n^{(1)} - \hat{H}') \psi_n^{(0)} \tag{9.172}$$

For a one-particle one-dimensional problem, Eq. (9.172) is

$$\frac{d^2 F}{dx^2} + \frac{2}{\psi_n^{(0)}} \frac{d\psi_n^{(0)}}{dx} \frac{dF}{dx} = \frac{2m}{\hbar^2} \frac{1}{\psi_n^{(0)}} (\hat{H}' - E_n^{(1)}) \psi_n^{(0)} \tag{9.173}$$

Equation (9.172) is a differential equation, which we attempt to solve for F. Having found F, we use Eqs. (9.41) and (9.166) to write

$$E_n^{(2)} = \langle \psi_n^{(0)}| \hat{H}' |F\psi_n^{(0)}\rangle - E_n^{(1)} \langle \psi_n^{(0)}|F\psi_n^{(0)}\rangle$$

$$E_n^{(2)} = \langle \psi_n^{(0)}| \hat{H}'F |\psi_n^{(0)}\rangle - \langle \psi_n^{(0)}| \hat{H}' |\psi_n^{(0)}\rangle \langle \psi_n^{(0)}| F |\psi_n^{(0)}\rangle \tag{9.174}$$

Thus, provided we can solve (9.172) for F, we can evaluate $E_n^{(2)}$ exactly, without having to do the infinite summation in (9.164). Using $\psi_n^{(1)}$, we can also evaluate $E_n^{(3)}$.

Equation (9.172) was used by Slater and Kirkwood in a perturbation treatment of van der Waals forces; more recently this method has been widely used, due to the efforts of Dalgarno and co-workers.[12] For the evaluation of more-general sums than (9.164), see A. Dalgarno, *Rev. Mod. Phys.*, **35**, 522 (1963).

PROBLEMS

9.1 Prove that the expression (9.46) for $E_n^{(2)}$ does not depend on the choice $a_n = 0$.

9.2 When Hylleraas began his calculations on helium, it was not known whether the isolated hydride ion H^- was a stable entity. Calculate the ground-state energy of H^- predicted by the trial function (9.77). Compare the result with the ground-state energy of the hydrogen atom, -13.60 eV, and show that this simple variation function (erroneously) indicates H^- is unstable with respect to ionization into a hydrogen atom and an electron. (More complicated variational functions give a ground state energy of -14.35 eV.)

9.3 Show that the secular equation (9.114) can be written as

$$\det [H_{mi} - \delta_{mi}(E_j^{(0)} + E_j^{(1)})] = 0$$

where $H_{mi} = \int \psi_m^{(0)*} \hat{H} \psi_i^{(0)} \, d\tau$.

9.4 For the anharmonic oscillator with Hamiltonian (9.3), calculate $E_0^{(1)}$ and $E_1^{(1)}$, the first-order corrections for the ground state and for the first excited state; use (9.4) for $\hat{H}^0$.

9.5 By considering Eq. (9.108) for the case $m > n$, derive Eq. (9.119).

9.6 Consider the perturbation treatment of the helium configurations $1s3s$, $1s3p$, and $1s3d$. Without setting up the secular equation, but simply by analogy to the results of Section 9.7, write down the 18 correct zeroth-order wave functions. How many energy levels correspond to each of these three configurations, and what is the degeneracy of each energy level? The levels of which configuration lie lowest? highest?

9.7 There is more than one way to divide a Hamiltonian $\hat{H}$ into an unperturbed part $\hat{H}^0$ and a perturbation $\hat{H}'$. Instead of the division (9.51) and (9.52) consider the following way of dividing up the helium-atom Hamiltonian:

$$\hat{H}^0 = -\frac{\hbar^2}{2m}\nabla_1^2 - \frac{\hbar^2}{2m}\nabla_2^2 - \left(Z - \frac{5}{16}\right)\frac{e^2}{r_1} - \left(Z - \frac{5}{16}\right)\frac{e^2}{r_2}$$

$$\hat{H}' = -\frac{5}{16}\frac{e^2}{r_1} - \frac{5}{16}\frac{e^2}{r_2} + \frac{e^2}{r_{12}}$$

What are the unperturbed wave functions? Calculate $E^{(0)}$ and $E^{(1)}$ for the ground state. (See Section 9.4.)

9.8 Verify the result (9.157) for the integral J_{1s2p}.

9.9 We have considered helium configurations in which only one electron is excited. Get a rough estimate of the energy of the $2s^2$ configuration from Eq. (9.59). Compare this to the ground-state energy of the He^+ ion to show that the $2s^2$ helium configuration is unstable with respect to ionization to He^+ and an electron. If we had obtained

[12] Some references are: J. C. Slater and J. G. Kirkwood, *Phys. Rev.*, **37**, 682 (1931); A. Dalgarno and J. T. Lewis, *Proc. Roy. Soc.*, **A233**, 70 (1955); A. Dalgarno and A. L. Stewart, *ibid.*, **A238**, 269, 276 (1956); **A240**, 274 (1957); C. Schwartz, *Annals of Physics*, **6**, 156 (1959).

a more accurate estimate of the $2s^2$ energy by including the first-order energy correction, would this increase or decrease our estimate of the $2s^2$ energy?

9.10 Most (but not all) of the effect of nuclear motion in helium can be corrected for by replacing the electron's mass m by the reduced mass (6.67) in the expression for the energy. The energy of helium is proportional to what power of m? [See Eq. (9.87).] Use of μ instead of m multiplies the energies calculated on the basis of infinite nuclear mass, by what factor?

9.11 For a hydrogen atom perturbed by a uniform applied electric field in the z direction, the perturbation Hamiltonian is

$$\hat{H}' = e\mathscr{E}z = e\mathscr{E}r\cos\theta$$

where $\mathscr{E}$ is the magnitude of the electric field. Consider the effect of $\hat{H}'$ on the $n = 2$ energy level, which is fourfold degenerate. Since $\hat{H}'$ commutes with the angular-momentum operator $\hat{L}_z$, the ideas of Section 9.6 lead us to set up the secular determinant using the complex hydrogen-atom orbitals $2s$, $2p_1$, $2p_0$, and $2p_{-1}$, which are eigenfunctions of $\hat{L}_z$. Set up the secular determinant using the fact that matrix elements of $\hat{H}'$ between states with different values of the quantum number m will vanish; also use parity considerations to show that certain other integrals are zero (see Problem 7.16d). Evaluate the nonzero integrals, find the first-order energy corrections and the correct zeroth-order wave functions.

9.12 For helium the first-order perturbation energy correction is e^2/r_{12} averaged over the correct unperturbed wave function. Show that if we evaluate $\langle e^2/r_{12}\rangle$ using the incorrect zeroth-order functions $1s(1)2s(2)$ or $1s(2)2s(1)$, we get J_{1s2s} in each case. Now show that when we use the correct functions (9.148) and (9.149) to evaluate $\langle e^2/r_{12}\rangle$, we get $J_{1s2s} \pm K_{1s2s}$ (as found from the secular equation). The exchange-integral contribution to the energy thus arises from the indistinguishability of electrons in the same atom.

9.13 Consider the one-dimensional potential-energy function

$$V = \infty \quad \text{for } x < 0 \quad \text{and} \quad x > a$$
$$V = 0 \quad \text{for } 0 \leqslant x \leqslant \tfrac{1}{4}a \quad \text{and} \quad \tfrac{3}{4}a \leqslant x \leqslant a$$
$$V = k \quad \text{for } \tfrac{1}{4}a < x < \tfrac{3}{4}a$$

where k is a constant. Treat the system as a perturbed particle in a box and find the first-order energy and wave-function corrections.

9.14 Assume that the charge of the proton is distributed uniformly throughout the volume of a sphere of radius 10^{-13} cm. Use perturbation theory to find the shift in the ground-state hydrogen-atom energy due to the finite proton size. The potential energy experienced by the electron when it has penetrated the nucleus and is at distance r from the nuclear center is $-eq/r$, where q is the amount of proton charge within the sphere of radius r (*Halliday and Resnick*, pp. 695–697). The evaluation of the integral is simplified by noting that the exponential factor in ψ is essentially equal to 1 within the nucleus.

Electron Spin and the Pauli Principle

10.1 Electron Spin

All chemists are familiar with the yellow color imparted to a flame by sodium atoms. Examining the emission spectrum of sodium, one finds that the strongest yellow line (the so-called D line) is actually two closely spaced lines. The sodium D line arises from a transition from the excited configuration $1s^2 2s^2 2p^6 3p$ to the ground state. The doublet nature of this and other lines in the Na spectrum indicates a doubling of the expected number of states available to the valence electron.

To explain this *fine structure* of atomic spectra, Uhlenbeck and Goudsmit proposed in 1925 that the electron has an *intrinsic* angular momentum in addition to the orbital angular momentum due to its motion about the nucleus. If one pictures the electron as a sphere of charge spinning about one of its diameters, one can see how such an intrinsic angular momentum can arise. Hence we have the term *spin angular momentum* or, more simply, *spin*. However, electron "spin" is not a classical effect, and the picture of an electron rotating about one of its axes should not be considered to represent physical reality. The intrinsic angular momentum is real, but there is no easily visualizable model that can explain its origin properly. We cannot hope to obtain a proper understanding of microscopic particles based on models taken from our experience in the macroscopic world. Other elementary particles besides the electron have "spin" angular momentum.

In 1928 Dirac developed the *relativistic* quantum mechanics of an electron and in his treatment electron "spin" arises naturally. Dirac's theory also indicated the existence of positively charged electrons, positrons, although Dirac did not fully realize this in 1928. Positrons were discovered in 1932. The positron is the anti-particle of the electron. Nowadays, speculation on the possible existence of galaxies composed of antimatter is commonplace.[1]

In the nonrelativistic quantum mechanics to which we are confining ourselves, electron spin must be introduced as an additional hypothesis. We have learned that each physical property has its corresponding linear Hermitian operator in quantum mechanics. For properties like orbital angular momentum we can construct the quantum-mechanical operator from the classical expression by replacing p_x, p_y, p_z by the appropriate operators. The inherent "spin" angular momentum of a microscopic particle has no analog in classical mechanics, so that we cannot use this method to construct operators for spin. For our purposes, we will simply use symbols for the spin operators, without giving an explicit form for them.

Analogous to the orbital angular-momentum operators $\hat{L}^2, \hat{L}_x, \hat{L}_y, \hat{L}_z$, we have the spin angular-momentum operators $\hat{S}^2, \hat{S}_x, \hat{S}_y, \hat{S}_z$. The operator $\hat{S}^2$ is for the square of the magnitude of the total spin angular momentum of a particle; $\hat{S}_z$ is the operator for the z component of the particle's spin angular momentum. We have

$$\hat{S}^2 = \hat{S}_x^2 + \hat{S}_y^2 + \hat{S}_z^2 \qquad (10.1)$$

We hypothesize that the spin angular-momentum operators obey the same commutation relations as the orbital angular-momentum operators. Analogous to Eqs. (5.70) and (5.72), we have

$$[\hat{S}_x, \hat{S}_y] = i\hbar\hat{S}_z, \qquad [\hat{S}_y, \hat{S}_z] = i\hbar\hat{S}_x, \qquad [\hat{S}_z, \hat{S}_x] = i\hbar\hat{S}_y \qquad (10.2)$$

From (10.1) and (10.2), it follows, by the same operator algebra used to obtain (5.73) and (5.74), that

$$[\hat{S}^2, \hat{S}_x] = [\hat{S}^2, \hat{S}_y] = [\hat{S}^2, \hat{S}_z] = 0 \qquad (10.3)$$

Since Eqs. (10.1) and (10.2) are of the form of Eqs. (5.149) and (5.150), it follows from the work of Section 5.4 (which depended only on the commutation relations and not the specific forms of the operators) that the eigenvalues of $\hat{S}^2$ are [Eq. (5.192)]

$$s(s+1)\hbar^2, \qquad s = 0, \tfrac{1}{2}, 1, \tfrac{3}{2}, \ldots \qquad (10.4)$$

and the eigenvalues of $\hat{S}_z$ are [Eq. (5.191)]

$$m_s\hbar, \qquad m_s = -s, -s+1, \ldots, s-1, s \qquad (10.5)$$

The quantum number s is called the *spin* of the particle. Although nothing in our work in Section 5.4 restricts electrons to a single value for s, experiment shows that all electrons do have a single value for s, namely $s = \tfrac{1}{2}$. (Protons and neutrons also have spin $\tfrac{1}{2}$; pi-mesons have $s = 0$.) Thus the magnitude of the total

---

[1] There have been suggestions that the enormous energy output of the mysterious quasars is due to matter-antimatter annihilation; see H. Alfvén, "Antimatter and Cosmology," *Scientific American*, April 1967, p. 106. It has been proposed that the still unexplained phenomenon of ball lightning might be due to minute fragments of meteoritic antimatter [D. E. T. F. Ashby and C. Whitehead, *Nature*, **230**, 180 (1971)].

intrinsic (spin) angular momentum of an electron is

$$[\tfrac{1}{2}(\tfrac{3}{2})\hbar^2]^{1/2} = \tfrac{1}{2}\sqrt{3}\,\hbar \tag{10.6}$$

Corresponding to $s = \tfrac{1}{2}$, we have two possible eigenvalues of $\hat{S}_z$: $+\tfrac{1}{2}\hbar$ and $-\tfrac{1}{2}\hbar$. The electron spin eigenfunctions corresponding to these eigenvalues of $\hat{S}_z$ are denoted by α and β:

$$\hat{S}_z\alpha = +\tfrac{1}{2}\hbar\alpha \tag{10.7}$$

$$\hat{S}_z\beta = -\tfrac{1}{2}\hbar\beta \tag{10.8}$$

Since $\hat{S}_z$ commutes with $\hat{S}^2$, we can take the eigenfunctions of $\hat{S}_z$ to be eigenfunctions of $\hat{S}^2$ also:

$$\hat{S}^2\alpha = \tfrac{3}{4}\hbar^2\alpha, \qquad \hat{S}^2\beta = \tfrac{3}{4}\hbar^2\beta \tag{10.9}$$

$\hat{S}_z$ does not commute with $\hat{S}_x$ or $\hat{S}_y$, so that α and β are not eigenfunctions of these operators. The terms "spin up" and "spin down" refer to $m_s = +\tfrac{1}{2}$ and $m_s = -\tfrac{1}{2}$, respectively. See Fig. 10.1. We will later show that the two possibilities for the quantum number m_s give the doubling of lines in the spectra of the alkali metals.

FIGURE 10.1   *The two possible orientations of the electronic spin vector with respect to the z axis.*

The wave functions we have dealt with previously are functions of the spatial coordinates of the particle: $\psi = \psi(x, y, z)$. We might ask, what is the variable for the spin eigenfunctions α and β? Sometimes one talks of a spin coordinate ω, without really specifying what this coordinate is. Most often, one takes the spin quantum number m_s as being the variable on which the spin eigenfunctions depend. This procedure is quite unusual as compared to the spatial wave functions, but because we have only two possible electronic spin eigenfunctions and eigenvalues, this is a convenient choice. We have

$$\alpha = \alpha(m_s), \qquad \beta = \beta(m_s) \tag{10.10}$$

As usual, we want our eigenfunctions to be normalized. The three variables of a one-particle space wave function range continuously from $-\infty$ to $+\infty$, so that normalization means

$$\int_{-\infty}^{\infty}\int_{-\infty}^{\infty}\int_{-\infty}^{\infty} |\psi(x, y, z)|^2\, dx\, dy\, dz = 1$$

The variable m_s of the electronic spin eigenfunctions takes on only the two discrete values $+\frac{1}{2}$ and $-\frac{1}{2}$, so that normalization of the one-particle spin eigenfunctions means

$$\sum_{m_s=-1/2}^{1/2} |\alpha(m_s)|^2 = 1, \qquad \sum_{m_s=-1/2}^{1/2} |\beta(m_s)|^2 = 1 \qquad (10.11)$$

Since the eigenfunctions α and β correspond to different eigenvalues of the Hermitian operator $\hat{S}_z$, they are orthogonal:

$$\sum_{m_s=-1/2}^{1/2} \alpha^*(m_s)\beta(m_s) = 0 \qquad (10.12)$$

To satisfy (10.11) and (10.12), we can take

$$\alpha(m_s) = 1 \qquad \text{for } m_s = +\tfrac{1}{2}$$
$$\alpha(m_s) = 0 \qquad \text{for } m_s = -\tfrac{1}{2}$$
$$\beta(+\tfrac{1}{2}) = 0, \qquad \beta(-\tfrac{1}{2}) = 1$$

which may be written more compactly using Kronecker deltas:

$$\alpha(m_s) = \delta_{m_s, 1/2}, \qquad \beta(m_s) = \delta_{m_s, -1/2} \qquad (10.13)$$

When we consider the complete wave function for an electron including both space and spin variables, we will normalize it according to

$$\sum_{m_s=-1/2}^{1/2} \int_{-\infty}^{\infty} \int_{-\infty}^{\infty} \int_{-\infty}^{\infty} |\psi(x,y,z,m_s)|^2 \, dx \, dy \, dz = 1 \qquad (10.14)$$

The notation

$$\int |\psi(x,y,z,m_s)|^2 \, d\tau$$

will denote summation over the spin variable and integration over the space variables, as in (10.14). The symbol $\int dv$ will denote integration over spatial variables.

10.2 Ladder Operators for Electron Spin

The spin angular-momentum operators obey the general angular-momentum commutation relations of Section 5.4, and it is often helpful to use spin angular-momentum ladder operators.

From (5.152) and (5.153), the raising and lowering operators for spin angular momentum are

$$\hat{S}_+ = \hat{S}_x + i\hat{S}_y \qquad (10.15)$$
$$\hat{S}_- = \hat{S}_x - i\hat{S}_y \qquad (10.16)$$

and we have [Eqs. (5.154) and (5.155)]

$$\hat{S}_+\hat{S}_- = \hat{S}^2 - \hat{S}_z^2 + \hbar\hat{S}_z \qquad (10.17)$$
$$\hat{S}_-\hat{S}_+ = \hat{S}^2 - \hat{S}_z^2 - \hbar\hat{S}_z \qquad (10.18)$$

The spin functions α and β are eigenfunctions of $\hat{S}_z$ with eigenvalues $+\frac{1}{2}\hbar$ and $-\frac{1}{2}\hbar$, respectively. Since $\hat{S}_+$ is the raising operator, the function $\hat{S}_+\beta$ is an eigenfunction of $\hat{S}_z$ with eigenvalue $+\frac{1}{2}\hbar$. The most general eigenfunction of $\hat{S}_z$ with this eigenvalue is an arbitrary constant times α. Hence

$$\hat{S}_+\beta = c\alpha \tag{10.19}$$

where c is some constant. To find c, we use Eq. (10.11):

$$1 = \sum_{m_s} \alpha^*(m_s)\alpha(m_s) = \sum \left(\frac{\hat{S}_+\beta}{c}\right)^*\left(\frac{\hat{S}_+\beta}{c}\right)$$

$$|c|^2 = \sum (\hat{S}_+\beta)^*\hat{S}_+\beta = \sum (\hat{S}_+\beta)^*(\hat{S}_x+i\hat{S}_y)\beta$$

$$|c|^2 = \sum (\hat{S}_+\beta)^*\hat{S}_x\beta + i\sum (\hat{S}_+\beta)^*\hat{S}_y\beta \tag{10.20}$$

We now use the Hermitian property of $\hat{S}_x$ and $\hat{S}_y$. For an operator $\hat{A}$ that acts on functions of a continuous variable like x, the Hermitian property is

$$\int f^*(x)\hat{A}g(x)\,dx = \int g(x)[\hat{A}f(x)]^*\,dx$$

For an operator like $\hat{S}_x$ which acts on functions of the variable m_s, which takes on discrete values, the Hermitian property is

$$\sum_{m_s} f^*(m_s)\hat{S}_x g(m_s) = \sum_{m_s} g(m_s)[\hat{S}_x f(m_s)]^* \tag{10.21}$$

Taking $f = \hat{S}_+\beta$ and $g = \beta$, we can write (10.20) as

$$c^*c = \sum \beta[\hat{S}_x\hat{S}_+\beta]^* + i\sum \beta[\hat{S}_y\hat{S}_+\beta]^*$$

Taking the complex conjugate of this equation, we have

$$cc^* = \sum \beta^*\hat{S}_x\hat{S}_+\beta - i\sum \beta^*\hat{S}_y\hat{S}_+\beta$$

$$|c|^2 = \sum \beta^*(\hat{S}_x-i\hat{S}_y)\hat{S}_+\beta = \sum \beta^*\hat{S}_-\hat{S}_+\beta$$

$$|c|^2 = \sum \beta^*(\hat{S}^2-\hat{S}_z^2-\hbar\hat{S}_z)\beta$$

$$|c|^2 = \sum \beta^*\left(\frac{3}{4}\hbar^2 - \frac{\hbar^2}{4} + \frac{\hbar^2}{2}\right)\beta = \hbar^2\sum \beta^*\beta = \hbar^2$$

$$|c| = \hbar$$

Choosing the phase of c as zero, we have $c = \hbar$ and (10.19) reads

$$\hat{S}_+\beta = \hbar\alpha \tag{10.22}$$

A similar calculation gives

$$\hat{S}_-\alpha = \hbar\beta \tag{10.23}$$

Since α is the eigenfunction with the highest possible value of m_s, the operàtor $\hat{S}_+$ acting on α must annihilate it [Eq. (5.181)]:

$$\hat{S}_+\alpha = 0 \tag{10.24}$$

Likewise

$$\hat{S}_-\beta = 0 \tag{10.25}$$

From these last four equations, we get

$$(\hat{S}_+ + \hat{S}_-)\beta = \hbar\alpha \tag{10.26}$$

$$(\hat{S}_+ - \hat{S}_-)\beta = \hbar\alpha \tag{10.27}$$

Use of Eqs. (10.15) and (10.16) in Eqs. (10.26) and (10.27) gives

$$\hat{S}_x\beta = \tfrac{1}{2}\hbar\alpha, \qquad \hat{S}_y\beta = -\tfrac{1}{2}i\hbar\alpha \tag{10.28}$$

Similarly we find

$$\hat{S}_x\alpha = \tfrac{1}{2}\hbar\beta, \qquad \hat{S}_y\alpha = \tfrac{1}{2}i\hbar\beta \tag{10.29}$$

10.3 Spin and the Hydrogen Atom

The wave function specifying the state of an electron depends not only on the coordinates x, y, and z, but also on the spin state of the electron. What effect does this have on the wave functions and energy levels of the hydrogen atom?

To a very good approximation, the Hamiltonian for a system of electrons does not involve the spin variables, but is a function only of spatial coordinates and derivatives with respect to spatial coordinates. As a result, we can separate the wave function of a single electron into a product of space and spin parts:

$$\psi(x, y, z)g(m_s) \tag{10.30}$$

where $g(m_s)$ is either one of the functions α and β, depending on whether $m_s = \tfrac{1}{2}$ or $-\tfrac{1}{2}$. Since the Hamiltonian operator has no effect on the spin function, we have

$$\hat{H}[\psi(x, y, z)g(m_s)] = g(m_s)\hat{H}\psi(x, y, z) = E[\psi(x, y, z)g(m_s)]$$

so that we get the same energies as previously found without taking spin into account. The only difference spin makes is to double the possible number of states; instead of the state $\psi(x, y, z)$, we have the two possible states $\psi(x, y, z)\alpha$ and $\psi(x, y, z)\beta$. Taking spin into account, the degeneracy of the hydrogen-atom energy levels is $2n^2$ rather than n^2, as given by Eq. (6.113).

10.4 The Pauli Principle

Suppose we have a system of several identical particles. In classical mechanics the identity of the particles leads to no special consequences. For example, consider n identical billiard balls rolling about on a billiard table. It is perfectly possible to follow the motion of any individual ball, say by taking a motion picture of the system. We can say that ball number one is moving along a certain path, ball two is on another definite path, and so on, the paths being determined by Newton's laws of motion. Thus, although the balls are identical, we can distinguish among them by specifying the path each one takes. The identity of the balls has no special effect on their motions.

In quantum mechanics, the uncertainty principle tells us that we cannot follow the exact path taken by a microscopic "particle." If the microscopic particles of our system all have different masses or charges or spins, etc., we can use one of these properties to distinguish the particles from one another. But if they are all identical, then the one way we had in classical mechanics of distinguishing them, namely by specifying their paths, is lost in quantum mechanics due to the uncertainty principle. Therefore, the wave function of a system of interacting identical particles must not distinguish among the particles. For example, in the perturbation treatment of the helium-atom excited states in Chapter 9, we saw that the function $1s(1)2s(2)$, which says that electron 1 is in the $1s$ orbital and electron 2 is in the $2s$ orbital, was not a correct zeroth-order wave function. Rather we had to use the functions (9.161) and (9.162), which do not specify which electron is in which orbital. (If the identical particles are well separated from each other, so that their wave functions do not overlap, they may be regarded as distinguishable.)

We now derive the restrictions on the wave function due to the requirement of indistinguishability of identical particles in quantum mechanics. We consider a system of n identical microscopic particles. The wave function depends on the space and spin variables of all the particles. For particle 1 these variables are x_1, y_1, z_1, m_{s1}. We will use the symbol q_1 to stand for all four of these variables. Thus:

$$\psi = \psi(q_1, q_2, ..., q_n)$$

We define the *permutation operator* $\hat{P}_{12}$ as the operator that interchanges all the coordinates of particles 1 and 2:

$$\hat{P}_{12} f(q_1, q_2, q_3, ..., q_n) = f(q_2, q_1, q_3, ...; q_n)$$

As an example, the effect of $\hat{P}_{12}$ on the function which has electron 1 in a $1s$ orbital with spin up and electron 2 in a $3s$ orbital with spin down is

$$\hat{P}_{12}[1s(1)\alpha(1)3s(2)\beta(2)] = 1s(2)\alpha(2)3s(1)\beta(1)$$

What are the eigenvalues of $\hat{P}_{12}$? Applying $\hat{P}_{12}$ twice has no net effect:

$$\hat{P}_{12}\hat{P}_{12} f(q_1, q_2, ..., q_n) = \hat{P}_{12} f(q_2, q_1, ..., q_n) = f(q_1, q_2, ..., q_n)$$

so that $\hat{P}_{12}^2 = \hat{1}$. We showed in Section 7.5 that an operator whose square is the unit operator has the eigenvalues $+1$ and -1. If h is an eigenfunction of $\hat{P}_{12}$ with eigenvalue $+1$, we have

$$\hat{P}_{12} h(q_1, q_2, ..., q_n) = +1 \cdot h(q_1, q_2, ..., q_n)$$

$$h(q_2, q_1, ..., q_n) = h(q_1, q_2, ..., q_n) \tag{10.31}$$

and we say that h is *symmetric* with respect to interchange of particles 1 and 2. For eigenvalue -1 we have

$$h(q_2, q_1, ..., q_n) = -h(q_1, q_2, ..., q_n) \tag{10.32}$$

If (10.32) holds, h is *antisymmetric* with respect to interchange of particles 1 and 2. There is no necessity for an arbitrary function $f(q_1, q_2, ..., q_n)$ to be either symmetric or antisymmetric with respect to interchange of 1 and 2. However, we can write an arbitrary function as the sum of functions symmetric and antisymmetric with respect to 1–2 interchange:

$$f(q_1, q_2, ..., q_n) = \tfrac{1}{2}[f(q_1, q_2, ..., q_n) + f(q_2, q_1, ..., q_n)]$$
$$+ \tfrac{1}{2}[f(q_1, q_2, ..., q_n) - f(q_2, q_1, ..., q_n)]$$

This equation shows that the eigenfunctions of $\hat{P}_{12}$ form a complete set.

Do not confuse the property of being symmetric or antisymmetric with respect to particle interchange, with the property of being even or odd with respect to inversion. The function $(x_1 + x_2)$ is symmetric with respect to 1–2 interchange and is an odd function of x_1 and x_2. The function $(x_1^2 + x_2^2)$ is symmetric with respect to 1–2 interchange and is an even function of x_1 and x_2.

The operator $\hat{P}_{ij}$ is defined by

$$\hat{P}_{ij} f(q_1, ..., q_i, ..., q_j, ..., q_n) = f(q_1, ..., q_j, ..., q_i, ..., q_n) \tag{10.33}$$

The eigenvalues of $\hat{P}_{ij}$ are, like $\hat{P}_{12}$, $+1$ and -1.

We now consider the wave function of a system of identical microscopic particles. Since the particles are indistinguishable, the way we label them cannot affect the state of the system. Thus the two wave functions

$$\psi(q_1, ..., q_i, ..., q_j, ..., q_n) \quad \text{and} \quad \psi(q_1, ..., q_j, ..., q_i, ..., q_n)$$

must correspond to the same state of the system. Two wave functions that correspond to the same state can differ at most by a multiplicative constant. Hence

$$\psi(q_1, ..., q_j, ..., q_i, ..., q_n) = c\psi(q_1, ..., q_i, ..., q_j, ..., q_n)$$
$$\hat{P}_{ij} \psi(q_1, ..., q_i, ..., q_j, ..., q_n) = c\psi(q_1, ..., q_i, ..., q_j, ..., q_n) \tag{10.34}$$

Equation (10.34) states that ψ is an eigenfunction of $\hat{P}_{ij}$. But we know that the only possible eigenvalues of $\hat{P}_{ij}$ are 1 and -1. We conclude that the wave function for a system of n identical particles must be symmetric or antisymmetric with respect to interchange of any two of the identical particles, i and j. Since the n particles are all identical, we could not have the wave function symmetric with respect to some interchanges and antisymmetric with respect to other interchanges. Thus the wave function of n identical particles must be either symmetric with respect to every possible interchange or antisymmetric with respect to every possible interchange of two particles.

We have shown that there are two possible cases for the wave function of a system of identical particles, the symmetric and the antisymmetric cases. Experimental evidence (such as the periodic table of the elements to be discussed later) shows that for electrons only the antisymmetric case occurs. Thus we have an additional postulate of quantum mechanics which states that *the wave function of a system of electrons must be antisymmetric with respect to interchange of any two electrons.* This important postulate is called the *Pauli principle* or the *exclusion principle.* The Pauli exclusion principle was originally stated by Pauli in a more restricted form to be discussed later.

Pauli has shown that relativistic quantum field theory indicates that particles with half-integral spin ($s = \tfrac{1}{2}, \tfrac{3}{2}$, etc.) require antisymmetric wave functions, while particles of integral spin ($s = 0, 1$, etc.) require symmetric wave functions. Experimental evidence leads to the same conclusion. Particles, such as electrons, requiring antisymmetric wave functions are called *fermions* (after E. Fermi), while particles such as pi-mesons, requiring symmetric wave functions are called *bosons* (after S. N. Bose).

The Pauli principle has an interesting consequence for a system of identical fermions. The antisymmetry requirement means that

$$\psi(q_1, q_2, q_3, \ldots, q_n) = -\psi(q_2, q_1, q_3, \ldots, q_n) \tag{10.35}$$

Consider the value of the wave function when electrons 1 and 2 have the same coordinates, i.e., when

$$x_1 = x_2, \qquad y_1 = y_2, \qquad z_1 = z_2, \qquad m_{s1} = m_{s2}$$

Putting $q_2 = q_1$ in (10.35), we have

$$\psi(q_1, q_1, q_3, \ldots, q_n) = -\psi(q_1, q_1, q_3, \ldots, q_n)$$

$$2\psi = 0$$

$$\psi(q_1, q_1, q_3, \ldots, q_n) = 0 \tag{10.36}$$

Thus, two electrons with the same spin have zero probability of being found at the same point in three-dimensional space. (By "the same spin," we mean the same value of m_s.) Since ψ is a continuous function, Eq. (10.36) means that the probability of finding two electrons with the same spin close to each other in space is quite small. Thus the Pauli antisymmetry principle forces electrons of like spin to keep apart from one another; to describe this, one often speaks of a *Pauli repulsion* between such electrons. This "repulsion" is not a real physical force, but a reflection of the fact that the electronic wave function must be antisymmetric with respect to exchange.

10.5 The Helium Atom

We now reconsider the helium atom from the standpoint of electron spin and the Pauli principle. In the perturbation treatment of helium in Section 9.3, we found the zeroth-order wave function for the ground state to be $1s(1)1s(2)$. To take spin into account, we must multiply this spatial function by a spin eigenfunction. We therefore consider the possible spin eigenfunctions for two electrons. We will use the notation $\alpha(1)\alpha(2)$ to indicate a state where electron 1 has spin up and electron two has spin up; $\alpha(1)$ stands for $\alpha(m_{s1})$. Since each electron has two possible spin states, we have at first sight the four possible spin functions:

$$\alpha(1)\alpha(2), \qquad \beta(1)\beta(2), \qquad \alpha(1)\beta(2), \qquad \alpha(2)\beta(1)$$

There is nothing wrong with the first two functions, but the third and fourth functions violate the principle of indistinguishability of identical particles. For example, the third function says that electron one has spin up and electron two has spin down which *does* distinguish between electrons one and two. More formally, if we apply the permutation operator $\hat{P}_{12}$ to these functions we find that the first two functions are symmetric with respect to interchange of the two electrons, but the third and fourth functions are neither symmetric nor antisymmetric, and so are unacceptable.

What now? Recall that we ran into essentially the same situation in treating the helium excited states (Section 9.7) where we started with the functions $1s(1)2s(2)$ and $2s(1)1s(2)$. We found that these two functions, which distinguished between electrons 1 and 2, were not the correct zeroth-order functions and that the correct zeroth-order functions were:

$$2^{-1/2}[1s(1)2s(2)\pm 2s(1)1s(2)]$$

This result suggests pretty strongly that instead of $\alpha(1)\beta(2)$ and $\beta(1)\alpha(2)$, we use the spin functions:

$$2^{-1/2}[\alpha(1)\beta(2)\pm\beta(1)\alpha(2)]$$

These two functions are the normalized linear combinations of $\alpha(1)\beta(2)$ and $\beta(1)\alpha(2)$ that are eigenfunctions of $\hat{P}_{12}$. To demonstrate that they are normalized, we have

$$\sum_{m_{s1}}\sum_{m_{s2}}\frac{1}{\sqrt{2}}[\alpha(1)\beta(2)\pm\beta(1)\alpha(2)]^*\frac{1}{\sqrt{2}}[\alpha(1)\beta(2)\pm\beta(1)\alpha(2)]$$

$$=\tfrac{1}{2}\sum_{m_{s1}}|\alpha(1)|^2\sum_{m_{s2}}|\beta(2)|^2\pm\tfrac{1}{2}\sum_{m_{s1}}\alpha^*(1)\beta(1)\sum_{m_{s2}}\beta^*(2)\alpha(2)$$

$$\pm\tfrac{1}{2}\sum_{m_{s1}}\beta^*(1)\alpha(1)\sum_{m_{s2}}\alpha^*(2)\beta(2)+\tfrac{1}{2}\sum_{m_{s1}}|\beta(1)|^2\sum_{m_{s2}}|\alpha(2)|^2=1$$

where we have used the orthonormality relations (10.11) and (10.12).

Therefore the four normalized two-electron spin eigenfunctions are

symmetric:
$$\begin{cases} \alpha(1)\alpha(2) & \textbf{(10.37)} \\ \beta(1)\beta(2) & \textbf{(10.38)} \\ [\alpha(1)\beta(2)+\beta(1)\alpha(2)]/\sqrt{2} & \textbf{(10.39)} \end{cases}$$

antisymmetric:
$$[\alpha(1)\beta(2)-\beta(1)\alpha(2)]/\sqrt{2} \qquad \textbf{(10.40)}$$

We now include spin in the zeroth-order ground-state wave function. The function $1s(1)1s(2)$ is symmetric with respect to exchange. According to the Pauli principle the over-all wave function including spin must be antisymmetric with respect to interchange of the two electrons. Hence we must multiply the symmetric space function $1s(1)1s(2)$ by an antisymmetric spin function. We have only one antisymmetric two-electron spin function, so that the ground-state zeroth-order wave function for the helium atom including spin is

$$\psi^{(0)}=1s(1)1s(2)\cdot 2^{-1/2}[\alpha(1)\beta(2)-\beta(1)\alpha(2)] \qquad \textbf{(10.41)}$$

The function $\psi^{(0)}$ is an eigenfunction of $\hat{P}_{12}$ with eigenvalue -1, as the Pauli principle requires.

To a very good approximation, the Hamiltonian does not contain spin terms, so that the energy is unaffected by inclusion of the spin factor in the ground-state wave function. Also, the ground state of helium is still nondegenerate when spin is considered. Since the ground-state helium wave function consists of a *symmetric* space function times an antisymmetric spin function, in doing variational calculations with functions of the form (9.91) we should include only even values of j, so that the factor $(r_1 - r_2)^j$ will be symmetric with respect to interchange of 1 and 2.

To further demonstrate that the spin factor has no effect on the value of the energy, we will assume we are doing a variational calculation for the helium ground state using the trial function

$$\varphi = f(r_1, r_2, r_{12}) 2^{-1/2} [\alpha(1)\beta(2) - \beta(1)\alpha(2)]$$

where f is a normalized function symmetric in the coordinates of the two electrons. The variational integral is

$$\int \varphi^* \hat{H} \varphi \, d\tau = \sum_{m_{s1}} \sum_{m_{s2}} \int \int f^*(r_1, r_2, r_{12}) \frac{1}{\sqrt{2}} [\alpha(1)\beta(2) - \beta(1)\alpha(2)]^*$$

$$\times \hat{H} f(r_1, r_2, r_{12}) \frac{1}{\sqrt{2}} [\alpha(1)\beta(2) - \beta(1)\alpha(2)] \, dv_1 \, dv_2$$

Since $\hat{H}$ has no effect on the spin functions, the variational integral becomes

$$\int \int f^* \hat{H} f \, dv_1 \, dv_2 \sum_{m_{s1}} \sum_{m_{s2}} \tfrac{1}{2} |\alpha(1)\beta(2) - \beta(1)\alpha(2)|^2$$

The spin function (10.40) is normalized, so that the variational integral reduces to

$$\int \varphi^* \hat{H} \varphi \, d\tau = \int \int f^* \hat{H} f \, dv_1 \, dv_2$$

which is the expression we used before we introduced spin.

Now consider the excited states of helium. We found the lowest excited state to have the zeroth-order space wave function

$$2^{-1/2} [1s(1) 2s(2) - 2s(1) 1s(2)]$$

Since this space function is antisymmetric, we must multiply it by a symmetric spin function. We can use any one of the three symmetric two-electron spin functions, so that instead of the nondegenerate level previously found, we have a triply degenerate level with the three zeroth-order wave functions

$$2^{-1/2} [1s(1) 2s(2) - 2s(1) 1s(2)] \alpha(1)\alpha(2) \tag{10.42}$$

$$2^{-1/2} [1s(1) 2s(2) - 2s(1) 1s(2)] \beta(1)\beta(2) \tag{10.43}$$

$$2^{-1/2} [1s(1) 2s(2) - 2s(1) 1s(2)] 2^{-1/2} [\alpha(1)\beta(2) + \beta(1)\alpha(2)] \tag{10.44}$$

For the next excited state, the requirement of antisymmetry of the over-all wave function leads to the zeroth-order wave function

$$2^{-1/2} [1s(1) 2s(2) + 2s(1) 1s(2)] 2^{-1/2} [\alpha(1)\beta(2) - \beta(1)\alpha(2)] \tag{10.45}$$

The same considerations apply for the $1s2p$ states.

10.6 The Lithium Atom

So far, we have not seen any very spectacular consequences of electron spin and the Pauli principle. In the hydrogen and helium atoms, the spin factors in the wave functions and the antisymmetry requirement simply affect the degeneracy of the levels but do not (except for very small effects to be considered later) affect the previously obtained energies. For lithium, the story is quite different.

The natural perturbation approach to the lithium atom is to take the inter-electronic repulsions as a perturbation on the remaining terms in the Hamiltonian. By the same steps used in the treatment of helium, the unperturbed wave functions are products of three hydrogenlike functions. For the ground state we have the zeroth-order wave function

$$\psi^{(0)} = 1s(1)\, 1s(2)\, 1s(3) \tag{10.46}$$

and the zeroth-order (unperturbed) energy is [Eq. (9.59)]:

$$E^{(0)} = -\left(\frac{1}{1^2} + \frac{1}{1^2} + \frac{1}{1^2}\right)\left(\frac{Z^2 e^2}{2a_0}\right) = -27\left(\frac{e^2}{2a_0}\right)$$

$$E^{(0)} = -27(13.606) \text{ eV} = -367.4 \text{ eV}$$

The first-order correction to the energy is given by (9.30). The perturbation consists of the interelectronic repulsions, so that

$$E^{(1)} = \int |1s(1)|^2 |1s(2)|^2 |1s(3)|^2 \frac{e^2}{r_{12}} \, dv + \int |1s(1)|^2 |1s(2)|^2 |1s(3)|^2 \frac{e^2}{r_{23}} \, dv$$

$$+ \int |1s(1)|^2 |1s(2)|^2 |1s(3)|^2 \frac{e^2}{r_{13}} \, dv$$

The way we label the dummy integration variables in these definite integrals cannot affect their value. If we interchange the labels 1 and 3 on the variables in the second integral, it is converted to the first integral. Hence these two integrals are equal. Interchange of the labels 2 and 3 in the third integral shows it to be equal to the first integral also. Hence

$$E^{(1)} = 3 \int\int |1s(1)|^2 |1s(2)|^2 \frac{e^2}{r_{12}} \, dv_1 \, dv_2 \int |1s(3)|^2 \, dv_3$$

The integral over electron 3 gives 1 (normalization). The integral over electrons 1 and 2 was evaluated in the perturbation treatment of helium, and we have [Eqs. (9.63) and (9.67)]:

$$E^{(1)} = 3\left(\frac{5Z}{4}\right)\left(\frac{e^2}{2a_0}\right) = 153.1 \text{ eV}$$

$$E^{(0)} + E^{(1)} = -214.3 \text{ eV}$$

Since we can use the zeroth-order perturbation wave function as a trial variation function (recall the discussion at the beginning of Section 9.4) the value of $E^{(0)} + E^{(1)}$ must be, according to the variation principle, equal to or greater than the true ground-state energy. The experimental value of the lithium ground-state energy is obtained by adding up the three ionization energies, which gives [2]

$$-(5.39 + 75.64 + 122.45) \text{ eV} = -203.5 \text{ eV}$$

We thus have $E^{(0)} + E^{(1)}$ as less than the true ground-state energy, which is a violation of the variation principle. Moreover, the supposed configuration $(1s)^3$ for the Li ground state is in complete disagreement with the low value of the first ionization potential and with all chemical evidence. If we continued on in this manner we would have a $(1s)^Z$ ground-state configuration for the element of atomic number Z. We would not get the well-known periodic behavior of the elements.

Of course, our error is failure to consider spin and the Pauli principle. The hypothetical zeroth-order wave function $1s(1)1s(2)1s(3)$ is symmetric with respect to interchange of any two electrons. If we are to satisfy the Pauli principle we must multiply this symmetric space function by an antisymmetric spin function. It is easy to construct completely symmetric spin functions for three electrons, such as $\alpha(1)\alpha(2)\alpha(3)$. However, try as we may, it is impossible to construct a completely antisymmetric spin function for three electrons.

Let us consider how we can systematically construct an antisymmetric function for three electrons. We will use f, g, and h to stand for three functions of electronic coordinates, without specifying whether we are considering space coordinates or spin coordinates or both. We start with the function

$$f(1)g(2)h(3) \tag{10.47}$$

which is certainly not antisymmetric. The antisymmetric function we desire must be converted into its negative by each of the permutation operators $\hat{P}_{12}$, $\hat{P}_{13}$, and $\hat{P}_{23}$. Applying each of these operators in turn to $f(1)g(2)h(3)$, we get the functions

$$f(2)g(1)h(3) \tag{10.48}$$

$$f(3)g(2)h(1) \tag{10.49}$$

$$f(1)g(3)h(2) \tag{10.50}$$

We might seek to construct the antisymmetric function as a linear combination of the four functions (10.47)–(10.50), but this could not succeed; the application of $\hat{P}_{12}$ to (10.49) and (10.50) gives

$$f(3)g(1)h(2) \tag{10.51}$$

$$f(2)g(3)h(1) \tag{10.52}$$

which are not included in (10.47)–(10.50), so that we must include all six functions (10.47)–(10.52) in our desired antisymmetric linear combination. These six functions are the six $(3 \cdot 2 \cdot 1)$ possible permutations of the three electrons among the three functions f, g, and h. If $f(1)g(2)h(3)$ is a solution of the Schroedinger equation with eigenvalue E, then, due to the identity of the particles, each of the functions (10.48)–(10.52) is also a solution with the same eigenvalue E (exchange degeneracy), and any linear combination of these functions is an eigenfunction with eigenvalue E.

---

[2] C. E. Moore, "Ionization Potentials and Ionization Limits," publication NSRDS-NBS 34 of the National Bureau of Standards (1970).

The antisymmetric linear combination will have the form

$$c_1 f(1)g(2)h(3) + c_2 f(2)g(1)h(3) + c_3 f(3)g(2)h(1) + c_4 f(1)g(3)h(2)$$

$$+ c_5 f(3)g(1)h(2) + c_6 f(2)g(3)h(1) \qquad (10.53)$$

Since $f(2)g(1)h(3) = \hat{P}_{12} f(1)g(2)h(3)$, in order to have (10.53) be an eigenfunction of $\hat{P}_{12}$ with eigenvalue -1, we must have

$$c_2 = -c_1$$

Likewise $f(3)g(2)h(1) = \hat{P}_{13} f(1)g(2)h(3)$ and $f(1)g(3)h(2) = \hat{P}_{23} f(1)g(2)h(3)$ so that $c_3 = -c_1$ and $c_4 = -c_1$. Since $f(3)g(1)h(2) = \hat{P}_{12} f(3)g(2)h(1)$, we must have $c_5 = -c_3 = c_1$. Similarly, we find $c_6 = c_1$. We thus arrive at the linear combination

$$c_1 [f(1)g(2)h(3) - f(2)g(1)h(3) - f(3)g(2)h(1) - f(1)g(3)h(2)$$

$$+ f(3)g(1)h(2) + f(2)g(3)h(1)] \qquad (10.54)$$

which is easily verified to be antisymmetric with respect to 1–2, 1–3, and 2–3 interchange.[3]

Let us assume f, g, and h to be orthonormal and choose c_1 so that (10.54) is normalized. Multiplying (10.54) by its complex conjugate, we get many terms, but because of the assumed orthogonality the integrals of all products involving two different terms of (10.54) vanish. For example

$$\int [f(1)g(2)h(3)]^* f(2)g(1)h(3) \, d\tau$$

$$= \int f^*(1)g(1) \, d\tau_1 \int g^*(2)f(2) \, d\tau_2 \int h^*(3)h(3) \, d\tau_3 = 0 \cdot 0 \cdot 1 = 0$$

Integrals involving the product of a term of (10.54) with its own complex conjugate are equal to one, because f, g, and h are normalized. Therefore

$$1 = \int |(10.54)|^2 \, d\tau = |c_1|^2 (1+1+1+1+1+1)$$

$$c_1 = 1/\sqrt{6}$$

We could work with (10.54) as its stands, but its properties are most easily determined if we recognize it as simply the expansion [Eq. (8.42)] of the following third-order determinant:

$$\frac{1}{\sqrt{6}} \begin{vmatrix} f(1) & g(1) & h(1) \\ f(2) & g(2) & h(2) \\ f(3) & g(3) & h(3) \end{vmatrix} \qquad (10.55)$$

(For the reader familiar with Problem 8.8, this should come as no surprise.) The antisymmetry property is easily seen to hold for (10.55), because interchange of two electrons amounts to interchanging two rows of the determinant, which multiplies it by -1.

---

[3] Taking all signs as plus in (10.54), we get a completely symmetric function.

We stated that it is impossible to construct an antisymmetric spin function for three electrons. We now use (10.55) to prove this statement. The functions f, g, and h may each be either α or β. We might take $f = \alpha$, $g = \beta$, $h = \alpha$, so that (10.55) becomes

$$\frac{1}{\sqrt{6}} \begin{vmatrix} \alpha(1) & \beta(1) & \alpha(1) \\ \alpha(2) & \beta(2) & \alpha(2) \\ \alpha(3) & \beta(3) & \alpha(3) \end{vmatrix} \qquad (10.56)$$

Although (10.56) is antisymmetric, we must reject it because it is equal to zero. The first and third columns of the determinant are identical, so (Section 8.3) the determinant vanishes. No matter how we choose f, g, and h, at least two columns of the determinant must be equal, so that we cannot construct a nonzero antisymmetric three-electron spin function.

We now use (10.55) to construct the zeroth-order ground-state wave function for lithium, including both space and spin variables. The functions f, g, and h will now involve both space and spin variables. We choose

$$f(1) = 1s(1)\alpha(1) \qquad (10.57)$$

We call a function like (10.57) a *spin-orbital*. A spin-orbital is the product of a one-electron space orbital and a one-electron spin function. If we were to take $g(1) = 1s(1)\alpha(1)$, this would make the first and second columns of (10.55) identical, and the wave function would vanish. This is a particular case of the original form of the Pauli exclusion principle: *No two electrons can occupy the same spin-orbital.* Another way of stating this is to say that no two electrons in an atom can have the same values for all their quantum numbers. These versions of the Pauli principle are consequences of the more general antisymmetry requirement and are less satisfying, since they are based on approximate (zeroth-order) wave functions. We therefore take

$$g(1) = 1s(1)\beta(1)$$

which puts two electrons with opposite spin in the $1s$ orbital. For the spin-orbital h, we cannot use either $1s(1)\alpha(1)$ or $1s(1)\beta(1)$, since these choices make the determinant vanish. We take $h(1) = 2s(1)\alpha(1)$, which gives the familiar Li ground-state configuration $1s^2 2s$ and the zeroth-order wave function

$$\psi^{(0)} = \frac{1}{\sqrt{6}} \begin{vmatrix} 1s(1)\alpha(1) & 1s(1)\beta(1) & 2s(1)\alpha(1) \\ 1s(2)\alpha(2) & 1s(2)\beta(2) & 2s(2)\alpha(2) \\ 1s(3)\alpha(3) & 1s(3)\beta(3) & 2s(3)\alpha(3) \end{vmatrix} \qquad (10.58)$$

Note especially that (10.58) is *not* simply a product of space and spin parts (as we found for H and He), but is a linear combination of terms, each of which is a product of space and spin parts.

We could just as well have taken $h(1) = 2s(1)\beta(1)$, so that the ground state of lithium is, like hydrogen, doubly degenerate, corresponding to the two possible orientations of the spin of the 2s electron. We might use the usual orbital diagrams

$$
\begin{array}{cc}
1s & 2s \\
\uparrow\downarrow & \uparrow \\
\rule{1em}{0.4pt} & \rule{1em}{0.4pt}
\end{array}
\quad \text{and} \quad
\begin{array}{cc}
1s & 2s \\
\uparrow\downarrow & \downarrow \\
\rule{1em}{0.4pt} & \rule{1em}{0.4pt}
\end{array}
$$

to indicate this. Each space orbital such as $1s$ or $2p_0$ can hold two electrons of opposite spin. A spin-orbital such as $2s\alpha$ can hold one electron.

Although the $1s^2 2p$ configuration will have the same unperturbed energy $E^{(0)}$ as the $1s^2 2s$ configuration, when we take electron repulsion into account by calculating $E^{(1)}$ and higher corrections, we will find that the $1s^2 2s$ configuration lies lower for the same reason as in helium.

We close this section by discussing some points about the original form of the Pauli exclusion principle, which we restate as follows: *In a system of identical fermions, no two particles can occupy the same state.* If we have a system of n interacting particles (e.g., an atom) there is a single wave function (involving $4n$ variables) for the entire system. Because of the interactions between the particles, the wave function cannot be written as the product of wave functions of the individual particles; hence, strictly speaking, we cannot talk of the states of individual particles, only the state of the whole system. If, however, the interactions between the particles are not too large, then as an initial approximation we can neglect them and write the zeroth-order wave function of the system as a product of wave functions of the individual particles. In this zeroth-order wave function, no two fermions can have the same wave function (state).

Since bosons require a wave function symmetric with respect to interchange, there is no restriction on the number of bosons in a given state.

10.7 Slater Determinants

Slater pointed out in 1929 that a determinant of the form (10.58) satisfies the antisymmetry requirement for a many-electron atom. A determinant like (10.58) is called a *Slater determinant*. All the elements in a given column of a Slater determinant involve the same spin-orbital, while elements in the same row all involve the same electron. Since interchanging rows and columns does not affect the value of a determinant, we could write the Slater determinant in another, equivalent form. For the sake of consistency we will always write Slater determinants in the form (10.58).

Consider how the zeroth-order helium wave functions which we found previously can be written as Slater determinants. For the ground-state configuration $(1s)^2$ we have the spin-orbitals $1s\alpha$ and $1s\beta$, which give the Slater determinant

$$
\frac{1}{\sqrt{2}} \begin{vmatrix} 1s(1)\alpha(1) & 1s(1)\beta(1) \\ 1s(2)\alpha(2) & 1s(2)\beta(2) \end{vmatrix} = 1s(1)1s(2)\frac{1}{\sqrt{2}}[\alpha(1)\beta(2)-\beta(1)\alpha(2)] \quad \textbf{(10.59)}
$$

which agrees with (10.41). For the states corresponding to the excited configuration $1s2s$, we have the possible spin-orbitals $1s\alpha, 1s\beta, 2s\alpha, 2s\beta$, which give the four

Slater determinants

$$D_1 = \frac{1}{\sqrt{2}} \begin{vmatrix} 1s(1)\alpha(1) & 2s(1)\alpha(1) \\ 1s(2)\alpha(2) & 2s(2)\alpha(2) \end{vmatrix} \qquad D_2 = \frac{1}{\sqrt{2}} \begin{vmatrix} 1s(1)\alpha(1) & 2s(1)\beta(1) \\ 1s(2)\alpha(2) & 2s(2)\beta(2) \end{vmatrix}$$

$$D_3 = \frac{1}{\sqrt{2}} \begin{vmatrix} 1s(1)\beta(1) & 2s(1)\alpha(1) \\ 1s(2)\beta(2) & 2s(2)\alpha(2) \end{vmatrix} \qquad D_4 = \frac{1}{\sqrt{2}} \begin{vmatrix} 1s(1)\beta(1) & 2s(1)\beta(1) \\ 1s(2)\beta(2) & 2s(2)\beta(2) \end{vmatrix}$$

Comparison with (10.42)–(10.45) shows that the $1s2s$ zeroth-order wave functions are related to these four Slater determinants as follows:

$$2^{-1/2}[1s(1)\,2s(2) - 2s(1)\,1s(2)]\,\alpha(1)\,\alpha(2) = D_1 \qquad \text{(10.60)}$$

$$2^{-1/2}[1s(1)\,2s(2) - 2s(1)\,1s(2)]\,\beta(1)\,\beta(2) = D_4 \qquad \text{(10.61)}$$

$$2^{-1/2}[1s(1)\,2s(2) - 2s(1)\,1s(2)]\,2^{-1/2}[\alpha(1)\,\beta(2) + \beta(1)\,\alpha(2)] = 2^{-1/2}(D_2 + D_3) \qquad \text{(10.62)}$$

$$2^{-1/2}[1s(1)\,2s(2) + 2s(1)\,1s(2)]\,2^{-1/2}[\alpha(1)\,\beta(2) - \beta(1)\,\alpha(2)] = 2^{-1/2}(D_2 - D_3) \qquad \text{(10.63)}$$

(To get a zeroth-order function that is an eigenfunction of the spin and orbital angular-momentum operators, we sometimes have to take a linear combination of the Slater determinants of a configuration; see Chapter 11.)

Next consider some notations used for Slater determinants. Instead of writing α and β for spin functions, one often puts a bar over the space function to indicate the spin function β, while a space function without a bar implies the spin factor α. With this notation (10.58) is written as

$$\psi^{(0)} = \frac{1}{\sqrt{6}} \begin{vmatrix} 1s(1) & \overline{1s}(1) & 2s(1) \\ 1s(2) & \overline{1s}(2) & 2s(2) \\ 1s(3) & \overline{1s}(3) & 2s(3) \end{vmatrix} \qquad \text{(10.64)}$$

Given the spin-orbitals occupied by the electrons, we can readily construct the Slater determinant. Thus it is redundant to write out the full determinant. Instead, a shorthand notation which simply specifies the spin-orbitals is often used. In this notation (10.64) is written as

$$\psi^{(0)} = |1s\overline{1s}2s| \qquad \text{(10.65)}$$

where the vertical lines indicate formation of the determinant and multiplication by $1/\sqrt{6}$.

We showed that the factor $1/\sqrt{6}$ normalizes a third-order Slater determinant constructed of orthonormal functions. The expansion of an nth-order determinant has $n!$ terms (Problem 8.10). For an nth-order Slater determinant of orthonormal spin-orbitals, the same reasoning used in the third-order case shows that the normalization constant is $1/\sqrt{n!}$. We always include a factor $1/\sqrt{n!}$ in defining a Slater determinant of order n.

10.8 Perturbation Treatment of the Lithium Ground State

Let us carry out a perturbation treatment of the ground state of the lithium atom.

We take

$$\hat{H}^0 = -\frac{\hbar^2}{2m}\nabla_1^2 - \frac{\hbar^2}{2m}\nabla_2^2 - \frac{\hbar^2}{2m}\nabla_3^2 - \frac{Ze^2}{r_1} - \frac{Ze^2}{r_2} - \frac{Ze^2}{r_3} \qquad (10.66)$$

$$\hat{H}' = \frac{e^2}{r_{12}} + \frac{e^2}{r_{23}} + \frac{e^2}{r_{13}} \qquad (10.67)$$

We found in Section 10.6 that to satisfy the Pauli principle the ground-state configuration must be $1s^2 2s$; the correct zeroth-order wave function is (10.58):

$$\psi^{(0)} = 6^{-1/2}[1s(1)1s(2)2s(3)\,\alpha(1)\beta(2)\,\alpha(3) - 1s(1)2s(2)1s(3)\,\alpha(1)\,\alpha(2)\beta(3)$$

$$- 1s(1)1s(2)2s(3)\beta(1)\,\alpha(2)\,\alpha(3) + 1s(1)2s(2)1s(3)\beta(1)\,\alpha(2)\,\alpha(3)$$

$$+ 2s(1)1s(2)1s(3)\,\alpha(1)\,\alpha(2)\beta(3) - 2s(1)1s(2)1s(3)\,\alpha(1)\beta(2)\,\alpha(3)] \qquad (10.68)$$

What is $E^{(0)}$? Each term in (10.68) contains the product of two $1s$ hydrogenlike functions and one $2s$ hydrogenlike function, multiplied by a spin factor. $\hat{H}^0$ is the sum of three hydrogenlike Hamiltonians, one for each electron, and does not involve spin. Thus $\psi^{(0)}$ is a linear combination of terms, each of which is an eigenfunction of $\hat{H}^0$ with eigenvalue $E_{1s}^{(0)} + E_{1s}^{(0)} + E_{2s}^{(0)}$, where these are hydrogenlike energies; hence $\psi^{(0)}$ is an eigenfunction of $\hat{H}^0$ with eigenvalue $E_{1s}^{(0)} + E_{1s}^{(0)} + E_{2s}^{(0)}$. Therefore [Eq. (6.107)]

$$E^{(0)} = -\left(\frac{1}{1^2} + \frac{1}{1^2} + \frac{1}{2^2}\right)\left(\frac{Z^2 e^2}{2a_0}\right) = -\frac{81}{4}(13.606 \text{ eV}) = -275.5 \text{ eV} \qquad (10.69)$$

To find $E^{(1)}$, we must evaluate the integral (9.30). We begin by grouping together terms in $\psi^{(0)}$ that have the same spin factor:

$$\psi^{(0)} = 6^{-1/2}[1s(1)2s(2)1s(3) - 1s(1)1s(2)2s(3)]\,\beta(1)\,\alpha(2)\,\alpha(3)$$

$$+ 6^{-1/2}[1s(1)1s(2)2s(3) - 2s(1)1s(2)1s(3)]\,\alpha(1)\beta(2)\,\alpha(3)$$

$$+ 6^{-1/2}[2s(1)1s(2)1s(3) - 1s(1)2s(2)1s(3)]\,\alpha(1)\,\alpha(2)\beta(3) \qquad (10.70)$$

$$\psi^{(0)} = a\beta(1)\,\alpha(2)\,\alpha(3) + b\alpha(1)\beta(2)\,\alpha(3) + c\alpha(1)\,\alpha(2)\beta(3) = A + B + C \qquad (10.71)$$

where the space function multiplying the spin function $\beta(1)\,\alpha(2)\,\alpha(3)$ in (10.70) is called a, and $A = a\beta(1)\,\alpha(2)\,\alpha(3)$, with similar definitions for b, c, B, and C. We have

$$E^{(1)} = \int |\psi^{(0)}|^2 H' \, d\tau$$

$$E^{(1)} = \int |A|^2 H' \, d\tau + \int |B|^2 H' \, d\tau + \int |C|^2 H' \, d\tau + \int A^* B H' \, d\tau$$

$$+ \int B^* C H' \, d\tau + \int A^* C H' \, d\tau + \int A B^* H' \, d\tau$$

$$+ \int B C^* H' \, d\tau + \int A C^* H' \, d\tau \qquad (10.72)$$

Because of the orthogonality of the different spin functions in A, B, and C, the last six integrals in (10.72) are zero. For example, the integral $\int A^*BH' \, d\tau$ involves summations over spins, as follows:

$$\sum_{m_{s1}} \sum_{m_{s2}} \sum_{m_{s3}} [\beta(1)\alpha(2)\alpha(3)]^*[\alpha(1)\beta(2)\alpha(3)]$$

$$= \sum_{m_{s1}} \beta^*(1)\alpha(1) \sum_{m_{s2}} \alpha^*(2)\beta(2) \sum_{m_{s3}} \alpha^*(3)\alpha(3) = 0 \cdot 0 \cdot 1 = 0$$

Since the spin functions are normalized, summation over spins in the first three integrals in (10.72) gives unity. Therefore

$$E^{(1)} = \int\int\int a^2 H' \, dv_1 \, dv_2 \, dv_3 + \int\int\int b^2 H' \, dv_1 \, dv_2 \, dv_3 + \int\int\int c^2 H' \, dv_1 \, dv_2 \, dv_3 \tag{10.73}$$

where spin is no longer involved. By relabeling dummy integration variables, we can prove that the three integrals in (10.73) are equal to one another. Using orthonormality of the $1s$ and $2s$ orbitals and relabeling of integration variables, we can then show that (Problem 10.12):

$$E^{(1)} = 2\int\int 1s^2(1) \, 2s^2(2)\frac{e^2}{r_{12}} \, dv_1 \, dv_2 + \int\int 1s^2(1) \, 1s^2(2)\frac{e^2}{r_{12}} \, dv_1 \, dv_2$$

$$- \int\int 1s(1) \, 2s(2) \, 1s(2) \, 2s(1)\frac{e^2}{r_{12}} \, dv_1 \, dv_2 \tag{10.74}$$

These integrals are Coulomb and exchange integrals:

$$E^{(1)} = 2J_{1s2s} + J_{1s1s} - K_{1s2s} \tag{10.75}$$

We have [Eqs. (9.63), (9.67), and (9.157)]:

$$J_{1s1s} = \frac{5}{8}\frac{Ze^2}{a_0}, \qquad J_{1s2s} = \frac{17}{81}\frac{Ze^2}{a_0}, \qquad K_{1s2s} = \frac{16}{729}\frac{Ze^2}{a_0} \tag{10.76}$$

$$E^{(1)} = \frac{5965}{972}\left(\frac{e^2}{2a_0}\right) = 83.5 \text{ eV} \tag{10.77}$$

The energy through first order is -192.0 eV, as compared to the true ground-state energy of lithium, -203.5 eV. To improve on this result, we must calculate higher-order wave-function and energy corrections. This will mix into the wave function contributions from Slater determinants involving configurations besides $1s^2 2s$ (configuration interaction).

10.9 Variation Treatments of the Lithium Ground State

The zeroth-order perturbation wave function (10.58) uses the full nuclear charge $(Z = 3)$ for both the $1s$ and $2s$ orbitals of lithium. We expect that the $2s$ electron, which is partially shielded from the nucleus by the two $1s$ electrons, will see an effective nuclear charge that is considerably less than 3. Even the $1s$ electrons partially shield each other (recall the treatment of the helium ground state). This reasoning suggests the introduction of two variational parameters ζ_1 and ζ_2 into (10.58).

Instead of using the $Z = 3$ $1s$ function in Table 6.2, we take

$$f \equiv \frac{1}{\pi^{1/2}} \left(\frac{\zeta_1}{a_0} \right)^{3/2} e^{-\zeta_1 r/a_0} \tag{10.78}$$

where ζ_1 is a variational parameter representing an effective nuclear charge for the $1s$ electrons. Instead of the $Z = 3$ $2s$ function in Table 6.2, we use

$$g = \frac{1}{4(2\pi)^{1/2}} \left(\frac{\zeta_2}{a_0} \right)^{3/2} \left(2 - \frac{\zeta_2 r}{a_0} \right) e^{-\zeta_2 r/2a_0} \tag{10.79}$$

Our trial variation function is then

$$\varphi = \frac{1}{\sqrt{6}} \begin{vmatrix} f(1)\alpha(1) & f(1)\beta(1) & g(1)\alpha(1) \\ f(2)\alpha(2) & f(2)\beta(2) & g(2)\alpha(2) \\ f(3)\alpha(3) & f(3)\beta(3) & g(3)\alpha(3) \end{vmatrix} \tag{10.80}$$

Note that using different charges ζ_1 and ζ_2 for the $1s$ and $2s$ orbitals destroys their orthogonality, so that (10.80) is not normalized. The best values of the variational parameters are found by setting

$$\frac{\partial W}{\partial \zeta_1} = 0, \qquad \frac{\partial W}{\partial \zeta_2} = 0$$

where the variational integral W is given by the left side of Eq. (8.13). The results are[4]

$$\zeta_1 = 2.686, \qquad \zeta_2 = 1.776 \tag{10.81}$$

$$W = -7.3922 \left(\frac{e^2}{a_0} \right) = -201.2 \text{ eV}$$

which is considerably closer to the true value -203.5 eV than the result -192.0 eV obtained in the last section using simple perturbation theory. The value of ζ_2 indicates substantial, but not complete, screening of the $2s$ electron by the $1s$ electrons.

We might try other forms for the orbitals besides (10.78) and (10.79) to improve the trial function. However, no matter what orbital functions we try, if we restrict ourselves to a trial function of the form of (10.80), we can never reach the true ground-state energy. To do this, we must either introduce r_{12}, r_{23}, and r_{13} into the trial function, or use a linear combination of several Slater determinants corresponding to various configurations (configuration interaction).

10.10 Spin Magnetic Moment

Recall that the orbital angular momentum $\mathbf{L}$ of an electron has a magnetic moment $-(e/2mc)\mathbf{L}$ associated with it [Eq. (6.152)]. It is natural to suppose that there is also a magnetic moment $\boldsymbol{\mu}_S$ associated with the electronic spin angular momentum $\mathbf{S}$. We might guess that $\boldsymbol{\mu}_S$ would be $-e/2mc$ times $\mathbf{S}$. Spin is a relativistic phenomenon, however, and we cannot expect $\boldsymbol{\mu}_S$ to be related to $\mathbf{S}$ in exactly the same way that $\boldsymbol{\mu}_L$ is related to $\mathbf{L}$. In fact, Dirac's relativistic treatment

---

[4] E. B. Wilson, Jr., J. Chem. Phys., 1, 211 (1933).

of the electron gave the result that

$$\mu_S = -g_e \frac{e}{2mc} \mathbf{S} = -\frac{e}{mc} \mathbf{S} \qquad (10.82)$$

where Dirac found an electron g factor equal to 2. The magnitude of the spin magnetic moment of an electron is

$$|\mu_S| = g_e \frac{e}{2mc} |\mathbf{S}| = \sqrt{3} \frac{e\hbar}{2mc} \qquad (10.83)$$

Theoretical and experimental work[5] subsequent to Dirac's treatment has shown that g_e is slightly greater than 2:

$$g_e = 2\left(1 + \frac{\alpha}{2\pi} + \cdots\right) = 2.0023$$

where the *fine-structure constant* α is defined as

$$\alpha \equiv \frac{e^2}{\hbar c} \qquad (10.84)$$

The constant α is a dimensionless combination of the three fundamental constants e, $\hbar$, and c, and is of great theoretical interest. In 1969, the mathematician Wyler gave relativistic quantum theory arguments for the contention that

$$1/\alpha \overset{(?)}{=} 2^{19/4} 3^{-7/4} 5^{1/4} \pi^{11/4} = 137.03608$$

a result in remarkable agreement with the experimental value 137.03604 ± 0.00011. Wyler also proposed that the ratio of the proton and electron masses equals $6\pi^5 = 1836.118$, in only fair agreement with experiment. The validity of such numerology is an open question. (See *Physics Today*, Aug. 1971, p. 17 and Nov. 1971, p. 9.)

The ferromagnetism of iron is due to the electron's magnetic dipole moment.

PROBLEMS

10.1 If electrons had a spin of zero, what would be the zeroth order (interelectronic repulsions neglected) wave functions for the ground state and first excited state of lithium?

10.2 (a) Show that $\hat{P}_{12}$ commutes with the Hamiltonian for the lithium atom. (b) Show that $\hat{P}_{12}$ and $\hat{P}_{23}$ do not commute with each other.

10.3 The antisymmetrization operator $\hat{A}$ is defined as the operator that anti-symmetrizes a product of n one-electron functions and multiplies them by $(n!)^{-1/2}$. For $n = 2$, we have

$$\hat{A}f(1)g(2) = \frac{1}{\sqrt{2}} \begin{vmatrix} f(1) & g(1) \\ f(2) & g(2) \end{vmatrix}$$

(a) For $n = 2$, express $\hat{A}$ in terms of $\hat{P}_{12}$. (b) For $n = 3$, express $\hat{A}$ in terms of $\hat{P}_{12}$, $\hat{P}_{13}$, and $\hat{P}_{23}$.

---

[5] For a review see P. Kusch, *Physics Today*, Feb. 1966, p. 23.

10.4 A *permanent* is defined by the same expansion as a determinant except that all terms are given a plus sign. Thus, the second order permanent is

$$\begin{vmatrix} \overset{+}{a} & \overset{+}{b} \\ c & d \end{vmatrix} = ad + bc$$

Can you think of a use for permanents in quantum mechanics?

10.5 Show that $\hat{P}_{12}$ is Hermitian.

10.6 If we had incorrectly used as the zeroth-order Li ground-state wave function, the non-antisymmetric function $1s(1)1s(2)2s(3)$, what would $E^{(1)}$ be calculated to be?

10.7 Verify that the spin functions (10.13) satisfy Eqs. (10.11) and (10.12).

10.8 Calculate the angle that the spin vector $\mathbf{S}$ makes with the z axis for an electron with spin function α.

10.9 Which of the following functions are: (a) completely symmetric? (b) completely antisymmetric?

(1) $f(1)g(2)\alpha(1)\alpha(2)$

(2) $f(1)f(2)[\alpha(1)\beta(2)-\beta(1)\alpha(2)]$

(3) $f(1)f(2)f(3)\beta(1)\beta(2)\beta(3)$

(4) $[f(1)g(2)-g(1)f(2)][\alpha(1)\beta(2)-\beta(1)\alpha(2)]$

(5) $r_{12}^2 e^{-a(r_1+r_2)}$

(6) $e^{-a(r_1-r_2)}$

10.10 Verify Eqs. (10.23) and (10.29).

10.11 (a) If the spin component S_x of an electron is measured, what possible values can result? (b) The functions α and β form a complete set, so that any one-electron spin function can be written as a linear combination of them. Use Eqs. (10.28)–(10.29) to construct the two normalized eigenfunctions of $\hat{S}_x$ with eigenvalues $+\frac{1}{2}\hbar$ and $-\frac{1}{2}\hbar$. (c) Suppose a measurement of S_z for an electron gives the value $+\frac{1}{2}\hbar$; if a measurement of S_x is then carried out, give the probabilities for each possible outcome.[6] (d) The same as (b) for $\hat{S}_y$ instead of $\hat{S}_x$.

10.12 Derive Eq. (10.74) from (10.73).

10.13 Let Y_{jm} be the *normalized* eigenfunction of the generalized angular-momentum operators (Section 5.4) $\hat{M}^2$ and $\hat{M}_z$:

$$\hat{M}^2 Y_{jm} = j(j+1)\hbar^2 Y_{jm}, \qquad \hat{M}_z Y_{jm} = m\hbar Y_{jm}$$

From Section 5.4, the effect of $\hat{M}_+$ on Y_{jm} is to increase the $\hat{M}_z$ eigenvalue by $\hbar$:

$$\hat{M}_+ Y_{jm} = AY_{j,m+1}$$

---

[6] In the Stern–Gerlach experiment, a beam of particles is sent through an inhomogeneous magnetic field, which splits the beam into several beams each having particles with a different component of magnetic dipole moment in the field direction. For example, a beam of ground-state sodium atoms is split into two beams, corresponding to the two possible orientations of the valence-electron's spin. Problem 10.11c corresponds to setting up a Stern–Gerlach apparatus with the field in the z direction and then allowing the $+\frac{1}{2}\hbar$ beam from this apparatus to enter a Stern–Gerlach apparatus that has the field in the x direction.

where A is a constant. Use the same procedure that led to Eqs. (10.22) and (10.23) to show that

$$\hat{M}_+ Y_{jm} = [j(j+1) - m(m+1)]^{1/2} \hbar Y_{j, m+1} \tag{10.85}$$

$$\hat{M}_- Y_{jm} = [j(j+1) - m(m-1)]^{1/2} \hbar Y_{j, m-1} \tag{10.86}$$

(b) Show that (10.85) and (10.86) are consistent with (10.22) and (10.23). (c) With $\mathbf{M} = \mathbf{L}$, the function Y_{jm} is the spherical harmonic $Y_l^m(\theta, \varphi)$. Verify (10.85) directly for $l = 2$, $m = -1$. [Actually, for consistency with the phase choice of Eqs. (10.85) and (10.86), one must add the factor $(-i)^{m+|m|}$ to the definition (5.146) of the spherical harmonics; this introduces a minus sign for odd positive values of m.]

10.14 A muon has the same charge and spin as an electron, but a heavier mass. What would be the ground-state configuration of a lithium atom with two electrons and one muon?

10.15 Show that α and β are each eigenfunctions of $\hat{S}_x^2$ (but not of $\hat{S}_x$).

CHAPTER
11

Many-Electron Atoms

11.1 The Hartree–Fock Self-Consistent-Field Method

For hydrogen the exact wave function is known. For helium and lithium, very accurate wave functions have been calculated by including interelectronic distances in the variation functions. For atoms of higher atomic number, the best approach to a good wave function lies in first calculating an approximate wave function using the Hartree–Fock procedure, which we will outline in this section. The Hartree–Fock method is the basis for the use of atomic and molecular orbitals in many-electron systems.

We begin by writing down the atomic Hamiltonian. For an n-electron atom we have,[1] assuming an infinitely heavy point nucleus,

$$\hat{H} = -\frac{\hbar^2}{2m} \sum_{i=1}^{n} \nabla_i^2 - \sum_{i=1}^{n} \frac{Ze^2}{r_i} + \sum_{i=1}^{n} \sum_{j>i}^{n} \frac{e^2}{r_{ij}} \tag{11.1}$$

The first sum in (11.1) contains the kinetic-energy operators for the n electrons; the second sum is the potential energy for the attractions between the electrons and the nucleus of charge Z (for a neutral atom $Z = n$); the last sum is the potential energy of the interelectronic repulsions—the restriction $j > i$ avoids counting the same interelectronic repulsion twice, and avoids terms like e^2/r_{ii}. The Schroedinger equation for the atom is not separable because of the interelectronic repulsion terms, e^2/r_{ij}. Recalling the perturbation treatment of helium (Section 9.3), we might obtain a zeroth-order wave function by neglecting these repulsions. The

---

[1] This Hamiltonian is not complete; it omits spin-orbit and other interactions; these terms are generally small and will be considered later in this chapter.

Schroedinger equation would then separate into n one-electron hydrogenlike equations. The zeroth-order wave function would be a product of n hydrogenlike (one-electron) orbitals:

$$\psi^{(0)} = f_1(r_1, \theta_1, \varphi_1) f_2(r_2, \theta_2, \varphi_2) \cdots f_n(r_n, \theta_n, \varphi_n) \qquad (11.2)$$

where the hydrogenlike orbitals are

$$f = R_{nl}(r) Y_l^m(\theta, \varphi) \qquad (11.3)$$

For the ground state of the atom, we would feed two electrons with opposite spin into each of the lowest orbitals, in accord with the Pauli exclusion principle, giving rise to the ground-state configuration. Although the approximate wave function (11.2) is qualitatively useful, it is gravely lacking in quantitative accuracy. For one thing, all the orbitals use the full nuclear charge Z. Recalling our variational treatments of helium and lithium, we know we can get a better approximation by using different effective atomic numbers for the different orbitals to account for screening of electrons. The use of effective atomic numbers gives considerable improvement, but we are still far from having an accurate wave function. The next step is to use a variation function that has the same form as (11.2), but is not restricted to using hydrogenlike or any other particular form of orbitals. Thus we take

$$\varphi = g_1(r_1, \theta_1, \varphi_1) g_2(r_2, \theta_2, \varphi_2) \cdots g_n(r_n, \theta_n, \varphi_n) \qquad (11.4)$$

and we seek to determine the functions $g_1, g_2, \ldots, g_n$ that minimize the variational integral $\int \varphi^* \hat{H} \varphi \, dv / \int \varphi^* \varphi \, dv$. Our task is considerably more difficult than in previous variational calculations where we guessed a trial function that included some parameters, and then varied the *parameters*. Here, we must vary the *functions* g_i. [After we have found the best possible functions g_i, Eq. (11.4) will still be only an approximate wave function. The many-electron Schroedinger equation is not separable, so that the true wave function cannot be written as the product of n one-electron functions.]

Finding the best possible approximate wave function of the form (11.4) is a formidable computational task for a many-electron atom. To simplify matters somewhat, we approximate the best possible orbitals with orbitals that are the product of a radial factor and a spherical harmonic:

$$g_i = h_i(r_i) Y_{l_i}^{m_i}(\theta_i, \varphi_i) \qquad (11.5)$$

This approximation is generally made in atomic calculations.

The procedure for calculating the g_i's was introduced by Hartree in 1928 and is called the Hartree *self-consistent-field* (SCF) method. Hartree arrived at the SCF procedure by intuitive physical arguments; the proof[2] that Hartree's procedure gives the best possible variation function of the form (11.4) was given in 1930 by Slater and by Fock.

Hartree's procedure is as follows. We first guess a product wave function

$$\varphi_0 = s_1(r_1, \theta_1, \varphi_1) s_2(r_2, \theta_2, \varphi_2) \cdots s_n(r_n, \theta_n, \varphi_n) \qquad (11.6)$$

---

[2] For a review of the SCF method, see S. M. Blinder, *Am. J. Phys.*, 33, 431 (1965).

where each s_i is a normalized function of r multiplied by a spherical harmonic. A reasonable guess for φ_0 would be a product of hydrogenlike orbitals with effective atomic numbers. For the function (11.6), the probability density of electron i is $|s_i|^2$. We now focus attention on electron 1 and regard electrons $2, 3, ..., n$ as being smeared out to form a static distribution of electric charge through which electron 1 moves; we are thus averaging out the instantaneous interactions between electron 1 and the other electrons. The potential energy of interaction between two point charges q_1 and q_2 is given by (6.66) as $V_{12} = q_1 q_2 / r_{12}$. We now take q_2 and smear it out into a continuous charge distribution such that ρ_2 is the charge density, the charge per unit volume. The infinitesimal charge in the infinitesimal volume dv_2 is $\rho_2 \, dv_2$ and summing up the interactions between q_1 and the infinitesimal elements of charge, we have

$$V_{12} = q_1 \int \frac{\rho_2}{r_{12}} \, dv_2 \tag{11.7}$$

For electron 2 (with charge $-e$) the charge density of the hypothetical charge cloud is $\rho_2 = -e|s_2|^2$. Hence

$$V_{12} = e^2 \int \frac{|s_2|^2}{r_{12}} \, dv_2 \tag{11.8}$$

Adding in the interactions with the other electrons, we have

$$V_{12} + V_{13} + \cdots + V_{1n} = \sum_{j=2}^{n} e^2 \int \frac{|s_j|^2}{r_{1j}} \, dv_j \tag{11.9}$$

The potential energy of interaction between electron 1 and the other electrons and the nucleus is then

$$V(r_1, \theta_1, \varphi_1) = \sum_{j=2}^{n} e^2 \int \frac{|s_j|^2}{r_{1j}} \, dv_j - \frac{Ze^2}{r_1} \tag{11.10}$$

We now make a further approximation beyond assuming the wave function to be a product of one-electron orbitals. We assume that the effective potential acting on an electron in an atom can be adequately approximated by a function of r only. This *central-field approximation* can be shown to be generally accurate. We therefore average $V(r_1, \theta_1, \varphi_1)$ over the angles to arrive at a potential energy which depends only on r_1:

$$V(r_1) = \frac{\int_0^{2\pi} \int_0^{\pi} V(r_1, \theta_1, \varphi_1) \sin \theta_1 \, d\theta_1 \, d\varphi_1}{\int_0^{2\pi} \int_0^{\pi} \sin \theta \, d\theta \, d\varphi} \tag{11.11}$$

We now use $V(r_1)$ as the potential energy in a one-electron Schroedinger equation

$$\left[-\frac{\hbar^2}{2m} \nabla_1^2 + V(r_1) \right] t_1(1) = \varepsilon_1 t_1(1) \tag{11.12}$$

and solve for $t_1(1)$, which will be an improved orbital for electron 1. In (11.12), ε_1 is the energy of the orbital of electron 1 at this stage of the approximation. Since the potential energy in (11.12) is spherically symmetric, the angular factor in $t_1(1)$ is a spherical harmonic involving quantum numbers l_1 and m_1 (Section 6.1). The radial factor $R(r_1)$ in t_1 is the solution of a one-dimensional Schroedinger equation of the form (6.21). We get a set of solutions $R(r_1)$, where the number of nodes k interior to the boundary points ($r = 0$ and ∞) starts at zero for the lowest energy and increases by one for each higher energy (Section 4.2). We now *define* the quantum number n as $n = l+1+k$, $k = 0, 1, 2, \ldots$. We thus have $1s, 2s, 2p$, etc. orbitals (with orbital energy ε increasing with n) just as in hydrogenlike atoms, and the number of interior radial nodes $(n-l-1)$ is the same as in hydrogenlike atoms (Section 6.5). However, since $V(r_1)$ is not a simple Coulomb potential, the radial factor $R(r_1)$ is not a hydrogenlike function. Of the set of solutions $R(r_1)$, we take the one that corresponds to the orbital we are improving. For example, if electron 1 is a $1s$ electron in the Be $1s^2 2s^2$ configuration, then $V(r_1)$ is calculated from the guessed orbitals of one $1s$ electron and two $2s$ electrons, and we use the radial solution of (11.12) with $k = 0$ to find an improved $1s$ orbital.

We now go to electron 2 and regard it as moving in a charge cloud of density

$$-e[|t_1(1)|^2 + |s_3(3)|^2 + |s_4(4)|^2 + \cdots + |s_n(n)|^2]$$

due to the other electrons. We calculate an effective potential energy $V(r_2)$ and solve a one-electron Schroedinger equation for electron 2 to obtain an improved orbital $t_2(2)$. We continue this process until we have a set of improved orbitals for all n electrons. Then we go back to electron 1 and repeat the process. We continue to calculate improved orbitals until there is no further change from one iteration to the next. The final set of orbitals gives the Hartree self-consistent-field wave function.

How do we get the energy of the atom in the SCF approximation? It seems natural to simply take the sum of the orbital energies of the electrons, $\varepsilon_1 + \varepsilon_2 + \cdots + \varepsilon_n$, and some texts give this expression. This is wrong. In calculating the orbital energy ε_1 we solved a one-electron Schroedinger equation like (11.12). The potential energy in (11.12) includes, in an average way, the energy of the repulsions between electrons 1 and 2, 1 and 3, ..., 1 and n. When we solve for ε_2, we solve a Schroedinger equation whose potential energy includes repulsions between electrons 2 and 1, 2 and 3, ..., 2 and n. If we take $\sum \varepsilon_i$ we will count each interelectronic repulsion twice. To obtain the total energy E of the atom, we must take

$$E = \sum_{i=1}^{n} \varepsilon_i - \sum_{i=1}^{n} \sum_{j>i} \int \int \frac{e^2 |g_i(i)|^2 |g_j(j)|^2}{r_{ij}} \, dv_i \, dv_j$$

$$E = \sum_{i=1}^{n} \varepsilon_i - \sum_{i=1}^{n} \sum_{j>i} J_{ij} \tag{11.13}$$

where we have subtracted the average repulsions of the electrons from the sum of the orbital energies, and have used the notation J_{ij} for Coulomb integrals [Eq. (9.144)].

The set of orbitals belonging to a given principal quantum number n constitutes a *shell*. The $n = 1, 2, 3, \ldots$ shells are the $K, L, M, \ldots$ shells, respectively.

The orbitals belonging to a given n and a given l constitute a *subshell*. Consider the sum of the Hartree probability densities for the electrons in a filled subshell. Using (11.5), we have

$$2 \sum_{m=-l}^{l} |h_{n,l}(r)|^2 |Y_l^m(\theta, \varphi)|^2 = 2|h_{n,l}(r)|^2 \sum_{m=-l}^{l} |Y_l^m(\theta, \varphi)|^2 \qquad (11.14)$$

where the factor 2 comes from the pair of electrons in each orbital. Now it is a result of the spherical-harmonic addition theorem (*Merzbacher*, Section 9.7) that the sum on the right side of (11.14) equals $(2l+1)/4\pi$. Hence the sum of the probability densities is $[(2l+1)/2\pi]|h_{n,l}(r)|^2$, which is independent of the angles. A closed subshell gives a spherically symmetric probability density, a result called *Unsöld's theorem*. For a half-filled subshell, the factor 2 is omitted from (11.14), and here also we get a spherically symmetric probability density.

The alert reader may have realized that there is something fundamentally wrong with the simple Hartree product wave function (11.4). Although we have paid some attention to spin and the Pauli principle by putting no more than two electrons in each spatial orbital, any approximation to the true wave function should include spin explicitly and should be antisymmetric to interchange of electrons (Chapter 10). Hence, instead of the spatial orbitals we must use spin-orbitals and must take an antisymmetric linear combination of products of spin-orbitals. This was pointed out by Fock (and by Slater) in 1930, and an SCF calculation that uses antisymmetrized spin-orbitals is called a *Hartree–Fock* calculation. We have seen that a Slater determinant of spin-orbitals provides the proper antisymmetry. For example, to carry out a Hartree–Fock calculation for the lithium ground state, we start with the function (10.80), where f and g are guesses for the 1s and 2s orbitals. We then carry out the SCF iterative process until we get no further improvement in f and g; this gives the lithium ground-state Hartree–Fock wave function. The differential equations for finding the Hartree–Fock orbitals have the same general form as (11.12), namely,

$$\hat{H}_i^{\text{eff}} f_i = \varepsilon_i f_i, \qquad i = 1, 2, ..., n \qquad (11.15)$$

where f_i is the spin-orbital of electron i, the operator $\hat{H}_i^{\text{eff}}$ is the effective Hartree–Fock Hamiltonian for electron i, and the eigenvalue ε_i is the orbital energy of electron i. However, the effective Hartree–Fock Hamiltonian has extra terms, as compared to the effective Hartree Hamiltonian given by the bracketed terms in (11.12). The Hartree–Fock expression for the total energy of the atom involves exchange integrals K_{ij} in addition to the Coulomb integrals that occur in the Hartree expression (11.13). See Section 13.16.

Originally, Hartree–Fock calculations were done numerically, and the resulting orbitals given as tables of the radial functions for various values of r. In 1951 Roothaan proposed representing the Hartree–Fock orbitals as linear combinations of a complete set of known functions, called *basis functions*. Thus, for lithium we would write the Hartree–Fock 1s and 2s spatial orbitals as

$$f = \sum_i b_i \chi_i, \qquad g = \sum_i c_i \chi_i$$

where the χ_i are some complete set of functions, and the b's and c's are the expansion coefficients to be determined by the SCF iterative procedure. Since the χ_i form a complete set, these expansions are valid.

The most commonly used set of basis functions is the set of *Slater-type orbitals* (STO's), which have the normalized form:

$$\frac{[2\zeta/a_0]^{n+1/2}}{[(2n)!]^{1/2}} r^{n-1} e^{-\zeta r/a_0} Y_l^m(\theta, \varphi) \tag{11.16}$$

The set of all such functions with n, l, and m being integers but with ζ having all possible positive values forms a complete set. The parameter ζ is called the *orbital exponent*. To get a truly accurate representation of the Hartree–Fock orbitals, we would have to include an infinite number of Slater orbitals in the expansions; in practice, one can get very accurate results by using only a few judiciously chosen Slater orbitals.

Clementi[3] performed analytic Hartree–Fock calculations for the ground state and some excited states of the first third of the periodic table. For example, consider the Hartree–Fock ground-state wave function of helium, which has the form [*cf*. Eq. (10.59)]:

$$f(1) f(2) \cdot 2^{-1/2} [\alpha(1) \beta(2) - \alpha(2) \beta(1)]$$

Clementi expresses the $1s$ orbital function f as the following combination of five $1s$ Slater-type orbitals:

$$f = \pi^{-1/2} \sum_{i=1}^{5} c_i \left(\frac{\zeta_i}{a_0}\right)^{3/2} e^{-\zeta_i r/a_0}$$

where the expansion coefficients c_i are

$$c_1 = 0.78503, \qquad c_2 = 0.20284, \qquad c_3 = 0.03693$$

$$c_4 = -0.00293, \qquad c_5 = 0.00325$$

and where the orbital exponents ζ_i are

$$\zeta_1 = 1.4300, \qquad \zeta_2 = 2.4415, \qquad \zeta_3 = 4.0996$$

$$\zeta_4 = 6.4843, \qquad \zeta_5 = 0.7978$$

The Hartree–Fock energy is -77.9 eV, as compared to the true value -79.0 eV.

Electron densities calculated from Hartree–Fock wave functions are quite accurate. Figure 11.1 compares the radial electron density of argon calculated by the Hartree–Fock method, with the density determined by electron diffraction. Note the electronic shell structure. The high nuclear charge causes the inner-shell electrons to have much smaller average distances from the nucleus than in hydrogen or helium. Thus there is only a moderate increase in atomic size as we go down a given group in the periodic table. Calculations show that the radius of a sphere containing 98 percent of the Hartree–Fock electron probability density gives an atomic radius in good agreement with the empirically determined van der Waals radius. [C. W. Kammeyer and D. R. Whitman, *J. Chem. Phys.*, **56**, 4419 (1972).]

---

[3] E. Clementi, *J. Chem. Phys.*, **38**, 996, 1001 (1962); **41**, 295, 303 (1964).

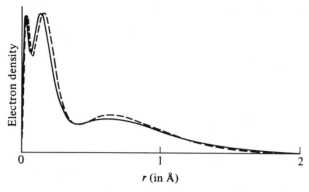

FIGURE 11.1 *Electron density in* Ar *as a function of r. The broken line is the result of a Hartree-Fock calculation. The solid line is the result of electron-diffraction data.* [*From L. S. Bartell and L. O. Brockway*, Phys. Rev. **90**, *833 (1953). Used by permission.*]

Accurate representation of a many-electron atomic orbital (AO) requires a linear combination of several Slater-type orbitals. For rough calculations it is convenient to have simple approximations for AO's. We might use hydrogenlike orbitals with effective nuclear charges, but Slater suggested an even simpler method, namely, to approximate an AO by a single function of the form (11.16) with the orbital exponent ζ taken as

$$\zeta = (Z - s)/n \tag{11.17}$$

where Z is the atomic number, n is the orbital's principal quantum number, and s is a screening constant calculated by a set of rules (see Problem 15.27). A Slater orbital replaces the polynomial in r in a hydrogenlike orbital with a single power of r; hence a Slater orbital does not have the proper number of radial nodes and does not represent well the inner part of an orbital.

It requires an enormous amount of computation to carry out a Hartree–Fock SCF calculation for a many-electron atom. Hartree did several SCF calculations in the 1930's, when electronic computers were not in existence. Fortunately, Hartree's father, a retired gentleman, enjoyed numerical computation as a hobby and helped his son. Nowadays computers have replaced Hartree's father.

11.2 Orbitals and the Periodic Table

The orbital concept and the Pauli exclusion principle allow us to understand the periodic table of the elements. An orbital is a one-electron wave function. We have used orbitals to obtain approximate wave functions for many-electron atoms, writing the wave function as a Slater determinant of one-electron orbitals. In the crudest approximation we neglect all interelectronic repulsions and obtain hydrogenlike orbitals. The best possible orbitals are the Hartree–Fock SCF functions. We build up the periodic table by feeding electrons into these orbitals, each of which can hold a pair of electrons with opposite spin.

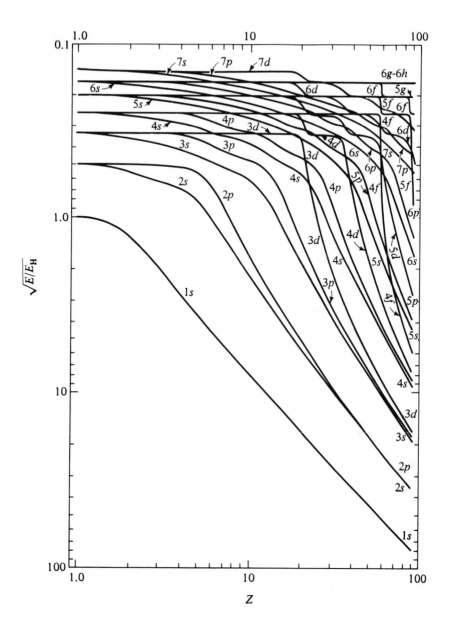

FIGURE 11.2 *Atomic-orbital energies as a function of atomic number for neutral atoms, as calculated by Latter.* [*Figure redrawn by M. Kasha from R. Latter,* Phys. Rev. **99**, *510 (1955). Used by permission.*] *Note the logarithmic scales.* E_H *is the ground-state hydrogen-atom energy,* -13.6 eV.

Figure 11.2 is a diagram of theoretically calculated AO energies for neutral atoms; these energies were calculated by the Thomas–Fermi–Dirac method, which uses ideas of statistical mechanics to get approximate atomic wave functions.[4] The orbital energies of Fig. 11.2 generally agree well with both Hartree–Fock and experimentally determined orbital energies.[5]

Orbital energies change with changing atomic number Z; as Z increases, the orbital energies decrease, due to the increased attraction between the nucleus and the electrons. This decrease is most rapid for the inner orbitals, which are less well-shielded from the nucleus.

For $Z > 1$, orbitals with the same value of n but different l have different energies. Thus for the $n = 3$ orbital energies, we have

$$E_{3s} < E_{3p} < E_{3d}, \qquad Z > 1$$

The splitting of these levels, which are degenerate in the hydrogen atom, arises from the interelectronic repulsions. (Recall the perturbation treatment of helium in Section 9.7.) In the limit $Z \to \infty$, orbitals with the same value of n are again degenerate, because the interelectronic repulsions become insignificant in comparison with the electron–nucleus attractions.

The relative positions of certain orbitals change with changing Z. Thus in hydrogen the $3d$ orbital lies below the $4s$ orbital, but for Z in the range 7 to 21 the $4s$ is below the $3d$. For large values of Z, the $3d$ is again lower. At $Z = 19$, the $4s$ is lower; hence $_{19}$K has the ground-state configuration $1s^2 2s^2 2p^6 3s^2 3p^6 4s$. Recall that s orbitals are more penetrating than p or d orbitals; this allows the $4s$ orbital to lie below the $3d$ orbital for some values of Z. Note the sudden drop in the $3d$ energy which starts at $Z = 21$, when filling of the $3d$ orbital begins. The electrons of the $3d$ orbital do not shield each other very well; hence the sudden drop in $3d$ energy. Similar drops occur for other orbitals.

Figure 11.2 shows that the separation between ns and np orbitals is much less than that between np and nd orbitals, giving the familiar $ns^2 np^6$ stable octet.

The orbital concept[6] is the basis for most qualitative discussions of the chemistry of atoms and molecules. The use of orbitals, however, is an approximation; to reach the true wave function we must go beyond a Slater determinant of spin-orbitals.

11.3 Electron Correlation

Energies calculated by the Hartree–Fock method are typically in error by about 1 percent. On an absolute basis this is not much, but for the chemist it is too large. For example, the total energy of the carbon atom is about 1000 eV, and 1 percent of this is 10 eV. Chemical bond energies run about 100 kcal/mole, which is

---

[4] For the Thomas-Fermi-Dirac method, see Chapter 5 of *Bethe and Jackiw*.
[5] See the figures on pp. 146, 147, 325, and 326 of J. C. Slater, *Quantum Theory of Matter*, Second Edition, McGraw-Hill, New York, 1968.
[6] Two review articles on atomic orbitals are: R. S. Berry, *J. Chem. Educ.*, **43**, 283 (1966); I. Cohen and T. Bustard, *ibid.*, **43**, 187.

5 eV/molecule. Attempting to calculate a bond energy by taking the difference between Hartree–Fock molecular and atomic energies, which are in error by several eV for light atoms, is an unreliable procedure. We must seek a way of improving on Hartree–Fock wave functions and energies. (Our discussion will be applicable to molecules as well as atoms.)

A Hartree–Fock SCF wave function takes into account the interactions between electrons only in an average way. Actually we must consider the instantaneous interactions between electrons. Since electrons repel each other, they tend to keep out of each other's way. For example, in helium, if one electron is close to the nucleus at a given instant, it is energetically more favorable for the other electron to be far from the nucleus at that instant. One sometimes speaks of a *Coulomb hole* surrounding each electron in an atom—this is a region in which the probability of finding another electron is small. The motions of electrons are correlated with each other, and we speak of *electron correlation*. We must find a way to introduce the instantaneous electron correlation into the wave function.

Actually, a Hartree–Fock wave function does have some instantaneous electron correlation built into it. A Hartree–Fock function satisfies the antisymmetry requirement of the Pauli principle; therefore [Eq. (10.36)] it vanishes when two electrons with the same spin have the same spatial coordinates. For a Hartree–Fock function, there is little probability of finding electrons of the same spin in the same region of space, so that a Hartree–Fock function has some correlation of the motions of electrons with the same spin. This causes the Hartree–Fock energy to be lower than the Hartree energy. (One sometimes refers to a *Fermi hole* around each electron in a Hartree–Fock wave function, thereby indicating a region in which the probability of finding another electron with the same spin is small.)

The *correlation energy* is the difference between the exact nonrelativistic energy and the Hartree–Fock energy. For helium the correlation energy is 1.1 eV (Section 11.1).

We have already indicated the two main ways in which we may provide for instantaneous electron correlation. The first method is to introduce the interelectronic distances r_{ij} into the wave function (Section 9.4). This method is only practicable for systems with a few electrons.

The second method is configuration interaction. We found (Sections 9.3 and 10.5) the zeroth-order wave function for the helium $1s^2$ ground state to be $1s(1)1s(2)[\alpha(1)\beta(2) - \beta(1)\alpha(2)]/\sqrt{2}$. We remarked that first-order and higher-order corrections to the wave function will mix in contributions from excited configurations, giving rise to *configuration interaction* (CI). We can also consider configuration interaction in terms of the variation method, using the Hartree–Fock scheme. Consider the Hartree–Fock wave functions for the states of all possible electron configurations of an atom, including configurations with one or more electrons in continuum states. This set of approximate wave functions forms a complete set, and we may expand the true wave function ψ for any particular state as a linear combination of the Hartree–Fock functions φ_i for all states:

$$\psi = \sum_i c_i \varphi_i \tag{11.18}$$

We then regard (11.18) as a linear variation function (Section 8.5). Variation of the coefficients c_i to minimize the variational integral leads to the determinantal equation

$$\det(H_{ij} - ES_{ij}) = 0 \qquad (11.19)$$

Since we have an infinite number of configurations, (11.19) is an infinite-order determinant. In practice, one uses a finite number of configurations.

As an example, consider the ground state of beryllium. The Hartree–Fock SCF method would find the best forms for the $1s$ and $2s$ orbitals in the Slater determinant $|1s\overline{1s}2s\overline{2s}|$ and use this for the ground-state wave function. [We are using the notation of Eq. (10.65).] Going beyond the Hartree–Fock method, we would calculate Hartree–Fock functions for excited configurations and include contributions from these configurations in a linear variation function for the ground state. Bunge did a configuration-interaction calculation[7] for the Be ground state, using a linear combination of 180 configurations. The Hartree–Fock energy is $-14.573(e^2/a_0)$, Bunge's CI result is $-14.664(e^2/a_0)$, and the experimental energy is $-14.667(e^2/a_0)$. Bunge was able to account for almost all the correlation energy. (He did not actually use Hartree–Fock functions for the excited configurations.)

As we add more and more configurations, a CI wave function will approach the true wave function. It generally takes a large number of configurations to give a truly satisfactory wave function; part of the "art" of the CI method is choosing those configurations that will make the greatest contributions. There is no necessity to use SCF functions for the excited configurations; any complete set of functions will do. Convergence of the configuration-interaction wave function to the true wave function may be faster if we use other than SCF excited-state functions.

11.4 Addition of Angular Momenta

For a many-electron atom, the operators for individual angular momenta of the electrons do not commute with the Hamiltonian, but their sum does. Hence we want to learn how to add angular momenta.

Suppose we have a system with two angular-momentum vectors $\mathbf{M}_1$ and $\mathbf{M}_2$. They might be the orbital angular-momentum vectors of two electrons in an atom, or they might be the spin angular-momentum vectors of two electrons, or one might be the spin and the other the orbital angular momentum of a single electron. The eigenvalues of $\hat{M}_1^2, \hat{M}_2^2, \hat{M}_{z1}$, and $\hat{M}_{z2}$ are $j_1(j_1+1)\hbar^2, j_2(j_2+1)\hbar^2$, $m_1\hbar$, and $m_2\hbar$, where the quantum numbers obey the usual restrictions. The components of $\hat{\mathbf{M}}_1$ and $\hat{\mathbf{M}}_2$ obey the angular-momentum commutation relations [Eq. (5.149)]:

$$[\hat{M}_{x1}, \hat{M}_{y1}] = i\hbar\hat{M}_{z1}, \text{ etc.} \qquad (11.20)$$

$$[\hat{M}_{x2}, \hat{M}_{y2}] = i\hbar\hat{M}_{z2}, \text{ etc.} \qquad (11.21)$$

We define the total angular momentum $\mathbf{M}$ of the system as the vector sum

$$\mathbf{M} = \mathbf{M}_1 + \mathbf{M}_2 \qquad (11.22)$$

---

[7] C. F. Bunge, *Phys. Rev.*, **168**, 92 (1968).

M is a vector with three components:

$$\mathbf{M} = M_x \mathbf{i} + M_y \mathbf{j} + M_z \mathbf{k} \tag{11.23}$$

The vector equation (11.22) gives the three scalar equations

$$M_x = M_{x1} + M_{x2}, \qquad M_y = M_{y1} + M_{y2}, \qquad M_z = M_{z1} + M_{z2} \tag{11.24}$$

For the operator $\hat{M}^2$, we have

$$\hat{M}^2 = \hat{\mathbf{M}} \cdot \hat{\mathbf{M}} = \hat{M}_x^2 + \hat{M}_y^2 + \hat{M}_z^2 \tag{11.25}$$

$$\hat{M}^2 = (\hat{\mathbf{M}}_1 + \hat{\mathbf{M}}_2) \cdot (\hat{\mathbf{M}}_1 + \hat{\mathbf{M}}_2)$$

$$= \hat{M}_1^2 + \hat{M}_2^2 + \hat{\mathbf{M}}_1 \cdot \hat{\mathbf{M}}_2 + \hat{\mathbf{M}}_2 \cdot \hat{\mathbf{M}}_1 \tag{11.26}$$

If $\hat{\mathbf{M}}_1$ and $\hat{\mathbf{M}}_2$ refer to different electrons, they will commute with each other, since each will affect only functions of the coordinates of one electron and not the other. Even if $\hat{\mathbf{M}}_1$ and $\hat{\mathbf{M}}_2$ are the orbital and spin angular momenta of the same electron, they will commute, as one will affect only functions of the spatial coordinates while the other will affect functions of the spin coordinates. Thus Eq. (11.26) becomes

$$\hat{M}^2 = \hat{M}_1^2 + \hat{M}_2^2 + 2\hat{\mathbf{M}}_1 \cdot \hat{\mathbf{M}}_2 \tag{11.27}$$

$$\hat{M}^2 = \hat{M}_1^2 + \hat{M}_2^2 + 2(\hat{M}_{x1}\hat{M}_{x2} + \hat{M}_{y1}\hat{M}_{y2} + \hat{M}_{z1}\hat{M}_{z2}) \tag{11.28}$$

We now show that the components of the total angular momentum obey the usual angular-momentum commutation relations. We have

$$[\hat{M}_x, \hat{M}_y] = [\hat{M}_{x1} + \hat{M}_{x2}, \hat{M}_{y1} + \hat{M}_{y2}]$$

$$= [\hat{M}_{x1}, \hat{M}_{y1} + \hat{M}_{y2}] + [\hat{M}_{x2}, \hat{M}_{y1} + \hat{M}_{y2}]$$

$$= [\hat{M}_{x1}, \hat{M}_{y1}] + [\hat{M}_{x1}, \hat{M}_{y2}] + [\hat{M}_{x2}, \hat{M}_{y1}] + [\hat{M}_{x2}, \hat{M}_{y2}]$$

Since all components of $\hat{\mathbf{M}}_1$ commute with all components of $\hat{\mathbf{M}}_2$, we have

$$[\hat{M}_x, \hat{M}_y] = [\hat{M}_{x1}, \hat{M}_{y1}] + [\hat{M}_{x2}, \hat{M}_{y2}] = i\hbar\hat{M}_{z1} + i\hbar\hat{M}_{z2}$$

$$[\hat{M}_x, \hat{M}_y] = i\hbar\hat{M}_z \tag{11.29}$$

Cyclic permutation of x, y, and z gives

$$[\hat{M}_y, \hat{M}_z] = i\hbar\hat{M}_x, \qquad [\hat{M}_z, \hat{M}_x] = i\hbar\hat{M}_y \tag{11.30}$$

The same commutator algebra used to derive (5.151) gives

$$[\hat{M}^2, \hat{M}_x] = [\hat{M}^2, \hat{M}_y] = [\hat{M}^2, \hat{M}_z] = 0 \tag{11.31}$$

Thus we can simultaneously quantize M^2 and one of its components, say M_z. Since the components of the total angular momentum obey the angular-momentum commutation relations, the work of Section 5.4 shows that the eigenvalues of $\hat{M}^2$ are

$$J(J+1)\hbar^2, \qquad J = 0, \tfrac{1}{2}, 1, \tfrac{3}{2}, 2, \dots \tag{11.32}$$

and the eigenvalues of $\hat{M}_z$ are

$$M_J \hbar, \qquad M_J = -J, -J+1, \dots, J-1, J \tag{11.33}$$

We want to find out how the total-angular-momentum quantum numbers

J and M_J are related to the quantum numbers j_1, j_2, m_1, m_2 of the two angular momenta we are adding in (11.22). We also want the eigenfunctions of $\hat{M}^2$ and $\hat{M}_z$. These eigenfunctions are characterized by the quantum numbers J and M_J and, using ket notation (Section 7.3), we write them as $|JM_J\rangle$. Similarly, let $|j_1 m_1\rangle$ denote the eigenfunctions of $\hat{M}_1^2$ and $\hat{M}_{z1}$ and $|j_2 m_2\rangle$ denote the eigenfunctions of $\hat{M}_2^2$ and $\hat{M}_{z2}$. Now it is readily shown (Problem 11.4a) that

$$[\hat{M}_x, \hat{M}_1^2] = [\hat{M}_y, \hat{M}_1^2] = [\hat{M}_z, \hat{M}_1^2] = [\hat{M}^2, \hat{M}_1^2] = 0 \qquad (11.34)$$

with similar equations with $\hat{M}_2^2$ replacing $\hat{M}_1^2$. Hence we can have simultaneous eigenfunctions of all four operators $\hat{M}_1^2, \hat{M}_2^2, \hat{M}^2, \hat{M}_z$ and the eigenfunctions $|JM_J\rangle$ can be more fully written as $|j_1 j_2 JM_J\rangle$. If we take the complete set of functions $|j_1 m_1\rangle$ for particle 1 and the complete set $|j_2 m_2\rangle$ for particle 2 and form all possible products of the form $|j_1 m_1\rangle |j_2 m_2\rangle$, we will have a complete set of functions for the two particles. Each unknown eigenfunction $|j_1 j_2 JM_J\rangle$ can then be expanded using this complete set:

$$|j_1 j_2 JM_J\rangle = \sum c(j_1 j_2 JM_J; m_1 m_2) |j_1 m_1\rangle |j_2 m_2\rangle \qquad (11.35)$$

where the expansion coefficients are the $c(j_1 \cdots m_2)$'s. Since the function being expanded is an eigenfunction of $\hat{M}_1^2$ with eigenvalue $j_1(j_1 + 1)\hbar^2$, we only include terms in the sum that have the same j_1 value as in the function $|j_1 j_2 JM_J\rangle$. [See the reasoning following Eq. (7.66).] Likewise, only terms with the same j_2 value as in $|j_1 j_2 JM_J\rangle$ are included in the sum. Hence the sum only goes over the m_1 and m_2 values. Furthermore, using $\hat{M}_z = \hat{M}_{z1} + \hat{M}_{z2}$, we can prove (Problem 11.4b) that the coefficient c vanishes unless

$$m_1 + m_2 = M_J \qquad (11.36)$$

To explicitly obtain the total-angular-momentum eigenfunctions, we must evaluate the coefficients in (11.35). These are called *Clebsch-Gordan* or *Wigner* or *vector addition* coefficients. We omit their evaluation (see *Merzbacher*, Section 16.6); *Anderson* gives 12 pages of tables of these coefficients.

Thus each total-angular-momentum eigenfunction $|j_1 j_2 JM_J\rangle$ is a linear combination of those product functions $|j_1 m_1\rangle |j_2 m_2\rangle$ whose m values satisfy $m_1 + m_2 = M_J$. We now find the relation between J and the j_1, j_2 values. Before discussing the general case, we consider the case with $j_1 = 1, j_2 = 2$. The possible values of m_1 are $-1, 0, +1$, and the possible values of m_2 are $-2, -1, 0, +1, +2$. If we describe the system by the quantum numbers j_1, j_2, m_1, m_2, then the total number of possible states is 15, corresponding to 3 possibilities for m_1 and 5 for m_2. Instead, we can describe the system using the quantum numbers, j_1, j_2, J, M_J, and we must have the same number of states in this description. Let us tabulate the 15 possible values of M_J using (11.36):

$$
\begin{array}{ccc|c}
m_1 = -1 & 0 & +1 & \\
\hline
-3 & -2 & -1 & -2 = m_2 \\
-2 & -1 & 0 & -1 \\
-1 & 0 & +1 & 0 \\
0 & +1 & +2 & +1 \\
+1 & +2 & +3 & +2 \\
\end{array}
$$

The number of times each value of M_J occurs is

value of M_J	3	2	1	0	-1	-2	-3
number of occurrences	1	2	3	3	3	2	1

The highest value of M_J is $+3$; since M_J ranges from $-J$ to $+J$, the highest value of J must be 3. Corresponding to $J = 3$, there are 7 values of M_J ranging from -3 to $+3$. Eliminating these 7 values, we are left with

value of M_J	2	1	0	-1	-2
number of occurrences	1	2	2	2	1

The highest remaining value, $M_J = 2$, must correspond to $J = 2$; for $J = 2$, we have 5 values of M_J, which when eliminated leave

value of M_J	1	0	-1
number of occurrences	1	1	1

These remaining values of M_J clearly correspond to $J = 1$. Thus for $j_1 = 1$, $j_2 = 2$, the possible values of J are 3, 2, and 1.

Now we consider the general case. We have $2j_1 + 1$ values of m_1 and $2j_2 + 1$ values of m_2; hence there are $(2j_1 + 1)(2j_2 + 1)$ possible states. The highest possible values of m_1 and m_2 are j_1 and j_2, respectively, so that the highest possible value of M_J is $j_1 + j_2$. Since M_J ranges from $-J$ to $+J$, the highest value of J must also be $j_1 + j_2$. The second-highest value of M_J is $j_1 + j_2 - 1$, which arises in two ways: $m_1 = j_1 - 1, m_2 = j_2$ and $m_1 = j_1, m_2 = j_2 - 1$. Linear combinations of these two states must give one state with $J = j_1 + j_2, M_J = j_1 + j_2 - 1$ and one state with $J = j_1 + j_2 - 1, M_J = j_1 + j_2 - 1$. Continuing on in this manner, we find the possible values of J to be $j_1 + j_2, j_1 + j_2 - 1, j_1 + j_2 - 2, ..., j_1 + j_2 - b$, where $j_1 + j_2 - b$ is the lowest value of J. We determine b by the requirement that the total number of states be $(2j_1 + 1)(2j_2 + 1)$. For the state with $J = j_1 + j_2 - k$, there are $2(j_1 + j_2 - k) + 1$ possible values of M_J. Hence

$$\sum_{k=0}^{b} [2(j_1 + j_2 - k) + 1] = (2j_1 + 1)(2j_2 + 1)$$

$$\sum_{k=0}^{b} (2j_1 + 2j_2 + 1) - 2\sum_{k=0}^{b} k = (2j_1 + 1)(2j_2 + 1) \tag{11.37}$$

The first sum has $b+1$ terms, each of which is the same; hence its value is $(b+1)(2j_1 + 2j_2 + 1)$. From Problem 6.25, the second sum equals $\frac{1}{2}b(b+1)$. Equation (11.37) becomes

$$b^2 - 2(j_1 + j_2)b + 4j_1 j_2 = 0$$

The roots of this quadratic equation are $b = 2j_1$ and $b = 2j_2$. Corresponding to these roots, we have the minimum values of J:

$$J_{min} = j_2 - j_1 \qquad J_{min} = j_1 - j_2 \qquad \text{(11.38)}$$

If $j_1 = j_2$, then $J_{min} = 0$. If $j_1 \neq j_2$, then one of the values in (11.38) is negative and must be rejected [Eq. (11.32)]. Thus

$$J_{min} = |j_2 - j_1| \qquad \text{(11.39)}$$

To summarize, we have shown that the addition of two angular momenta characterized by quantum numbers j_1 and j_2 results in a total angular momentum whose quantum number J has the possible values

$$J = j_1 + j_2, j_1 + j_2 - 1, ..., |j_1 - j_2| \qquad \text{(11.40)}$$

For example, if $j_1 = 2, j_2 = 3$, we have the possibilities $J = 5, 4, 3, 2, 1$. For $j_1 = 3, j_2 = 3/2$, we have $J = 9/2, 7/2, 5/2, 3/2$.

To add more than two angular momenta, we apply (11.40) repeatedly. Thus to add three angular momenta with $j_1 = 1, j_2 = 2, j_3 = 3$, we first add j_1 and j_2 to give the possible values $3, 2, 1$. Adding j_3 to each of these values, we get the following possibilities for the total angular-momentum quantum number

$$6, 5, 4, 3, 2, 1, 0; 5, 4, 3, 2, 1; 4, 3, 2 \qquad \text{(11.41)}$$

We have one set of states with total-angular-momentum quantum number 6, two sets of states with angular momentum 5, etc.

11.5 Angular Momentum in Many-Electron Atoms

We define the total orbital angular momentum $\mathbf{L}$ of an n-electron atom as the vector sum of the orbital angular momenta of the individual electrons:

$$\mathbf{L} = \sum_{i=1}^{n} \mathbf{L}_i \qquad \text{(11.42)}$$

Although the individual orbital angular momenta of the electrons do not commute with the atomic Hamiltonian (11.1), it can be shown [8] that the total orbital angular momentum operator does commute with the Hamiltonian. We may therefore characterize an atomic state by a quantum number L, where $L(L+1)\hbar^2$ is the square of the magnitude of the total electronic orbital angular momentum.

As an example, consider an excited state of carbon with the electron configuration $1s^2 2s^2 2p3d$. The s electrons have zero orbital angular momentum; combining the orbital angular momenta of the p and d electrons, we find that L can be 3 or 2 or 1. [The Hartree–Fock central-field approximation has each electron moving in a central-field potential, $V = V(r)$; hence, within this approximation the individual electronic orbital angular momenta are constant, giving rise to a wave function composed of a single configuration which specifies the individual orbital angular momenta. When we go beyond the SCF central-field approximation, we

---

[8] *Pilar*, Section 12-1. This statement is true provided spin-orbit interaction (Section 11.6) is neglected.

mix in other configurations, so that we no longer specify precisely the individual orbital angular momenta; even so, we can still use the rule (11.40) for finding the possible values of the total orbital angular momentum.]

We indicate the total orbital angular momentum of an atom by a letter, as follows:

L	0	1	2	3	4	5	6	7	8
letter	S	P	D	F	G	H	I	K	L

The total orbital angular momentum is designated by a capital letter, while lower-case letters are used for orbital angular momenta of individual electrons. The configuration $1s^2 2s^2 2p3d$ gives rise to P, D, and F states.

We define the total electronic spin angular momentum as the vector sum of the spins of the individual electrons of the atom:

$$\mathbf{S} = \sum_{i=1}^{n} \mathbf{S}_i \tag{11.43}$$

The total electronic spin angular-momentum operator commutes with the Hamiltonian (11.1). We may characterize an atomic state by a quantum number S, where $S(S+1)\hbar^2$ is the square of the magnitude of the total electronic spin angular momentum.[9] For example, for two electrons, the individual spin quantum numbers s_1 and s_2 are both 1/2, and the rule (11.40) gives the possibilities $S = 0, 1$, corresponding to the two spins being antiparallel or parallel.

The quantity $2S+1$ is written as a left superscript to the letter designating L. As an example, we again consider the configuration $1s^2 2s^2 2p3d$. Consider first the two $1s$ electrons. To satisfy the exclusion principle, one of these electrons must have $m_s = +\frac{1}{2}$, while the other has $m_s = -\frac{1}{2}$. If M_S is the quantum number specifying the z component of the total spin of the $1s$ electrons, then the only possible value of M_S is zero [Eq. (11.36)]. This single value of M_S clearly means that the total spin of the two $1s$ electrons is zero. Thus, although in general we have the two possibilities $S = 0$, $S = 1$ when adding the spins of two electrons, the restriction imposed by the Pauli principle leaves $S = 0$ as the only possibility in this case. Likewise, the spins of the $2s$ electrons add up to 0. The Pauli principle imposes no restriction on the $2p$ and $3d$ electrons, and we get both possibilities, $S = 0$, $S = 1$, for the sum of their spins. The total atomic spin quantum number is 0 or 1 for this configuration, so that $2S+1$ is 1 or 3. We thus have the possibilities

$$^1P, \,^3P, \,^1D, \,^3D, \,^1F, \,^3F \tag{11.44}$$

for the $1s^2 2s^2 2p3d$ configuration. The symbols in (11.44) are called *term symbols*. Atomic states arising from the same electron configuration and having the same value of L and of S are said to belong to the same *term*. States belonging to different terms have different energies, since the amount of interelectronic repulsion is different for each term. For example, see the discussion of helium at the end of this section.

---

[9] The proof often given is that since $\hat{H}$ does not involve spin, it must commute with $\hat{S}$. This proof is not quite adequate; see *Bethe and Jackiw*, pp. 103–104.

The total electronic angular momentum **J** of the atom is the vector sum of the total electronic orbital and spin angular momenta:

$$\mathbf{J} = \mathbf{L} + \mathbf{S} \tag{11.45}$$

The operator for the total electronic angular momentum commutes with the Hamiltonian, and we may characterize an atomic state by a quantum number J, which has the possible values [Eq. (11.40)]

$$L + S, L + S - 1, ..., |L - S| \tag{11.46}$$

The value of J is written as a subscript on the term symbol. Thus for a ^3P term, $L = 1$ and $S = 1$, so that J can be 2, 1, or 0, giving the possibilities $^3P_2$, $^3P_1$, and $^3P_0$. States belonging to the same term and having the same value of J are said to belong to the same *level*. As far as the Hamiltonian (11.1) is concerned, all states belonging to the same term have the same energy, but when we include spin-orbit interaction in the Hamiltonian (Section 11.6) we find that the value of J affects the energy slightly; hence the energies of different levels belonging to the same term are slightly different (see Fig. 11.6).

The quantity $2S+1$ is called the *multiplicity* of the term. If $L \geqslant S$, the possible values of J range from $L+S$ to $L-S$ and are $2S+1$ in number; in this case the multiplicity gives the number of levels arising from a given term. For $L < S$, the values of J range from $S+L$ to $S-L$ and are $2L+1$ in number; in this case the multiplicity is greater than the number of levels. Thus if $L = 0$ and $S = 1$, we designate the term as ^3S although there is only one possible value for J: $J = 1$. For $2S+1 = 1, 2, 3, 4, 5, 6, ...$, we use the words *singlet, doublet, triplet, quartet, quintet, sextet, ...* to designate the multiplicity. We read $^3P_1$ as "triplet P one."

We now show how to derive the terms that arise from a given electron configuration. We first consider configurations that contain only completely filled subshells. In such configurations, for each electron with $m_s = +\frac{1}{2}$, there is an electron with $m_s = -\frac{1}{2}$. Let the quantum number specifying the z component of the total electronic spin angular momentum be M_S; the only possible value for M_S is zero ($M_S = \sum m_s = 0$); hence S must be zero. For each electron in a closed subshell with magnetic quantum number m, there is an electron with magnetic quantum number $-m$; e.g., for a $2p^6$ configuration we have two electrons with $m = +1$, two with $m = -1$, and two with $m = 0$. Denoting the quantum number specifying the z component of the total electronic orbital angular momentum by M_L, we have $M_L = \sum m = 0$; we conclude that L must be zero. In summary, a configuration of closed subshells gives rise to only one term: ^1S. For configurations consisting of closed subshells and open subshells, the closed subshells make no contribution to L or S and may be ignored in finding the terms. (Note that our conclusions are consistent with Unsöld's theorem.)

We now consider two electrons in different subshells; such electrons are called *nonequivalent*. Nonequivalent electrons have different values of n or l or both, and we need not worry about any restrictions imposed by the exclusion principle when we derive the terms. We simply find the possible values of L from l_1 and l_2 according to (11.40); combining s_1 and s_2 gives $S = 0, 1$. We previously worked out the pd case, which gives the terms in (11.44). If we have more than two nonequivalent electrons, we combine the individual l's to find the values of L, and we combine the individual s's to find the values of S. For example, consider a pdf configuration. The possible values of L are given by (11.41). Combining three angular momenta, each of which is $\frac{1}{2}$, gives $S = \frac{3}{2}, \frac{1}{2}, \frac{1}{2}$. Each of the three possibilities in (11.41) with $L = 3$ may be combined with each of the two possibilities for $S = \frac{1}{2}$, giving six ^2F terms. Continuing in this manner, we find the terms arising from a pdf configuration to be: $^2S(2)$, $^2P(4)$, $^2D(6)$, $^2F(6)$, $^2G(6)$, $^2H(4)$, $^2I(2)$, ^4S, $^4P(2)$, $^4D(3)$, $^4F(3)$, $^4G(3)$, $^4H(2)$, ^4I, where the number of times each term occurs is in parentheses.

Now consider two electrons in the same subshell (*equivalent* electrons). Equivalent electrons have the same value of n and of l, and the situation is complicated by the necessity to avoid giving two electrons the same four quantum numbers; hence not all the terms derived for nonequivalent electrons are possible. As an example consider the terms arising from two equivalent p electrons, an np^2 configuration. (The carbon ground-state configuration is $1s^2 2s^2 2p^2$.) We list the possible values of m and m_s for the two electrons in Table 11.1, which also gives M_L and M_S.

Table 11.1   Quantum Numbers for Two Equivalent p Electrons

m_1	m_{s1}	m_2	m_{s2}	$M_L = \sum m$	$M_S = \sum m_s$
1	$\frac{1}{2}$	1	$-\frac{1}{2}$	2	0
1	$\frac{1}{2}$	0	$\frac{1}{2}$	1	1
1	$\frac{1}{2}$	0	$-\frac{1}{2}$	1	0
1	$-\frac{1}{2}$	0	$\frac{1}{2}$	1	0
1	$-\frac{1}{2}$	0	$-\frac{1}{2}$	1	-1
1	$\frac{1}{2}$	-1	$\frac{1}{2}$	0	1
1	$\frac{1}{2}$	-1	$-\frac{1}{2}$	0	0
1	$-\frac{1}{2}$	-1	$\frac{1}{2}$	0	0
1	$-\frac{1}{2}$	-1	$-\frac{1}{2}$	0	-1
0	$\frac{1}{2}$	0	$-\frac{1}{2}$	0	0
0	$\frac{1}{2}$	-1	$\frac{1}{2}$	-1	1
0	$\frac{1}{2}$	-1	$-\frac{1}{2}$	-1	0
0	$-\frac{1}{2}$	-1	$\frac{1}{2}$	-1	0
0	$-\frac{1}{2}$	-1	$-\frac{1}{2}$	-1	-1
-1	$\frac{1}{2}$	-1	$-\frac{1}{2}$	-2	0

Note that certain combinations are missing from this table. For example, we do not have $m_1 = 1$, $m_{s1} = \frac{1}{2}$, $m_2 = 1$, $m_{s2} = \frac{1}{2}$, as this violates the exclusion principle. Another missing combination is $m_1 = 1$, $m_{s1} = -\frac{1}{2}$, $m_2 = 1$, $m_{s2} = \frac{1}{2}$. This combination differs from $m_1 = 1$, $m_{s1} = \frac{1}{2}$, $m_2 = 1$, $m_{s2} = -\frac{1}{2}$ solely by interchange of electrons 1 and 2. Each row in Table 11.1 stands for a Slater determinant, which when expanded contains terms for all possible electron interchanges among the spin-orbitals. Two rows that differ from each other solely by interchange of two electrons correspond to the same Slater determinant, and we include only one of them in the table.

The highest value of M_L in Table 11.1 is 2, which must correspond to a term with $L = 2$, a D term. The $M_L = 2$ value occurs in conjunction with $M_S = 0$, indicating that $S = 0$ for the D term; thus we have a ^1D term corresponding to the five states

$$
\begin{array}{ccccc}
M_L = 2 & 1 & 0 & -1 & -2 \\
M_S = 0 & 0 & 0 & 0 & 0
\end{array}
\tag{11.47}
$$

The highest value of M_S in Table 11.1 is 1, indicating a term with $S = 1$, a triplet term. $M_S = 1$ occurs in conjunction with $M_L = 1, 0, -1$, which indicates a P term. Hence we have a ^3P term corresponding to the nine states

$$
\begin{array}{ccccccccc}
M_L = 1 & 1 & 1 & 0 & 0 & 0 & -1 & -1 & -1 \\
M_S = 1 & 0 & -1 & 1 & 0 & -1 & 1 & 0 & -1
\end{array}
\tag{11.48}
$$

Elimination of the states of (11.47) and (11.48) from Table 11.1 leaves only a single state, which has $M_L = 0$, $M_S = 0$, corresponding to a ^1S term. Thus a p^2 configuration gives rise to the terms $^1S, ^3P, ^1D$. (In contrast, two nonequivalent p electrons give rise to six terms: $^1S, ^3S, ^1P, ^3P, ^1D, ^3D$.)

Table 11.2a lists the terms arising from various configurations of equivalent electrons. These results may be derived in the same manner that we found the p^2 terms, but this procedure can become quite involved; to derive the terms of the f^7 configuration would require a table with 3432 rows. A more efficient method[10] uses group theory. Note that the terms for a subshell containing N electrons are the same as the terms for a subshell that is N electrons short of being full; e.g., the terms for p^2 and p^4 are the same. We can divide the electrons of a closed subshell into two groups and find the terms for each group; because a closed subshell gives only a ^1S term, the terms for each of these two groups must be the same. One sometimes speaks of the absence of an electron from a subshell as a "hole." Table 11.2b gives the terms arising from some nonequivalent electron configurations.

To deal with a configuration containing both equivalent and nonequivalent electrons, we first find separately the terms from the nonequivalent electrons and the terms from the equivalent electrons. We then take all possible combinations of the L and S values of these two sets of terms. For example, consider an sp^3 configuration. From the s electron, we get a ^2S term. From the three equivalent p electrons, we get the terms $^2P, ^2D$, and ^4S. Combining the L and S values of these terms, we have as the terms of an sp^3 configuration:

$$
^3P, ^1P, ^3D, ^1D, ^5S, ^3S
$$

We now consider the terms and levels for the hydrogen and helium atoms. For hydrogen we have one electron; hence, $L = l$ and $S = s = \frac{1}{2}$. The possible values of J are $L \pm \frac{1}{2}$ except for $L = 0$, where we can have only $J = \frac{1}{2}$. Each configuration gives rise to a single term, which is composed of one or two levels. The

---

[10] See R. F. Curl, Jr., and J. E. Kilpatrick, *Am. J. Phys.*, **28**, 357 (1960).

Table 11.2 Terms Arising from Various Electron Configurations

(a) *Equivalent electrons*[1]

Configuration	Terms
$s^2; p^6; d^{10}$	^1S
$p; p^5$	^2P
$p^2; p^4$	$^3P, \,^1D, \,^1S$
p^3	$^4S, \,^2D, \,^2P$
$d; d^9$	^2D
$d^2; d^8$	$^3F, \,^3P, \,^1G, \,^1D, \,^1S$
$d^3; d^7$	$^4F, \,^4P, \,^2H, \,^2G, \,^2F, \,^2D(2), \,^2P$
$d^4; d^6$	$\begin{cases} ^5D, \,^3H, \,^3G, \,^3F(2), \,^3D, \,^3P(2) \\ ^1I, \,^1G(2), \,^1F, \,^1D(2), \,^1S(2) \end{cases}$
d^5	$\begin{cases} ^6S, \,^4G, \,^4F, \,^4D, \,^4P, \,^2I, \,^2H, \,^2G(2) \\ ^2F(2), \,^2D(3), \,^2P, \,^2S \end{cases}$

(b) *Nonequivalent electrons*

ss	$^1S, \,^3S$
sp	$^1P, \,^3P$
sd	$^1D, \,^3D$
pp	$^3D, \,^1D, \,^3P, \,^1P, \,^3S, \,^1S$

[1] "Equivalent" electrons have the same values of n and l.

ground-state configuration $1s$ gives the term ^2S, which is composed of the single level $^2S_{1/2}$; the level is twofold degenerate, corresponding to the two possible orientations $M_J = +\frac{1}{2}$ and $-\frac{1}{2}$. The $2s$ configuration also gives a $^2S_{1/2}$ level. For the $2p$ configuration we have the levels $^2P_{3/2}$ and $^2P_{1/2}$; the $^2P_{3/2}$ level is four-fold degenerate ($M_J = -\frac{3}{2}, -\frac{1}{2}, \frac{1}{2}, \frac{3}{2}$) and the $^2P_{1/2}$ level is twofold degenerate. All told, we have 8 states with quantum number $n = 2$; omitting spin-orbit inter-action, these states all have the same energy. Previously we discussed the degeneracy in terms of possible values for m and m_s; now we are representing things in terms of the quantum numbers J and M_J. We get the same number of states no matter how we view things.

For helium the ground-state configuration $1s^2$ is a closed subshell and gives the single level $^1S_0$; we have $M_J = 0$, and the level is nondegenerate. The $1s2s$ excited configuration gives rise to two terms, ^1S and ^3S, each of which has one level. The $^1S_0$ level is nondegenerate, while the $^3S_1$ level is threefold degenerate ($M_J = 1, 0, -1$). (Although in this case the multiplicity is equal to the degeneracy, this is certainly not true in general.) In Section 10.5 we found the lower of the two energy levels of the $1s2s$ helium configuration to be triply degenerate, corresponding to the three zeroth-order wave functions (10.42)–(10.44). This must be the $^3S_1$ level. The nondegenerate $^1S_0$ level has the zeroth-order wave function (10.45).

Since $S = 1$ for the $^3S_1$ level, we should find the three spin functions in (10.42)–(10.44) to be eigenfunctions of $\hat{S}^2$ with eigenvalue $2\hbar^2$, and eigenfunctions of $\hat{S}_z$

with eigenvalues $\hbar, 0, -\hbar$ ($M_S = 1, 0, -1$). The spin function in (10.45) should be an eigenfunction of $\hat{S}^2$ and $\hat{S}_z$ with eigenvalue zero in each case, since $S = 0$ here. We now verify these assertions. From Eq. (11.43), the total electronic spin operator is the sum of the spin operators for each electron:

$$\hat{\mathbf{S}} = \hat{\mathbf{S}}_1 + \hat{\mathbf{S}}_2 \tag{11.49}$$

Taking the z components of (11.49), we have

$$\hat{S}_z = \hat{S}_{z1} + \hat{S}_{z2} \tag{11.50}$$

$$\hat{S}_z \alpha(1) \alpha(2) = \hat{S}_{z1} \alpha(1) \alpha(2) + \hat{S}_{z2} \alpha(1) \alpha(2)$$

$$= \alpha(2) \hat{S}_{z1} \alpha(1) + \alpha(1) \hat{S}_{z2} \alpha(2)$$

$$= \tfrac{1}{2}\hbar \alpha(1) \alpha(2) + \tfrac{1}{2}\hbar \alpha(1) \alpha(2)$$

$$= \hbar \alpha(1) \alpha(2) \tag{11.51}$$

where Eq. (10.7) has been used. Similarly we find

$$\hat{S}_z \beta(1) \beta(2) = -\hbar \beta(1) \beta(2) \tag{11.52}$$

$$\hat{S}_z [\alpha(1) \beta(2) + \beta(1) \alpha(2)] = 0 \tag{11.53}$$

$$\hat{S}_z [\alpha(1) \beta(2) - \beta(1) \alpha(2)] = 0 \tag{11.54}$$

Consider now $\hat{S}^2$. We have [Eq. (11.28)]

$$\hat{S}^2 = (\hat{\mathbf{S}}_1 + \hat{\mathbf{S}}_2) \cdot (\hat{\mathbf{S}}_1 + \hat{\mathbf{S}}_2)$$

$$= \hat{S}_1^2 + \hat{S}_2^2 + 2(\hat{S}_{x1}\hat{S}_{x2} + \hat{S}_{y1}\hat{S}_{y2} + \hat{S}_{z1}\hat{S}_{z2}) \tag{11.55}$$

$$\hat{S}^2 \alpha(1) \alpha(2) = \alpha(2) \hat{S}_1^2 \alpha(1) + \alpha(1) \hat{S}_2^2 \alpha(2) + 2\hat{S}_{x1} \alpha(1) \hat{S}_{x2} \alpha(2)$$

$$+ 2\hat{S}_{y1} \alpha(1) \hat{S}_{y2} \alpha(2) + 2\hat{S}_{z1} \alpha(1) \hat{S}_{z2} \alpha(2) \tag{11.56}$$

Using Eqs. (10.7)–(10.9) and (10.28) and (10.29), we find

$$\hat{S}^2 \alpha(1) \alpha(2) = 2\hbar^2 \alpha(1) \alpha(2)$$

showing that $\alpha(1) \alpha(2)$ is an eigenfunction of $\hat{S}^2$ corresponding to $S = 1$. Similarly we find

$$\hat{S}^2 \beta(1) \beta(2) = 2\hbar^2 \beta(1) \beta(2)$$

$$\hat{S}^2 [\alpha(1) \beta(2) + \beta(1) \alpha(2)] = 2\hbar^2 [\alpha(1) \beta(2) + \beta(1) \alpha(2)]$$

$$\hat{S}^2 [\alpha(1) \beta(2) - \beta(1) \alpha(2)] = 0$$

Thus the spin eigenfunctions in (10.42)–(10.45) correspond to the following values for the total spin quantum numbers:

		S	M_S	
	$\alpha(1) \alpha(2)$	1	1	(11.57)
triplet	$2^{-1/2} [\alpha(1) \beta(2) + \beta(1) \alpha(2)]$	1	0	(11.58)
	$\beta(1) \beta(2)$	1	-1	(11.59)
singlet	$\{2^{-1/2} [\alpha(1) \beta(2) - \beta(1) \alpha(2)]$	0	0	(11.60)

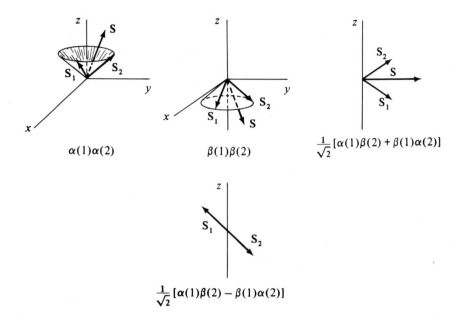

FIGURE 11.3 *Vector addition of the spins of two electrons. For* $\alpha(1)\alpha(2)$ *and* $\beta(1)\beta(2)$, *the projections of* $\mathbf{S}_1$ *and* $\mathbf{S}_2$ *in the xy plane make an angle of* $90°$ *with each other.*

Figure 11.3 shows the vector addition of $\mathbf{S}_1$ and $\mathbf{S}_2$ to form $\mathbf{S}$. It might seem surprising that the spin function (11.58), which has the z components of the spins of the two electrons pointing in opposite directions, could have total spin quantum number $S = 1$. Figure 11.3 shows how this is possible.

In Section 10.7 we showed that two of the four zeroth-order wave functions for the $1s2s$ helium configuration could be written as single Slater determinants, but the remaining two functions had to be expressed as linear combinations of two Slater determinants. Since $\hat{L}^2$ and $\hat{S}^2$ commute with the Hamiltonian (11.1), the zeroth-order functions should be eigenfunctions of $\hat{L}^2$ and $\hat{S}^2$. The Slater determinants D_2 and D_3 of Section 10.7 are not eigenfunctions of these operators and hence are not suitable zeroth-order functions. We have just shown that the linear combinations (10.62) and (10.63) are eigenfunctions of $\hat{S}^2$, and we can also show them to be eigenfunctions of $\hat{L}^2$.

For a configuration of closed subshells (e.g., the helium ground state) we can write only a single Slater determinant; this determinant is an eigenfunction of $\hat{L}^2$ and $\hat{S}^2$ and is the correct zeroth-order function for the nondegenerate $^1S_0$ level. A configuration with one electron outside closed subshells (e.g., the lithium ground-state) gives rise to only one term; the Slater determinants for such a configuration differ from one another only in the m and m_s values of this electron, and are the correct zeroth-order functions for the states of the term. Aside from these two kinds of configurations (and a configuration that is one electron short of having closed subshells), we generally have to take linear combinations of the Slater determinants to obtain the correct zeroth-order functions, which are eigenfunctions of $\hat{L}^2$ and $\hat{S}^2$. The correct linear combinations can be found by solving the secular equation of degenerate perturbation theory, or by operator techniques. Tabulations of the correct combinations for various configurations are available.[11] Hartree–Fock calculations of atomic term energies use these linear combinations and find the best possible orbital functions for the Slater determinants.

To decide which of the terms arising from a given atomic configuration is lowest in energy, we use the empirical *Hund's rule: The term with the highest multiplicity is lowest in energy; if there is more than one term with the highest multiplicity, then the term with the highest multiplicity and the largest value of L lies lowest.* For example, the ground-state configuration of carbon $1s^2 2s^2 2p^2$ gives the terms ^1S, ^3P, and ^1D. Hund's rule tells us that ^3P is the lowest term, in agreement with experiment. For a d^2 configuration (Table 11.2) the ^3F term lies lowest according to Hund's rule. Hund's rule gives only the lowest term, and should not be used to decide the order of the remaining terms. Thus for the $1s^2 2s2p^3$ configuration of carbon, the experimental order of the terms is

$$^5S < {}^3D < {}^3P < {}^1D < {}^3S < {}^1P$$

The ^3S term lies above the ^1D term, even though ^3S has the higher multiplicity. For the $1s^2 2s^2 2p^6 3s^2 3p^6 3d^2 4s^2$ titanium configuration, the lowest singlet term is ^1D and not ^1G, even though ^1G has the larger value of L.

We can rationalize Hund's rule as follows. Electrons with the same spin tend to keep out of each other's way (recall the idea of Fermi holes) thereby minimizing the Coulombic repulsion between them. The term that has the greatest number of parallel spins (i.e., the greatest value of S) will therefore be lowest in energy. For example, the ^3S term of the helium $1s2s$ configuration has an anti-symmetric space function which vanishes when the spatial coordinates of the two electrons are equal; hence the ^3S term is lower than the ^1S term.

It is not necessary to consult Table 11.2a to find the lowest term of a partly filled subshell configuration. We simply put the electrons in the orbitals so as to give the greatest number of parallel spins. Thus for a d^3 configuration, we have

$$\begin{array}{ccccc} \uparrow & \uparrow & \uparrow & \underline{} & \underline{} \\ \underline{} & \underline{} & \underline{} & & \\ m: \quad +2 & +1 & 0 & -1 & -2 \end{array}$$

The lowest term thus has three parallel spins, so that $S = \frac{3}{2}$, giving a quartet term. The maximum value of M_L is 3, corresponding to $L = 3$, an F term. Hund's rule thus predicts ^4F as the lowest term of a d^3 configuration.

An important concept is the parity of atomic states. Consider the atomic Hamiltonian (11.1). We showed in Section 7.5 that the parity operator $\hat{\Pi}$ commutes with the kinetic-energy operator. The quantity $1/r_i$ is given by

$$r_i^{-1} = [x_i^2 + y_i^2 + z_i^2]^{-1/2}$$

Replacement of each coordinate by its negative leaves $1/r_i$ unchanged. Also

$$r_{ij}^{-1} = [(x_i - x_j)^2 + (y_i - y_j)^2 + (z_i - z_j)^2]^{-1/2}$$

---

[11] *Slater, Atomic Structure, Vol. II.*

so that inversion has no effect on $1/r_{ij}$. Thus $\hat{\Pi}$ commutes with the atomic Hamiltonian and we can choose atomic eigenfunctions to have definite parity.

For a one-electron atom the spatial wave function has the form

$$\psi = R(r) Y_l^m(\theta, \varphi)$$

The radial function is unchanged on inversion, so that the parity is determined by the angular factor. In Problem 7.16 we showed that Y_l^m is an even function when l is even, and is an odd function when l is odd. Thus the states of one-electron atoms have even or odd parity according to whether l is even or odd.

Now consider an n-electron atom. In the Hartree–Fock central-field approximation, we write the wave function as a Slater determinant (or linear combination of Slater determinants) of spin-orbitals. The wave function is the sum of terms, the spatial factor in each term having the form

$$R_1(r_1) \cdots R_n(r_n) Y_{l_1}^{m_1}(\theta_1, \varphi_1) \cdots Y_{l_n}^{m_n}(\theta_n, \varphi_n)$$

The parity of this product is determined by the spherical-harmonic factors; we see that the product is an even or odd function according to whether $l_1 + l_2 + \cdots + l_n$ is an even or odd number. Thus the sum of the l values of the electrons determines the parity. For example, the configuration $1s^2 2s 2p^3$ has $\sum l_i = 3$, and all states arising from this configuration have odd parity. (Our argument was based on the SCF approximation to the wave function, but the conclusions are valid for the true wave function.)

11.6 Spin-Orbit Interaction

Up to now, we have used an atomic Hamiltonian [Eq. (11.1)] that does not involve electron spin. In reality, the existence of spin adds an additional term, usually small, to the Hamiltonian. This term, called the *spin-orbit interaction*, causes the fine structure of atomic spectra. Spin-orbit interaction is a relativistic effect and is properly derived using Dirac's relativistic treatment of the electron. We will give a rough "derivation."

If we imagine ourselves riding on an electron in an atom, from our viewpoint the nucleus is moving around the electron (as the sun appears to move about the earth). This apparent motion of the nucleus gives rise to a magnetic field which interacts with the intrinsic (spin) magnetic moment of the electron, giving the spin-orbit interaction term in the Hamiltonian. The electron's spin magnetic moment is proportional to its spin $\mathbf{S}$ and the magnetic field arising from the apparent nuclear motion is proportional to the electron's orbital angular momentum $\mathbf{L}$; hence the spin-orbit interaction term is proportional to $\mathbf{L} \cdot \mathbf{S}$. The dot product of $\mathbf{L}$ and $\mathbf{S}$ depends on the relative orientation of these two vectors. The total angular momentum $\mathbf{J} = \mathbf{L} + \mathbf{S}$ also depends on the relative orientation of $\mathbf{L}$ and $\mathbf{S}$ and therefore the spin-orbit interaction energy depends on J [Eq. (11.74)].

From the viewpoint of the electron, the magnetic field produced by the apparent nuclear motion is [Eq. (6.148)]

$$\mathbf{B} = \frac{Ze}{cr^3} \mathbf{v}_N \times \mathbf{r} \tag{11.61}$$

(a)   (b)

FIGURE 11.4   (a) *Nucleus viewed from an electron.* (b) *Laboratory view of things.*

where v_N is the apparent velocity of the nucleus, and $\mathbf{r}$ is the vector from the nucleus to the electron (Fig. 11.4). We have $\mathbf{v}_N = -\mathbf{v}$, where $\mathbf{v}$ is the actual velocity of the electron. Hence

$$\mathbf{B} = \frac{Ze}{cr^3}\mathbf{r} \times \mathbf{v}$$

The electric field $\mathbf{E}$ of the nucleus at the electron is $Ze\mathbf{r}/r^3$, so that

$$\mathbf{B} = \frac{\mathbf{E} \times \mathbf{v}}{c} \tag{11.62}$$

For the energy of the spin-orbit interaction between $\mathbf{B}$ and the spin magnetic moment $\boldsymbol{\mu}_S$ of the electron, we have [Eq. (6.155)]

$$E_{\text{s.o.}} = -\mathbf{B} \cdot \boldsymbol{\mu}_S = -\frac{(\mathbf{E} \times \mathbf{v}) \cdot \boldsymbol{\mu}_S}{c} \tag{11.63}$$

The product of the electric field at the electron and its charge gives the force on the electron:

$$\mathbf{F} = -e\mathbf{E} = -\nabla V \tag{11.64}$$

where Eq. (5.46) has been used. Hence

$$E_{\text{s.o.}} = -\frac{(\nabla V \times \mathbf{v}) \cdot \boldsymbol{\mu}_S}{ec} \tag{11.65}$$

At this point we must break the news that (11.65) is wrong. It turns out that there is an additional relativistic effect,[12] discovered by L. H. Thomas in 1926, which when added in gives for the spin-orbit interaction energy:

$$E_{\text{s.o.}} = -\frac{(\nabla V \times \mathbf{v}) \cdot \boldsymbol{\mu}_S}{2ec} \tag{11.66}$$

If we assume the validity of the central-field approximation (Section 11.1), we can accurately approximate the potential energy of an electron in an atom by a function of r only: $V = V(r)$, so that [Eqs. (5.46) and (6.4)]

$$\nabla V = \frac{dV}{dr}\frac{\mathbf{r}}{r} \tag{11.67}$$

---

[12] For a discussion, see W. H. Furry, *Am. J. Phys.*, **23**, 517 (1955).

Substitution of (11.67), (10.82), and $\mathbf{v} = \mathbf{p}/m$ (where $\mathbf{p}$ is the linear momentum of the electron) into (11.66) gives

$$E_{\text{s.o.}} = \frac{1}{2m^2c^2}\frac{1}{r}\frac{dV}{dr}(\mathbf{r} \times \mathbf{p}) \cdot \mathbf{S} \tag{11.68}$$

The quantity $\mathbf{r} \times \mathbf{p}$ is the electronic orbital angular momentum $\mathbf{L}$, and introduction of operators into (11.68) gives the following term in the Hamiltonian due to spin-orbit interaction:

$$\hat{H}_{\text{s.o.}} = \frac{1}{2m^2c^2}\frac{1}{r}\frac{dV}{dr}\hat{\mathbf{L}} \cdot \hat{\mathbf{S}} \tag{11.69}$$

Equation (11.69) is for one electron; for the many-electron case we sum over the individual spin-orbit interactions to get

$$\hat{H}_{\text{s.o.}} = \frac{1}{2m^2c^2}\sum_i \frac{1}{r_i}\frac{dV(r_i)}{dr_i}\hat{\mathbf{L}}_i \cdot \hat{\mathbf{S}}_i = \sum_i \xi_i(r_i)\hat{\mathbf{L}}_i \cdot \hat{\mathbf{S}}_i \tag{11.70}$$

where the definition of ξ_i is clear.

An exact calculation of the effect of the spin-orbit interaction requires that we find the eigenvalues and eigenfunctions of the Hamiltonian $\hat{H} + \hat{H}_{\text{s.o.}}$, where $\hat{H}$ is the Hamiltonian of Eq. (11.1). Such a calculation is too difficult, and we will use an approximate treatment. The effect of $\hat{H}_{\text{s.o.}}$ is generally small compared to the terms in $\hat{H}$, so that we may use first-order perturbation theory to calculate the energy correction. We have [Eq. (9.30)]

$$E_{\text{s.o.}} = \int \psi^* \hat{H}_{\text{s.o.}} \psi \, d\tau = \langle H_{\text{s.o.}} \rangle \tag{11.71}$$

where ψ is an eigenfunction of $\hat{H}$. For a one-electron atom,

$$E_{\text{s.o.}} = \int \psi^* \xi(r)\hat{\mathbf{L}} \cdot \hat{\mathbf{S}}\psi \, d\tau \tag{11.72}$$

Now

$$\mathbf{J} \cdot \mathbf{J} = (\mathbf{L}+\mathbf{S}) \cdot (\mathbf{L}+\mathbf{S}) = L^2 + S^2 + 2\mathbf{L} \cdot \mathbf{S}$$

$$\mathbf{L} \cdot \mathbf{S} = \tfrac{1}{2}(J^2 - L^2 - S^2)$$

$$\hat{\mathbf{L}} \cdot \hat{\mathbf{S}}\psi = \tfrac{1}{2}(\hat{J}^2 - \hat{L}^2 - \hat{S}^2)\psi = \tfrac{1}{2}[J(J+1) - L(L+1) - S(S+1)]\hbar^2\psi$$

since the unperturbed ψ is an eigenfunction of $\hat{L}^2$, $\hat{S}^2$, and $\hat{J}^2$. Therefore

$$E_{\text{s.o.}} = \tfrac{1}{2}\langle \xi \rangle \hbar^2 [J(J+1) - L(L+1) - S(S+1)] \tag{11.73}$$

For a many-electron atom, it can be shown (*Bethe and Jackiw*, p. 163) that the spin-orbit interaction energy is:

$$E_{\text{s.o.}} = \tfrac{1}{2}A\hbar^2 [J(J+1) - L(L+1) - S(S+1)] \tag{11.74}$$

where A is a constant for a given term; i.e., A depends on L and S but not on J. Equation (11.74) shows that when we include the spin-orbit interaction, the energy of an atomic state depends on its total electronic angular momentum J. Thus each

$1s^2\,2s^2\,2p^6\,3p$ $^2P_{3/2}$
               $^2P_{1/2}$

5890 Å   5896 Å

$1s^2\,2s^2\,2p^6\,3s$ $^2S_{1/2}$

FIGURE 11.5   *Fine structure of the sodium D line.*

atomic term is split into levels, each level having a different value of J. For example, the $1s^2\,2s^2\,2p^6\,3p$ configuration of sodium has the single term ^2P, which is composed of the two levels $^2P_{3/2}$ and $^2P_{1/2}$. The splitting of these levels gives the observed *fine structure* of the sodium D line (Fig. 11.5). The levels of a given term are said to form its *multiplet structure*.

What about the order of levels within a given term? Since L and S are the same for such levels, their relative energies are determined, according to Eq. (11.74), by $AJ(J+1)$. If A is positive, the level with the lowest value of J lies lowest, and the multiplet is said to be *regular*; if A is negative, the level with the highest value of J lies lowest, and the multiplet is said to be *inverted*. The following rule usually applies to a configuration with only one partly filled subshell: If this subshell is less than half filled, the multiplet is regular; if this subshell is more than half filled, the multiplet is inverted. (A few exceptions exist.) For example, according to this rule, the multiplets of the $1s^2\,2s^2\,2p^2$ carbon configuration are regular; previously we used Hund's rule to conclude that the lowest term was ^3P, and we now conclude that $^3P_0$ is the lowest level of this term. For a subshell that is half-filled, Hund's rule tells us that the lowest-lying term has $L = 0$. For example, we have for the lowest term of a d^5 configuration:

$$\uparrow \quad \uparrow \quad \uparrow \quad \uparrow \quad \uparrow$$

$$m:\quad +2 \quad +1 \quad 0 \quad -1 \quad -2$$

With $L = 0$, there is only one possible value of J, and the lowest term has but one level. Thus, we don't need a rule to find the lowest level of the lowest term of a half-filled subshell.

The tables[13] of C. E. Moore give the spectroscopically determined atomic energy levels for all atoms except the rare earths and actinides. Also given are the levels of various atomic ions. Spectroscopists use the symbol I to indicate a neutral atom, the symbol II to indicate a singly ionized atom, etc. Thus C III refers to the C^{++} ion.

---

[13] C. E. Moore, *Atomic Energy Levels*, National Bureau of Standards Circular 467, vols. I, II, and III, 1949, 1952, and 1958, Washington, D.C.

11.7 The Atomic Hamiltonian

The Hamiltonian of an atom can be divided into three parts:

$$\hat{H} = \hat{H}^0 + \hat{H}_{rep} + \hat{H}_{s.o.} \tag{11.75}$$

where $\hat{H}^0$ is the sum of hydrogenlike Hamiltonians

$$\hat{H}^0 = \sum_{i=1}^{n} \left[-\frac{\hbar^2}{2m} \nabla_i^2 - \frac{Ze^2}{r_i} \right] \tag{11.76}$$

$\hat{H}_{rep}$ consists of the interelectronic repulsions

$$\hat{H}_{rep} = \sum_{i=1}^{n} \sum_{j>i} \frac{e^2}{r_{ij}} \tag{11.77}$$

and $\hat{H}_{s.o.}$ is the spin-orbit interaction

$$\hat{H}_{s.o.} = \sum_{i=1}^{n} \xi_i \hat{\mathbf{L}}_i \cdot \hat{\mathbf{S}}_i \tag{11.78}$$

If we consider just $\hat{H}^0$, all atomic states corresponding to the same electronic *configuration* are degenerate. Adding in $\hat{H}_{rep}$, we lift the degeneracy between states with different L or S or both, thus splitting each configuration into *terms*. Next, we add in $\hat{H}_{s.o.}$, which splits each term into *levels*; each level is composed of *states* with the same value of J, and is $(2J+1)$-fold degenerate, corresponding to the possible values of M_J.

We can remove the degeneracy of the levels by applying an external magnetic field (the *Zeeman effect*). If $\mathbf{B}$ is the applied field, we have the additional term in the Hamiltonian [Eq. (6.155)]:

$$\hat{H}_B = -\hat{\boldsymbol{\mu}} \cdot \mathbf{B} = -(\hat{\boldsymbol{\mu}}_L + \hat{\boldsymbol{\mu}}_S) \cdot \mathbf{B} \tag{11.79}$$

where we have included both the orbital and the spin magnetic moments. Using Eqs. (6.152), (6.154), and (10.82), we have

$$\hat{H}_B = \beta_e \hbar^{-1}(\hat{\mathbf{L}} + 2\hat{\mathbf{S}}) \cdot \mathbf{B} = \beta_e \hbar^{-1}(\hat{\mathbf{J}} + \hat{\mathbf{S}}) \cdot \mathbf{B} = \beta_e B \hbar^{-1}(\hat{J}_z + \hat{S}_z) \tag{11.80}$$

where β_e is the Bohr magneton; we have taken the z axis along the direction of the field. If the external field is reasonably weak, its effect will be less than that of the spin-orbit interaction, and we can calculate the effect of the field by using first-order perturbation theory on the levels. Since

$$\hat{J}_z \psi = M_J \hbar \psi$$

we have for the energy of interaction with the applied field:

$$E_B = \beta_e B M_J + \beta_e B \hbar^{-1} \langle S_z \rangle$$

Evaluation[14] of the average value of S_z gives the final result:

$$E_B = \beta_e g B M_J \tag{11.81}$$

---

[14] See *Bethe and Jackiw*, p. 168, or *Landau and Lifshitz*, p. 428.

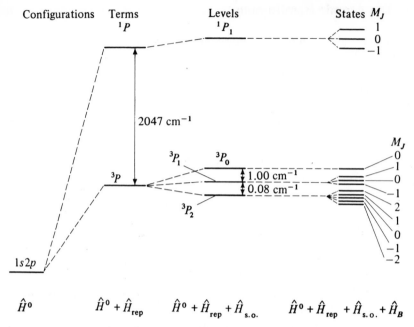

Configurations   Terms   Levels   States M_J

^1P

$^1P_1$

2047 cm^{-1}

$^3P_1$ $^3P_0$

^3P

1.00 cm^{-1}

0.08 cm^{-1}

$^3P_2$

$1s2p$

M_J

$\hat{H}^0$ $\hat{H}^0 + \hat{H}_{rep}$ $\hat{H}^0 + \hat{H}_{rep} + \hat{H}_{s.o.}$ $\hat{H}^0 + \hat{H}_{rep} + \hat{H}_{s.o.} + \hat{H}_B$

FIGURE 11.6 *Effect of inclusion of successive terms in the atomic Hamiltonian for the $1s2p$ helium configuration.* ($\hat{H}_B$ *is not part of the atomic Hamiltonian but is due to an applied magnetic field.*)

where g (*the Landé g factor*) is given by

$$g = 1 + \frac{[J(J+1) - L(L+1) + S(S+1)]}{2J(J+1)} \qquad (11.82)$$

Thus the external field splits each level into $2J+1$ states, each state having a different value of M_J.

Figure 11.6 illustrates what happens when we consider successive interactions in an atom, using the $1s2p$ configuration of helium as the example.

We have based our discussion on a scheme in which we first added the individual electronic orbital angular momenta to form a total orbital angular-momentum vector, and did the same for the spins: $\mathbf{L} = \sum \mathbf{L}_i$, $\mathbf{S} = \sum \mathbf{S}_i$. We then combined $\mathbf{L}$ and $\mathbf{S}$ to get $\mathbf{J}$. This scheme is known as *Russell–Saunders* coupling (or *L–S* coupling) and is appropriate where the spin-orbit interaction energy is small compared to the interelectronic repulsion energy. Although $\hat{L}$ and $\hat{S}$ commute with $\hat{H}^0 + \hat{H}_{rep}$, when we include $\hat{H}_{s.o.}$ in the Hamiltonian, $\hat{L}$ and $\hat{S}$ no longer commute with $\hat{H}$. If the spin-orbit interaction is small, then $\hat{L}$ and $\hat{S}$ "almost" commute with $\hat{H}$, and *L–S* coupling is valid.

As the atomic number increases, the average speed v of the electrons increases; as v/c increases, relativistic effects such as the spin-orbit interaction increase. For atoms with very high atomic number, the spin-orbit interaction exceeds the interelectronic repulsion energy, and we can no longer consider $\hat{L}$ and $\hat{S}$ to commute with $\hat{H}$; the operator $\hat{\mathbf{J}}$, however, still commutes with $\hat{H}$. In this case we first add in $\hat{H}_{\text{s.o.}}$ to $\hat{H}^0$ and then consider $\hat{H}_{\text{rep}}$. This corresponds to first combining the spin and orbital angular momenta of each electron to give a total angular momentum $\mathbf{j}_i$ for each electron: $\mathbf{j}_i = \mathbf{L}_i + \mathbf{S}_i$. We then add the $\mathbf{j}_i$ to get the total electronic angular momentum: $\mathbf{J} = \sum \mathbf{j}_i$. This scheme is called *j–j coupling*. For most heavy atoms, the situation is intermediate between *j–j* and *L–S* coupling, and computations are complex.

There are several other effects which should be included in the atomic Hamiltonian. The finite size of the nucleus and the effect of nuclear motion cause slight changes[15] in the energy. There is a small relativistic term due to the interaction between the spin magnetic moments of the electrons (*spin–spin interaction*). We should also take into account the relativistic change of electronic mass with velocity; this effect is of appreciable magnitude for inner-shell electrons of heavy atoms, where average electronic speeds are not negligible in comparison with the speed of light.

If the nucleus has a nonzero spin, there is an interaction between the nuclear spin magnetic moment and the electronic spin and orbital magnetic moments, giving rise to atomic *hyperfine structure*. The nuclear spin angular momentum $\mathbf{I}$ adds vectorially to the total electronic angular momentum $\mathbf{J}$ to give the total angular momentum $\mathbf{F}$ of the atom: $\mathbf{F} = \mathbf{I} + \mathbf{J}$. For example, consider the ground state of the hydrogen atom. The spin of a proton is $\frac{1}{2}$, so that $I = \frac{1}{2}$; also $J = \frac{1}{2}$. Hence the quantum number F can be 0 or 1, corresponding to the proton and electron spins being antiparallel or parallel. The transition $F = 1 \rightarrow 0$ gives a line at 1420 megacycles per second, the famous 21-centimeter line emitted by hydrogen atoms in outer space. In 1951 Ewen and Purcell (who is also codiscoverer of nuclear magnetic resonance) stuck a horn-shaped antenna out the window of a Harvard physics laboratory and detected this line. The frequency of the hyperfine splitting in the ground state of hydrogen is probably the most accurately measured physical constant[16]:

$$(1,420,405,751.786 \pm 0.002) \text{ cycles per second}$$

PROBLEMS

11.1 How many electrons can be put in each of the following: (a) a shell with principal quantum number n; (b) a subshell with quantum numbers n and l; (c) an orbital; (d) a spin-orbital?

11.2 Give the designations for the ground-state energy levels of the first 10 elements; e.g., $^3P_0$ for carbon.

11.3 What terms does the electron configuration $1s^2 2s^2 2p^6 3s^2 3p5g$ give rise to?

11.4 (a) Verify Eq. (11.34). (b) Apply $\hat{M}_z = \hat{M}_{z1} + \hat{M}_{z2}$ to (11.35), combine terms, and use the linear independence of the functions involved to prove (11.36).

11.5 Verify Eqs. (11.52)–(11.54) and the four equations following (11.56).

11.6 How many states belong to a term that has quantum numbers L and S?

[15] See *Bethe and Salpeter*, pp. 102, 166, 351; *Landau and Lifshitz*, p. 462.
[16] R. Vessot *et al.*, *IEEE Trans. Instr. Meas.*, **IM-15**, 165 (1966).

11.7 Draw a diagram similar to Fig. 11.6 for the carbon $1s^2 2s^2 2p^2$ configuration. (The ^1S term is the highest.)

11.8 (a) Calculate the angle in Fig. 11.3 between the z axis and $\mathbf{S}$ for the spin function $\alpha(1)\,\alpha(2)$. (b) Calculate the angle between $\mathbf{S}_1$ and $\mathbf{S}_2$ for each of the functions (11.57)–(11.60).

11.9 Which STO's have the same form as hydrogenlike AO's?

11.10 Does Fig. 11.6 contain a violation of the rule given in Section 11.6 for determining whether a multiplet is regular or inverted?

11.11 Find the $\hat{S}^2$ and $\hat{S}_z$ eigenvalues for the spin function

$$3^{-1/2}\,[\alpha(1)\,\alpha(2)\,\beta(3)+\alpha(1)\,\beta(2)\,\alpha(3)+\beta(1)\,\alpha(2)\,\alpha(3)]$$

11.12 Estimate the nonrelativistic $1s$ orbital energy in Ar; check with Fig. 11.2.

11.13 At what atomic number does the second crossing of the $3d$ and $4s$ orbital energies occur in Fig. 11.2. Take account of the logarithmic scale.

11.14 If $R(r_1)$ is the radial factor in the function t_1 in the Hartree differential equation (11.12), write down the differential equation satisfied by R.

11.15 Verify the terms in Table 11.2b.

11.16 Give the level designations for the ground states of elements 21 through 30. Which of these elements has the most degenerate ground level?

11.17 How many states belong to the carbon configurations: (a) $1s^2 2s^2 2p^2$; (b) $1s^2 2s^2 2p3p$?

11.18 Use Eq. (11.73) to calculate the separation between the $^2P_{3/2}$ and $^2P_{1/2}$ levels of the hydrogen-atom $2p$ configuration. (Because of other relativistic effects, the result will not agree accurately with experiment.)

11.19 Use Eq. (11.81) to calculate the energy separation between the $M_J = \frac{1}{2}$ and $M_J = -\frac{1}{2}$ states of the $2p$ $^2P_{1/2}$ hydrogen-atom level, if a magnetic field of 2000 gauss is applied.

11.20 Consult Moore's table of atomic energy levels (footnote at the end of Section 11.6) and find a configuration of the neutral carbon atom for which Hund's rule does not correctly predict the lowest term.

11.21 Explain why it would be incorrect to calculate the experimental ground-state energy of lithium by taking $E_{2s} + 2E_{1s}$, where E_{2s} is the experimental energy needed to remove the $2s$ electron from lithium, and E_{1s} is the experimental energy needed to remove a $1s$ electron from lithium.

11.22 Which of the first 10 elements have ground states of odd parity?

Molecular Symmetry

12.1 Symmetry Elements and Operations

The quantum-mechanical treatment of molecules is difficult; hence it is heartening to know that we can often obtain qualitative information about molecular wave functions and properties from the symmetry of the molecule. By the symmetry of a molecule, we will mean the symmetry of the framework formed by the nuclei held fixed in their equilibrium positions. (Our starting point for molecular quantum mechanics will be the Born–Oppenheimer approximation, which regards the nuclei as fixed when solving for the electronic wave function; see Section 13.1.) It should be noted that the symmetry of a molecule can be different in different electronic states. For example, HCN is linear in its ground electronic state, but nonlinear in certain excited states. Unless otherwise specified, we will be considering the symmetry of the ground electronic state.

By a *symmetry operation* we mean a transformation of a body such that the final position is physically indistinguishable from the initial position, and such that the distances between all pairs of points in the body are preserved. For example, consider the trigonal-planar molecule BF_3 (Fig. 12.1a), where for convenience we have numbered the fluorine nuclei. If we rotate the molecule counterclockwise through 120° about an axis through the boron nucleus and perpendicular to the plane of the molecule, the new position will be as in Fig. 12.1b. Since in reality the fluorine nuclei are physically indistinguishable from one another, we have carried out a symmetry operation. The axis about which we rotated is an example of a *symmetry element*. Symmetry elements and symmetry operations are related but different things which are often confused. A symmetry *element* is a geometrical entity (point, line, or plane) with respect to which a symmetry *operation* is carried out.

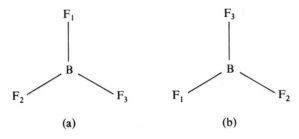

(a)   (b)

FIGURE 12.1   (a) *The* BF_3 *molecule.* (b) BF_3 *after a* 120° *rotation.*

We say that a body has an *n-fold axis of symmetry* (also called an *n-fold proper axis* or an *n-fold rotation axis*) if rotation about this axis by $2\pi/n$ radians (where n is an integer) gives a configuration physically indistinguishable from the original position; n is called the *order* of the axis. For example, BF_3 has a threefold axis of symmetry perpendicular to the molecular plane. The symbol for an *n*-fold rotation axis is C_n. The threefold axis in BF_3 is a C_3 axis. To denote the operation of counterclockwise rotation by $2\pi/n$ radians, we use the symbol $\hat{C}_n$. The "hat" distinguishes symmetry operations from symmetry elements. BF_3 has three more rotation axes; each B—F bond is a twofold symmetry axis (Fig. 12.2).

A second kind of symmetry element is a *plane of symmetry*. A molecule has a plane of symmetry if reflection of all the nuclei through that plane gives a configuration physically indistinguishable from the original one. The symbol for a symmetry plane is σ. (*Spiegel* is the German word for mirror.) The symbol for the operation of reflection is $\hat{\sigma}$. BF_3 has four symmetry planes. The plane of the molecule is a symmetry plane, since nuclei lying in a reflection plane undergo no change in position when a reflection is carried out. The plane passing through the B and F_1 nuclei and perpendicular to the plane of the molecule is a symmetry plane, since reflection in this plane merely interchanges F_2 and F_3. It might be thought that this reflection is the same symmetry operation as rotation by 180° about the C_2 axis passing through B and F_1, which also interchanges F_2 and F_3. This is not so; the reflection carries points lying above the plane of the molecule into points that also lie above the molecular plane, whereas the $\hat{C}_2$ rotation carries points lying

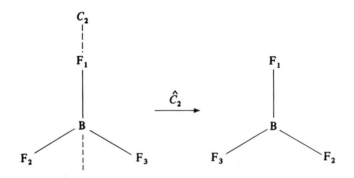

FIGURE 12.2   *A* C_2 *axis in* BF_3.

above the plane of the molecule into points below the molecular plane. Two symmetry operations are equal only when they represent the same transformation of three-dimensional space. The remaining two symmetry planes in BF_3 pass through $B—F_2$ and $B—F_3$ and are perpendicular to the molecular plane.

The third kind of symmetry element is a *center of symmetry*, symbolized by i (no connection with $\sqrt{-1}$). A molecule has a center of symmetry if the operation of inverting all the nuclei through the center gives a configuration indistinguishable from the original one. If we set up a Cartesian coordinate system, the operation of inversion through the origin (symbolized by $\hat{i}$) carries a nucleus originally at (x, y, z) to $(-x, -y, -z)$. Does BF_3 have a center of symmetry? With the origin at the boron nucleus, inversion gives the result shown in Fig. 12.3. Since we get a configuration that is physically distinguishable from the original one, BF_3 does not

FIGURE 12.3 *Effect of inversion in BF_3.*

have a center of symmetry. For SF_6, inversion through the sulfur nucleus is shown in Fig. 12.4, and it is clear that SF_6 has a center of symmetry. (An operation such as $\hat{i}$, $\hat{C}_n$, etc., may or may not be a symmetry operation; thus $\hat{i}$ is a symmetry operation in SF_6 but not in BF_3.)

The fourth and final kind of symmetry element is an *n-fold alternating axis of symmetry* (also called an *improper axis* or a *rotation-reflection axis*), symbolized by S_n. A body has an S_n axis if rotation by $2\pi/n$ radians (n integral) about the axis, followed by reflection in a plane perpendicular to the axis, carries the body into a position physically indistinguishable from the original one. Clearly, if a body has a C_n axis and also has a plane of symmetry perpendicular to this axis, then the C_n axis is also an S_n axis. Thus the C_3 axis in BF_3 is also an S_3 axis. It is possible to have an S_n axis that is not a C_n axis. An example is CH_4. In Fig. 12.5 we have first carried out a 90° proper rotation ($\hat{C}_4$) about what we assert is an S_4 axis. As can

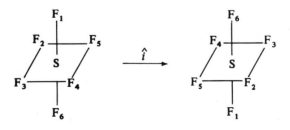

FIGURE 12.4 *Effect of inversion in SF_6.*

FIGURE 12.5   *An S_4 axis in methane.*

be seen, this operation does not result in an equivalent configuration. When we follow the $\hat{C}_4$ operation by reflection in the plane perpendicular to the axis and passing through the carbon atom, we do get a configuration equivalent to the one existing before we performed the rotation and reflection; hence we have an S_4 axis. The S_4 axis is not a C_4 axis, although it is a C_2 axis. There are two other S_4 axes in methane, each one perpendicular to a pair of faces of the cube in which the tetrahedral molecule is inscribed.

The operation of rotation by $2\pi/n$ radians about an axis, followed by reflection in a plane perpendicular to the axis, is denoted by $\hat{S}_n$. An $\hat{S}_1$ operation is a 360° rotation about an axis, followed by a reflection in a plane perpendicular to the axis. Since a 360° rotation restores the body to its original position, an $\hat{S}_1$ operation is the same as reflection in a plane, $\hat{S}_1 = \hat{\sigma}$; any plane of symmetry has an S_1 axis perpendicular to it.

Consider now the $\hat{S}_2$ operation. We choose the coordinate system so that the S_2 axis is the z axis (Fig. 12.6). Rotation by 180° about the S_2 axis changes the x and y coordinates of a point to $-x$ and $-y$, respectively, and leaves the z coordinate unaffected. Reflection in the xy plane then converts the z coordinate to $-z$. The net effect of the $\hat{S}_2$ operation is to bring a point originally at (x, y, z) to $(-x, -y, -z)$, which amounts to an inversion through the origin: $\hat{S}_2 = \hat{\imath}$. Any axis passing through a center of symmetry is an S_2 axis. Reflection in a plane and inversion are special cases of the $\hat{S}_n$ operation.

The $\hat{S}_n$ operation may seem an arbitrary kind of operation, but it must be included as one of the kinds of symmetry operations. Thus, the transformation

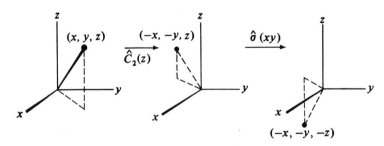

FIGURE 12.6   *The $\hat{S}_2$ operation.*

from the first to the third CH_4 configuration in Fig. 12.5 certainly meets the definition of a symmetry operation, but it is neither a proper rotation nor a reflection nor an inversion.

Performing a symmetry operation on a molecule gives a nuclear configuration physically indistinguishable from the original one; hence the center of mass must have the same position in space before and after a symmetry operation. For the operation $\hat{C}_n$, the only points that do not move are those on the C_n axis; therefore a C_n symmetry axis must pass through the molecular center of mass. Similarly, a center of symmetry must coincide with the center of mass; a plane of symmetry and an alternating axis of symmetry must pass through the center of mass. The center of mass is the common intersection of all the symmetry elements of the molecule.

In discussing the symmetry of a molecule, we often place it in a Cartesian coordinate system with the molecular center of mass at the origin. We make the rotational axis of highest order, the z axis. A plane of symmetry containing this axis is designated σ_v (for *vertical*); a plane of symmetry perpendicular to this axis is designated σ_h (for *horizontal*).

What is the relation between the symmetry operations of a molecule and quantum mechanics? To classify the states of a quantum-mechanical system, we consider those operators that commute with the Hamiltonian and with each other. For example, we classified the states of many-electron atoms using the quantum numbers L, S, J, and M_J, which correspond to the operators $\hat{L}^2$, $\hat{S}^2$, $\hat{J}^2$, and $\hat{J}_z$, all of which commute with each other and with the Hamiltonian (omitting spin-orbit interaction). The symmetry operations discussed in this chapter act on *points* in three-dimensional space, transforming each point to a corresponding point. All the quantum-mechanical operators we have discussed act on *functions*, transforming each function to a corresponding function. Corresponding to each symmetry operation $\hat{R}$, we define an operator $\hat{O}_R$ that acts on functions in the following manner. Let $\hat{R}$ bring a point originally at (x, y, z) to the location (x', y', z'):

$$\hat{R}(x, y, z) \rightarrow (x', y', z') \tag{12.1}$$

The operator $\hat{O}_R$ is defined so that the function $\hat{O}_R f$ has the same value at (x', y', z') that the function f has at (x, y, z):

$$\hat{O}_R f(x', y', z') = f(x, y, z) \tag{12.2}$$

We shall illustrate this definition with an example. Let $\hat{R}$ be a counter-clockwise 90° proper rotation about the z axis: $\hat{R} = \hat{C}_4(z)$. Let f be a $2p_x$ hydrogen orbital:

$$f = 2p_x = Nxe^{-k(x^2+y^2+z^2)^{1/2}}$$

where N and k are constants. A contour showing where f has its maximum positive value is a distorted ellipsoid of revolution about the positive x axis (Section 6.6); likewise, f has its maximum negative value on an ellipsoid lying on the negative x axis. Let us say that these ellipsoids are "centered" about the points $(a, 0, 0)$ and $(-a, 0, 0)$. The operator $\hat{C}_4(z)$ has the following effect (Fig. 12.7):

$$\hat{C}_4(z)(x, y, z) \rightarrow (-y, x, z) \tag{12.3}$$

For example, the point originally at $(a, 0, 0)$ is moved to $(0, a, 0)$, while the point

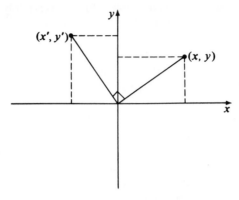

FIGURE 12.7 *Effect of a $\hat{C}_4(z)$ rotation. A little trigonometry shows that $x' = -y, y' = x$.*

at $(-a, 0, 0)$ is moved to $(0, -a, 0)$. From (12.2), the function $\hat{O}_{C_4(z)} 2p_x$ must have its contours of maximum positive and negative values centered about $(0, a, 0)$ and $(0, -a, 0)$, respectively. We conclude that

$$\hat{O}_{C_4(z)} 2p_x = 2p_y \tag{12.4}$$

For the inversion operation, we have

$$\hat{i}(x, y, z) \rightarrow (-x, -y, -z)$$

so that (12.2) reads

$$\hat{O}_i f(-x, -y, -z) = f(x, y, z)$$

We now carry out the following renaming of the variables:

$$\bar{x} = -x, \qquad \bar{y} = -y, \qquad \bar{z} = -z$$

Hence

$$\hat{O}_i f(\bar{x}, \bar{y}, \bar{z}) = f(-\bar{x}, -\bar{y}, -\bar{z})$$

The point $(\bar{x}, \bar{y}, \bar{z})$ is a general point in space and we can drop the bars to get

$$\hat{O}_i f(x, y, z) = f(-x, -y, -z)$$

We conclude that $\hat{O}_i$ is the parity operator:

$$\hat{O}_i = \hat{\Pi} \tag{12.5}$$

The wave function of an n-particle system is a function of $4n$ variables, and we extend the definition (12.2) of $\hat{O}_R$ to read

$$\hat{O}_R f(x'_1, y'_1, z'_1, m_{s1}, \ldots, x'_n, y'_n, z'_n, m_{sn}) = f(x_1, y_1, z_1, m_{s1}, \ldots, x_n, y_n, z_n, m_{sn})$$

Note that $\hat{O}_R$ does not affect the spin coordinates. Thus, in looking at the parity of atomic states in Section 11.5, we looked at the spatial factors in each term of the expansion of the Slater determinant and omitted consideration of the spin factors, since these are unaffected by $\hat{\Pi}$.

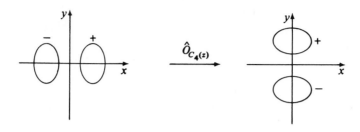

FIGURE 12.8 *Effect of $\hat{O}_{C_4}(z)$ on a p_x orbital.*

When a system is characterized by the symmetry operations $\hat{R}_1, \hat{R}_2, ...,$ then the corresponding operators $\hat{O}_{R_1}, \hat{O}_{R_2}, ...$ commute with the Hamiltonian.[1] For example, if the nuclear framework of a molecule has a center of symmetry, then the parity operator $\hat{\Pi}$ commutes with the Hamiltonian for the electronic motion. We can then choose the electronic states (wave functions) as even or odd, according to the eigenvalue of $\hat{\Pi}$. Of course, all the symmetry operations may not commute among themselves (see the next section); hence, the wave functions cannot in general be chosen as eigenfunctions of all the operators $\hat{O}_R$. (Since the correspondence between the symmetry transformation $\hat{R}$ and the operator $\hat{O}_R$ is so close, one often doesn't distinguish between them.)

There is a close connection between symmetry and the *constants of the motion* (these are properties whose operators commute with the Hamiltonian $\hat{H}$). For a system whose Hamiltonian is invariant (i.e., doesn't change) under any translation of spatial coordinates, the linear-momentum operator $\hat{p}$ will commute with $\hat{H}$, and $\hat{p}$ can be assigned a definite value in a stationary state. (An example is the free particle.) For a system with $\hat{H}$ invariant under any rotation of coordinates, the operators for the angular momentum components commute with $\hat{H}$ and the total angular momentum and one of its components are specifiable. (An example is an atom.) A linear molecule has axial symmetry, rather than the spherical symmetry of an atom; here only the axial component of angular momentum can be specified (Chapter 13).

12.2 Products of Symmetry Operations

Symmetry operations are operators that cause transformations of three-dimensional space, and (as with any operators) we define the product of two such operators as meaning successive application of the operators, the operator on the right of the product being applied first. Clearly, the product of any two symmetry operations of a molecule must also be a symmetry operation.

As an example, consider BF_3. The product of the $\hat{C}_3$ operator with itself, $\hat{C}_3 \hat{C}_3 = \hat{C}_3^2$, rotates the molecule 240° counterclockwise. If we take $\hat{C}_3 \hat{C}_3 \hat{C}_3 = \hat{C}_3^3$,

---

[1] For a careful discussion, see *Schonland*, Sections 7.1 and 7.2.

we have a 360° rotation, which restores the molecule to its original position. We define the *identity operation* $\hat{E}$ as the operation that does nothing to a body. We have $\hat{C}_3^3 = \hat{E}$. (The symbol comes from the German word *Einheit*, meaning unity. The symbol $\hat{I}$ is sometimes used instead of $\hat{E}$.) The operator $\hat{O}_E$ is the unit operator: $\hat{O}_E = \hat{1}$.

Now consider a molecule with a sixfold axis of symmetry, e.g., C_6H_6. The operation $\hat{C}_6$ is a 60° rotation, and $\hat{C}_6^2$ is a 120° rotation; hence $\hat{C}_6^2 = \hat{C}_3$. Also $\hat{C}_6^3 = \hat{C}_2$. We conclude that a C_6 symmetry axis is also a C_3 and a C_2 axis. In general, a C_n axis is also a C_m axis if n/m is an integer.

Since two successive reflections in the same plane bring all nuclei back to their original positions, we have $\hat{\sigma}^2 = \hat{E}$. Also $\hat{\imath}^2 = \hat{E}$. More generally, $\hat{\sigma}^n = \hat{E}$, $\hat{\imath}^n = \hat{E}$ for even n, while $\hat{\sigma}^n = \hat{\sigma}$, $\hat{\imath}^n = \hat{\imath}$ for odd n.

Do symmetry operators always commute? Consider SF_6. We examine the products of a $\hat{C}_4$ rotation about the z axis and a $\hat{C}_2$ rotation about the x axis. Figure 12.9 shows that $\hat{C}_4(z)\,\hat{C}_2(x) \neq \hat{C}_2(x)\,\hat{C}_4(z)$. Thus symmetry operations do not always commute. [Note that we describe symmetry operations with respect

(a)

(b)

FIGURE 12.9 *Products of symmetry operations in* SF_6: (a) $\hat{C}_2(x)\,\hat{C}_4(z)$; (b) $\hat{C}_4(z)\,\hat{C}_2(x)$.

to a fixed coordinate system; our convention is that the symmetry elements do not move with the molecule when we perform a symmetry operation, but remain fixed in space. For example, the $C_2(x)$ axis does not move when we perform the $\hat{C}_4(z)$ operation.]

12.3 Symmetry and Dipole Moments

As an application of symmetry, we consider molecular dipole moments. Since a symmetry operation produces a configuration physically indistinguishable from the original one, the direction of the dipole-moment vector must remain unchanged after a symmetry operation. (This is a nonrigorous, unsophisticated argument.) Hence, if we have a proper axis of symmetry, the dipole moment must lie along this axis. If we have two or more noncoincident symmetry axes, the molecule cannot have a dipole moment, since the dipole moment cannot lie on two different axes. CH_4, which has four noncoincident C_3 axes, has no dipole moment. If there is a plane of symmetry, the dipole moment must lie in this plane. If there are several symmetry planes, the dipole moment must lie along the line of intersection of these planes. In H_2O the dipole moment lies on the C_2 axis, which is also the intersection of the two symmetry planes (Fig. 12.10). A molecule with a center of symmetry cannot have a dipole moment, since inversion reverses the direction of a vector. A monatomic molecule has a center of symmetry; hence, atoms don't have dipole moments. (There is one exception to this statement—see Problem 13.30.) Thus we can use symmetry to discover whether a molecule has a dipole moment; in many cases symmetry considerations also tell us along what line the dipole moment lies.

FIGURE 12.10 *The symmetry elements of* H_2O.

12.4 Symmetry and Optical Activity

The ability of certain molecules to rotate the plane of polarization of plane-polarized light is well-known. Experimental evidence and a quantum-mechanical treatment[2] both show that the optical rotary powers of two molecules that are

_____
[2] *Kauzmann*, pp. 703–713.

mirror images of each other are equal in magnitude but opposite in sign. A simple way to see this is from the fact that physical processes occur in the same manner for a system and for its mirror image. Reflection of an optical-rotation experiment in a mirror converts the molecules to their mirror images and converts a clockwise optical rotation to a counterclockwise rotation of equal magnitude. (Interestingly, for the physical processes that occur in elementary-particle decay, nature *does* distinguish between a system and its mirror image; Yang and Lee won the 1957 Nobel Prize in physics for suggesting this possibility. See M. Gardner, *The Ambidextrous Universe*, Mentor–New American Library, 1969.) Hence if a molecule is its own mirror image, it is optically inactive: $R = -R$, $2R = 0$, $R = 0$, where R is the optical rotary power. If a molecule is not superimposable on its mirror image, it may be optically active. (If the conformation of the mirror image differs from that of the original molecule only by rotation about a bond with a low rotational barrier, then we will not have optical activity.)

What is the connection between symmetry and optical activity? Consider the $\hat{S}_n$ operation. It consists of a rotation ($\hat{C}_n$) and a reflection ($\hat{\sigma}$). The reflection part of the $\hat{S}_n$ operation converts the molecule to its mirror image, and if the $\hat{S}_n$ operation is a symmetry operation for the molecule, then the $\hat{C}_n$ rotation will superimpose the molecule and its mirror image:

$$\text{molecule} \xrightarrow{\hat{C}_n} \text{rotated molecule} \xrightarrow{\hat{\sigma}} \text{rotated mirror image}$$

We conclude that a molecule with an S_n axis is optically inactive; if the molecule has no S_n axis, it may be optically active.

Since $\hat{S}_1 = \hat{\sigma}$ and $\hat{S}_2 = \hat{i}$, a molecule with either a plane or a center of symmetry is optically inactive (as you probably learned in organic chemistry). However, an S_n axis of any order rules out optical activity. As an example consider the molecule of Fig. 12.11, which has two mutually perpendicular rings with one atom in common. The molecule has neither a plane nor a center of symmetry, but is optically inactive due to the presence of an S_4 axis. As a check, it is easily verified that the mirror image generated by reflection in a plane perpendicular to the S_4 axis is superimposable on the original molecule after a $\hat{C}_4$ rotation.

FIGURE 12.11 *A molecule that is optically inactive due to an S_4 axis.*

A molecule can have a symmetry element and still be optically active; if a C_n axis is present, and there is no S_n axis, we can have optical activity. An example is the molecule in Fig. 12.12, which has a C_2 axis but no S_n axis. As a check, we readily verify that this molecule is not superimposable on its mirror image.

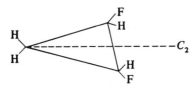

FIGURE 12.12   *An optically active molecule with a C_2 axis.*

We have made no reference to asymmetric carbon atoms. There are optically active organic compounds that have no asymmetric carbons; there are optically inactive molecules that have two or more asymmetric carbons.

12.5   Symmetry Point Groups

We now systematically consider the possible combinations of symmetry elements. We cannot have arbitrary combinations of symmetry elements in a molecule. For example, suppose we have a molecule with one and only one C_3 axis. Any symmetry operation must send this axis into itself. We cannot, therefore, have a plane of symmetry at an arbitrary angle to the C_3 axis; any plane of symmetry must either contain this axis or be perpendicular to it. (In BF_3 there are three σ_v planes and one σ_h plane.) The only possibility for a C_n axis noncoincident with the C_3 axis is a C_2 axis perpendicular to the C_3 axis; the corresponding $\hat{C}_2$ operation will send the C_3 axis into itself. Since $\hat{C}_3$ and $\hat{C}_3^2$ are symmetry operations, if we have one C_2 axis perpendicular to the C_3 axis, we must have a total of three such axes (as in BF_3).

The set of all the symmetry operations of a molecule forms a mathematical group. A *group* is a set of entities and a rule for forming the product of these entities, such that certain requirements are met. (The rule of combination of symmetry operations is successive performance of them.) We will not make explicit use of the mathematics of group theory. Note that it is the symmetry *operations*, not the symmetry elements, that constitute the group. For any symmetry operation of a molecule, the point that is the center of mass remains fixed. Hence the symmetry groups of isolated molecules are called *point groups*. For a crystal of infinite extent, we can have symmetry operations (e.g., translations) that leave no point fixed, giving rise to *space groups*. We omit consideration of space groups.

Any molecule can be classified as belonging to one of the symmetry point groups that we now list. For convenience, we have divided the point groups into four divisions. (Script letters denote point groups.)

I. Groups with no C_n axis: $\mathscr{C}_1, \mathscr{C}_s, \mathscr{C}_i$

(a) $\mathscr{C}_1$

If a molecule has no symmetry elements at all, it belongs to this group. The only symmetry operation is $\hat{E}$ (which is a $\hat{C}_1$ rotation). CHFClBr belongs to point group $\mathscr{C}_1$.

(b) $\mathscr{C}_s$

A molecule whose only symmetry element is a plane of symmetry belongs to this group. The symmetry operations are $\hat{E}$ and $\hat{\sigma}$. An example is HOCl (Fig. 12.13).

(c) $\mathscr{C}_i$

A molecule whose only symmetry element is a center of symmetry belongs to this group. The symmetry operations are $\hat{\imath}$ and $\hat{E}$.

II. Groups with a single C_n axis: $\mathscr{C}_n, \mathscr{C}_{nh}, \mathscr{C}_{nv}, \mathscr{S}_{2n}$

(a) $\mathscr{C}_n$, $n = 2, 3, 4, ...$

A molecule whose only symmetry element is a C_n axis belongs to this group. The symmetry operations are $\hat{C}_n, \hat{C}_n^2, ..., \hat{C}_n^{n-1}, \hat{E}$. Examples of molecules belonging to $\mathscr{C}_2$ are shown in Figs. 12.14 and 12.12.

(b) $\mathscr{C}_{nh}$, $n = 2, 3, 4, ...$

If we add a plane of symmetry perpendicular to the C_n axis, we have a molecule belonging to this group. Since $\hat{\sigma}_h \hat{C}_n = \hat{S}_n$, the C_n axis is also an S_n axis. If n is even, the C_n axis is also a C_2 axis, and we have the symmetry operation

$$\hat{\sigma}_h \hat{C}_2 = \hat{S}_2 = \hat{\imath}$$

Thus for n even, a molecule belonging to $\mathscr{C}_{nh}$ has a center of symmetry. (The group $\mathscr{C}_{1h}$ is the group $\mathscr{C}_s$ discussed previously.) Examples of molecules belonging to groups $\mathscr{C}_{2h}$ and $\mathscr{C}_{3h}$ are shown in Fig. 12.14.

(c) $\mathscr{C}_{nv}$, $n = 2, 3, 4, ...$

A molecule in this group has a C_n axis and n vertical symmetry planes (passing through the C_n axis). (Group $\mathscr{C}_{1v}$ is the group $\mathscr{C}_s$.) Water, with a C_2 axis and two vertical symmetry planes, belongs to $\mathscr{C}_{2v}$. Ammonia belongs to $\mathscr{C}_{3v}$. (See Fig. 12.14.)

FIGURE 12.13 *Molecules with no C_n axis.*

H_2O_2; the O—O bond is perpendicular to the plane of the paper

$\mathscr{C}_2$

$\mathscr{C}_{2h}$　　　　　$\mathscr{C}_{3h}$　　　　　$\mathscr{C}_{3v}$

FIGURE 12.14　*Molecules with a single C_n axis.*

(d) $\mathscr{S}_n$, $n = 4, 6, 8, \ldots$

$\mathscr{S}_n$ is the group of symmetry operations associated with an S_n axis. First consider the case of odd n. We have $\hat{S}_n = \hat{\sigma}_h \hat{C}_n$. The operation $\hat{C}_n$ affects the x and y coordinates only, while the $\hat{\sigma}_h$ operation affects the z coordinate only; hence these operations commute, and we have

$$\hat{S}_n^n = (\hat{\sigma}_h \hat{C}_n)^n = \hat{\sigma}_h \hat{C}_n \hat{\sigma}_h \hat{C}_n \cdots \hat{\sigma}_h \hat{C}_n = \hat{\sigma}_h^n \hat{C}_n^n$$

Now $\hat{C}_n^n = \hat{E}$, and for odd n $\hat{\sigma}_h^n = \hat{\sigma}_h$. Hence the symmetry operation $\hat{S}_n^n$ equals $\hat{\sigma}_h$ for odd n, and the group $\mathscr{S}_n$ has a horizontal symmetry plane if n is odd. Also

$$\hat{S}_n^{n+1} = \hat{S}_n^n \hat{S}_n = \hat{\sigma}_h \hat{S}_n = \hat{\sigma}_h \hat{\sigma}_h \hat{C}_n = \hat{C}_n, \qquad n \text{ odd}$$

so that we have a C_n axis if n is odd. We conclude that the group $\mathscr{S}_n$ is identical with the group $\mathscr{C}_{nh}$ if n is odd.

Now consider even values of n. Since $\hat{S}_2 = \hat{\imath}$, the group $\mathscr{S}_2$ is identical with $\mathscr{C}_i$. Thus it is only for $n = 4, 6, 8, \ldots$ that we get new groups. The S_{2n} axis is also a C_n axis:

$$\hat{S}_{2n}^2 = \hat{\sigma}_h^2 \hat{C}_{2n}^2 = \hat{E}\hat{C}_n = \hat{C}_n$$

The spiran of Fig. 12.11 belongs to the group $\mathscr{S}_4$.

III. Groups with one C_n axis and n C_2 axes: $\mathscr{D}_n, \mathscr{D}_{nh}, \mathscr{D}_{nd}$

(a) $\mathscr{D}_n$, $n = 2, 3, 4, \ldots$

A molecule with a C_n axis and n C_2 axes perpendicular to the C_n axis (and no

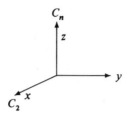

FIGURE 12.15   *Two of the symmetry axes in a $\mathscr{D}_{nh}$ molecule.*

symmetry planes) belongs to group $\mathscr{D}_n$. The angle between adjacent C_2 axes is π/n radians. For the group $\mathscr{D}_2$ we have three mutually perpendicular C_2 axes, and the symmetry operations are $\hat{E}, \hat{C}_2(x), \hat{C}_2(y), \hat{C}_2(z)$.

(b) $\mathscr{D}_{nh}$, $n = 2, 3, 4, \ldots$
    This is the group of a molecule with a C_n axis, n C_2 axes, and a σ_h symmetry plane perpendicular to the C_n axis. As in $\mathscr{C}_{nh}$, the C_n axis is also an S_n axis. If n is even, the C_n axis is a C_2 and an S_2 axis, and we have a center of symmetry. Molecules in $\mathscr{D}_{nh}$ also have n vertical planes of symmetry, each such plane passing through the C_n axis and a C_2 axis. We now prove this assertion. We set up a coordinate system with the C_n axis as the z axis, and let one of the C_2 axes be the x axis (Fig. 12.15). This makes the xy plane the σ_h symmetry plane. Looking at the effect of the product $\hat{\sigma}(xy)\,\hat{C}_2(x)$ on a point originally at (x, y, z), we have

$$(x, y, z) \xrightarrow{\hat{C}_2(x)} (x, -y, -z) \xrightarrow{\hat{\sigma}(xy)} (x, -y, z)$$

We also have

$$(x, y, z) \xrightarrow{\hat{\sigma}(xz)} (x, -y, z)$$

Since $\hat{\sigma}(xy)\,\hat{C}_2(x)$ and $\hat{\sigma}(xz)$ both bring a point originally at (x, y, z) to the final position $(x, -y, z)$, they are equal:

$$\hat{\sigma}(xy)\,\hat{C}_2(x) = \hat{\sigma}(xz)$$

$\hat{C}_2(x)$ and $\hat{\sigma}(xy)$ are symmetry operations and their product must be a symmetry operation; hence the xz plane is a symmetry plane. The same argument holds for any C_2 axis, so that we have n σ_v planes. BF_3 belongs to $\mathscr{D}_{3h}$; $PtCl_4^{--}$ belongs to $\mathscr{D}_{4h}$; benzene belongs to $\mathscr{D}_{6h}$ (Fig. 12.16).

(c) $\mathscr{D}_{nd}$, $n = 2, 3, 4, \ldots$
    A molecule with a C_n axis, n C_2 axes, and n vertical planes of symmetry, which pass through the C_n axis and bisect the angles between adjacent C_2 axes, belongs to this group. The n vertical planes are called *diagonal* planes and are symbolized by σ_d. The C_n axis can be shown to be an S_{2n} axis. The staggered conformation of ethane is an example of group $\mathscr{D}_{3d}$ (Fig. 12.16). [The symmetry of molecules with internal rotation (e.g., ethane) actually requires special consideration, which we omit.[3]]

---

[3] See H. C. Longuet-Higgins, *Mol. Phys.*, **6**, 445 (1963).

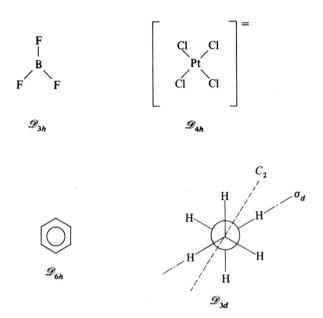

FIGURE 12.16 *Molecules with a C_n axis and n C_2 axes.*

IV. Groups with more than one C_n axis, $n > 2$: $\mathscr{T}_d, \mathscr{T}, \mathscr{T}_h, \mathcal{O}_h, \mathcal{O}, \mathscr{I}_h, \mathscr{I}, \mathscr{K}_h$

These groups are related to the symmetries of the Platonic solids, solids bounded by congruent regular polygons and having congruent polyhedral angles. There are five such solids: the tetrahedron has 4 triangular faces, the cube has 6 square faces, the octahedron has 8 triangular faces, the pentagonal dodecahedron has 12 pentagonal faces, the icosahedron has 20 triangular faces. (The pentagonal dodecahedron should not be confused with the triangular dodecahedron; the latter has 12 triangular faces and is not a Platonic solid.)

(a) $\mathscr{T}_d$

The symmetry operations of a regular tetrahedron constitute this group. The prime example is CH_4. The symmetry elements of methane are four C_3 axes (each C—H bond), three S_4 axes which are also C_2 axes (Fig. 12.5), and six symmetry planes, each such plane containing two C—H bonds. (The number of combinations of 4 things taken 2 at a time is $4!/2!\,2! = 6$.)

(b) $\mathcal{O}_h$

The symmetry operations of a cube or a regular octahedron constitute this group. The cube and octahedron are said to be *dual* to each other—if we connect the midpoints of adjacent faces of a cube, we get an octahedron, and vice versa. Hence the cube and octahedron have the same symmetry elements and operations. A cube has six faces, eight vertices, and twelve edges; its symmetry elements are: a center of symmetry, three C_4 axes passing through the centers of opposite faces of the cube (these are also S_4 and C_2 axes), four C_3 axes passing through opposite corners of the cube (these are also S_6 axes), six C_2 axes connecting the midpoints of pairs of opposite edges, three planes of symmetry parallel to pairs of opposite faces, six planes of symmetry passing through pairs of opposite edges. Octahedral molecules, e.g., SF_6, belong to $\mathcal{O}_h$.

(c) $\mathcal{I}_h$

The symmetry operations of a regular pentagonal dodecahedron or icosahedron (which are dual to each other) constitute this group. The $B_{12}H_{12}^{-2}$ ion belongs to group $\mathcal{I}_h$; the 12 boron atoms lie at the vertices of a regular icosahedron (Fig. 12.17).

(d) $\mathcal{K}_h$

This is the group of symmetry operations of a sphere. (*Kugel* is the German word for sphere.) An atom belongs to this group.

For completeness, we mention the remaining groups related to the Platonic solids; these groups are chemically unimportant. The groups $\mathcal{T}$, $\mathcal{O}$, and $\mathcal{I}$ are the groups of symmetry proper *rotations* of a tetrahedron, cube, and icosahedron, respectively; these groups do not have the symmetry reflections and improper rotations of these solids or the inversion operation of the cube and icosahedron. The group $\mathcal{T}_h$ contains the symmetry rotations of a tetrahedron, the inversion operation, and certain reflections and improper rotations.

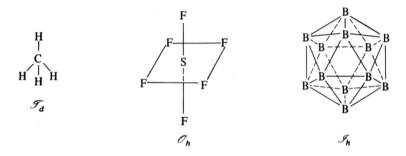

FIGURE 12.17 *Molecules with more than one C_n axis, $n > 2$. (For the $B_{12}H_{12}^{-2}$ ion, the hydrogen atoms have been omitted for clarity.)*

What groups do linear molecules belong to? A rotation by any angle about the internuclear axis of a linear molecule is a symmetry operation. A regular polygon of n sides has a C_n axis, and taking the limit as $n \to \infty$ we get a circle, which has a C_∞ axis. The internuclear axis of a linear molecule is a C_∞ axis. Any plane containing this axis is a symmetry plane. If the linear molecule does not have a center of symmetry (e.g., CO, HCN), it belongs to the group $\mathscr{C}_{\infty v}$. If the linear molecule has a center of symmetry (e.g., H_2, C_2H_2), then it also has a σ_h symmetry plane and an infinite number of C_2 axes perpendicular to the molecular axis; hence it belongs to $\mathscr{D}_{\infty h}$.

How do we find what point group a molecule belongs to? One way is to find all the symmetry elements and then compare with the above list of groups. A

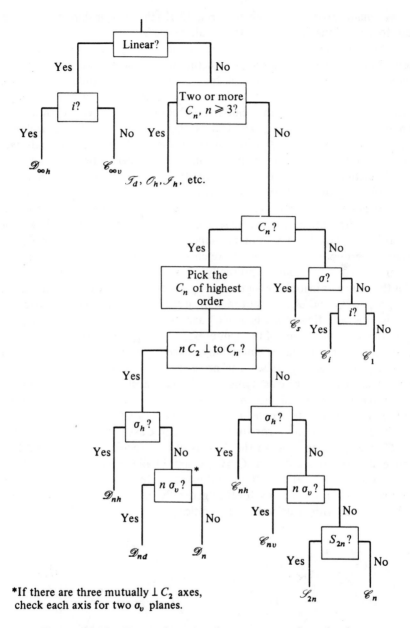

*If there are three mutually $\perp C_2$ axes,
check each axis for two σ_v planes.

FIGURE 12.18　*How to determine the point group of a molecule.*

more systematic procedure[4] is given in Fig. 12.18; the relationship of this procedure to our four divisions of point groups should be clear.

We begin by checking whether the molecule is linear; linear molecules are classified in $\mathscr{D}_{\infty h}$ or $\mathscr{C}_{\infty v}$ according to whether or not there is a center of symmetry. If the molecule is nonlinear, we look for two or more rotational axes of 3-fold or higher order; if these are present, the molecule is classified in one of the groups related to the symmetry of the regular polyhedra (division IV). If these axes are not present, we look for any C_n axis at all. If there is no C_n axis, the molecule belongs to one of the groups $\mathscr{C}_s, \mathscr{C}_i, \mathscr{C}_1$ (division I). If there is at least one C_n axis, we pick the C_n axis of highest order as the main symmetry axis before proceeding to the next step. (Sometimes there will be three mutually perpendicular C_2 axes; in these cases we may pick any one of these axes as the main axis.) We next check for n C_2 axes at right angles to the main C_n axis. If these are present, we have one of the division III groups; if these are absent, we have one of the division II groups. If we find the n C_2 axes, we look for a symmetry plane perpendicular to the main C_n axis; if present, the group is $\mathscr{D}_{nh}$. If absent, we check for n planes of symmetry containing the main C_n axis (if we have 3 mutually perpendicular C_2 axes, we must try each axis as the main axis in looking for the two σ_v planes—the three C_2 axes are equivalent in the groups $\mathscr{D}_{nh}$ and $\mathscr{D}_n$, but not in $\mathscr{D}_{nd}$); if we find n σ_v planes, the group is $\mathscr{D}_{nd}$, otherwise it is $\mathscr{D}_n$. If we don't have n C_2 axes perpendicular to the main C_n axis, we classify the molecule in one of the groups $\mathscr{C}_{nh}, \mathscr{C}_{nv}, \mathscr{S}_{2n}$, or $\mathscr{C}_n$, by looking first for a σ_h plane, then for n σ_v planes, and finally, if these are absent, checking whether or not the C_n axis is an S_{2n} axis. The procedure of Fig. 12.18 does not locate all symmetry elements; after classifying a molecule, check that all the required symmetry elements are indeed present. Although the above procedure might seem involved, it is really quite simple and is easily memorized.

The most common error students make in classifying a molecule is to miss the n C_2 axes perpendicular to the C_n axis of a molecule belonging to $\mathscr{D}_{nd}$. For example, it is easy to see that the C=C=C axis of allene is a C_2 axis, but the other two C_2 axes (Fig. 12.19) are often overlooked. Molecules with two equal halves "staggered" with respect to each other generally belong to $\mathscr{D}_{nd}$. Models may be helpful for those with visualization difficulties.

(a)   (b)

FIGURE 12.19 *Two views of allene. The C=C=C axis is perpendicular to the plane of the paper in (a).*

[4] J. B. Calvert, *Am. J. Phys.*, **31**, 569 (1963).

PROBLEMS

12.1 Two people play the following game. Each in turn places a penny on the surface of a large chessboard. The pennies can be put anywhere on the board, so long as they do not overlap previously placed pennies. A penny may overlap more than one square if desired. Once placed, a penny cannot be moved. When one of the players finds there is no room to place another penny on the board, she loses. With best play, will the person placing the first penny or her opponent win? Give the winning strategy.

12.2 Give all the symmetry elements of each of the following molecules: (a) H_2S; (b) NH_3; (c) CHF_3; (d) HOCl; (e) 1,3,5-trichlorobenzene; (f) CH_2F_2; (g) CHFClBr.

12.3 For SF_6, which of the following pairs of operations commute: (a) $\hat{C}_4(z)$, $\hat{\sigma}_h$; (b) $\hat{C}_4(z)$, $\hat{\sigma}(yz)$; (c) $\hat{C}_2(z)$, $\hat{C}_2(x)$; (d) $\hat{\sigma}_h$, $\hat{\sigma}(yz)$; (e) $\hat{i}$, $\hat{\sigma}_h$?

12.4 What information does symmetry give about the dipole moment of each of the molecules in Problem 12.2?

12.5 Verify directly that the molecule in Fig. 12.11 is superimposable on its mirror image, while the molecule in Fig. 12.12 is not superimposable on its mirror image.

12.6 (a) What Platonic solid is dual to the regular tetrahedron? (b) How many vertices does a pentagonal dodecahedron have?

12.7 (a) Does H_2O_2 have an S_n axis? (b) Is it optically active? Explain.

12.8 For which point groups can a molecule have a dipole moment?

12.9 For which point groups can a molecule be optically active?

12.10 (a) For what values of n does the presence of an S_n axis imply the presence of a plane of symmetry? (b) For what values of n does the presence of an S_n axis imply the presence of a center of symmetry? (c) The group $\mathcal{D}_{nd}$ has an S_{2n} axis; for what values of n does it have a center of symmetry?

12.11 Give the point group of each of the following molecules. (a) CH_4; (b) CH_3F; (c) CH_2F_2; (d) CHF_3; (e) SF_6; (f) SF_5Br; (g) trans-SF_4Br_2; (h) CDH_3.

12.12 Give the point group of (a) $CH_2{=}CH_2$; (b) $CH_2{=}CHF$; (c) $CH_2{=}CF_2$; (d) cis-CHF{=}CHF; (e) trans-CHF{=}CHF.

12.13 Give the point group of: (a) benzene; (b) fluorobenzene; (c) o-difluorobenzene; (d) m-difluorobenzene; (e) p-difluorobenzene; (f) 1,3,5-trifluorobenzene; (g) 1,4-difluoro-2,5-dibromobenzene; (h) naphthalene; (i) 2-chloronaphthalene.

12.14 Give the point group of: (a) HCN; (b) H_2S; (c) CO_2; (d) CO; (e) C_2H_2; (f) CH_3OH; (g) ND_3; (h) OCS; (i) P_4; (j) PCl_3; (k) PCl_5; (l) $B_{12}Cl_{12}{}^{-2}$; (m) UF_6; (n) Ar.

12.15 Give the point group of: (a) $FeF_6{}^{-3}$; (b) IF_5; (c) $CH_2{=}C{=}CH_2$; (d) C_8H_8, cubane; (e) $C_6H_6Cr(CO)_3$; (f) B_2H_6; (g) XeF_4; (h) F_2O; (i) spiropentane; (j) $B_{10}H_{10}{}^{-2}$ (for the structure, see E. L. Muetterties and W. H. Knoth, *Chem. Eng. News*, May 9, 1966, p. 88).

12.16 The structure of ferrocene, $C_5H_5FeC_5H_5$, is an iron atom sandwiched midway between two parallel regular pentagons. For the eclipsed conformation, the vertices of the two pentagons are aligned; for the staggered conformation, one pentagon is rotated $2\pi/10$ radians with respect to the other. Electron diffraction results show that the gas-phase equilibrium conformation is the eclipsed one, with a quite low barrier to internal rotation of the rings. [A. Haaland and J. E. Nilsson, *Acta Chem. Scand.*, **22**, 2653 (1968).] What is the point group of (a) eclipsed ferrocene; (b) staggered ferrocene?

12.17 What is the point group of the tris(ethylenediamine)cobalt(III) complex ion? (Each $NH_2CH_2CH_2NH_2$ group occupies two adjacent positions of the octahedral coordination sphere.)

12.18 Give the point group of: (a) a square-based pyramid; (b) a right circular cone; (c) a square lamina; (d) a square lamina with the top and bottom sides painted different colors; (e) a right circular cylinder; (f) a right circular cylinder with the two ends painted different colors; (g) a right circular cylinder with a stripe painted parallel to the axis; (h) a snowflake; (i) a doughnut; (j) a baseball (Fig. 12.20); (k) a $2p_z$ orbital; (l) a human being (ignore internal organs and slight external left–right asymmetries).

FIGURE 12.20 *A baseball. The dashed and solid parts of the seam are in different hemispheres.*

12.19 (a) What are the eigenvalues of $\hat{O}_{C_4}$? (b) Is this operator Hermitian?

12.20 The same as Problem 12.19 for $\hat{O}_{C_2}$.

12.21 To what function is a $2p_z$ hydrogenlike orbital converted by: (a) $\hat{O}_{C_4(z)}$; (b) $\hat{O}_{C_4(y)}$?

12.22 Consider the following transformation:

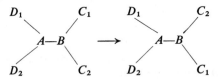

where C_1 and C_2 are identical and D_1 and D_2 are identical. Does it meet the definition of a symmetry operation (Section 12.1)? If so, express it in terms of some combination of the four kinds of symmetry operations discussed.

12.23 It is common to use rotation-inversion axes (rather than rotation-reflection axes) to classify the symmetry of crystals. Any S_n axis is equivalent to a rotation-inversion axis (symbolized by $\bar{p}$) whose order p may differ from n. A rotation-inversion operation consists of rotation by $2\pi/p$ radians followed by inversion. Show that

$$\hat{S}_n(z) = \hat{i}[\hat{C}_n(z)\,\hat{C}_2(z)]$$

Thus we have the following correspondence:

S_n	1	2	3	4
$\bar{p}$	$\bar{2}$	$\bar{1}$	$\bar{6}$	$\bar{4}$

Give the next 3 pairs of entries in this table.

CHAPTER

13

Electronic Structure
of Diatomic Molecules

13.1 The Born–Oppenheimer Approximation

We now begin the study of molecular quantum mechanics. If we assume the nuclei and electrons to be point masses and neglect spin-orbit and other relativistic interactions (Sections 11.6 and 11.7), then the molecular Hamiltonian is:

$$\hat{H} = -\frac{\hbar^2}{2} \sum_\alpha \frac{1}{m_\alpha} \nabla_\alpha^2 - \frac{\hbar^2}{2m} \sum_i \nabla_i^2 + \sum_\alpha \sum_{\beta > \alpha} \frac{Z_\alpha Z_\beta e^2}{r_{\alpha\beta}} - \sum_\alpha \sum_i \frac{Z_\alpha e^2}{r_{i\alpha}} + \sum_j \sum_{i>j} \frac{e^2}{r_{ij}}$$

(13.1)

where α and β refer to nuclei and i and j refer to electrons. The first term in (13.1) is the operator for the kinetic energy of the nuclei; the second term is the operator for the kinetic energy of the electrons; the third term represents the repulsions between the nuclei, $r_{\alpha\beta}$ being the distance between nuclei α and β of atomic numbers Z_α and Z_β; the fourth term represents the attractions between the electrons and the nuclei, $r_{i\alpha}$ being the distance between electron i and nucleus α; the last term represents the repulsions between the electrons, r_{ij} being the distance between electrons i and j.

As an example, consider H_2. Let α and β be the two protons, 1 and 2 be the two electrons, and let M be the proton mass; we have

$$\hat{H} = -\frac{\hbar^2}{2M} \nabla_\alpha^2 - \frac{\hbar^2}{2M} \nabla_\beta^2 - \frac{\hbar^2}{2m} \nabla_1^2 - \frac{\hbar^2}{2m} \nabla_2^2 + \frac{e^2}{r_{\alpha\beta}} - \frac{e^2}{r_{1\alpha}} - \frac{e^2}{r_{1\beta}} - \frac{e^2}{r_{2\alpha}} - \frac{e^2}{r_{2\beta}} + \frac{e^2}{r_{12}}$$

(13.2)

The wave functions and energies of a molecule are found from the Schroedinger equation:

$$\hat{H}\psi(q_i, q_\alpha) = E\psi(q_i, q_\alpha) \tag{13.3}$$

where q_i and q_α symbolize the electronic and nuclear coordinates, respectively. The molecular Hamiltonian (13.1) is formidable enough to strike terror in the heart of any quantum chemist; fortunately there exists a highly accurate, simplifying approximation. The key lies in the fact that nuclei are much heavier than electrons: $m_\alpha \gg m$. Hence the electrons move much faster than the nuclei, and to a good approximation as far as the electrons are concerned, we can regard the nuclei as fixed while the electrons carry out their motions. Speaking classically, during the time of a cycle of electronic motion, the change in nuclear configuration is negligible. Thus, considering the nuclei as fixed, we omit the nuclear kinetic-energy terms from (13.1) to obtain the Schroedinger equation for electronic motion:

$$(\hat{H}_{el} + V_{NN})\psi_{el} = U\psi_{el} \tag{13.4}$$

where the *purely electronic Hamiltonian* $\hat{H}_{el}$ is

$$\hat{H}_{el} = -\frac{\hbar^2}{2m}\sum_i \nabla_i^2 - \sum_\alpha \sum_i \frac{Z_\alpha e^2}{r_{i\alpha}} + \sum_j \sum_{i>j} \frac{e^2}{r_{ij}} \tag{13.5}$$

The electronic Hamiltonian including nuclear repulsion is $\hat{H}_{el} + V_{NN}$. The nuclear-repulsion term V_{NN} is given by

$$V_{NN} = \sum_\alpha \sum_{\beta > \alpha} \frac{Z_\alpha Z_\beta e^2}{r_{\alpha\beta}} \tag{13.6}$$

The energy U in (13.4) is the electronic energy including the energy of nuclear repulsion. The internuclear distances $r_{\alpha\beta}$ in (13.4) are not variables, but are each fixed at some constant value. Of course, there are an infinite number of possible nuclear configurations, and for each of these we may solve the electronic Schroedinger equation (13.4) to get a set of electronic wave functions (and corresponding electronic energies); each member of the set corresponds to a different molecular electronic state. The electronic wave functions and energies thus depend parametrically on the nuclear configuration:

$$\psi_{el} = \psi_{el,n}(q_i; q_\alpha)$$
$$U = U_n(q_\alpha)$$

where n symbolizes the electronic quantum numbers.

The variables in the electronic Schroedinger equation (13.4) are the electronic coordinates. The quantity V_{NN} is independent of these coordinates and is a constant for a given nuclear configuration. Now it is easily proved (Problem 4.20) that the omission of a constant term C from the Hamiltonian doesn't affect the wave functions, and simply decreases each energy eigenvalue by C. Hence if V_{NN} is omitted from (13.4), we get

$$\hat{H}_{el}\psi_{el} = E_{el}\psi_{el} \tag{13.7}$$

where the *purely electronic energy* E_{el} is related to the electronic energy including internuclear repulsion by

$$U = E_{el} + V_{NN} \qquad (13.8)$$

We can thus omit the internuclear repulsion from the electronic Schroedinger equation and simply add it to E_{el} after solving (13.7).

For the hydrogen molecule, with the two protons at a fixed distance $r_{\alpha\beta} = R$, the purely electronic Hamiltonian is given by (13.2) with the first, second, and fifth terms omitted; the nuclear repulsion V_{NN} equals e^2/R. The purely electronic Hamiltonian involves the six electronic coordinates $x_1, y_1, z_1, x_2, y_2, z_2$, and involves the nuclear coordinates as parameters.

The electronic Schroedinger equation (13.4) can be dealt with by approximate methods to be discussed later. If we plot the electronic energy including nuclear repulsion for a bound state of a diatomic molecule against the internuclear distance R, we find a curve like Fig. 13.1. At $R = 0$, the internuclear repulsion causes U to go to infinity. The internuclear separation at the minimum in this curve is called the *equilibrium internuclear distance* R_e. The difference between the limiting value of U at infinite internuclear separation and its value at R_e is called the *equilibrium dissociation energy* D_e:

$$D_e \equiv U(\infty) - U(R_e) \qquad (13.9)$$

It should be noted that D_e differs from the experimental dissociation energy. When one considers nuclear motion (*Gatz*, Chap. 19), one finds that although the lowest molecular state has zero rotational energy, it has a nonzero vibrational energy—the zero-point energy. (Recall the harmonic oscillator.) The dissociation energy of a diatomic molecule in the ground state of nuclear motion for a particular electronic state is designated D_0. If we approximate the nuclear vibrations by those of a harmonic oscillator of frequency ν, we have $D_0 \approx D_e - \frac{1}{2}h\nu$.

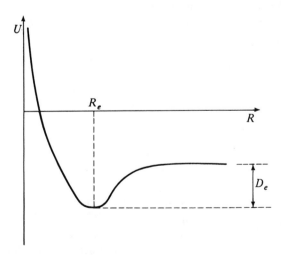

FIGURE 13.1 *Electronic energy of a diatomic molecule bound state, nuclear repulsion included.*

No doubt you are familiar with tables of bond energies. It might be thought that D_0 of the ground electronic state is identical with the tabulated bond energy, but this is not so. Bond energies[1] are usually tabulated as the enthalpy change for the dissociation reaction at 25°C and one atmosphere pressure. For $H_2 \rightarrow 2H$, we have $\Delta H^\circ_{298} = 104.16$ kcal/mole. For an ideal-gas reaction at constant pressure and temperature, the enthalpy and energy changes are related by $\Delta H = \Delta E + RT \Delta n$, where Δn is the change in number of moles of gas, and R is the gas constant. For the dissociation of H_2, we find $\Delta E^\circ_{298} = 103.57$ kcal/mole, which is an energy change of 4.491 eV/molecule. This is not D_0, however. The ground electronic state D_0 is the energy change for the dissociation reaction with all species in their ground states of electronic and nuclear motion, i.e., at 0°K. At 298°K, we have translational energy for the atoms and the molecule, and rotational energy for the molecule. Usually the energy differences between the ground and first excited electronic states and the ground and first excited vibrational states are too large to have appreciable population of excited electronic or vibrational states at room temperature. (Recall the form of the Boltzmann distribution law.) When we allow for the energy change on raising the atoms and molecules from absolute zero to 298°K, we find (Problem 13.2) that for H_2 $D_0 = 4.478$ eV.

For some electronic states of a molecule, the solution of the electronic Schroedinger equation gives a $U(R)$ curve with no minimum. For this case, we don't have a stable bound state, and the molecule will dissociate. (Examples are some of the states in Fig. 13.4.)

It occasionally happens that an electronic state shows two minima in its potential-energy curve. We shall not consider this case.

Assuming that we have solved the electronic Schroedinger equation (which is quite an assumption), we next consider nuclear motions. According to our picture, the electrons move much faster than the nuclei; when the nuclei change their configuration slightly, say from q'_α to q''_α, the electrons immediately adjust to the change, with the electronic wave function changing from $\psi_{el}(q_i; q'_\alpha)$ to $\psi_{el}(q_i; q''_\alpha)$, and the electronic energy changing from $U(q'_\alpha)$ to $U(q''_\alpha)$. Thus, as the nuclei move, the electronic energy varies smoothly as a function of the parameters defining the nuclear configuration, and $U(q_\alpha)$ becomes, in effect, the potential energy for the nuclear motion. The electrons act like a spring connecting the nuclei; as the inter-nuclear distance changes, the energy stored in the spring changes. Hence the Schroedinger equation for nuclear motion is

$$\hat{H}_N \psi_N = E\psi_N \tag{13.10}$$

$$\hat{H}_N = -\frac{\hbar^2}{2} \sum_\alpha \frac{1}{m_\alpha} \nabla_\alpha^2 + U(q_\alpha) \tag{13.11}$$

The variables in the nuclear Schroedinger equation are the nuclear coordinates, symbolized by q_α. The energy eigenvalue E in (13.10) is the *total* energy of the molecule, since the Hamiltonian (13.11) includes operators for both nuclear energy and electronic energy. E is of course simply a number, and does not depend on any

---

[1] See S. W. Benson, *J. Chem. Educ.*, **42**, 502 (1965).

coordinates. Note that for each electronic state of a molecule, one must solve a different nuclear Schroedinger equation, since U differs from state to state. In this chapter we will concentrate on the electronic Schroedinger equation (13.4).

The approximation of separating electronic and nuclear motion is called the *Born–Oppenheimer approximation*,[2] and is basic to quantum chemistry. Born and Oppenheimer's mathematical treatment showed that the true molecular wave function is adequately approximated as:

$$\psi(q_i, q_\alpha) = \psi_{el}(q_i; q_\alpha)\psi_N(q_\alpha) \tag{13.12}$$

if $(m/m_\alpha)^{1/4} \ll 1$. The Born–Oppenheimer approximation introduces little error for the ground electronic states of diatomic molecules. Corrections for excited electronic states are larger than for the ground state, but still are generally negligible as compared to the errors introduced by the approximations used to solve the electronic Schroedinger equation of a many-electron molecule. Hence, we will not worry about corrections to the Born–Oppenheimer approximation.

13.2 Atomic Units

Up to this point, we have used cgs Gaussian units; however, most quantum chemists report the results of their calculations in atomic units. *Atomic units* (also called Hartree units) are defined as follows.[3] The unit of mass is the electron's mass m, rather than the gram; the unit of charge is the proton's charge e, rather than the statcoulomb; the unit of angular momentum is $\hbar$ rather than the g cm^2/sec. (The atomic unit of mass used in quantum chemistry should not be confused with the quantity 1 amu, which is $\frac{1}{12}$th the mass of a C^{12} atom.)

In cgs Gaussian units the hydrogenlike-atom Hamiltonian is (assuming infinite nuclear mass):

$$-\frac{\hbar^2}{2m}\nabla^2 - \frac{Ze^2}{r} \tag{13.13}$$

When we switch to atomic units, $\hbar$, m, and e each have a numerical value of 1; hence, to change a formula from cgs units to atomic units, we simply set these quantities equal to 1. Thus, in atomic units the hydrogenlike Hamiltonian is $-\frac{1}{2}\nabla^2 - Z/r$, where r is now measured in atomic units of length, rather than in centimeters as in (13.13). The ground-state energy of the hydrogenlike atom is given by (6.107) as $-\frac{1}{2}Z^2(e^2/a_0)$. Since [Eq. (6.125)] $a_0 = \hbar^2/me^2$, the numerical value of a_0 in atomic units is 1, and the ground-state energy of the hydrogenlike atom has the numerical value (neglecting nuclear motion) $-\frac{1}{2}Z^2$ in atomic units.

The atomic unit of energy, e^2/a_0, is called the *hartree*:

$$1 \text{ hartree} = e^2/a_0 = 27.212 \text{ eV} \tag{13.14}$$

---

[2] The American physicist J. Robert Oppenheimer was a postdoctoral student of Born in 1927.
[3] H. Shull and G. G. Hall, *Nature*, **184**, 1559 (1959).

The ground-state energy of the hydrogen atom is $-\frac{1}{2}$ hartree, if nuclear motion is neglected. Unfortunately, some workers report energies in *rydbergs*, where 1 rydberg $= e^2/2a_0 = \frac{1}{2}$ hartree.

The atomic unit of length is called the *bohr*:

$$1 \text{ bohr} = a_0 = 0.52918 \text{ Å} \tag{13.15}$$

Use of atomic units saves time by eliminating m, e, and $\hbar$ from equations. Also, if the results of a quantum-mechanical calculation are reported in eV or ergs, the value given depends on the currently accepted values of the physical constants; reporting results in atomic units avoids this.

Atomic units will be used in Chapters 13 and 15.

13.3 The Hydrogen Molecule Ion

We now begin the study of the electronic energies of molecules. We will use the Born–Oppenheimer approximation, keeping the nuclei fixed while we solve, as best we can, the Schroedinger equation for the motion of the electrons. We will always be considering an isolated molecule, ignoring intermolecular interactions. Our results will be most applicable to molecules in the gas phase at low pressure.

We start with diatomic molecules, the simplest of which is H_2^+, the hydrogen molecule ion, consisting of two protons and one electron. (H_2^+ was discovered by J. J. Thomson in cathode rays.) Just as the one-electron hydrogen atom serves as a starting point in the discussion of many-electron atoms, the one-electron hydrogen molecular ion furnishes many ideas useful for discussing many-electron diatomic molecules. The electronic Schroedinger equation for H_2^+ is separable, and we can obtain exact solutions for the eigenfunctions and eigenvalues.

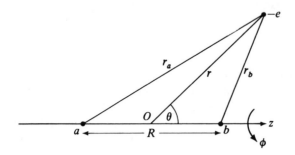

FIGURE 13.2 *The H_2^+ molecule.*

Figure 13.2 shows H_2^+. The nuclei are at a and b; R is the internuclear distance; r_a and r_b are the distances from the electron to nuclei a and b. Since the nuclei are fixed, we have a one-particle problem whose Hamiltonian is [Eq. (13.5)]:

$$-\frac{\hbar^2}{2m}\nabla^2 - \frac{e^2}{r_a} - \frac{e^2}{r_b}$$

The first term is the electronic kinetic-energy operator; the second and third terms are the attractions between the electron and the nuclei. In atomic units, the purely electronic Hamiltonian for H_2^+ is:

$$\hat{H}_{el} = -\tfrac{1}{2}\nabla^2 - \frac{1}{r_a} - \frac{1}{r_b} \tag{13.16}$$

In Fig. 13.2 the coordinate origin is on the internuclear axis, midway between the nuclei, with the z axis lying along the internuclear axis. We might attempt to solve the electronic Schroedinger equation using the spherical polar coordinates (r, θ, φ) of the electron, expressing r_a and r_b in these coordinates (Problem 13.5). We would find that the Schroedinger equation is not separable in spherical polar coordinates. However, Burrau showed in 1927 that separation of variables is possible using *confocal elliptic coordinates* ξ, η, φ. The coordinate φ is the angle of rotation of the electron about the internuclear (z) axis, the same as in spherical polar coordinates. The coordinates ξ (xi) and η (eta) are defined by

$$\xi = \frac{r_a + r_b}{R}, \qquad \eta = \frac{r_a - r_b}{R} \tag{13.17}$$

The ranges of these coordinates are (Problem 13.5):

$$0 \leqslant \varphi \leqslant 2\pi, \qquad 1 \leqslant \xi \leqslant \infty, \qquad -1 \leqslant \eta \leqslant 1 \tag{13.18}$$

(Instead of ξ and η, some people use λ and μ, respectively; still another notation for these coordinates is μ and ν.)

We must put the Hamiltonian (13.16) into these coordinates. We have

$$r_a = \tfrac{1}{2}R(\xi + \eta), \qquad r_b = \tfrac{1}{2}R(\xi - \eta) \tag{13.19}$$

We also need the expression for the Laplacian in confocal elliptic coordinates. One way to find this is to express ξ, η, and φ in terms of x, y, and z, the Cartesian coordinates of the electron, and then use the chain rule to find $\partial/\partial x$, $\partial/\partial y$, and $\partial/\partial z$ in terms of $\partial/\partial\xi$, $\partial/\partial\eta$, and $\partial/\partial\varphi$. We then form the operator (3.55). [We used this procedure to derive Eq. (6.6).] We omit the long, tiresome details and simply state the result[4]:

$$\nabla^2 = \frac{4}{R^2(\xi^2 - \eta^2)}\left[(\xi^2 - 1)\frac{\partial^2}{\partial\xi^2} + 2\xi\frac{\partial}{\partial\xi} + (1 - \eta^2)\frac{\partial^2}{\partial\eta^2} - 2\eta\frac{\partial}{\partial\eta}\right.$$

$$\left. + \left(\frac{1}{\xi^2 - 1} + \frac{1}{1 - \eta^2}\right)\frac{\partial^2}{\partial\varphi^2}\right] \tag{13.20}$$

The H_2^+ electronic Hamiltonian (13.16) in atomic units is

$$\hat{H}_{el} = -\frac{2}{R^2(\xi^2 - \eta^2)}\left[(\xi^2 - 1)\frac{\partial^2}{\partial\xi^2} + 2\xi\frac{\partial}{\partial\xi} + (1 - \eta^2)\frac{\partial^2}{\partial\eta^2} - 2\eta\frac{\partial}{\partial\eta}\right.$$

$$\left. + \left(\frac{1}{\xi^2 - 1} + \frac{1}{1 - \eta^2}\right)\frac{\partial^2}{\partial\varphi^2}\right] - \frac{2}{R(\xi + \eta)} - \frac{2}{R(\xi - \eta)} \tag{13.21}$$

[4] For a systematic discussion, see *Margenau and Murphy*, Chapter 5.

We could now form the electronic Schroedinger equation (13.7) and carry out a separation of variables. However, we can save time by considering the electronic angular momentum. For the hydrogen atom, the operators $\hat{L}^2$ and $\hat{L}_z$ both commute with the Hamiltonian. For H_2^+ we no longer have spherical symmetry, and we would find that $[\hat{L}^2, \hat{H}_{el}] \neq 0$. However, we do have axial symmetry, and we can show that $\hat{L}_z$ commutes with $\hat{H}_{el}$. $\hat{L}_z$ is given by (5.96) and involves only φ; hence in calculating the commutator, we need only consider the part of $\hat{H}_{el}$ that involves φ; we have (in atomic units):

$$[\hat{L}_z, \hat{H}_{el}] = \left[-i\frac{\partial}{\partial\varphi}, -\frac{2}{R^2(\xi^2 - \eta^2)}\left(\frac{1}{\xi^2 - 1} + \frac{1}{1 - \eta^2}\right)\frac{\partial^2}{\partial\varphi^2} \right] = 0$$

Therefore the electronic wave functions can be chosen to be eigenfunctions of $\hat{L}_z$; the eigenfunctions of $\hat{L}_z$ are [Eq. (5.114)]

$$\text{constant} \cdot (2\pi)^{-1/2} e^{im\varphi} \tag{13.22}$$

$$m = 0, \pm 1, \pm 2, \pm 3, \dots \tag{13.23}$$

The z component of electronic orbital angular momentum in H_2^+ is $m\hbar$ in cgs units or m in atomic units. The total electronic orbital angular momentum is not a constant for H_2^+.

The "constant" in (13.22) is a constant only as far as $\partial/\partial\varphi$ is concerned, so that the H_2^+ wave functions have the form

$$\psi_{el} = F(\xi, \eta)(2\pi)^{-1/2} e^{im\varphi} \tag{13.24}$$

We now try a separation of variables:

$$\psi_{el} = L(\xi) M(\eta)(2\pi)^{-1/2} e^{im\varphi} \tag{13.25}$$

Substitution of (13.25) into the electronic Schroedinger equation (13.7) leads to an equation in which the variables are separable; we are led to the two ordinary differential equations (Problem 13.3):

$$(\xi^2 - 1)L'' + 2\xi L' + \left(A + 2R\xi + \tfrac{1}{2}E_{el}R^2\xi^2 - \frac{m^2}{\xi^2 - 1}\right)L = 0 \tag{13.26}$$

$$(1 - \eta^2)M'' - 2\eta M' - \left(A + \tfrac{1}{2}E_{el}R^2\eta^2 + \frac{m^2}{1 - \eta^2}\right)M = 0 \tag{13.27}$$

where A is the separation constant.

Solving these equations is involved, and we simply sketch the results. The solution for $M(\eta)$ is an infinite series of associated Legendre functions. $L(\xi)$ also involves an infinite series. The values of the coefficients in the series for L and M are available. The requirement that the wave function be well behaved leads to the conclusion that for a fixed value of R, only certain values of E_{el} are allowed; this gives a series of electronic states. There is no algebraic formula for E_{el}; it must be calculated numerically for each desired value of R for each state. Tables of E_{el} are available.[5]

For the ground electronic state, the quantum number m is zero. At $R = \infty$ the H_2^+ ground state is dissociated into a proton and a ground-state hydrogen atom; hence $E_{el}(\infty) = -\frac{1}{2}$ hartree. At $R = 0$, the two protons have come together to form the He^+ ion with ground-state energy: $-\frac{1}{2}(2)^2$ hartrees $= -2$ hartrees. Addition of the internuclear repulsion $1/R$ (in atomic units) to $E_{el}(R)$ gives the $U(R)$ potential-energy curve for nuclear motion. Plots of the ground-state $E_{el}(R)$ and $U(R)$, as found from solution of the electronic Schroedinger equation are shown in Fig. 13.3. At $R = \infty$ the internuclear repulsion is 0, and U is $-\frac{1}{2}$ hartree.

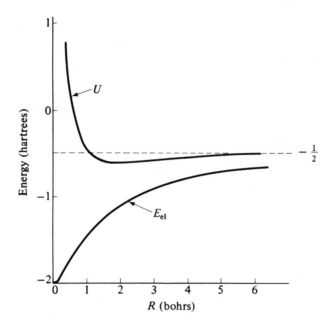

FIGURE 13.3 *Electronic energy with (U) and without (E_{el}) nuclear repulsion for the H_2^+ ground state.*

The $U(R)$ curve is found to have a minimum at [see J. L. Schaad and W. V. Hicks, *J. Chem. Phys.*, **53**, 851 (1970)]:

$$R_e = 1.9972 \text{ bohrs} \approx 2.00 \text{ bohrs} = 1.06 \text{ Å}$$

indicating that the H_2^+ ground electronic state is a stable bound state. The calculated value of E_{el} at 1.9972 bohrs is -1.1033 hartrees; addition of the internuclear repulsion $1/R$ gives $U(R_e) = -0.6026$ hartree, compared to -0.5000 hartree at

[5] D. R. Bates, K. Ledsham, and A. L. Stewart, *Phil. Trans. Roy. Soc.*, **A246**, 215 (1953). The wave functions given by Bates *et al.* are not normalized. For the normalization constants, see E. M. Roberts, M. R. Foster, and F. F. Selig, *J. Chem. Phys.*, **37**, 485 (1962). For accurate ground-state energy values, see H. Wind, *J. Chem. Phys.*, **42**, 2371 (1965).

$R = \infty$. Thus the ground-state binding energy is

$$D_e = 0.1026 \text{ hartree} = 2.79 \text{ eV} = 64.4 \text{ kcal/mole} \qquad \textbf{(13.28)}$$

The binding energy is only 17 percent of the total energy at the equilibrium inter-nuclear distance. Thus a reasonably small error in the total energy can correspond to a large error in the binding energy. For heavier molecules the situation is even worse, since chemical binding energies are of the same order of magnitude (100 kcal/mole) for most diatomic molecules, but the total electronic energy increases markedly for heavier molecules.

Note that the single electron in H_2^+ is sufficient to give a stable bound state.

Figure 13.4 shows the $U(R)$ curves for the first several electronic energy levels of H_2^+, as calculated from the solutions to the Schroedinger equation. Each H_2^+ state has a definite value for m. Of course, since this is a three-dimensional

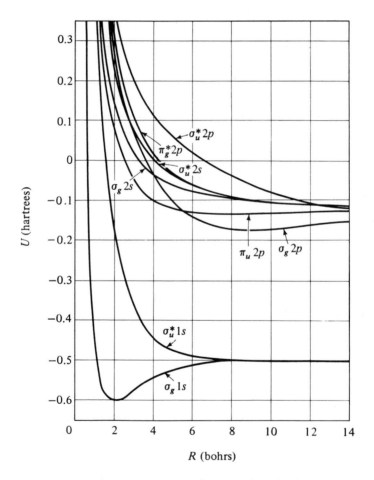

FIGURE 13.4 *Potential-energy curves for several* H_2^+ *electronic states.* [*Curves taken from J. C. Slater,* Quantum Theory of Molecules and Solids, *vol. 1, McGraw-Hill, New York, 1963. Used by permission.*]

problem, the value of the single quantum number m does not specify the state uniquely; we have two other quantum numbers, which specify which solutions of the two differential equations (13.27) and (13.26) are used. These quantum numbers give the number of nodes in the ξ and η factors of the wave function; we shall not make any further reference to them.

Note that m enters Eqs. (13.27) and (13.26) as m^2; hence the electronic energy depends only on $|m|$. Each electronic energy level with $m \neq 0$ is doubly degenerate, corresponding to states with quantum numbers $+|m|$ and $-|m|$. In the standard notation[6] for diatomic molecules, the absolute value of m is called λ:

$$\lambda = |m|$$

(Some texts define λ as identical to m.) Somewhat similar to the s, p, d, f notation for hydrogen-atom states, a letter code is used to specify λ, the absolute value (in atomic units) of the component along the molecular axis of the electron's orbital angular momentum:

λ	0	1	2	3	4
letter	σ	π	δ	φ	γ

Thus the lowest H_2^+ electronic state is a σ state.

Besides classifying the states of H_2^+ according to λ, we can also classify them according to their parity (Section 7.5). From Fig. 13.11, inversion of the electron's coordinates through the origin O changes φ to $\varphi + \pi$, r_a to r_b, and r_b to r_a; this leaves the potential-energy part of the electronic Hamiltonian (13.16) unchanged. We previously showed the kinetic-energy operator to be invariant under inversion. Hence the parity operator commutes with the Hamiltonian (13.16), and the H_2^+ electronic wave functions can be classified as either even or odd. For even electronic wave functions, we use the subscript g (from the German word *gerade*, meaning even); for odd wave functions, we use u (from *ungerade*).

We further classify the H_2^+ electronic energy levels according to the state of the hydrogen atom obtained on dissociation, writing this state following the symbol for λ. Thus the two lowest levels dissociate to a $1s$ hydrogen atom. The significance of the star in Fig. 13.4 will be explained later.

For completeness we must take spin into account by multiplying each spatial H_2^+ electronic wave function by α or β, depending on whether the component of electron spin along the internuclear axis is $+\frac{1}{2}$ or $-\frac{1}{2}$ (in atomic units). Inclusion of spin doubles the degeneracy of all levels.

The Schroedinger equation for any one-electron diatomic molecule is separable in elliptical coordinates; thus the electronic energies for the heteronuclear diatomic molecule HeH^{++} are available.[7]

In the rest of this chapter, we will drop the subscript el from the electronic wave function, Hamiltonian, and energy; it will be understood in Chapters 13 and 15 that ψ means ψ_{el}.

---

[6] F. A. Jenkins, *J. Opt. Soc. Am.*, **43**, 425 (1953).
[7] D. R. Bates and T. R. Carson, *Proc. Roy. Soc.*, **A234**, 207 (1956).

13.4 Approximate Treatments of the H_2^+ Ground Electronic State

For a many-electron atom, the self-consistent-field (SCF) method is used to construct an approximate wave function as a Slater determinant of (one-electron) spin-orbitals. The one-electron spatial part of a spin-orbital is an atomic orbital (AO). We took each AO as a product of a spherical harmonic and a radial factor; as an initial approximation to the radial factors, we can use hydrogenlike radial functions with effective nuclear charges.

For many-electron molecules, which (unlike H_2^+) cannot be solved exactly, we want to use many of the ideas of the SCF treatment of atoms. We will write an approximate molecular electronic wave function as a Slater determinant of (one-electron) spin-orbitals. The one-electron spatial part of a molecular spin-orbital will be called a *molecular orbital* (MO). Because of the Pauli principle, each MO can hold no more than two electrons, just as for AO's. What kind of functions do we use for the MO's? Ideally, the analytic form of each MO is found by an SCF calculation. Such calculations are difficult for molecules, and accurate SCF molecular wave functions first became available in the 1960's. We seek a simple approximation for the MO's which will enable us to gain some qualitative understanding of chemical bonding. Just as we took the angular part of each AO to be the same kind of function (a spherical harmonic) as in the one-electron hydrogenlike atom, we will take the angular part of each diatomic MO to be $(2\pi)^{-1/2}e^{im\varphi}$, as in H_2^+. However, the ξ and η factors in the H_2^+ wave functions are complicated functions and do not readily lend themselves for use in MO calculations. We therefore seek simpler functions that will provide reasonably accurate approximations to the H_2^+ wave functions, and which can serve to construct molecular orbitals for many-electron diatomic molecules. With this discussion as motivation for looking at approximate solutions in a case where the Schroedinger equation is exactly soluble, we consider approximate treatments of H_2^+.

We will use the variation method, writing down some function containing several parameters, and varying them to minimize the variational integral. This will give an approximation to the ground-state wave function and an upper bound to the ground-state energy. By use of the factor $e^{im\varphi}$ in the trial function, we can get an upper bound to the energy of the lowest H_2^+ level for any given value of m (see Section 8.2). By using linear variation functions, we can get approximations for excited states.

The H_2^+ ground state has $m = 0$ and the wave function depends only on ξ and η. We could try any well-behaved function of these coordinates as a trial variation function; we will, however, use a more systematic approach based on the idea of a molecule as being formed from the interaction of atoms.

Consider what the H_2^+ wave function would look like for large values of the internuclear separation R. When the electron is near nucleus a, nucleus b is so far away that we essentially have a hydrogen atom with origin at a; thus when r_a is small, the ground-state H_2^+ electronic wave function should resemble the ground-state hydrogen-atom wave function of Eq. (6.120). We have $Z = 1$, and the Bohr radius a_0 has the numerical value 1 in atomic units; hence (6.120) becomes

$$\pi^{-1/2}e^{-r_a} \tag{13.29}$$

Similarly, we conclude that when the electron is near nucleus b, the H_2^+ ground-state wave function will be approximated by

$$\pi^{-1/2}e^{-r_b} \tag{13.30}$$

These considerations suggest that we try as a variation function:

$$c_1\pi^{-1/2}e^{-r_a} + c_2\pi^{-1/2}e^{-r_b} \tag{13.31}$$

where c_1 and c_2 are variational parameters. When the electron is near nucleus a, the variable r_a is small and r_b is large, so that the first term in (13.31) predominates, giving a function resembling (13.29). The function (13.31) is a linear variation function, and we are led to solve a secular equation, which has the form (8.87), where the subscripts 1 and 2 refer to the functions (13.29) and (13.30).

We can also approach the problem using perturbation theory. We take the unperturbed system as the H_2^+ molecule with $R = \infty$. For $R = \infty$, the electron can be bound to nucleus a with wave function (13.29), or it can be bound to nucleus b with wave function (13.30). In either case the energy is $-\frac{1}{2}$ hartree, so that we have a doubly degenerate unperturbed energy level. Bringing the nuclei in from infinity gives rise to a perturbation which splits the doubly degenerate unperturbed level into two levels; this is illustrated by the $U(R)$ curves for the two lowest H_2^+ electronic states, which both dissociate to a ground-state hydrogen atom (see Fig. 13.4). The correct zeroth-order wave functions for the perturbed levels are linear combinations of the form (13.31), and we are led to a secular equation of the form (8.87) with W replaced by $E^{(0)} + E^{(1)}$ (see Problem 9.3).

Before proceeding with the solution of (8.87), let us improve the trial function (13.31). Consider the limiting behavior of the H_2^+ ground-state electronic wave function as R goes to zero. In this limit we get the He^+ ion, which has the ground-state wave function [put $Z = 2$ in (6.120)]

$$2^{3/2}\pi^{-1/2}e^{-2r} \tag{13.32}$$

From Fig. 13.2 we see that as R goes to zero, both r_a and r_b go to r; hence as R goes to zero, the trial function (13.31) goes to $(c_1+c_2)\pi^{-1/2}e^{-r}$. Comparing with (13.32), we see that our trial function has the wrong limiting behavior at $R = 0$; it should go to e^{-2r}, not e^{-r}. We can fix things by multiplying r_a and r_b in the exponentials by a variational parameter k, which will be some function of R: $k = k(R)$. For the correct limiting behavior at zero and at infinite internuclear distance, we have

$$k(0) = 2, \qquad k(\infty) = 1$$

for the ground state of H_2^+. Physically, k is some sort of effective nuclear charge, which increases as the nuclei come together. We thus take as the trial function

$$c_a 1s_a + c_b 1s_b \tag{13.33}$$

where the c's are variational parameters, and

$$1s_a = k^{3/2}\pi^{-1/2}e^{-kr_a}, \qquad 1s_b = k^{3/2}\pi^{-1/2}e^{-kr_b} \qquad (13.34)$$

The factor $k^{3/2}$ normalizes $1s_a$ and $1s_b$ [see Eq. (6.120)]. The molecular-orbital function (13.33) is a *linear combination of atomic orbitals*, an LCAO-MO. The trial function (13.33) was first used by Finkelstein and Horowitz in 1928.

For the function (13.33), the secular equation (8.87) is

$$\begin{vmatrix} H_{aa}-WS_{aa} & H_{ab}-WS_{ab} \\ H_{ba}-WS_{ba} & H_{bb}-WS_{bb} \end{vmatrix} = 0 \qquad (13.35)$$

The integrals H_{aa} and H_{bb} are

$$H_{aa} = \int 1s_a^* \hat{H} 1s_a \, dv, \qquad H_{bb} = \int 1s_b^* \hat{H} 1s_b \, dv \qquad (13.36)$$

where the H_2^+ electronic Hamiltonian operator $\hat{H}$ is given by (13.16). These two integrals are called *Coulomb integrals*. [Their form differs considerably from that of the Coulomb integral (9.144); the designation of (13.36) as Coulomb integrals is not really appropriate.] We can relabel the variables in a definite integral without affecting its value; changing a to b and b to a changes $1s_a$ to $1s_b$, but leaves $\hat{H}$ unaffected (this would not be true for a heteronuclear diatomic molecule). Hence $H_{aa} = H_{bb}$. We have

$$H_{ab} = \int 1s_a^* \hat{H} 1s_b \, dv, \qquad H_{ba} = \int 1s_b^* \hat{H} 1s_a \, dv \qquad (13.37)$$

Since $\hat{H}$ is Hermitian and the functions in these integrals are real, we conclude that $H_{ab} = H_{ba}$. The integral H_{ab} is called a *resonance* (or *bond*) *integral*. Since $1s_a$ and $1s_b$ are normalized and real, we have

$$S_{aa} = \int 1s_a^* 1s_a \, dv = 1 = S_{bb} \qquad (13.38)$$

$$S_{ab} = \int 1s_a^* 1s_b \, dv = S_{ba} \qquad (13.39)$$

The secular equation (13.35) becomes

$$\begin{vmatrix} H_{aa}-W & H_{ab}-S_{ab}W \\ H_{ab}-S_{ab}W & H_{aa}-W \end{vmatrix} = 0 \qquad (13.40)$$

$$H_{aa} - W = \pm(H_{ab}-S_{ab}W) \qquad (13.41)$$

$$W_1 = \frac{H_{aa}+H_{ab}}{1+S_{ab}}, \qquad W_2 = \frac{H_{aa}-H_{ab}}{1-S_{ab}} \qquad (13.42)$$

These two roots are upper bounds for the energies of the ground and first excited electronic states of H_2^+.

We now find the coefficients in (13.33) for each of the roots of the secular equation. From Eq. (8.86), we have

$$(H_{aa}-W)c_a + (H_{ab}-S_{ab}W)c_b = 0 \tag{13.43}$$

Substituting in W_1 from (13.42) [or using (13.41)], we get

$$c_a/c_b = 1 \tag{13.44}$$

$$\varphi_1 = c_a(1s_a+1s_b) \tag{13.45}$$

We fix c_a by normalization:

$$|c_a|^2 \int (1s_a^2 + 1s_b^2 + 2 \cdot 1s_a 1s_b) \, dv = 1$$

$$|c_a| = \frac{1}{[2+2S_{ab}]^{1/2}} \tag{13.46}$$

The normalized trial function corresponding to the energy W_1 is thus:

$$\varphi_1 = \frac{1s_a+1s_b}{\sqrt{2}(1+S_{ab})^{1/2}} \tag{13.47}$$

For the root W_2, we find $c_b = -c_a$ and

$$\varphi_2 = \frac{1s_a-1s_b}{\sqrt{2}(1-S_{ab})^{1/2}} \tag{13.48}$$

Equations (13.47) and (13.48) come as no surprise. Since the nuclei are identical, we expect $|\varphi|^2$ to remain unchanged on interchanging a and b; in other words, we expect no polarity in the bond.

Let us now evaluate H_{aa}, H_{ab}, and S_{ab}. [This can be skimmed, if desired; begin reading again after Eq. (13.58).] We begin with the *overlap integral* S_{ab}. From (13.34) and (13.17), we have

$$1s_a 1s_b = k^3 \pi^{-1} e^{-k(r_a+r_b)} = k^3 \pi^{-1} e^{-kR\xi}$$

We need the expression for the volume element dv in elliptic coordinates; this turns out to be (*Eyring, Walter, and Kimball*, Appendix III):

$$dv = \tfrac{1}{8}R^3(\xi^2 - \eta^2) \, d\xi \, d\eta \, d\varphi \tag{13.49}$$

We have

$$S_{ab} = \frac{k^3 R^3}{8\pi} \int_0^{2\pi} d\varphi \int_{-1}^{1} \left[\int_1^{\infty} e^{-kR\xi}(\xi^2 - \eta^2) \, d\xi \right] d\eta \tag{13.50}$$

Using the Appendix integral (A.7), we find

$$\int_1^{\infty} e^{-kR\xi}\xi^2 \, d\xi - \int_1^{\infty} e^{-kR\xi}\eta^2 \, d\xi = \frac{2e^{-kR}}{k^3 R^3}\left(1 + kR + \frac{k^2 R^2}{2}\right) - \eta^2 \frac{e^{-kR}}{kR}$$

Substituting in (13.50) and doing the eta integration, we get

$$S_{ab} = e^{-kR}[1 + kR + \tfrac{1}{3}k^2 R^2] \tag{13.51}$$

Now for H_{aa}. Adding and subtracting k/r_a in (13.16), we get:

$$\hat{H} = \left[-\tfrac{1}{2}\nabla^2 - \frac{k}{r_a} \right] + \frac{(k-1)}{r_a} - \frac{1}{r_b} = \hat{H}_a + \frac{(k-1)}{r_a} - \frac{1}{r_b} \tag{13.52}$$

where $\hat{H}_a$ is the Hamiltonian operator for a hydrogenlike atom of nuclear charge k located at a. Since $1s_a$ is a $1s$ hydrogenlike function for nuclear charge k, we have (Section 13.2):

$$\hat{H}_a 1s_a = -\tfrac{1}{2}k^2 1s_a \tag{13.53}$$

Hence

$$H_{aa} = \int 1s_a^* \left[\hat{H}_a + \frac{(k-1)}{r_a} - \frac{1}{r_b} \right] 1s_a \, dv$$

$$H_{aa} = -\tfrac{1}{2}k^2 + (k-1) \int \frac{1s_a^* 1s_a}{r_a} \, dv - \int \frac{1s_a^* 1s_a}{r_b} \, dv \tag{13.54}$$

The first integral in (13.54) can be done in elliptical coordinates, but it is faster to use spherical polar coordinates with origin at a:

$$\int \frac{1s_a^2}{r_a} \, dv = \frac{k^3}{\pi} \int_0^\infty \frac{e^{-2kr_a}}{r_a} r_a^2 \, dr_a \int_0^{2\pi} d\varphi \int_0^\pi \sin\theta \, d\theta = k \tag{13.55}$$

where Eq. (A.4) has been used. Equations (13.49), (13.34), and (13.19) give for the second integral in (13.54):

$$\int \frac{1s_a^2}{r_b} \, dv = \frac{k^3 R^2}{4\pi} \int_0^{2\pi} d\varphi \int_{-1}^1 e^{-kR\eta} \left[\int_1^\infty e^{-kR\xi}(\xi+\eta) \, d\xi \right] d\eta$$

$$\int \frac{1s_a^2}{r_b} \, dv = \frac{1}{R} - e^{-2kR}\left(\frac{1}{R} + k \right) \tag{13.56}$$

Therefore

$$H_{aa} = \tfrac{1}{2}k^2 - k - \frac{1}{R} + e^{-2kR}\left(k + \frac{1}{R} \right) \tag{13.57}$$

The evaluation of H_{ab} is left as an exercise. We find

$$H_{ab} = -\tfrac{1}{2}k^2 S_{ab} + k(k-2)(1+kR)e^{-kR} \tag{13.58}$$

Substituting the values for the integrals into (13.42), we get

$$W_{1,2} = -\tfrac{1}{2}k^2 + \frac{k^2 - k - R^{-1} + R^{-1}(1+kR)e^{-2kR} \pm k(k-2)(1+kR)e^{-kR}}{1 \pm e^{-kR}(1+kR+k^2R^2/3)} \tag{13.59}$$

where the upper signs are for W_1.

The final task is to vary the parameter k, setting

$$\frac{\partial W_1}{\partial k} = 0, \qquad \frac{\partial W_2}{\partial k} = 0$$

For the procedure used, see Problem 13.8. The results[8] are that for the $1s_a + 1s_b$

---

[8] C. A. Coulson, *Trans. Faraday Soc.*, **33**, 1479 (1937).

function (13.47), the parameter k increases monotonically from 1 to 2 as R decreases from ∞ to 0; for the $1s_a - 1s_b$ function (13.48), k decreases monotonically from 1.0 to 0.4 as R decreases from ∞ to 0. Since k is positive and never greater than 2, and since the overlap integral S_{ab} is positive, we see from (13.58) that the resonance integral H_{ab} is always negative. We conclude from (13.42) that the root W_1 corresponds to the ground electronic state $\sigma_g 1s$ of $H_2{}^+$. For the ground state, one finds

$$k(R_e) = 1.24$$

We might ask why the variational parameter k for the $\sigma_u^* 1s$ state goes to 0.4, rather than to 2, as R goes to zero. The answer is that this state of $H_2{}^+$ does not go to the ground state ($1s$) of He^+ as R goes to zero. The $\sigma_u^* 1s$ state has odd parity and must correlate with an odd state of He^+. The lowest odd states of He^+ are the $2p$ states (Section 11.5); since the $\sigma_u^* 1s$ state has zero electronic orbital angular momentum along the internuclear (z) axis, this state must go to an atomic $2p$ state with $m = 0$, i.e., to the $2p_0 = 2p_z$ state.

Having found $k(R)$ for each root, we can calculate the variational approximation to the energies from (13.59). To find the $U(R)$ curves, we add the internuclear repulsion $1/R$ to W. The calculated ground-state $U(R)$ curve has a minimum at 2.02 bohrs, in good agreement with the true value 2.00 bohrs; the total energy at this distance is found to be 15.95 eV, giving a binding energy of 2.35 eV, as compared to the true value 2.79 eV [Eq. (13.28)]. (If we omit varying k, but simply set it equal to 1, we get $R_e = 2.50$ bohrs, $D_e = 1.76$ eV.)

Now consider the appearance of the trial functions for the $\sigma_g 1s$ and $\sigma_u^* 1s$ states at intermediate values of R. Figure 13.5 shows the values of the functions $(1s_a)^2$ and $(1s_b)^2$ at points on the internuclear axis (see also Fig. 6.6). For the $\sigma_g 1s$ function $1s_a + 1s_b$, we get a buildup of electronic probability density between the

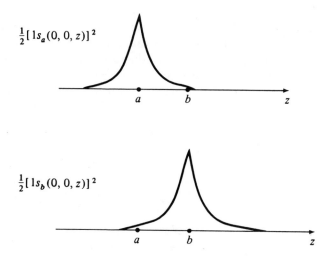

FIGURE 13.5 *Atomic charge probability densities for* $H_2{}^+$. *Note the cusps at the nuclei.*

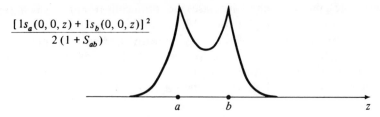

$$\frac{[1s_a(0, 0, z) + 1s_b(0, 0, z)]^2}{2(1 + S_{ab})}$$

a   b   z

FIGURE 13.6 *Charge probability density for the* LCAO-MO *function* $1s_a + 1s_b$.

nuclei, as shown in Fig. 13.6. It is especially significant that the buildup of charge between the nuclei is greater than that obtained by simply taking the sum of the separate atomic charge densities. The charge probability density for an electron in a $1s_a$ atomic orbital is $-(1s_a)^2$. (The electron's charge is -1 in atomic units.) If we add the charge probability density for half an electron in a $1s_a$ atomic orbital and half an electron in a $1s_b$ atomic orbital, we get

$$-\tfrac{1}{2}[1s_a^2 + 1s_b^2] \tag{13.60}$$

However, in quantum mechanics we don't add the separate atomic charge probability densities; instead, we add the wave functions, as in (13.47). The charge probability density for the H_2^+ ground state is then

$$-\varphi_1^2 = -\frac{1}{2(1 + S_{ab})}[1s_a^2 + 1s_b^2 + 2 \cdot 1s_a 1s_b] \tag{13.61}$$

The difference between (13.61) and (13.60) is

$$-\frac{1}{2(1 + S_{ab})}[2 \cdot 1s_a 1s_b - S_{ab}(1s_a^2 + 1s_b^2)] \tag{13.62}$$

Putting $R = 2.00$ and $k = 1.24$ in Eq. (13.51), we find that the overlap integral S_{ab} equals 0.46 at R_e. (It might be thought that because of the orthogonality of different AO's, the integral S_{ab} should be zero. However, the AO's $1s_a$ and $1s_b$ are eigenfunctions of *different* Hamiltonian operators, one for a hydrogen atom at a, and one for a hydrogen atom at b; hence the orthogonality theorem doesn't apply.) Consider

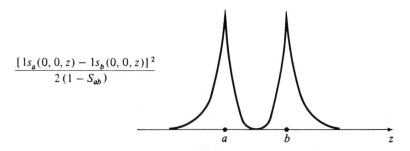

$$\frac{[1s_a(0, 0, z) - 1s_b(0, 0, z)]^2}{2(1 - S_{ab})}$$

a   b   z

FIGURE 13.7 *Charge probability density for the* LCAO-MO *function* $1s_a - 1s_b$.

now the relative magnitudes of the two terms in brackets in (13.62) for points on the molecular axis. To the left of nucleus a, the function $1s_b$ is very small; to the right of nucleus b, the function $1s_a$ is very small. Hence in the regions outside the nuclei, the product $1s_a 1s_b$ is small, and the second term in (13.62) is dominant. This gives a subtraction of electronic charge density in the regions outside the nuclei, as compared to the sum of the densities of the individual atoms. Now consider the region between the nuclei. At the midpoint of the internuclear axis (and anywhere on the plane perpendicular to the axis and bisecting it), we have $1s_a = 1s_b$, and the bracketed terms in (13.62) become $2(1s_a)^2 - 0.92(1s_a)^2 \approx 1s_a^2$, which is positive. We thus get a buildup of charge probability density between the nuclei in the molecule, as compared to the sum of the densities of the individual atoms. This buildup of electronic charge between the nuclei allows the electron to feel the attractions of both nuclei at the same time, which lowers its potential energy. The greater the overlap in the internuclear region between the atomic orbitals forming the bond, the greater the charge buildup in this region, giving the familiar "principle of maximum overlap." [Our argument has been based on the approximate wave function (13.47). If we plot Fig. 13.6 using the true wave function, we get a very similar graph, except that the true wave function is somewhat larger between the nuclei, and somewhat smaller outside the internuclear region, than (13.47).]

The preceding discussion seems to attribute the bonding in H_2^+ mainly to the lowering in the average electronic potential energy that results from having the shared electron interact with two nuclei instead of one. This, however, is an incomplete picture. Calculations on H_2^+ by Feinberg and Ruedenberg show that the decrease in electronic potential energy due to the sharing is of the same order of magnitude as the nuclear repulsion energy $1/R$, and hence is insufficient by itself to give binding. Two other effects also contribute to the bonding. The increase in atomic orbital exponent ($k = 1.24$ at R_e versus 1.0 at ∞) causes charge to accumulate near the nuclei (as well as in the internuclear region) and this further lowers the electronic potential energy. Moreover, the buildup of charge in the internuclear region makes $\partial\psi/\partial z$ zero at the midpoint of the molecular axis and small in the region close to this point; hence the z component of the average electronic kinetic energy [which can be expressed as $\frac{1}{2}\int |\partial\psi/\partial z|^2 \, d\tau$; Problem 7.3] is lowered as compared to the atomic $\langle T_z \rangle$. (However, the *total* average electronic kinetic energy is raised; see Section 14.2.) For further details, see M. J. Feinberg and K. Ruedenberg, *J. Chem. Phys.*, **54**, 1495 (1971). Wilson and Goddard have also emphasized the important role of kinetic energy in bonding. [C. W. Wilson and W. A. Goddard, *Chem. Phys. Letters*, **5**, 45 (1970); *Theor. Chim. Acta*, **26**, 195 (1972); W. A. Goddard and C. W. Wilson, *ibid.*, **26**, 211.] Further study is needed before the origin of the covalent bond can be considered a settled question.

The $\sigma_u^* 1s$ trial function $1s_a - 1s_b$ is proportional to: $e^{-r_a} - e^{-r_b}$. On a plane perpendicular to the internuclear axis and midway between the nuclei, we have $r_a = r_b$, so that this plane is a nodal plane for the $\sigma_u^* 1s$ function. We don't get a buildup of charge between the nuclei for this state, and the $U(R)$ curve has no minimum. We say that the $\sigma_g 1s$ orbital is *bonding* and the $\sigma_u^* 1s$ orbital is *antibonding*.

Reflection of the electron's coordinates in the σ_h symmetry plane perpendicular to the molecular axis and midway between the nuclei converts r_a to r_b, r_b to

r_a, and leaves φ unchanged (Eq. 13.75). The operator $\hat{O}_{\sigma_h}$ (Section 12.1) commutes with the electronic Hamiltonian (13.16) and with the parity (inversion) operator. Hence, we can choose the H_2^+ wave functions to be eigenfunctions of this reflection operator, as well as of the parity operator. Since the square of this reflection operator is the unit operator, its eigenvalues must be $+1$ and -1 (Section 7.5). States of H_2^+ for which the wave function changes sign upon reflection in this plane (eigenvalue -1) are indicated by a star as a superscript to the letter that specifies λ; states whose wave functions are unchanged on reflection in this plane are left unstarred. Since orbitals with eigenvalue -1 for this reflection have a nodal plane between the nuclei, starred orbitals are antibonding.

Instead of using graphs, we can make contour diagrams of the orbitals (Section 6.6); see Fig. 13.8.

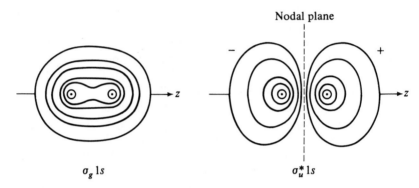

FIGURE 13.8   *Contours of constant $|\psi|$ for the $\sigma_g 1s$ and $\sigma_u^* 1s$ MO's. The three-dimensional contour surfaces are generated by rotating these figures about the z axis. Note the resemblance of the antibonding MO contours to those of a $2p_z$ AO.*

We might compare the preceding treatment of H_2^+ with the perturbation treatment of the helium $1s2s$ levels (Section 9.7). There we started with the degenerate functions $1s(1) 2s(2)$ and $1s(2) 2s(1)$. Because of the symmetry of the Hamiltonian with respect to interchange of the identical electrons, we found the correct zeroth-order functions to be (9.161) and (9.162). For H_2^+ we started with the degenerate functions $1s_a$ and $1s_b$. Because of the symmetry of the electronic Hamiltonian with respect to the identical nuclei, we found the correct zeroth-order functions to be (13.47) and (13.48).

Sometimes one speaks of a resonance "phenomenon" in H_2^+, saying that the electron resonates back and forth between the $1s$ orbital on nucleus a and the $1s$ orbital on nucleus b. Just as with "exchange" in helium, there is no physical reality to such a "phenomenon." The electron in the ground state of H_2^+ is in neither the $1s_a$ orbital nor the $1s_b$ orbital, but is in a molecular orbital that (in the zeroth-order approximation) is a linear combination of both AO's. A state where the electron "resonated" between different orbitals would be a nonstationary state, whereas we are dealing with the stationary states of the molecule.

Sometimes one attributes the binding in H_2^+ to the resonance integral H_{ab}, since in the approximate treatment we have given, it provides most of the binding energy. This viewpoint is misleading; in the exact treatment of Section 13.3, there arose no such resonance integral. The resonance integral arises simply out of the nature of the LCAO approximation we used.

The resonance integral H_{ab} is often called an exchange integral; however, the following distinction is worth preserving. An exchange integral such as K_{1s2s} in Eq. (9.145) involves two functions that differ from each other in the interchange of two electrons. A resonance integral such as H_{ab} in (13.37) involves only a single electron, and two functions that differ from each other in the spatial location of this electron.

In summary, we have formed the two H_2^+ MO's (13.47) and (13.48), one bonding and one antibonding, from the AO's $1s_a$ and $1s_b$. The MO energies are given by Eq. (13.42) as

$$W_{1,2} = H_{aa} \pm \frac{H_{ab} - H_{aa} S_{ab}}{1 \pm S_{ab}} \qquad (13.63)$$

where H_{aa} is the energy of each AO. A schematic representation of MO formation from AO's is given in Fig. 13.20.

We have described the H_2^+ states according to the state of the hydrogen atom obtained on dissociation; this is a *separated-atoms* description. Alternatively, we can use the state of the atom formed as the internuclear distance goes to zero; this is a *united-atom* description. We have seen that for the two lowest electronic states of H_2^+, the united-atom states are the $1s$ and $2p_0$ states of He^+. The united-atom designation is put on the left of the symbol for λ. The $\sigma_g 1s$ state thus has the united-atom designation $1s\sigma_g$. The $\sigma_u^* 1s$ state has the united-atom designation $2p\sigma_u^*$. It is not necessary to write this state as $2p_0 \sigma_u^*$, because the fact that it is a σ state tells us that it correlates with the united-atom $2p_0$ state. For the united-atom description, the subscripts g and u are redundant, in that molecular states correlating with $s, d, g, \ldots$ atomic states must be g, while states correlating with $p, f, h, \ldots$ atomic states must be u. From the separated-atoms states, we cannot tell whether the molecular wave function is g or u. Thus from the $1s$ separated-atoms state, we formed both a g and a u function for H_2^+.

Before constructing approximate molecular orbitals for other H_2^+ states, we consider how the trial function (13.47) can be improved. From the viewpoint of perturbation theory, (13.47) is the correct zeroth-order wave function. We know that the perturbation of molecule formation will mix in other hydrogen-atom states besides $1s$. Dickinson in 1933 used a trial function with some $2p_0$ character mixed in (since the ground state of H_2^+ is a σ state, it would not do to mix in $2p_{\pm 1}$ functions); he took

$$\varphi = [1s_a + c(2p_0)_a] + [1s_b + c(2p_0)_b] \qquad (13.64)$$

where c is a variational parameter, and where (Table 6.2)

$$1s_a = k^{3/2} \pi^{-1/2} e^{-kr_a}$$

$$(2p_0)_a = (2p_z)_a = \frac{\zeta^{5/2}}{4(2\pi)^{1/2}} r_a e^{-\zeta r_a/2} \cos \theta_a$$

with k and ζ being two other variational parameters. We have similar expressions for $1s_b$ and $(2p_0)_b$. The angles θ_a and θ_b refer to two sets of spherical polar coordinates, one set at each nucleus; see Fig. 13.9. The definitions of θ_a and θ_b correspond to using a right-handed coordinate system on atom a and a left-handed system on atom b; this is the usual convention. Naturally, c goes to zero as R goes to either zero or infinity.

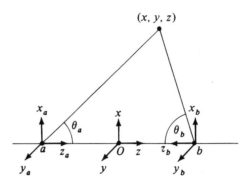

FIGURE 13.9   *Coordinate systems for a homonuclear diatomic molecule.*

The function $(1s + c2p_0)$ is a *hybridized* atomic orbital. Since the $2p_0$ function is positive in one lobe and negative in the other, its inclusion leads to further building up of charge between the nuclei, giving a greater binding energy. The hybridization allows for the polarization of the $1s_a$ and $1s_b$ atomic orbitals that occurs on molecule formation. The function (13.64) gives a $U(R)$ curve with a minimum at 2.01 bohrs. At this distance the parameters have the values [F. Weinhold, *J. Chem. Phys.*, **54**, 530 (1971)]:

$$k = 1.246, \qquad \zeta = 2.965, \qquad c = 0.138$$

The binding energy is calculated to be 2.73 eV, in good agreement with the true value 2.79 eV.

Besides the variational functions discussed in this section, many others[9] have been used for the H_2^+ ground state.

13.5   Molecular Orbitals for H_2^+ Excited States

In the last section, we used the approximate functions (13.47) and (13.48) for the two lowest H_2^+ electronic states. Now we construct approximate functions for further excited states, so as to build up a supply of H_2^+-like molecular orbitals. We will then use these MO's to give a qualitative discussion of many-electron diatomic molecules, just as we used hydrogenlike AO's to discuss many-electron atoms.

---

[9] For a partial listing, see M. Geller, A. A. Frost, and P. G. Lykos, *J. Chem. Phys.*, **36**, 2693 (1962); F. Weinhold and A. B. Chinen, *ibid.*, **56**, 3798 (1972).

To get approximations to higher H_2^+ MO's, we can use the method of the linear variation function. We saw that it was natural to take our variation functions for H_2^+ as linear combinations of hydrogenlike atomic-orbital functions, giving LCAO-MO's. To get approximate MO's for higher states, we add in more AO's to the linear combination. Thus, to get approximate wave functions for the six lowest H_2^+ σ states, we use a linear combination of the three lowest $m = 0$ hydrogenlike functions on each atom:

$$\varphi = c_1 1s_a + c_2 2s_a + c_3 (2p_0)_a + c_4 1s_b + c_5 2s_b + c_6 (2p_0)_b$$

As found in the last section for the function (13.33), the symmetry of the homonuclear diatomic molecule makes the coefficients of the atom b orbitals equal to ± 1 times the corresponding atom a orbital coefficients:

$$\varphi = [c_1 1s_a + c_2 2s_a + c_3 (2p_0)_a] \pm [c_1 1s_b + c_2 2s_b + c_3 (2p_0)_b] \qquad \text{(13.65)}$$

where the upper sign goes with the even (g) states.

Consider the relative magnitudes of the coefficients in (13.65). For the two electronic states that dissociate into a $1s$ hydrogen atom, we expect that c_1 will be considerably greater than c_2 or c_3, since c_2 and c_3 vanish in the limit of R going to infinity. Thus the Dickinson function (13.64) had the $2p_0$ coefficient about one-seventh the $1s$ coefficient at R_e. (This function does not include a $2s$ term, but if it did, we no doubt would find its coefficient to be small compared to the $1s$ coefficient.) As a first approximation, we therefore set c_2 and c_3 equal to zero, taking

$$\varphi = c_1(1s_a \pm 1s_b) \qquad \text{(13.66)}$$

as an approximation for the wave functions of these two states (as we already have done). The same argument for the two states that dissociate to a $2s$ hydrogen atom gives as approximate wave functions for them:

$$\varphi = c_2(2s_a \pm 2s_b) \qquad \text{(13.67)}$$

since c_1 and c_3 will be small for these states. The functions (13.67) are only an approximation to what we would find if we carried out the linear variation treatment; to find rigorous upper bounds to the energies of these two H_2^+ states, we must use the trial function (13.65) and solve the appropriate sixth-order determinantal equation.

From the viewpoint of perturbation theory, taking the separated atoms as the unperturbed problem, the functions (13.66) and (13.67) are the correct zeroth-order wave functions.

In general, we have two H_2^+ states correlating with each separated-atom state, and rough approximations to the wave functions of these two states will be the LCAO functions $f_a + f_b$ and $f_a - f_b$, where f is a hydrogenlike wave function. The functions (13.66) give the $\sigma_g 1s$ and $\sigma_u^* 1s$ states. Similarly, the functions (13.67) give the $\sigma_g 2s$ and $\sigma_u^* 2s$ molecular orbitals. The outer contour lines for these orbitals are like those for the corresponding MO's made from $1s$ AO's. However, since the $2s$ AO has a nodal sphere, while the $1s$ AO does not, each of these MO's has one more nodal surface than the corresponding $\sigma_g 1s$ or $\sigma_u^* 1s$ MO.

Next, we have the combinations

$$(2p_0)_a \pm (2p_0)_b = (2p_z)_a \pm (2p_z)_b \qquad \text{(13.68)}$$

giving the $\sigma_g 2p$ and $\sigma_u^* 2p$ molecular orbitals (Fig. 13.10); these are σ MO's even though they correlate with $2p$ separated AO's, since they have $m = 0$.

[The preceding discussion is oversimplified. For the hydrogen atom, the $2s$ and $2p$ AO's are degenerate, so that we can expect the correct zeroth-order functions for the $\sigma_g 2s$, $\sigma_u^* 2s$, $\sigma_g 2p$, and $\sigma_u^* 2p$ MO's of H_2^+ to each be mixtures of $2s$ and $2p$ AO's rather than containing only $2s$ or only $2p$ character. For molecules that dissociate into many-electron atoms, the separated-atom $2s$ and $2p$ AO's are not degenerate, but do lie close together in energy; hence the first-order corrections to the wave functions will mix substantial $2s$ character into the $\sigma 2p$ MO's and substantial $2p$ character into the $\sigma 2s$ MO's. Thus the designation of an MO as $\sigma 2s$ or $\sigma 2p$ should not be taken too literally. For H_2^+ and H_2, the united-atom designations of the MO's are preferable to the separated-atom designations, but we shall use mostly the latter.]

For the other two $2p$ atomic orbitals, we can use either the $2p_{+1}$ and $2p_{-1}$ complex functions, or the $2p_x$ and $2p_y$ real functions. If we want MO's that are eigenfunctions of $\hat{L}_z$, we will choose the complex p orbitals. We then have the 4 MO's:

$$(2p_{+1})_a + (2p_{+1})_b \qquad \text{(13.69)}$$

$$(2p_{+1})_a - (2p_{+1})_b \qquad \text{(13.70)}$$

$$(2p_{-1})_a + (2p_{-1})_b \qquad \text{(13.71)}$$

$$(2p_{-1})_a - (2p_{-1})_b \qquad \text{(13.72)}$$

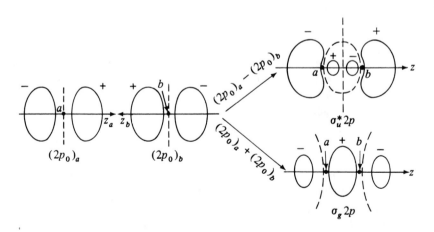

FIGURE 13.10   *Formation of $\sigma_g 2p$ and $\sigma_u^* 2p$ MO's from $2p_z$ AO's. The dashed lines indicate nodal surfaces. The signs on the contours give the sign of the wave function. The contours are symmetric about the z axis. (Because of substantial 2s–2p hybridization, these contours are not accurate representations of true MO shapes; for accurate contours, see the reference to Fig. 13.18.)*

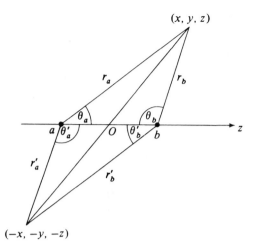

(x, y, z)

r_a

r_b

θ_a

θ_b

a

θ_a'

O

θ_b'

b

z

r_a'

r_b'

(−x, −y, −z)

FIGURE 13.11 *The effect of inversion of the electron's coordinates in* $H_2{}^+$. *We have* $r_a' = r_b$, $r_b' = r_a$, *and* $\varphi' = \varphi + \pi$.

From Eq. (6.131) we have, since $\varphi_a = \varphi_b = \varphi$:

$$(2p_{+1})_a + (2p_{+1})_b = \tfrac{1}{8}\pi^{-1/2}[r_a e^{-r_a/2}\sin\theta_a + r_b e^{-r_b/2}\sin\theta_b]e^{i\varphi} \qquad (13.73)$$

Since $\lambda = |m| = 1$, this is a π orbital. The inversion operation amounts to the coordinate transformation (Fig. 13.11)

$$r_a \rightarrow r_b, \qquad r_b \rightarrow r_a, \qquad \varphi \rightarrow \varphi + \pi \qquad (13.74)$$

We have

$$e^{i(\varphi+\pi)} = (\cos\pi + i\sin\pi)e^{i\varphi} = -e^{i\varphi}$$

From Fig. 13.11, we see that inversion converts θ_a to θ_b, and vice versa. Thus inversion converts (13.73) to its negative, meaning it is a u orbital. Reflection in the plane perpendicular to the axis and midway between the nuclei causes the following transformations (Problem 13.13):

$$r_a \rightarrow r_b, \qquad r_b \rightarrow r_a, \qquad \varphi \rightarrow \varphi, \qquad \theta_a \rightarrow \theta_b, \qquad \theta_b \rightarrow \theta_a \qquad (13.75)$$

This leaves (13.73) unchanged, so that we have an unstarred (bonding) orbital. The designation of (13.73) is then $\pi_u 2p_{+1}$.

The function (13.73) is complex; taking its absolute value, we can plot the orbital contours of constant probability density (Section 6.6). Since $|e^{i\varphi}| = 1$, the probability density is independent of φ, giving a density that is symmetric about the z (internuclear) axis. Figure 13.12 shows a cross section of this orbital in a plane containing the nuclei; the three-dimensional shape is found by rotating this figure about the z axis, giving a sort of fat doughnut. (Sometimes this orbital is pictured as having the shape of a right circular cylinder; this is inaccurate, since the probability density is not constant as we move parallel to the z axis.)

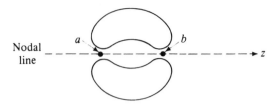

FIGURE 13.12   *Cross section of the* $\pi_u 2p_{+1}$ *(or* $\pi_u 2p_{-1}$*) molecular orbital. To obtain the three-dimensional contour surface, rotate the figure about the z axis. The z axis is a nodal line for this* MO *(as it is for the* $2p_{+1}$ AO*).*

The molecular orbital (13.71) differs from (13.73) only in having $e^{i\varphi}$ replaced by $e^{-i\varphi}$, and is designated $\pi_u 2p_{-1}$. The coordinate φ enters the Hamiltonian (13.21) as $\partial^2/\partial\varphi^2$. We have

$$\frac{\partial^2 e^{i\varphi}}{\partial\varphi^2} = \frac{\partial^2 e^{-i\varphi}}{\partial\varphi^2}$$

so that the states (13.69) and (13.71) have the same energy.   Recall (Section 13.3) that the $\lambda = 1$ energy levels are doubly degenerate, corresponding to $m = \pm 1$. Since $|e^{i\varphi}| = |e^{-i\varphi}|$, the $\pi_u 2p_{+1}$ and $\pi_u 2p_{-1}$ MO's have the same shapes, just as the $2p_{+1}$ and $2p_{-1}$ AO's have the same shapes.

The functions (13.70) and (13.72) give the $\pi_g^* 2p_{+1}$ and $\pi_g^* 2p_{-1}$ MO's.   These functions don't give charge buildup between the nuclei, as can be seen from Fig. 13.13.

Let us now consider the more familiar alternative of using the $2p_x$ and $2p_y$ AO's to make our MO's.   The linear combination

$$(2p_x)_a + (2p_x)_b \tag{13.76}$$

gives the $\pi_u 2p_x$ MO (Fig. 13.14).   This MO is not symmetric about the internuclear axis, but builds up electronic charge probability density in two lobes, one above and one below the yz plane, which is a nodal plane for this function.   The wave function

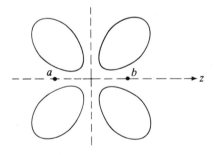

FIGURE 13.13   *Cross section of the* $\pi_g^* 2p_{+1}$ *(or* $\pi_g^* 2p_{-1}$*)* MO. *To obtain the three-dimensional contour surface, rotate about the z axis. The z axis and the xy plane are nodes.*

has opposite signs on each side of this plane. The linear combination

$$(2p_x)_a - (2p_x)_b \tag{13.77}$$

gives the $\pi_g^*2p_x$ MO (Fig. 13.14). Since the $2p_y$ functions differ from the $2p_x$ functions solely by a rotation of $90°$ about the internuclear axis, they give molecular orbitals differing from those of Fig. 13.14 by a $90°$ rotation about the z axis. The linear combinations

$$(2p_y)_a + (2p_y)_b \tag{13.78}$$

$$(2p_y)_a - (2p_y)_b \tag{13.79}$$

give the π_u2p_y and $\pi_g^*2p_y$ molecular orbitals. The MO's (13.76) and (13.78) have the same energy; the MO's (13.77) and (13.79) have the same energy. (Note that the $g \ \pi2p$ MO's are antibonding, while the $u \ \pi2p$ MO's are bonding.)

Just as the $2p_x$ and $2p_y$ AO's are linear combinations of the $2p_{+1}$ and $2p_{-1}$ AO's [Eqs. (6.135) and (6.139)], the π_u2p_x and π_u2p_y MO's are linear combinations of the π_u2p_{+1} and π_u2p_{-1} MO's. We can use any linear combination of the eigenfunctions of a degenerate energy level, and still have an energy eigenfunction. Just as the $2p_{+1}$ and $2p_{-1}$ AO's are eigenfunctions of $\hat{L}_z$ and the $2p_x$ and $2p_y$ AO's are not, the π_u2p_{+1} and π_u2p_{-1} MO's are eigenfunctions of $\hat{L}_z$ and the π_u2p_x and π_u2p_y MO's are not. Although the molecular orbitals $\pi_u2p_{+1}, \ \pi_u2p_{-1}, \ \pi_u2p_x, \ \pi_u2p_y$ all have the same energy, they represent different states of the system, since they have different

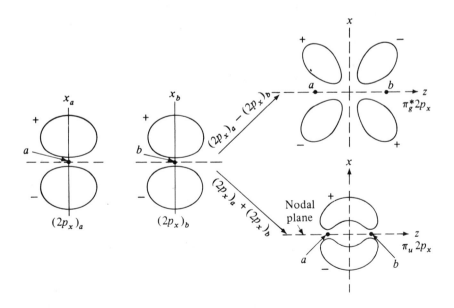

FIGURE 13.14 *Formation of the π_u2p_x and $\pi_g^*2p_x$ MO's. Since the coordinate φ has the value zero in the xz plane, the cross sections of these MO's in the xz plane are the same as for the corresponding π_u2p_{+1} and $\pi_g^*2p_{+1}$ MO's. However, the $\pi2p_x$ MO's are not symmetrical about the z axis; rather, they consist of blobs of probability density above and below the nodal yz plane.*

wave functions. The question arises: Given an H_2^+ molecule in the $\pi_u 2p$ energy level, what is its wave function (state)? The answer is that the state depends on the past history of the system. Thus if we have just measured L_z for a $\pi_u 2p$ H_2^+ molecule and found the result $+\hbar$, then we know that the molecule is in the state $\pi_u 2p_{+1}$. This assertion holds just after the measurement, but not just before. If the state just before the measurement were either $\pi_u 2p_x$ or $\pi_u 2p_y$, then (since these states are superpositions of the $\pi_u 2p_{+1}$ and $\pi_u 2p_{-1}$ states with coefficients equal in magnitude) we would have had a 50 percent chance of finding each of the results $+\hbar$ and $-\hbar$; the measurement of L_z changes the state to either $\pi_u 2p_{+1}$ or $\pi_u 2p_{-1}$, depending on what the outcome of the measurement is (reduction of the wave function—Section 7.8). For the H_2^+ $\pi_u 2p$ energy level, we can use the pair of real MO's (13.76) and (13.78), or the pair of complex MO's (13.69) and (13.71), or any two linearly independent linear combinations of these functions. (It might be argued that since $\hat{L}_z$ commutes with the Hamiltonian for H_2^+, the $\pi_u 2p_{+1}$ and $\pi_u 2p_{-1}$ molecular orbitals are preferable, since they are eigenfunctions of $\hat{L}_z$. However, for degenerate levels, there is no necessity that the molecule be in an eigenstate of $\hat{L}_z$; linear combinations that are not eigenfunctions of $\hat{L}_z$ are just as valid stationary states as those that are eigenfunctions of $\hat{L}_z$. For nondegenerate (σ) levels, there is no element of choice in the wave function and the wave functions must be eigenfunctions of $\hat{L}_z$.)

We have shown the correlation of the H_2^+ MO's with the separated-atom AO's. We can also show how they correlate with the united-atom AO's. As R goes to zero, the $\sigma_u^* 1s$ MO (Fig. 13.8) resembles more and more the $2p_z$ AO, with which it correlates. Similarly, the $\pi_u 2p$ MO's correlate with p united-atom states, while the $\pi_g^* 2p$ MO's correlate with d united-atom states.

We can treat a molecule by applying perturbation theory to the corresponding united atom, taking the perturbation $\hat{H}'$ as the difference between the molecular and united-atom Hamiltonians:

$$\hat{H}' = \hat{H}_{mol} - \hat{H}_{UA}$$

It has been shown[10] that the expression for the purely electronic energy of a diatomic molecule can be written as

$$E_{el} = E_{UA} + aR^2 + bR^3 + cR^4 + \cdots \tag{13.80}$$

where E_{UA} is the corresponding united-atom energy, R is the internuclear distance, and $a, b, c, \ldots$ are constants. Note the absence of a term linear in R. The matrix elements of $\hat{H}'$ between the various united-atom states turn out to be proportional to R^2 for small values of R; since the second-order perturbation energy correction $E^{(2)}$ [Eq. (9.46)] involves the squares of H'_{ij}, it was thought that $E^{(2)}$ was proportional to R^4 for small R, so that a and b could be evaluated from the first-order energy correction $E^{(1)}$. However, this is not so.[11] Although the individual terms in Eq. (9.46) are proportional to R^4, when the infinite summation over bound states and integration over continuum states is performed, the resulting $E^{(2)}$ is proportional to R^3. (See Problem 13.11.) The series (13.80) converges slowly.

---

[10] W. A. Bingel, *J. Chem. Phys.*, **30**, 1250 (1959).

[11] I. N. Levine, *J. Chem. Phys.*, **40**, 3444 (1964); **41**, 2044 (1964); W. Byers Brown and E. Steiner, *J. Chem. Phys.*, **44**, 3934 (1966). This last reference shows the presence of an $R^5 \ln R$ term in (13.80).

13.6 Molecular-Orbital Configurations of Homonuclear Diatomic Molecules

We now use the H_2^+ MO's developed in the last section to discuss many-electron homonuclear diatomic molecules. If we ignore the interelectronic repulsions, the zeroth-order wave function is a Slater determinant of H_2^+-like one-electron spin-orbitals. We approximate the spatial part of the H_2^+ spin-orbitals by the LCAO-MO's of the last section. Treatments that go beyond this crude first approximation will be discussed later.

The sizes and energies of the MO's vary with varying internuclear distance for each molecule, and vary as we go from one molecule to another. Thus we saw how the orbital exponent k in the H_2^+ trial function (13.47) varied with R. As we go to molecules with higher nuclear charge, the parameter k for the $\sigma_g 1s$ MO will increase, giving a more compact MO. We want to consider the order of the MO energies. Because of the variation of these energies with R and variations from molecule to molecule, numerous crossings occur, just as for atomic-orbital energies (Fig. 11.2). Hence we cannot give a definitive order. However, the following is the order in which the MO's fill as we go across the periodic table:

$$\sigma_g 1s < \sigma_u^* 1s < \sigma_g 2s < \sigma_u^* 2s < \pi_u 2p_{+1} = \pi_u 2p_{-1} < \sigma_g 2p < \pi_g^* 2p_{+1}$$
$$= \pi_g^* 2p_{-1} < \sigma_u^* 2p$$

Each bonding orbital fills before the corresponding antibonding orbital. The $\pi_u 2p$ orbitals are close in energy to the $\sigma_g 2p$ orbital, and it was formerly believed that the $\sigma_g 2p$ MO filled first.

Besides the separated-atom designation, there are other ways of referring to these MO's; see Table 13.1. The second column of this table gives the united-atom designations. The nomenclature of the third column uses $1\sigma_g$ for the lowest σ_g MO, $2\sigma_g$ for the second lowest σ_g MO, etc.

Table 13.1 Molecular-Orbital Nomenclature for Homonuclear Diatomic Molecules

Separated-Atoms Description	United-Atom Description	Numbering by Symmetry	Mulliken Notation
$\sigma_g 1s$	$1s\sigma_g$	$1\sigma_g$	K
$\sigma_u^* 1s$	$2p\sigma_u^*$	$1\sigma_u$	K
$\sigma_g 2s$	$2s\sigma_g$	$2\sigma_g$	$z\sigma$
$\sigma_u^* 2s$	$3p\sigma_u^*$	$2\sigma_u$	$y\sigma$
$\pi_u 2p$	$2p\pi_u$	$1\pi_u$	$w\pi$
$\sigma_g 2p$	$3s\sigma_g$	$3\sigma_g$	$x\sigma$
$\pi_g^* 2p$	$3d\pi_g^*$	$1\pi_g$	$v\pi$
$\sigma_u^* 2p$	$4p\sigma_u^*$	$3\sigma_u$	$u\sigma$

A diagram showing how the MO's correlate with the separated-atom and united-atom states is shown in Fig. 13.15. Because of the variation of MO energies from molecule to molecule, this diagram is not quantitative.

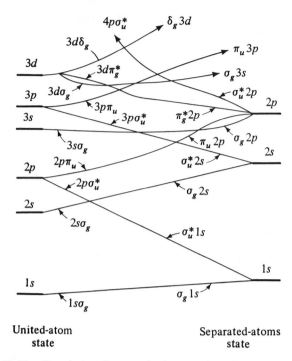

FIGURE 13.15 *Correlation diagram for homonuclear diatomic* MO's. (*This diagram doesn't hold for* H_2^+.)

Just as we discussed atoms by filling in the AO's, giving rise to atomic configurations such as $1s^2 2s^2$, we will discuss homonuclear diatomic molecules by filling in the MO's, giving rise to molecular electronic configurations such as $(\sigma_g 1s)^2 (\sigma_u^* 1s)^2$. (Recall that with a single atomic configuration, there is associated a hierarchy of terms, levels, and states; the same is true for a molecular configuration —see Section 13.7.)

For H_2^+ we have the ground-state configuration $\sigma_g 1s$, which gives a one-electron bond. For excited states, the electron is in one of the higher MO's.

For H_2 we put the two electrons in the $\sigma_g 1s$ MO with opposite spins, giving the ground-state configuration $(\sigma_g 1s)^2$. The two bonding electrons give a single bond. The ground-state dissociation energy D_e is 4.75 eV. In the crudest approximation, the H_2 dissociation energy would be twice the H_2^+ dissociation energy, or 5.6 eV [Eq. (13.28)]. Because of interelectronic repulsion, the true binding energy is somewhat less than this.

Now consider He_2. Two electrons go in the $\sigma_g 1s$ MO, thereby filling it. The other two go in the next highest MO, $\sigma_u^* 1s$. The ground-state configuration is $(\sigma_g 1s)^2 (\sigma_u^* 1s)^2$. With two bonding and two antibonding electrons, we expect no net bonding, in agreement with the well-known fact that the ground electronic state of He_2 is unstable, showing no minimum in the potential-energy curve. However, if an electron is excited from the antibonding $\sigma_u^* 1s$ MO to a higher MO that is bonding, we will have three bonding electrons and only one antibonding electron, so that there should be bonding excited states, with a minimum in each $U(R)$ curve. Indeed, about two dozen such bound excited states of He_2 have been spectroscopically observed in gas discharge tubes. Of course, such excited states decay to the ground electronic state, and then the molecule dissociates.

The repulsion of two $1s^2$ helium atoms can be ascribed to the Pauli repulsion between electrons with parallel spins (Section 10.4). Each helium atom has a pair of electrons with opposite spin and each pair tends to exclude the other pair from occupying the same region of space.

Removal of an antibonding electron from He_2 gives the He_2^+ ion, with ground-state configuration $(\sigma_g 1s)^2 (\sigma_u^* 1s)$; we have one net bonding electron. Ground-state properties of this molecule are quite close to those for H_2^+; see Table 13.2.

For Li_2 we have the ground-state configuration $(\sigma_g 1s)^2 (\sigma_u^* 1s)^2 (\sigma_g 2s)^2$ with two net bonding electrons, leading to the description of the molecule as containing an Li—Li single bond. Experimentally, Li_2 is found to be a stable species. In Li_2, the orbital exponent of the $1s$ AO's is considerably greater than in H_2^+ or H_2, due to the increase in the nuclear charges from 1 to 3. This shrinks the $1s_a$ and $1s_b$ AO's in closer to the corresponding nuclei; there is thus only very slight overlap between these two AO's, and the integrals S_{ab} and H_{ab} are very small for these AO's. As a result, the energies of the $\sigma_g 1s$ and $\sigma_u^* 1s$ MO's in Li_2 are nearly equal to each other and to the energy of a $1s$ Li AO. (For very small R, the $1s_a$ and $1s_b$ AO's do overlap appreciably and their energies then differ considerably.) The Li_2 ground-state configuration is frequently written as $KK(\sigma_g 2s)^2$ to indicate the negligible change in inner-shell orbital energies on molecule formation, which is in accord with the chemist's usual idea of bonding involving only the valence electrons. The orbital exponent of the $2s$ AO's in Li_2 is not much greater than 1, because these electrons are screened from the nucleus by the $1s$ electrons.

Be_2 has the ground-state configuration $KK(\sigma_g 2s)^2 (\sigma_u^* 2s)^2$ with no net bonding electrons, in agreement with the failure to observe a stable ground state. There should, however, be bound excited states.

B_2 has the ground-state configuration $KK(\sigma_g 2s)^2 (\sigma_u^* 2s)^2 (\pi_u 2p)^2$ with two net bonding electrons, indicating a stable ground state, as is found experimentally. The bonding electrons are π electrons, which is at variance with the notion that single bonds are always σ bonds. We have two degenerate $\pi_u 2p$ MO's. Recall that when we had an atomic configuration such as $1s^2 2s^2 2p^2$, we obtained several terms, which because of interelectronic repulsions had different energies. We saw that the term with the highest total spin was generally the lowest (Hund's rule). With the molecular configuration of B_2 given above, we will also have a number of terms. Since the lower (σ) MO's are all filled, their electrons must be paired, and contribute nothing to the total spin. If the two $\pi_u 2p$ electrons are both in the same MO (e.g., both in $\pi_u 2p_{+1}$) their spins must be paired (antiparallel), giving a total molecular electronic spin of zero. If, however, we have one electron in the $\pi_u 2p_{+1}$ MO and the other in the $\pi_u 2p_{-1}$ MO, their spins can be parallel, giving a net spin of one; by Hund's rule, this term will be lowest, and the ground state of B_2 will have $2S+1 = 3$. Experimentally, the ground state of B_2 is observed to be a triplet. [Actually, the experimental evidence is not conclusive. Moreover, theoretical calculations—C. F. Bender and E. R. Davidson, *J. Chem. Phys.*, **46**, 3313 (1967)—indicate that the quintet term of the $KK(\sigma_g 2s)^2 (\sigma_u^* 2s)(\pi_u 2p)^2 (\sigma_g 2p)$ configuration may be slightly lower in energy than the above-mentioned triplet term. Thus the ground state is uncertain.]

C_2 has the ground-state configuration $KK(\sigma_g 2s)^2 (\sigma_u^* 2s)^2 (\pi_u 2p)^4$ with four net bonding electrons, indicating a stable ground state with a double bond. As mentioned, the $\pi_u 2p$ and $\sigma_g 2p$ MO's have nearly the same energy in many molecules. It was formerly believed that the ground-state configuration of C_2 was $KK(\sigma_g 2s)^2 (\sigma_u^* 2s)^2 (\pi_u 2p)^3 (\sigma_g 2p)$. This configuration would allow two of the electrons to have their spins parallel, giving a triplet state; because of the minimization of the repulsion between these two electrons, the triplet state of this configuration was thought to be lower than the $(\pi_u 2p)^4$ configuration, which can only give a singlet state. (Recall that the ground-state configuration of Cr is $3d^5 4s$, rather than $3d^4 4s^2$.) However, experimental evidence[12] shows $(\pi_u 2p)^4$ to be the ground-state configuration of gas-phase C_2.

The N_2 ground-state electronic configuration is

$$KK(\sigma_g 2s)^2 (\sigma_u^* 2s)^2 (\pi_u 2p)^4 (\sigma_g 2p)^2$$

The six net bonding electrons indicate a triple bond, in accord with the Lewis structure $:N\!\equiv\!N:$.

The O_2 ground-state configuration is

$$KK(\sigma_g 2s)^2 (\sigma_u^* 2s)^2 (\sigma_g 2p)^2 (\pi_u 2p)^4 (\pi_g^* 2p)^2$$

Spectroscopic evidence indicates that in O_2 (and in F_2) the $\sigma_g 2p$ MO is lower in energy than the $\pi_u 2p$ MO. The four net bonding electrons give a double bond. The $\pi_g^* 2p_{+1}$ and $\pi_g^* 2p_{-1}$ MO's have the same energy, and by putting one electron in each we get a triplet state. By Hund's rule, this is the ground state. This explanation of the paramagnetism of O_2 was one of the early triumphs of molecular-orbital theory.

For F_2 the ground-state configuration is

$$KK(\sigma_g 2s)^2 (\sigma_u^* 2s)^2 (\sigma_g 2p)^2 (\pi_u 2p)^4 (\pi_g^* 2p)^4$$

The two net bonding electrons give a single bond.

For Ne_2 we have

$$KK(\sigma_g 2s)^2 (\sigma_u^* 2s)^2 (\sigma_g 2p)^2 (\pi_u 2p)^4 (\pi_g^* 2p)^4 (\sigma_u^* 2p)^2$$

There are no net bonding electrons and thus there is no bonding, in agreement with experiment.

We can go on to describe homonuclear diatomic molecules of higher atomic number. Thus the lowest electron configuration of Na_2 is $KKLL(\sigma_g 3s)^2$.

Table 13.2 lists D_e and R_e for the ground states of some homonuclear diatomic molecules; it also lists the bond order, which is one-half the difference between the number of bonding and antibonding electrons. The dissociation energy increases

---

[12] E. A. Ballik and D. A. Ramsay, *J. Chem. Phys.*, **31**, 1128 (1959); *Astrophys. J.*, **137**, 61, 84 (1963).

and the bond length decreases as the bond order increases. The spectroscopic designations in this table will be explained in the next section.

The criterion of whether an MO is bonding or antibonding is whether removal of an electron from the MO results in a decrease or an increase in D_e. (Note that as R decreases in Fig. 13.15, the energies of bonding MO's decrease, while the energies of antibonding MO's increase.) For example, the highest filled MO in N_2 is bonding, and Table 13.2 shows that in going from the ground state of N_2 to that of N_2^+, the dissociation energy decreases (and the bond length increases). In contrast, the

Table 13.2 Properties of Homonuclear Diatomic Molecules in their Ground Electronic States

Molecule	Ground Term	Bond Order	D_e (eV)	R_e (Å)
H_2^+	$^2\Sigma_g^+$	$\frac{1}{2}$	2.8	1.06
H_2	$^1\Sigma_g^+$	1	4.75	0.742
He_2^+	$^2\Sigma_u^+$	$\frac{1}{2}$	3	1.08
He_2	$^1\Sigma_g^+$	0	—	—
Li_2	$^1\Sigma_g^+$	1	1.1	2.67
Be_2	$^1\Sigma_g^+$	0	—	—
B_2	$^3\Sigma_g^-$ (?)	1	2.9	1.59
C_2	$^1\Sigma_g^+$	2	6.4	1.24
N_2^+	$^2\Sigma_g^+$	$2\frac{1}{2}$	8.9	1.12
N_2	$^1\Sigma_g^+$	3	9.9	1.10
O_2^+	$^2\Pi_g$	$2\frac{1}{2}$	6.8	1.12
O_2	$^3\Sigma_g^-$	2	5.2	1.21
F_2	$^1\Sigma_g^+$	1	1.6_5	1.42
Ne_2	$^1\Sigma_g^+$	0	—	—

highest filled MO of O_2 is antibonding, and in going from O_2 to O_2^+, the dissociation energy increases (and R_e decreases). The designation of bonding or antibonding does not refer to the effect of the electrons on the total energy of the molecule. It always requires energy to ionize a stable molecule, no matter which electron is removed. Hence, both bonding and antibonding electrons in a stable molecule decrease the total molecular energy.

13.7 Molecular Electronic Terms

We now consider the terms arising from a given molecular electronic configuration.

For atoms, each set of degenerate atomic orbitals constitutes an atomic subshell. For example, the $2p_{+1}$, $2p_0$, and $2p_{-1}$ AO's constitute the $2p$ subshell. An atomic electronic configuration is defined by giving the number of electrons in each subshell; e.g., $1s^2 2s^2 2p^4$. For molecules, each set of degenerate molecular orbitals constitutes a molecular subshell. For example, the $\pi_u 2p_{+1}$ and $\pi_u 2p_{-1}$ MO's constitute the $\pi_u 2p$ subshell. Each σ subshell consists of one MO, while each $\pi, \delta, \varphi, \ldots$ subshell consists of two MO's; σ subshells are filled with two electrons, while non-σ subshells hold up to 4 electrons. We define a molecular electronic configuration by giving the number of electrons in each subshell, e.g.,

$$(\sigma_g 1s)^2 (\sigma_u^* 1s)^2 (\sigma_g 2s)^2 (\sigma_u^* 2s)^2 (\pi_u 2p)^3$$

For H_2^+, we saw that although $\hat{L}^2$ does not commute with $\hat{H}$, the operator $\hat{L}_z$ does commute with $\hat{H}$. For a many-electron diatomic molecule, one finds that the operator for the axial component of the total electronic orbital angular momentum commutes with $\hat{H}$. The component of electronic orbital angular momentum along the molecular axis has the possible values $M_L \hbar$ where $M_L = 0, \pm 1, \pm 2, \pm \ldots$. To calculate M_L, we simply add algebraically the m's of the individual electrons. Analogous to the symbol λ for the one-electron molecule, we define Λ as

$$\Lambda \equiv |M_L| \tag{13.81}$$

The following code is used to indicate the value of Λ:

Λ	0	1	2	3	4
letter	Σ	Π	Δ	Φ	Γ

For $\Lambda \neq 0$, there are two possible values of M_L: $+\Lambda$ and $-\Lambda$; as in H_2^+, the electronic energy depends on M_L^2, so that there is a double degeneracy associated with the two values of M_L. (Note that lowercase letters refer to individual electrons, while capital letters refer to the whole molecule.)

Just as in atoms, the individual electronic spins add vectorially to give a total electronic spin $\mathbf{S}$, whose magnitude has the possible values $\sqrt{S(S+1)}\hbar$, with $S = 0, \frac{1}{2}, 1, \frac{3}{2}, \ldots$. The component of $\mathbf{S}$ along an axis has the possible values $M_S \hbar$, where $M_S = S, S-1, \ldots, -S$. As in atoms, the quantity $(2S+1)$ is called the *multiplicity* and is written as a left superscript to the code letter for Λ. Diatomic electronic states that have the same value for Λ and the same value for S are said to belong to the same electronic *term*. We now consider how the terms belonging to a given electronic configuration are derived. (We are assuming Russell–Saunders coupling, which holds for molecules composed of atoms of not-too-high atomic number.)

A filled molecular subshell consists of one or two filled molecular orbitals. The Pauli principle requires that for two electrons in the same molecular orbital, one have $m_s = +\frac{1}{2}$, while the other have $m_s = -\frac{1}{2}$. Hence the quantum number M_S, which is the algebraic sum of the individual m_s values, must be zero for a filled molecular-subshell configuration; therefore we must have $S = 0$ for a configuration containing only filled molecular subshells. A filled σ subshell has two electrons with $m = 0$, so that M_L is zero. A filled π subshell has two electrons with $m = +1$ and two electrons with $m = -1$, so that M_L (which is the algebraic sum of the m's) is zero. The same situation holds for filled $\delta, \varphi, \ldots$ subshells. Thus a closed-subshell molecular configuration has both S and Λ equal to zero and gives rise to a single $^1\Sigma$ term. An example is the ground electronic configuration of H_2. (Recall that a filled-subshell atomic configuration gives only a ^1S term.) In deriving molecular terms, we need only consider electrons outside filled subshells.

A single σ electron has $s = \frac{1}{2}$, so that S must be $\frac{1}{2}$, and we get a $^2\Sigma$ term. An example is the ground electronic configuration of H_2^+. A single π electron gives a $^2\Pi$ term. And so on.

Now consider more than one electron. Electrons that are in different subshells are called *nonequivalent*, just as for atoms. For such electrons, we don't have to worry about giving two of them the same set of quantum numbers, and the terms are easily derived. Consider two nonequivalent σ electrons, a $\sigma\sigma$ configuration. Since both m's are zero, we have $M_L = 0$. Each s is $\frac{1}{2}$, so that S can be 1 or 0. We thus have the terms $^1\Sigma$ and $^3\Sigma$. Similarly a $\sigma\pi$ configuration gives $^1\Pi$ and $^3\Pi$ terms.

For a $\pi\delta$ configuration, we have singlet and triplet terms. The π electron can have $m = \pm 1$, and the δ electron can have $m = \pm 2$. The possible values for M_L are thus $+3$, -3, $+1$, and -1. This gives $\Lambda = 3$ or 1, and we have the terms $^1\Pi$, $^3\Pi$, $^1\Phi$, $^3\Phi$. (In atoms, we add the *vectors* $\mathbf{L}_i$ to get the total $\mathbf{L}$; hence a pd atomic configuration gives P, D, and F terms. In molecules, however, we add the z *components* of the orbital angular momenta; this is an algebraic rather than a vectorial addition, so that a $\pi\delta$ molecular configuration gives Π and Φ terms, and no Δ terms.)

For a $\pi\pi$ configuration of two nonequivalent electrons, each electron has $m = \pm 1$, and we have the M_L values: $2, -2, 0, 0$. The values of Λ are 2, 0, and 0; the terms are $^1\Delta$, $^3\Delta$, $^1\Sigma$, $^3\Sigma$, $^1\Sigma$, and $^3\Sigma$. The values $+2$ and -2 correspond to the two degenerate states of the same Δ term. However, Σ terms are nondegenerate (apart from spin degeneracy) and the two values of M_L that are zero indicate two different Σ terms (which become four Σ terms when we consider spin).

Consider the forms of the wave functions for the terms. We shall call the two π subshells π and π', and shall use a subscript to indicate the m value. For the Δ terms, both electrons have $m = +1$, or both have $m = -1$. For $M_L = +2$, we might write as the spatial factor in the wave function $\pi_{+1}(1)\pi'_{+1}(2)$ or $\pi_{+1}(2)\pi'_{+1}(1)$. However, these functions are neither symmetric nor antisymmetric with respect to exchange of the indistinguishable electrons, and are unacceptable. Instead, we must take the two linear combinations (we won't bother with normalization constants)

$$^1\Delta: \quad \pi_{+1}(1)\pi'_{+1}(2) + \pi_{+1}(2)\pi'_{+1}(1) \tag{13.82}$$

$$^3\Delta: \quad \pi_{+1}(1)\pi'_{+1}(2) - \pi_{+1}(2)\pi'_{+1}(1) \tag{13.83}$$

Similarly, with both electrons having $m = -1$, we have the spatial factors

$$^1\Delta: \quad \pi_{-1}(1)\pi'_{-1}(2) + \pi_{-1}(2)\pi'_{-1}(1) \tag{13.84}$$

$$^3\Delta: \quad \pi_{-1}(1)\pi'_{-1}(2) - \pi_{-1}(2)\pi'_{-1}(1) \tag{13.85}$$

The functions (13.82) and (13.84) are symmetric with respect to exchange; they therefore go with the antisymmetric two-electron spin factor (11.60), which has $S = 0$; thus (13.82) and (13.84) are the spatial factors in the wave functions for the two states of the doubly degenerate $^1\Delta$ term. The antisymmetric functions (13.83) and (13.85) must go with the symmetric two-electron spin functions (11.57), (11.58), and (11.59), giving the six states of the $^3\Delta$ term. These states all have the same energy (if we neglect spin-orbit interaction).

Now consider the wave functions of the Σ terms. These have one electron with $m = +1$ and one electron with $m = -1$. We start with the four functions

$$\pi_{+1}(1)\,\pi'_{-1}(2) \qquad \pi_{+1}(2)\,\pi'_{-1}(1) \qquad \pi_{-1}(1)\,\pi'_{+1}(2) \qquad \pi_{-1}(2)\,\pi'_{+1}(1)$$

Combining them to get symmetric and antisymmetric functions, we get

$^1\Sigma^+$: $\quad \pi_{+1}(1)\,\pi'_{-1}(2) + \pi_{+1}(2)\,\pi'_{-1}(1) + \pi_{-1}(1)\,\pi'_{+1}(2) + \pi_{-1}(2)\,\pi'_{+1}(1)$

$^1\Sigma^-$: $\quad \pi_{+1}(1)\,\pi'_{-1}(2) + \pi_{+1}(2)\,\pi'_{-1}(1) - \pi_{-1}(1)\,\pi'_{+1}(2) - \pi_{-1}(2)\,\pi'_{+1}(1)$

$^3\Sigma^+$: $\quad \pi_{+1}(1)\,\pi'_{-1}(2) - \pi_{+1}(2)\,\pi'_{-1}(1) + \pi_{-1}(1)\,\pi'_{+1}(2) - \pi_{-1}(2)\,\pi'_{+1}(1)$

$^3\Sigma^-$: $\quad \pi_{+1}(1)\,\pi'_{-1}(2) - \pi_{+1}(2)\,\pi'_{-1}(1) - \pi_{-1}(1)\,\pi'_{+1}(2) + \pi_{-1}(2)\,\pi'_{+1}(1)$

$$\text{(13.86)}$$

The first two functions in (13.86) are symmetric; they therefore go with the anti-symmetric singlet spin function (11.60). Clearly these two spatial functions have different energies. The last two functions in (13.86) are antisymmetric and hence are the spatial factors in the wave functions of the two $^3\Sigma$ terms. These four functions are found to have eigenvalue $+1$ or -1 with respect to reflection of electronic coordinates in the xz σ_v symmetry plane containing the molecular (z) axis (Problem 13.31); the superscripts $+$ and $-$ refer to this eigenvalue.

Examination of the Δ terms (13.82)–(13.85) shows that they are not eigenfunctions of $\hat{O}_{\sigma_v}$. Since there is a twofold degeneracy (apart from spin degeneracy) associated with these terms, there is no necessity that their wave functions be eigenfunctions of this operator; however, since $\hat{O}_{\sigma_v}$ commutes with the Hamiltonian, we can *choose* the eigenfunctions to be eigenfunctions of $\hat{O}_{\sigma_v}$. Thus we can combine the functions (13.82) and (13.84), which belong to a degenerate energy level, as follows:

$$(13.82) + (13.84) \qquad \text{and} \qquad (13.82) - (13.84)$$

These two linear combinations are eigenfunctions of $\hat{O}_{\sigma_v}$ with eigenvalues $+1$ and -1, and we could refer to them as $^1\Delta^+$ and $^1\Delta^-$ states. Since they have the same energy, there is no point in using the $+$ and $-$ superscripts. Thus the $+$ and $-$ designations are used only for Σ terms. However, when one considers the inter-action between the molecular rotational angular momentum and the electronic orbital angular momentum, there is a very slight splitting (called Λ-type doubling) of the two states of a $^1\Delta$ term; it turns out that the correct zeroth-order wave functions for this perturbation are the linear combinations that are eigenfunctions of $\hat{O}_{\sigma_v}$, so that in this case there is a point to distinguishing between Δ^+ and Δ^- states. Note that the linear combinations (13.82)$\pm$(13.84), which are eigenfunctions of $\hat{O}_{\sigma_v}$, are not eigenfunctions of $\hat{L}_z$, but are superpositions of $\hat{L}_z$ eigenfunctions with eigenvalues $+2$ and -2.

We can distinguish $+$ and $-$ terms for one-electron configurations. The wave function of a single σ electron has no phi factor and hence must correspond to a Σ^+ term. For a π electron, the MO's that are eigenfunctions of $\hat{L}_z$ are the π_{+1} and π_{-1} functions (whose probability densities are each symmetric about the z axis—Fig. 13.12). The π_{+1} and π_{-1} functions are not eigenfunctions of $\hat{O}_{\sigma_v}$, but the linear combinations $\pi_{+1} + \pi_{-1} = \pi_x$ and $\pi_{+1} - \pi_{-1} = \pi_y$ are; the π_x and π_y MO's (whose probability densities are not symmetric about the z axis—Fig. 13.14) are the correct zeroth-order functions if the perturbation of the electronic wave functions due to molecular rotation is considered. The π_x and π_y MO's have eigenvalues $+1$ and -1, respectively, for reflection in the xz plane and eigenvalues -1 and $+1$, respectively, for reflection in the yz plane. (The operators $\hat{L}_z$ and $\hat{O}_{\sigma_v}$ do not commute—Problem 13.25. Hence we cannot have all the eigenfunctions of $\hat{H}$ being eigenfunctions of both these operators as well. However, since each of these operators commutes with the electronic Hamiltonian and since there is no element of choice in the wave function of a nondegenerate level, all the σ MO's must be eigenfunctions of both $\hat{L}_z$ and $\hat{O}_{\sigma_v}$.)

Electrons in the same molecular subshell are called *equivalent*. For equivalent electrons, there are fewer terms than for the corresponding nonequivalent electron configuration, due to the Pauli principle. Thus for a π^2 configuration of two equivalent π electrons, four of the eight functions (13.82)–(13.86) vanish; the remaining functions give a $^1\Delta$ term, a $^1\Sigma^+$ term, and a $^3\Sigma^-$ term. Alternatively, we can make a table similar to Table 11.1, and use it to derive the terms for equivalent electrons.

Table 13.3 lists terms arising from various electron configurations. A filled subshell always gives the single term $^1\Sigma^+$. A π^3 configuration gives the same result as a π configuration, since we can view things in terms of "holes," instead of electrons.

Table 13.3 Molecular Electronic Terms

Configuration	Terms
$\sigma\sigma$	$^1\Sigma^+,\ ^3\Sigma^+$
$\sigma\pi$	$^1\Pi,\ ^3\Pi$
$\pi\pi$	$^1\Sigma^+,\ ^3\Sigma^+,\ ^1\Sigma^-,\ ^3\Sigma^-,\ ^1\Delta,\ ^3\Delta$
$\pi\delta$	$^1\Pi,\ ^3\Pi,\ ^1\Phi,\ ^3\Phi$
σ	$^2\Sigma^+$
$\sigma^2;\ \pi^4;\ \delta^4$	$^1\Sigma^+$
$\pi;\ \pi^3$	$^2\Pi$
π^2	$^1\Sigma^+,\ ^3\Sigma^-,\ ^1\Delta$
$\delta;\ \delta^3$	$^2\Delta$
δ^2	$^1\Sigma^+,\ ^3\Sigma^-,\ ^1\Gamma$

For homonuclear diatomic molecules, a g or u right subscript is added to the term symbol to show the parity of the electronic states belonging to the term. Terms arising from an electron configuration that has an odd number of electrons in molecular orbitals of odd parity are odd; otherwise they are even. (This is the same rule as for atoms.)

The term symbols given in Table 13.2 are readily derived from the MO configurations. For example, O_2 has a π^2 configuration, which gives the three terms $^1\Sigma_g^+$, $^3\Sigma_g^-$, and $^1\Delta_g$. Hund's rule tells us that $^3\Sigma_g^-$ is the lowest term, as listed. Nearly all stable diatomic molecules have a $^1\Sigma^+$ ground term ($^1\Sigma_g^+$ for homonuclear diatomics). Exceptions include B_2 and O_2, and NO, which has a $^2\Pi$ ground term.

Spectroscopists prefix the ground term of a molecule by the symbol X. Excited terms of the same multiplicity as the ground term are designated as $A, B, C, \ldots$, while excited terms of different multiplicity from the ground term are designated as $a, b, c, \ldots$. Exceptions are C_2 and N_2, where the ground terms are $^1\Sigma_g^+$, but the letters $A, B, C, \ldots$ are used for excited triplet terms.

Just as for atoms, spin-orbit interaction can split a molecular term into closely spaced energy levels, giving a multiplet structure to the term. The projection of the total electronic spin S on the molecular axis is $M_S\hbar$; in molecules the quantum number M_S is called Σ (not to be confused with the symbol meaning $\Lambda = 0$):

$$\Sigma = S, S-1, \ldots, -S$$

The axial components of electronic orbital and spin angular momenta add, giving as the total axial component of electronic angular momentum: $(\Lambda + \Sigma)\hbar$. (Recall that Λ is the absolute value of M_L; we consider Σ to be positive when it has the same direction as Λ, and negative when it has the opposite direction as Λ.) The possible values of $\Lambda + \Sigma$ are

$$\Lambda + S, \Lambda + S-1, \ldots, \Lambda - S$$

The value of $\Lambda + \Sigma$ is written as a right subscript to the term symbol to distinguish the energy levels of the term. Thus a $^3\Delta$ term has $\Lambda = 2$ and $S = 1$, and gives rise to the levels $^3\Delta_3$, $^3\Delta_2$, and $^3\Delta_1$. In a sense, $\Lambda + \Sigma$ is the analog in molecules of the quantum number J in atoms. However, $\Lambda + \Sigma$ is the quantum number of the z *component* of total electronic angular momentum, and therefore can take on negative values. Thus a $^4\Pi$ term has the four levels $^4\Pi_{5/2}$, $^4\Pi_{3/2}$, $^4\Pi_{1/2}$, and $^4\Pi_{-1/2}$. The absolute value of $\Lambda + \Sigma$ is called Ω:

$$\Omega \equiv |\Lambda + \Sigma| \tag{13.87}$$

It is the value of $\Lambda + \Sigma$, and not the value of Ω, which is written as a subscript on the term symbol.

The spin–orbit interaction energy in diatomic molecules can be shown to be well approximated by $A\Lambda\Sigma$, where A depends on Λ and on the internuclear distance R, but not on Σ. The spacing between levels of the multiplet is thus constant. When A is positive, the level with the lowest value of $\Lambda + \Sigma$ lies lowest, and the multiplet is *regular*. When A is negative, the multiplet is *inverted*. Note that for $\Lambda \neq 0$, the multiplicity $(2S + 1)$ always equals the number of multiplet components; this is not always true for atoms.

Each energy level of a multiplet with $\Lambda \neq 0$ is doubly degenerate, corresponding to the two values for M_L. Thus a $^3\Delta$ term has six different wave functions [Eqs. (13.83), (13.85), (11.57)–(11.59)] and therefore six different molecular electronic states. Spin–orbit interaction splits the $^3\Delta$ term into three levels, each doubly degenerate. (The double degeneracy of the levels is removed by the Λ-type doubling mentioned previously.)

For Σ terms ($\Lambda = 0$), the spin–orbit interaction is very small (zero in the first approximation), and the quantum numbers Σ and Ω are not defined.

A $^1\Sigma$ term always corresponds to a single nondegenerate energy level.

13.8 The Hydrogen Molecule

The hydrogen molecule is the simplest molecule containing an electron-pair bond, and is probably the most studied molecule in quantum chemistry. Many of the ideas applied in treating H_2 are used in discussing more complicated molecules. We will devote most of our attention to the ground electronic state.

The purely electronic Hamiltonian for H_2 is

$$\hat{H} = -\tfrac{1}{2}\nabla_1^2 - \tfrac{1}{2}\nabla_2^2 - \frac{1}{r_{a1}} - \frac{1}{r_{a2}} - \frac{1}{r_{b1}} - \frac{1}{r_{b2}} + \frac{1}{r_{12}} \qquad (13.88)$$

where 1 and 2 are the electrons, and a and b are the nuclei (Fig. 13.16). Just as in the helium atom, the $1/r_{12}$ interelectronic-repulsion term prevents the Schroedinger equation from being separable. We therefore use approximation methods.

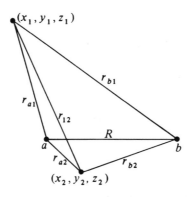

FIGURE 13.16 *The hydrogen molecule.*

We start with the molecular-orbital approach. The ground-state electronic configuration of H_2 is $(\sigma_g 1s)^2$, and we can write an approximate wave function as the Slater determinant:

$$\frac{1}{\sqrt{2}} \begin{vmatrix} \sigma_g 1s(1)\alpha(1) & \sigma_g 1s(1)\beta(1) \\ \sigma_g 1s(2)\alpha(2) & \sigma_g 1s(2)\beta(2) \end{vmatrix} = \sigma_g 1s(1)\,\sigma_g 1s(2)\,2^{-1/2}[\alpha(1)\beta(2) - \beta(1)\alpha(2)]$$

$$= f(1)\,f(2)\,2^{-1/2}[\alpha(1)\beta(2) - \beta(1)\alpha(2)] \qquad (13.89)$$

which is similar to (10.41) for the helium atom. To save time, we write f instead of $\sigma_g 1s$. As we saw in Section 10.5, omission of the spin factor does not affect the variational integral for a two-electron problem. Hence we want to choose f so as to minimize

$$\frac{\iint f^*(1)\,f^*(2)\,\hat{H}f(1)\,f(2)\,dv_1\,dv_2}{\iint |f(1)|^2\,|f(2)|^2\,dv_1\,dv_2} \qquad (13.90)$$

where the integration is over the space coordinates of the two electrons. Ideally f should be found by an SCF calculation. For simplicity, we can use an H_2^+-like MO.

(The H_2 Hamiltonian becomes the sum of two $H_2{}^+$ Hamiltonians if we omit the $1/r_{12}$ term.)   We saw in Section 13.4 that the function [Eq. (13.47)]

$$\frac{k^{3/2}}{(2\pi)^{1/2}(1+S_{ab})^{1/2}}(e^{-kr_a}+e^{-kr_b})$$

gave a good approximation to the ground-state $H_2{}^+$ wave function.   Hence we try as a variation function φ for H_2 the product of two such LCAO functions, one for each electron:

$$\varphi = \frac{\zeta^3}{2\pi(1+S_{ab})}(e^{-\zeta r_{a1}}+e^{-\zeta r_{b1}})(e^{-\zeta r_{a2}}+e^{-\zeta r_{b2}}) \tag{13.91}$$

$$\varphi = \frac{1}{2(1+S_{ab})}[1s_a(1)+1s_b(1)][1s_a(2)+1s_b(2)] \tag{13.92}$$

where the effective nuclear charge ζ will differ from k for $H_2{}^+$.   Since

$$\hat{H} = \hat{H}_1^0 + \hat{H}_2^0 + 1/r_{12}$$

where $\hat{H}_1^0$ and $\hat{H}_2^0$ are $H_2{}^+$ Hamiltonians for each electron, we have

$$\int\int \varphi^*\hat{H}\varphi \, dv_1 \, dv_2 = 2W_1 + \int\int \frac{\varphi^2}{r_{12}} \, dv_1 \, dv_2 \tag{13.93}$$

where W_1 is given by (13.59) with k replaced by ζ.   The evaluation of the $1/r_{12}$ integral is involved, and is omitted.   Coulson in 1937 carried out the variational calculation using (13.91).   He found[13] $R_e = 0.732$ Å, rather close to the true value 0.742 Å; the minimum in the calculated $U(R)$ curve gave $D_e = 3.49$ eV, which is not spectacular, as compared to the true value 4.75 eV (Table 13.2).   (Of course, the percent error in the total electronic energy is much less than the percent error in D_e, but D_e is the quantity of chemical interest.)   The value of ζ at 0.732 Å is 1.197, which is less than the value of k for $H_2{}^+$.   We attribute this to the screening of the nuclei from each electron by the other electron.

How can we improve on the above MO result?   We can try for a better approximation to the SCF molecular orbital by looking for the best possible function f in (13.89).   Coulson did such a calculation in 1938.   He used an expansion for f in elliptic coordinates.   Since $m = 0$ for the ground-state MO, the $e^{im\varphi}$ factor in the SCF MO is equal to 1, and f is a function of ξ and η only.   The expansion used is

$$f = e^{-\alpha\xi}\sum_{p,q} a_{pq}\xi^p\eta^q \tag{13.94}$$

where p and q are integers, and α and a_{pq} are variational parameters.   Coulson's calculation was improved by Kolos and Roothaan in 1960.   At $R = 0.74$ Å they found a dissociation energy of 3.64 eV, which is not much improvement on the value 3.49 eV given by the simple LCAO molecular orbital.   The correlation energy for H_2 is thus 1.11 eV, about the same as the value 1.1 eV for the two-electron helium atom (Section 11.1).   To get a truly accurate binding energy we must go beyond the SCF

---

[13] For the literature references of H_2 calculations mentioned in this and later sections, consult the bibliography given in A. D. McLean, A. Weiss, and M. Yoshimine, *Rev. Mod. Phys.*, **32**, 211 (1960).

approximation of writing the wave function in the form $f(1) f(2)$. We use the same methods we used for atoms, namely, configuration interaction, and introduction of r_{12} into the trial function.

First consider configuration interaction (CI). To reach the exact ground-state wave function, we include contributions from SCF (or other) functions for all the excited states (including continuum states) with the same symmetry as the ground state. In the first approximation, only contributions from the lowest-lying excited states are included. The first excited configuration of H_2 is $(\sigma_g 1s)(\sigma_u^* 1s)$, which gives the terms $^1\Sigma_u^+$ and $^3\Sigma_u^+$. (We have one g and one u electron, so the terms are of odd parity.) The ground-state configuration $(\sigma_g 1s)^2$ is a $^1\Sigma_g^+$ state. Hence we don't get any contribution from the $(\sigma_g 1s)(\sigma_u^* 1s)$ states, since they have different parity from the ground state. Next consider the configuration $(\sigma_u^* 1s)^2$. This is a closed-subshell configuration having the single state $^1\Sigma_g^+$. This is of the right symmetry to contribute to the ground-state wave function. As a simple CI trial function we can take a linear combination of the SCF wave functions for the $(\sigma_g 1s)^2$ and $(\sigma_u^* 1s)^2$ configurations. To simplify things, we will use the LCAO-MO's as approximations to the SCF functions. Thus we take

$$\varphi = \sigma_g 1s(1)\, \sigma_g 1s(2) + c\sigma_u^* 1s(1)\, \sigma_u^* 1s(2) \qquad \textbf{(13.95)}$$

where $\sigma_g 1s$ and $\sigma_u^* 1s$ are given by (13.47) and (13.48), and c is a variational parameter. This calculation was performed by Weinbaum in 1933. The result is a bond length of 0.75 Å and a dissociation energy of 4.02 eV, a considerable improvement over the SCF result $D_e = 3.64 \text{ eV}$. The orbital exponent has the optimum value 1.19. We can improve on this result in two ways: by using a better form for the MO's of each configuration, and by including more configurations. Hagstrom did a CI calculation in which the MO's were represented by expansions in elliptic coordinates; with 33 configurations, he found $D_e = 4.71$ eV, quite close to the true value 4.75 eV. [S. Hagstrom and H. Shull, *Rev. Mod. Phys.*, **35**, 624 (1963).]

Now consider the use of r_{12} in H_2 trial functions. The first really accurate calculation of the hydrogen-molecule ground state was done by James and Coolidge in 1933. They used the trial function

$$\exp\left[-\delta(\xi_1 + \xi_2)\right] \sum c_{mnjkp} \left[\xi_1^m \xi_2^n \eta_1^j \eta_2^k + \xi_1^n \xi_2^m \eta_1^k \eta_2^j\right] r_{12}^p \qquad \textbf{(13.96)}$$

where the summation is over integral values of m, n, j, k, and p. The variational parameters are δ and the c_{mnjkp}. Note the resemblance of this function to the helium trial function (9.91). The James and Coolidge function is symmetric with respect to interchange of electrons 1 and 2, as it should be, since we have an antisymmetric ground-state spin function. With 13 terms in the sum, James and Coolidge found $D_e = 4.72$ eV, only 0.03 eV in error. Their work has been extended by Kolos, Wolniewicz, and Roothaan. These workers used trial functions with as many as 100 terms in the sum. Including relativistic corrections and corrections to the Born–Oppenheimer approximation, Kolos and Wolniewicz found $D_e/hc = 38,297 \text{ cm}^{-1}$. Their 100-term wave function is nearly indistinguishable from the true wave function, but its great complexity allows no simple physical interpretation.[14] At the time

---

[14] W. Kolos and C. C. J. Roothaan, *Rev. Mod. Phys.*, **32**, 219 (1960); W. Kolos and L. Wolniewicz, *J. Chem. Phys.*, **41**, 3663 (1964); **49**, 404 (1968).

their calculation was completed, the accepted experimental D_e/hc was $(38{,}293 \pm 1)$ cm^{-1} and the 4 cm^{-1} discrepancy caused much consternation among theoreticians, who kept looking for additional theoretical corrections, without success. Finally a reinvestigation [G. Herzberg, *J. Mol. Spectry.*, **33**, 147 (1970)] of the H_2 spectrum gave a new experimental value in full agreement with the Kolos–Wolniewicz value, thereby vindicating the theoreticians.

13.9 The Valence-Bond Treatment of H_2

The first quantum-mechanical treatment of the hydrogen molecule was by Heitler and London in 1927. Their ideas have been extended to give a general theory of chemical bonding, known as the *valence-bond* (VB) theory, or the HLSP theory, after Heitler, London, Slater, and Pauling. The valence-bond method is more closely related to the chemist's idea of molecules as consisting of atoms held together by localized bonds than is the molecular-orbital method. The VB method views molecules as composed of atomic cores (nuclei plus inner-shell electrons) and bonding valence electrons. For H_2, both electrons are valence electrons.

The starting point of the Heitler–London treatment of the H_2 ground state is to approximate the molecule as two ground-state hydrogen atoms. The wave function for two such noninteracting atoms is

$$f_1 = 1s_a(1)\,1s_b(2) \tag{13.97}$$

where a and b refer to the nuclei, and 1 and 2 refer to the electrons. Of course, the function

$$f_2 = 1s_a(2)\,1s_b(1) \tag{13.98}$$

is also a valid wave function. This then suggests the trial variation function

$$c_1 f_1 + c_2 f_2 = c_1\,1s_a(1)\,1s_b(2) + c_2\,1s_a(2)\,1s_b(1) \tag{13.99}$$

This is a linear variation function, which leads to the determinantal equation (8.87), where

$$H_{11} = \int f_1^* \hat{H} f_1 \, dv, \qquad S_{11} = \int f_1^* f_1 \, dv, \qquad \text{etc.} \tag{13.100}$$

We can also consider the problem using perturbation theory (as Heitler and London did). A ground-state hydrogen molecule dissociates to two neutral ground-state hydrogen atoms. We therefore take as our unperturbed problem two ground-state hydrogen atoms at infinite separation. One possible zeroth-order (unperturbed) wave function is $1s_a(1)\,1s_b(2)$; however, electron 2 could just as well be bound to nucleus a, giving the unperturbed wave function $1s_a(2)\,1s_b(1)$. These two unperturbed wave functions belong to a doubly degenerate energy level (exchange degeneracy). Under the perturbation of molecule formation, the doubly degenerate level is split into two levels, and the *correct* zeroth-order wave functions are linear combinations of the two unperturbed wave functions:

$$c_1\,1s_a(1)\,1s_b(2) + c_2\,1s_a(2)\,1s_b(1)$$

This leads to a 2×2 secular determinant which is the same as (8.87), except that W is replaced by $E^{(0)} + E^{(1)}$; see Problem 9.3.

We now solve (8.87). The Hamiltonian is Hermitian, all functions are real, and f_1 and f_2 are normalized; hence

$$H_{12} = H_{21}, \qquad S_{12} = S_{21}, \qquad S_{11} = S_{22} = 1 \qquad \textbf{(13.101)}$$

Consider H_{11} and H_{22}:

$$H_{11} = \langle 1s_a(1) 1s_b(2) | \hat{H} | 1s_a(1) 1s_b(2) \rangle$$

$$H_{22} = \langle 1s_a(2) 1s_b(1) | \hat{H} | 1s_a(2) 1s_b(1) \rangle$$

Interchange of the coordinate labels 1 and 2 in H_{22} converts H_{22} to H_{11}, since this relabeling leaves $\hat{H}$ unchanged. Hence $H_{11} = H_{22}$. The secular equation (8.87) becomes

$$\begin{vmatrix} H_{11} - W & H_{12} - W S_{12} \\ H_{12} - W S_{12} & H_{11} - W \end{vmatrix} = 0 \qquad \textbf{(13.102)}$$

This equation has the same form as Eq. (13.40), and by analogy to Eqs. (13.42), (13.47), and (13.48) the approximate energies and wave functions are:

$$W_1 = \frac{H_{11} + H_{12}}{1 + S_{12}}, \qquad W_2 = \frac{H_{11} - H_{12}}{1 - S_{12}} \qquad \textbf{(13.103)}$$

$$\varphi_1 = \frac{f_1 + f_2}{\sqrt{2}(1 + S_{12})^{1/2}}, \qquad \varphi_2 = \frac{f_1 - f_2}{\sqrt{2}(1 - S_{12})^{1/2}} \qquad \textbf{(13.104)}$$

For S_{12}, we have

$$S_{12} = \int f_1^* f_2 \, dv = \iint 1s_a(1) 1s_b(2) 1s_a(2) 1s_b(1) \, dv_1 \, dv_2$$

$$S_{12} = \langle 1s_a(1) | 1s_b(1) \rangle \langle 1s_a(2) | 1s_b(2) \rangle = S_{ab}^2 \qquad \textbf{(13.105)}$$

where the overlap integral S_{ab} is defined by (13.39).

The numerators of (13.104) are

$$f_1 \pm f_2 = 1s_a(1) 1s_b(2) \pm 1s_a(2) 1s_b(1) \qquad \textbf{(13.106)}$$

From our previous discussion in this chapter, we know that the ground state of H_2 is a $^1\Sigma$ state with the antisymmetric spin factor (11.60) and a symmetric spatial factor. Hence φ_1 must be the ground state. The Heitler–London ground-state wave function is

$$\frac{1s_a(1) 1s_b(2) + 1s_a(2) 1s_b(1)}{\sqrt{2}(1 + S_{ab}^2)^{1/2}} \frac{1}{\sqrt{2}} [\alpha(1) \beta(2) - \alpha(2) \beta(1)] \qquad \textbf{(13.107)}$$

The Heitler–London wave functions for the three states of the lowest $^3\Sigma$ term are

$$\frac{1s_a(1) 1s_b(2) - 1s_a(2) 1s_b(1)}{\sqrt{2}(1 - S_{ab}^2)^{1/2}} \begin{cases} \alpha(1) \alpha(2) \\ 2^{-1/2} [\alpha(1) \beta(2) + \beta(1) \alpha(2)] \\ \beta(1) \beta(2) \end{cases} \qquad \textbf{(13.108)}$$

Now consider the ground-state energy expression. We divide the molecular electronic Hamiltonian into the sum of two hydrogen-atom Hamiltonians plus perturbing terms:

$$\hat{H} = \hat{H}_a(1) + \hat{H}_b(2) + \hat{H}' \tag{13.109}$$

$$\hat{H}_a(1) = -\tfrac{1}{2}\nabla_1^2 - \frac{1}{r_{a1}}, \qquad \hat{H}_b(2) = -\tfrac{1}{2}\nabla_2^2 - \frac{1}{r_{b2}} \tag{13.110}$$

$$\hat{H}' = -\frac{1}{r_{b1}} - \frac{1}{r_{a2}} + \frac{1}{r_{12}}$$

We then have

$$H_{11} = \langle 1s_a(1)\,1s_b(2)|\,\hat{H}_a(1) + \hat{H}_b(2) + \hat{H}'\,|1s_a(1)\,1s_b(2)\rangle \tag{13.111}$$

For the integral involving $\hat{H}_a(1)$, we have

$$\langle 1s_a(1)\,1s_b(2)|\,\hat{H}_a(1)\,|1s_a(1)\,1s_b(2)\rangle = \langle 1s_a(1)|\,\hat{H}_a(1)\,|1s_a(1)\rangle \langle 1s_b(2)|1s_b(2)\rangle$$

The Heitler–London calculation does not introduce an effective nuclear charge into the $1s$ function; hence, $1s_a(1)$ is an eigenfunction of $\hat{H}_a(1)$ with eigenvalue $-\tfrac{1}{2}$ hartree, the hydrogen-atom ground-state energy. The $1s$ function is normalized, and we conclude that the $\hat{H}_a(1)$ integral equals $-\tfrac{1}{2}$ in atomic units. Similarly, the $\hat{H}_b(2)$ integral in (13.111) equals $-\tfrac{1}{2}$. Defining the Coulomb integral Q as

$$Q \equiv \langle 1s_a(1)\,1s_b(2)|\,\hat{H}'\,|1s_a(1)\,1s_b(2)\rangle \tag{13.112}$$

we have

$$H_{11} = Q - 1 \tag{13.113}$$

For H_{12} we have

$$H_{12} = H_{21} = \langle 1s_a(2)\,1s_b(1)|\,\hat{H}_a(1) + \hat{H}_b(2) + \hat{H}'\,|1s_a(1)\,1s_b(2)\rangle \tag{13.114}$$

The $\hat{H}_a(1)$ integral is easily evaluated as

$$\langle 1s_a(2)|1s_b(2)\rangle \langle 1s_b(1)|\,\hat{H}_a(1)\,|1s_a(1)\rangle = -\tfrac{1}{2}S_{ab}^2$$

Defining the exchange integral A as

$$A \equiv \langle 1s_a(2)\,1s_b(1)|\,\hat{H}'\,|1s_a(1)\,1s_b(2)\rangle \tag{13.115}$$

we have

$$H_{12} = A - S_{ab}^2 \tag{13.116}$$

Substitution into (13.103) gives

$$W_1 = -1 + \frac{Q+A}{1+S_{ab}^2} \tag{13.117}$$

$$W_2 = -1 + \frac{Q-A}{1-S_{ab}^2} \tag{13.118}$$

The quantity -1 hartree in these expressions is the energy of two ground-state hydrogen atoms. To obtain the $U(R)$ potential-energy curves, we add the inter-nuclear repulsion $1/R$ to these expressions.

Many of the integrals needed to evaluate W_1 and W_2 have been evaluated in the treatment of H_2^+ in Section 13.4; the only new integrals are those involving $1/r_{12}$. The hardest one is the two-center two-electron exchange integral:

$$\int \int 1s_a(1)\, 1s_b(2)\frac{1}{r_{12}} 1s_a(2)\, 1s_b(1)\, dv_1\, dv_2$$

("Two-center" means that the integrand contains functions centered on two different nuclei, a and b; "two electron" means that the coordinates of two electrons occur in the integrand.) This must be evaluated using an expansion for $1/r_{12}$ in confocal elliptic coordinates, similar to the expansion (9.64) in spherical polar coordinates. (Heitler and London only approximated this integral. Its exact evaluation was given by Sugiura.) We omit the integral evaluations.[15] The results of the Heitler–London treatment are: $D_e = 3.20$ eV, $R_e = 0.80$ Å. The agree-ment with the experimental values $D_e = 4.75$ eV, $R_e = 0.74$ Å, is only fair. In this treatment, most of the binding energy is provided by the exchange integral A. However, as discussed for helium, "exchange" is not a real physical process. The Heitler–London treatment of H_2 bears some resemblance to the Heisenberg treat-ment of the helium $1s2s$ configuration given in Section 9.7. However, for H_2 the exchange integral is negative, whereas for helium it is positive.

Consider some improvements on the Heitler–London function (13.107). One obvious step is the introduction of an orbital exponent ζ in the $1s$ function. This was done by Wang in 1928. The optimum value of ζ is 1.166 at R_e and the binding energy is improved to 3.78 eV. Recall that Dickinson in 1933 improved the Finkelstein–Horowitz H_2^+ trial function by mixing in some $2p_z$ character into the atomic orbitals (hybridization). In 1931 Rosen used this idea to improve the Heitler–London–Wang function. He took the trial function

$$\varphi = \varphi_a(1)\, \varphi_b(2) + \varphi_a(2)\, \varphi_b(1)$$

where the atomic orbital φ_a is given by $\varphi_a = e^{-\zeta r_a}(1 + cz_a)$, with a similar expression for φ_b. This allows for the polarization of the AO's on molecule formation. The result is a binding energy of 4.04 eV. Another improvement, the use of ionic structures, will be considered in the next section.

13.10 Preliminary Comparison of the MO and VB Theories

Let us compare the molecular-orbital and valence-bond treatments of the hydrogen-molecule ground state.

If φ_a symbolizes an atomic orbital centered on nucleus a, the spatial factor of the (unnormalized) LCAO-MO wave function for the H_2 ground state is

$$[\varphi_a(1)+\varphi_b(1)][\varphi_a(2)+\varphi_b(2)] \tag{13.119}$$

---

[15] See *Slater, Quantum Theory of Molecules and Solids*, vol. 1, Appendix 6.

In the simplest treatment, φ is a $1s$ AO. The function (13.119) equals

$$\varphi_a(1)\,\varphi_a(2) + \varphi_b(1)\,\varphi_b(2) + \varphi_a(1)\,\varphi_b(2) + \varphi_b(1)\,\varphi_a(2) \qquad \textbf{(13.120)}$$

What is the physical significance of the terms? The last two terms have each electron in an atomic orbital centered on a different nucleus; these are covalent terms, corresponding to equal sharing of the electrons between the atoms. The first two terms have both electrons in AO's centered on the same nucleus; these are ionic terms, corresponding to the chemical structures

$$\text{H}^-\ \text{H}^+ \qquad \text{and} \qquad \text{H}^+\ \text{H}^- \qquad \textbf{(13.121)}$$

The covalent and ionic terms occur with equal weight, so that according to this simple MO function, there is a 50–50 chance as to whether the H_2 ground state dissociates to two neutral hydrogen atoms or to a proton and a hydride ion. Actually, the H_2 ground state dissociates to two neutral hydrogen atoms. Thus the simple MO function gives the wrong limiting value of the energy as R goes to infinity.

How can we remedy this? Since H_2 is nonpolar, chemical intuition tells us that ionic terms should make substantially less contribution to the wave function than covalent terms. The simplest procedure is to omit the ionic terms of the MO function (13.120). This gives

$$\varphi_a(1)\,\varphi_b(2) + \varphi_b(1)\,\varphi_a(2) \qquad \textbf{(13.122)}$$

We immediately recognize (13.122) as being the Heitler–London function (13.107).

Although interelectronic repulsion causes the electrons to avoid each other, there is some probability to find both electrons near the same nucleus, corresponding to an ionic structure. Therefore, instead of simply dropping the ionic terms from (13.120) we might try

$$\varphi_{\text{VB, imp}} = \varphi_a(1)\,\varphi_b(2) + \varphi_b(1)\,\varphi_a(2) + \delta[\varphi_a(1)\,\varphi_a(2)+\varphi_b(1)\,\varphi_b(2)] \qquad \textbf{(13.123)}$$

where $\delta(R)$ is a variational parameter, and the subscript indicates an improved VB function. In the language of valence-bond theory, this trial function represents *ionic–covalent resonance*. Of course, the ground-state wave function of H_2 does not undergo a time-dependent change back and forth from a covalent function corresponding to the structure H—H to ionic functions corresponding to the structures (13.121). Rather (in the particular approximation we are considering), the wave function is a time-independent mixture of covalent and ionic functions. Since H_2 dissociates to neutral atoms, we know that $\delta(\infty) = 0$. A variational calculation done by Weinbaum in 1933 using $1s$ AO's with an orbital exponent gave the result that at R_e the parameter δ has the value 0.26; the orbital exponent was found to be 1.19, and the dissociation energy was calculated as 4.02 eV, a modest improvement over the Heitler–London–Wang value of 3.78 eV. With δ equal to zero in (13.123), we get the VB function (13.122); with δ equal to 1, we get the LCAO-MO function (13.120). The optimum value of δ turns out to be closer to zero than to 1, and, in fact, the Heitler–London–Wang VB function gives a better dissociation energy than the LCAO-MO function.

Let us compare the improved valence-bond trial function (13.123) with the simple LCAO-MO function improved by configuration interaction. The LCAO-MO CI trial function (13.95) has the (unnormalized) form

$$\varphi_{MO, imp} = [\varphi_a(1)+\varphi_b(1)][\varphi_a(2)+\varphi_b(2)] + \gamma[\varphi_a(1)-\varphi_b(1)][\varphi_a(2)-\varphi_b(2)]$$

Since we have not yet normalized this function, there is no harm in multiplying it by the constant $1/(1-\gamma)$. Doing so, and rearranging terms, we get

$$\varphi_{MO, imp} = \varphi_a(1)\varphi_b(2) + \varphi_b(1)\varphi_a(2) + \frac{1+\gamma}{1-\gamma}[\varphi_a(1)\varphi_a(2)+\varphi_b(1)\varphi_b(2)]$$

There is also no harm done if we define a new constant δ as

$$\delta = (1+\gamma)/(1-\gamma)$$

We see then that this improved MO function and the improved VB function (13.123) are *identical*. Weinbaum viewed his H_2 calculation as a valence-bond calculation with inclusion of ionic terms. We have shown that we can just as well view the Weinbaum calculation as an MO calculation with configuration interaction. (This was the viewpoint adopted in Section 13.8.)

In the past, there has been much debate between the advocates of the MO and VB methods. Actually, both methods in their initial stages are rough approximations, neither being particularly more reliable. As we have just seen, when refinements are included in each method, they approach each other in their results.

The MO function (13.120) underestimates electron correlation, in that it says that structures with both electrons on the same atom are just as likely as structures with each electron on a different atom. The VB function (13.122) overestimates electron correlation, in that it has no contribution from structures with both electrons on the same atom. In MO theory electron correlation is introduced by configuration interaction. In VB theory, electron correlation is reduced by ionic–covalent resonance. The simple VB method is more reliable at large R than the simple MO method, since the latter predicts the wrong dissociation products.

To fix further the differences between the MO and VB approaches, consider how each method divides the H_2 electronic Hamiltonian into unperturbed and perturbation Hamiltonians. For the MO method we write

$$\hat{H} = \left[\left(-\tfrac{1}{2}\nabla_1^2 - \frac{1}{r_{a1}} - \frac{1}{r_{b1}}\right) + \left(-\tfrac{1}{2}\nabla_2^2 - \frac{1}{r_{a2}} - \frac{1}{r_{b2}}\right)\right] + \frac{1}{r_{12}} \qquad \textbf{(13.124)}$$

where the unperturbed Hamiltonian consists of the bracketed terms. In MO theory, the unperturbed Hamiltonian for H_2 is the sum of two H_2^+ Hamiltonians, one for each electron. Accordingly, the zeroth-order MO wave function is a product of two H_2^+-like wave functions, one for each electron. Since the H_2^+ functions are rather complicated, we approximate the H_2^+-like MO's as LCAO's. The effect of the $1/r_{12}$ perturbation is taken into account in an average way by using self-consistent-field molecular orbitals; to take instantaneous electron correlation into account, we use configuration interaction, giving a kind of calculation called LCAO-MO SCF CI.

For the valence-bond method, the terms in the Hamiltonian are grouped in either of two ways:

$$\hat{H} = \left[\left(-\tfrac{1}{2}\nabla_1^2 - \frac{1}{r_{a1}}\right) + \left(-\tfrac{1}{2}\nabla_2^2 - \frac{1}{r_{b2}}\right)\right] - \frac{1}{r_{a2}} - \frac{1}{r_{b1}} + \frac{1}{r_{12}} \qquad (13.125)$$

$$\hat{H} = \left[\left(-\tfrac{1}{2}\nabla_1^2 - \frac{1}{r_{b1}}\right) + \left(-\tfrac{1}{2}\nabla_2^2 - \frac{1}{r_{a2}}\right)\right] - \frac{1}{r_{a1}} - \frac{1}{r_{b2}} + \frac{1}{r_{12}} \qquad (13.126)$$

The unperturbed system is two hydrogen atoms. We have two zeroth-order functions consisting of products of hydrogen-atom wave functions, and these belong to a degenerate level. The correct ground-state zeroth-order function is the linear combination (13.107).

The majority of quantitative molecular calculations are done using the MO method, because it is computationally much simpler than the VB method. The MO method was developed by Hund, Mulliken, and Lennard-Jones in the late 1920's. Originally it was used largely for qualitative descriptions of molecules, but the electronic digital computer has made possible the calculation of accurate MO functions (Section 13.16).

13.11 Electron Probability Density

We now consider how the wave function of a system is related to the electron probability density. We want the probability of finding an electron in the rectangular volume element at point (x, y, z) in space with edges dx, dy, dz. The electronic wave function ψ is a function of the space and spin coordinates of the n electrons. (For simplicity, the parametric dependence on the nuclear configuration will not be explicitly indicated.) We know that

$$|\psi(x_1, \ldots, z_n, m_{s1}, \ldots, m_{sn})|^2 \, dx_1 \, dy_1 \, dz_1 \cdots dx_n \, dy_n \, dz_n \qquad (13.127)$$

is the probability of simultaneously finding electron 1 with spin m_{s1} in the volume element $dx_1 \, dy_1 \, dz_1$ at (x_1, y_1, z_1), electron 2 with spin m_{s2} in the volume element $dx_2 \, dy_2 \, dz_2$ at (x_2, y_2, z_2), etc. Since we are not interested in what spin the electron we find at (x, y, z) has, we sum the probability (13.127) over all possible spin states of all electrons, to give the probability of simultaneously finding each electron in the appropriate volume element with no regard for spin:

$$\sum_{m_{s1}} \cdots \sum_{m_{sn}} |\psi|^2 \, dx_1 \cdots dz_n \qquad (13.128)$$

Suppose we ask for the probability of finding electron 1 in the volume element $dx \, dy \, dz$ at (x, y, z). For this probability we don't care where electrons 2 through n are; we therefore add the probabilities for all possible locations for these electrons. This amounts to integrating (13.128) over the coordinates of electrons $2, 3, \ldots, n$:

$$\left[\sum_{\text{all } m_s} \int \cdots \int |\psi(x, y, z, x_2, y_2, z_2, \ldots, x_n, y_n, z_n, m_{s1}, \ldots, m_{sn})|^2 \, dx_2 \cdots dz_n\right] dx \, dy \, dz$$
$$(13.129)$$

where there is a $(3n-3)$-fold integration over x_2 through z_n.

Now suppose we ask for the probability of finding electron 2 in the volume element $dx\,dy\,dz$ at (x, y, z). By analogy to (13.129), this is

$$\left[\sum_{\text{all } m_s} \int \cdots \int |\psi(x_1, y_1, z_1, x, y, z, x_3, \ldots, z_n, m_{s1}, \ldots, m_{sn})|^2\right.$$

$$\left. \times dx_1\,dy_1\,dz_1\,dx_3 \cdots dz_n\right]dx\,dy\,dz \qquad (13.130)$$

Of course electrons don't come with labels, and because of this indistinguishability (Chapter 10), we know that the probabilities (13.129) and (13.130) must be equal. This equality is readily proved. ψ is antisymmetric with respect to electron exchange, and therefore $|\psi|^2$ is unchanged by such an exchange. Interchanging the space and spin coordinates of electrons 1 and 2 in ψ in (13.130) and doing some relabeling of dummy variables, we see that (13.130) is equal to (13.129). Thus (13.129) gives the probability of finding any one particular electron in the volume element. Since we have n electrons, the probability for finding *an* electron in the volume element is n times (13.129). (In drawing this conclusion, we are assuming that the probability of finding more than one electron in the infinitesimal volume element is negligible compared to the probability of finding one electron; this is certainly valid, since the probability of finding two electrons will involve the product of six infinitesimal quantities as compared to the product of three infinitesimal quantities for the probability of finding one electron.)

Thus the probability density ρ for finding an electron in the neighborhood of point (x, y, z) is

$$\rho(x, y, z) = n \sum_{\text{all } m_s} \int \cdots \int |\psi(x, y, z, x_2, \ldots, z_n, m_{s1}, \ldots, m_{sn})|^2\,dx_2 \cdots dz_n$$

$$(13.131)$$

[Experimental determination of ρ in molecules involves measurement of electron diffraction intensities or x-ray diffraction intensities; see D. A. Kohl and L. S. Bartell, *J. Chem. Phys.*, **51**, 2891, 2896 (1969).] The units of ρ are electrons/bohr^3.

To illustrate (13.131), we calculate the electron density for the simple VB and MO ground-state H_2 functions. The wave function is a product of a spatial factor and the spin function (11.60). (For more than two electrons, the wave function cannot be factored into a simple product of space and spin parts; see Chapter 10.) Summation of (11.60) over m_{s1} and m_{s2} gives unity (Section 10.5). Thus (13.131) becomes for H_2

$$\rho(x, y, z) = 2 \int \int \int |\varphi(x, y, z, x_2, y_2, z_2)|^2\,dx_2\,dy_2\,dz_2 \qquad (13.132)$$

where φ is the spatial factor. The valence-bond function (13.107) gives

$$|\varphi(1, 2)|^2 = \frac{[1s_a(1)]^2[1s_b(2)]^2 + [1s_b(1)]^2[1s_a(2)]^2 + 2\cdot 1s_a(1)\,1s_a(2)\,1s_b(1)\,1s_b(2)}{2(1 + S_{ab}^2)}$$

$$\rho_{VB} = \frac{2}{2(1+S_{ab}^2)} \left[1s_a^2 \int [1s_b(2)]^2 \, dv_2 + 1s_b^2 \int [1s_a(2)]^2 \, dv_2 \right.$$

$$\left. + 2 \cdot 1s_a 1s_b \int 1s_a(2) 1s_b(2) \, dv_2 \right]$$

$$\rho_{VB} = \frac{1s_a^2 + 1s_b^2 + 2S_{ab} 1s_a 1s_b}{1 + S_{ab}^2} \tag{13.133}$$

The MO function (13.92) gives (Problem 13.19b)

$$\rho_{MO} = \frac{1s_a^2 + 1s_b^2 + 2 \cdot 1s_a 1s_b}{1 + S_{ab}} \tag{13.134}$$

Let us compare ρ_{MO} and ρ_{VB}. Both functions pile up more charge between the nuclei than is given by the sum of the atomic charge densities ($1s_a^2 + 1s_b^2$). (Recall the discussion of H_2^+ in Section 13.4.) Midway between the nuclei, we have $1s_a = 1s_b$ and $\rho_{MO} - \rho_{VB}$ is

$$\frac{2(S_{ab}-1)^2}{(1+S_{ab})(1+S_{ab}^2)} 1s_a^2 \tag{13.135}$$

The numerator of (13.135) is zero for S_{ab} equal to one, and positive for all other values of S_{ab}. Since the overlap integral S_{ab} is less than one, the MO function piles up more charge between the nuclei than the VB function. The VB function gives a lower energy (higher dissociation energy) than the MO function, so that the MO function must pile up too much charge between the nuclei. This is unfavorable because of increased interelectronic repulsion. Recall that the MO function underestimates electron correlation.

The MO probability density (13.134) is just twice the probability density for an H_2^+-like $\sigma_g 1s$ molecular orbital [Eq. (13.61)]. We can prove that for a molecular-orbital trial function, the probability density is found by multiplying the probability-density function of each MO by the number of electrons occupying it, and summing the results:

$$\rho(x, y, z) = \sum_j n_j |\varphi_j|^2 \tag{13.136}$$

where the sum is over all the different spatial MO's, and where n_j ($=0$ or 1 or 2) is the number of electrons in the orbital φ_j. [We used (13.136) in Eq. (11.14).]

13.12 Dipole Moments

We now show how to calculate molecular dipole moments from wave functions.

The classical expression for the electric dipole moment $\mathbf{d}_{cl}$ of a set of discrete charges q_i is

$$\mathbf{d}_{cl} = \sum_i q_i \mathbf{r}_i \tag{13.137}$$

where $\mathbf{r}_i$ is the position vector from the origin to the ith charge. The electric dipole moment is a vector; its x component is

$$d_{x,\,\mathrm{cl}} = \sum_i q_i x_i \tag{13.138}$$

with similar expressions for the other components. (The symbol $\boldsymbol{\mu}$ is commonly used for the electric dipole moment, but this can be confused with the symbol for magnetic dipole moment.) For a continuous charge distribution with charge density $\rho_q(x, y, z)$, $\mathbf{d}_{\mathrm{cl}}$ is found by summing over the infinitesimal elements of charge $dq_i = \rho_q(x, y, z)\, dx\, dy\, dz$:

$$\mathbf{d}_{\mathrm{cl}} = \int \rho_q(x, y, z) \mathbf{r}\, dx\, dy\, dz \tag{13.139}$$

$$\mathbf{r} = x\mathbf{i} + y\mathbf{j} + z\mathbf{k} \tag{13.140}$$

    Now consider the quantum-mechanical definition of the electric dipole moment. Suppose we apply a uniform external electric field $\mathbf{E}$ to an atom or molecule, and ask for the effect on the energy of the system. To form the Hamiltonian operator, we first need the classical expression for the energy. The definition of an electric field is the force $\mathbf{F}$ it exerts on a charge q, divided by q: $\mathbf{E} = \mathbf{F}/q$. We take the z direction as the direction of the applied field: $\mathbf{E} = \mathscr{E}_z \mathbf{k}$. The potential energy V is [Eq. (4.26)]:

$$\frac{dV}{dz} = -F_z = -q\mathscr{E}_z \tag{13.141}$$

$$V = -q\mathscr{E}_z z \tag{13.142}$$

This is the potential energy of a single charge in the field. For a system of charges, we have

$$V = -\mathscr{E}_z \sum_i q_i z_i \tag{13.143}$$

where z_i is the z coordinate of charge q_i. The extension of (13.143) to the case where the electric field points in an arbitrary direction follows from (4.26) and is

$$V = -\mathscr{E}_x \sum_i q_i x_i - \mathscr{E}_y \sum_i q_i y_i - \mathscr{E}_z \sum_i q_i z_i \tag{13.144}$$

$$V = -\mathbf{E} \cdot \mathbf{d}_{\mathrm{cl}} \tag{13.145}$$

This is the classical-mechanical expression for the energy of an electric dipole in a uniform applied electric field.

    To calculate the quantum-mechanical expression, we use perturbation theory. The perturbation operator $\hat{H}'$ corresponding to (13.145) is

$$\hat{H}' = -\mathbf{E} \cdot \hat{\mathbf{d}} \tag{13.146}$$

where the *electric dipole-moment operator* $\hat{\mathbf{d}}$ is given by

$$\hat{\mathbf{d}} = \sum_i q_i \hat{\mathbf{r}}_i = \mathbf{i}\, \hat{d}_x + \mathbf{j}\, \hat{d}_y + \mathbf{k}\, \hat{d}_z \tag{13.147}$$

$$\hat{d}_x = \sum_i q_i x_i, \qquad \hat{d}_y = \sum_i q_i y_i, \qquad \hat{d}_z = \sum_i q_i z_i \tag{13.148}$$

The first-order correction to the energy is [Eq. (9.30)]:

$$E^{(1)} = -\mathbf{E} \cdot \int \psi^{(0)*} \hat{\mathbf{d}} \psi^{(0)}\, d\tau \tag{13.149}$$

where $\psi^{(0)}$ is the unperturbed wave function. Comparison of (13.149) and (13.145) shows that the quantum-mechanical quantity that corresponds to $\mathbf{d}_{el}$ is the integral

$$\mathbf{d} = \int \psi^{(0)*} \hat{\mathbf{d}} \psi^{(0)} \, d\tau \tag{13.150}$$

The quantity $\mathbf{d}$ in (13.150) is the quantum-mechanical *electric dipole moment* of the system.

An objection to taking (13.150) as the dipole moment is that we only considered the first-order energy correction. If we had included $E^{(2)}$ in (13.149), the comparison with (13.145) would not give (13.150) as the dipole moment. Actually, (13.150) is the dipole moment of the system in the absence of an applied electric field, and is the *permanent* electric dipole moment. Application of the field distorts the wave function from $\psi^{(0)}$ giving rise to an *induced* electric dipole moment, in addition to the permanent dipole moment; the induced dipole moment corresponds[16] to the energy correction $E^{(2)}$. The induced dipole moment $\mathbf{d}_{ind}$ is related to the applied electric field by

$$\mathbf{d}_{ind} = \alpha \mathbf{E} \tag{13.151}$$

where α is the *polarizability* of the atom or molecule. The polarizability is important in discussions of van der Waals forces,[17] and determines the index of refraction and dielectric constant of a gas.

The shift in the energy of a quantum-mechanical system caused by an applied electric field is called the *Stark effect* (after a German physicist). The *first-order* (or *linear*) Stark effect is given by (13.149) and from (13.150) it vanishes for a system with no permanent electric dipole moment. The *second order* (or *quadratic*) Stark effect is given by the energy correction $E^{(2)}$ and is proportional to the square of the applied field.

The electric dipole-moment operator (13.147) is an odd function of the coordinates. If the wave function in (13.150) is either even or odd, then the integrand in (13.150) is an odd function, and the integral over all space vanishes. We conclude that the permanent electric dipole moment $\mathbf{d}$ is zero for states of definite parity.

The permanent electric dipole moment of a molecule whose electronic state is ψ_{el} is

$$\mathbf{d} = \int \psi_{el}^* \hat{\mathbf{d}} \psi_{el} \, d\tau_{el} \tag{13.152}$$

We have seen that the electronic wave functions of homonuclear diatomic molecules can be classified as g or u, according to their parity. Hence a homonuclear diatomic molecule has a zero permanent electric dipole moment, a not too astonishing result. The same holds true for any molecule with a center of symmetry.[18] The electric dipole-moment operator for a molecule includes summation over both the electronic and nuclear charges:

$$\hat{\mathbf{d}} = \sum_i (-e\mathbf{r}_i) + \sum_\alpha Z_\alpha e\mathbf{r}_\alpha \tag{13.153}$$

where $\mathbf{r}_\alpha$ is the vector from the origin to the nucleus of atomic number Z_α, and $\mathbf{r}_i$ is the vector to electron i. Since both the dipole-moment operator (13.153) and the electronic wave function depend on the parameters defining the nuclear configuration, the molecular electronic dipole moment $\mathbf{d}$ depends on the nuclear configuration. To indicate this, the quantity (13.152) can be called the dipole-moment *function* of the molecule. In writing

---

[16] For the details, see *Merzbacher*, Section 17.4.
[17] See *Kauzmann*, Chapter 13.
[18] Of course, there are other cases where $\mathbf{d}$ vanishes; see Section 12.3.

(13.152), we ignore the nuclear motion; when the dipole moment of a molecule is experimentally determined, what is measured is the quantity (13.152) averaged over the zero-point vibrations (assuming the temperature is not high enough to have appreciable population of higher vibrational levels). We might use $\mathbf{d}_0$ and $\mathbf{d}_e$ to indicate the dipole moment averaged over zero-point vibrations and the dipole moment at the equilibrium nuclear configuration, respectively.

Since the second sum in (13.153) is independent of the electronic coordinates, we have

$$\mathbf{d} = \int \psi_{el}^* \sum_i (-e\mathbf{r}_i) \psi_{el} \, d\tau_{el} + \sum_\alpha Z_\alpha e\mathbf{r}_\alpha \int \psi_{el}^* \psi_{el} \, d\tau_{el} \qquad \textbf{(13.154)}$$

$$\mathbf{d} = -e \int |\psi_{el}|^2 \sum_i \mathbf{r}_i \, d\tau_{el} + e \sum_\alpha Z_\alpha \mathbf{r}_\alpha \qquad \textbf{(13.155)}$$

Because of the indistinguishability of the electrons, we can write (13.155) as

$$\mathbf{d} = -en \int |\psi_{el}|^2 \mathbf{r}_1 \, d\tau_{el} + e \sum_\alpha Z_\alpha \mathbf{r}_\alpha \qquad \textbf{(13.156)}$$

where n is the number of electrons in the molecule, and $\mathbf{r}_1$ is the position vector of electron 1. Introducing the electronic probability density (13.131), we write

$$\mathbf{d} = -e \int \int \int \rho(x, y, z) \mathbf{r} \, dx \, dy \, dz + e \sum_\alpha Z_\alpha \mathbf{r}_\alpha \qquad \textbf{(13.157)}$$

The formula (13.157) is sometimes derived by considering the electronic charge as being smeared out into a continuous charge distribution whose charge density is found from (13.131); the classical expression (13.139) is then used to give the contribution of the electronic "charge cloud" to the molecular dipole moment. As mentioned in Section 6.6, the electrons are *not* smeared out into a charge cloud. However, the quantum-mechanical expression (13.150) for the electric dipole moment involves a spatial average over the electrons' positions. To determine $\langle \psi | \mathbf{r} | \psi \rangle$, we make a single measurement of $\mathbf{r}$ on a large number of identical noninteracting systems, each in the same state ψ, and average the result. Mathematically, the result is the same as if we considered the electrons in a single system to be smeared out into a charge cloud and calculated $\langle \mathbf{r} \rangle$ on this basis.

13.13 MO and VB Wave Functions for Homonuclear Diatomic Molecules

The molecular-orbital approximation puts the electrons of a molecule in molecular orbitals, which extend over the whole molecule. As an approximation to the molecular orbitals, we usually use linear combinations of atomic orbitals. The valence-bond method puts the electrons of a molecule in atomic orbitals and constructs the molecular wave function by allowing for "exchange" of the valence electron pairs between the atomic orbitals of the bonding atoms. We have compared the two methods for H_2; we now consider other homonuclear diatomic molecules.

We begin with the ground state of He_2. The separated helium atoms each have the ground-state configuration $1s^2$; for this closed-subshell configuration, we don't have any unpaired electrons to form valence bonds, and the VB wave function is simply the antisymmetrized product of the atomic-orbital functions:

$$\frac{1}{\sqrt{24}} \begin{vmatrix} 1s_a(1) & \overline{1s_a}(1) & 1s_b(1) & \overline{1s_b}(1) \\ 1s_a(2) & \overline{1s_a}(2) & 1s_b(2) & \overline{1s_b}(2) \\ 1s_a(3) & \overline{1s_a}(3) & 1s_b(3) & \overline{1s_b}(3) \\ 1s_a(4) & \overline{1s_a}(4) & 1s_b(4) & \overline{1s_b}(4) \end{vmatrix} \qquad (13.158)$$

The $1s$ function in this wave function is a helium-atom $1s$ function, which ideally is an SCF atomic function, but can be approximated by a hydrogenlike function with an effective nuclear charge. The subscripts a and b refer to the two atoms, and the bar indicates spin function β. In the shorthand notation of (10.65), the wave function (13.158) is

$$|1s_a \overline{1s_a} 1s_b \overline{1s_b}| \qquad (13.159)$$

The valence-bond wave function for He_2 has each electron paired with another electron in an orbital on the *same* atom and hence predicts no bonding.

In the MO approach, He_2 has the ground-state configuration $(\sigma_g 1s)^2 (\sigma_u^* 1s)^2$; with no net bonding electrons, no bonding is predicted, in agreement with the VB method. The MO approximation to the wave function is

$$|\sigma_g 1s \overline{\sigma_g 1s} \sigma_u^* 1s \overline{\sigma_u^* 1s}| \qquad (13.160)$$

The simplest approximation to the (unnormalized) MO's is to take them as linear combinations of the helium-atom AO's:

$$\sigma_g 1s \doteq 1s_a + 1s_b, \qquad \sigma_u^* 1s = 1s_a - 1s_b$$

With this approximation, (13.160) becomes

$$|(1s_a + 1s_b) \overline{(1s_a + 1s_b)} (1s_a - 1s_b) \overline{(1s_a - 1s_b)}| \qquad (13.161)$$

We can add or subtract one column of the determinant from another column without changing the determinant's value. If we add column 1 to column 3 and column 2 to column 4, we simplify (13.161) to

$$4|(1s_a + 1s_b) \overline{(1s_a + 1s_b)} 1s_a \overline{1s_a}|$$

We now subtract column 3 from column 1 and column 4 from column 2 to get

$$4|1s_b \overline{1s_b} 1s_a \overline{1s_a}| \qquad (13.162)$$

The interchange of columns 1 and 3 and of columns 2 and 4 multiplies the determinant by $(-1)^2$, so that (13.162) is equal to

$$4|1s_a \overline{1s_a} 1s_b \overline{1s_b}| \qquad (13.163)$$

which is identical (after normalization) to the valence-bond function (13.159). This result is easily generalized to the statement that the simple VB and simple LCAO-MO methods give the same approximate wave functions for diatomic molecules formed from separated atoms with completely filled atomic subshells. For example, the two methods give the same wave function for the Be_2 ground state. We could now substitute the trial function (13.163) into the variational integral and calculate the repulsive curve for the interaction of two ground-state helium atoms.

Before going on to Li_2, let us express the Heitler–London valence-bond functions for H_2 as Slater determinants. The ground-state Heitler–London function (13.107) can be written as

$$\tfrac{1}{2}(1+S_{ab}^2)^{-1/2}\left\{\begin{vmatrix} 1s_a(1)\alpha(1) & 1s_b(1)\beta(1) \\ 1s_a(2)\alpha(2) & 1s_b(2)\beta(2) \end{vmatrix} - \begin{vmatrix} 1s_a(1)\beta(1) & 1s_b(1)\alpha(1) \\ 1s_a(2)\beta(2) & 1s_b(2)\alpha(2) \end{vmatrix}\right\}$$

$$= (2+2S_{ab}^2)^{-1/2}\left\{|1s_a\,\overline{1s_b}| - |\overline{1s_a}\,1s_b|\right\} \tag{13.164}$$

In each Slater determinant the electron on atom a is paired with an electron of opposite spin on atom b, corresponding to the Lewis structure H—H. The Heitler–London functions (13.108) for the lowest H_2 triplet state can also be written as Slater determinants. Omitting normalization constants, we write the Heitler–London H_2 functions as

$$\text{Singlet:} \quad |1s_a\,\overline{1s_b}| - |\overline{1s_a}\,1s_b| \tag{13.165}$$

$$\text{Triplet:} \quad \begin{cases} |1s_a\,1s_b| \\ |1s_a\,\overline{1s_b}| + |\overline{1s_a}\,1s_b| \\ |\overline{1s_a}\,\overline{1s_b}| \end{cases} \tag{13.166}$$

Now consider Li_2. The ground-state configuration of Li is $1s^2 2s$ and the Lewis structure of Li_2 is Li—Li, with the two $2s$ Li electrons paired and the $1s$ electrons remaining in the inner shell of each atom. The part of the valence-bond wave function involving the $1s$ electrons will be like the He_2 function (13.159), while the part of the VB wave function involving the $2s$ electrons (which form the bond) will be like the Heitler–London H_2 function (13.165). Of course, because of the indistinguishability of the electrons, there is complete electronic democracy, and we must allow every electron to be in every orbital; hence, we write the ground-state valence-bond function for Li_2 using 6×6 Slater determinants:

$$|1s_a\,\overline{1s_a}\,1s_b\,\overline{1s_b}\,2s_a\,\overline{2s_b}| - |1s_a\,\overline{1s_a}\,1s_b\,\overline{1s_b}\,\overline{2s_a}\,2s_b| \tag{13.167}$$

We have written down (13.167) simply by analogy to (13.159) and (13.165)—for a fuller justification of it, we should show that it is an eigenfunction of the spin operators $\hat{S}^2$ and $\hat{S}_z$ with eigenvalue zero for each operator, which corresponds to a singlet state. This can be shown, but we omit doing so. To save space, (13.167) is sometimes written as

$$|1s_a\,\overline{1s_a}\,1s_b\,\overline{1s_b}\,\overset{\frown}{2s_a\,2s_b}| \tag{13.168}$$

where the curved line indicates the pairing (bonding) of the $2s_a$ and $2s_b$ AO's.

The MO wave function for the Li_2 ground state is

$$|\sigma_g 1s\,\overline{\sigma_g 1s}\,\sigma_u^*1s\,\overline{\sigma_u^*1s}\,\sigma_g 2s\,\overline{\sigma_g 2s}| \tag{13.169}$$

If we approximate the two lowest MO's by $1s_a \pm 1s_b$ and carry out the same manipulations we did for the He_2 MO function, we can write (13.169) as

$$|1s_a \overline{1s_a} 1s_b \overline{1s_b} \sigma_g 2s \overline{\sigma_g 2s}| \qquad (13.170)$$

[Recall the notation $KK(\sigma_g 2s)^2$ for the Li_2 ground-state configuration.] From (13.170) it might be thought that the contribution of the $\sigma_g 1s$ and $\sigma_u^* 1s$ electrons to the probability density in Li_2 is the same as for the sum of two $1s_a$ and two $1s_b$ electrons, but this is not quite so. The theorem stated at the end of Section 13.11 that allows the addition of orbital probability densities applies only to orthogonal orbitals, and the $1s_a$ and $1s_b$ orbitals are not orthogonal. However, as mentioned earlier, the overlap between these AO's in Li_2 is slight, so that they are nearly orthogonal.

Now consider the VB treatment of the N_2 ground state. The lowest configuration of N is $1s^2 2s^2 2p^3$; Hund's rule gives the ground level as $^4S_{3/2}$, with one electron in each of the three $2p$ AO's. We can thus pair the two $2p_x$ electrons, the two $2p_y$ electrons, and the two $2p_z$ electrons to form a triple bond; the Lewis structure is :N≡N:. How is this Lewis structure translated into the VB wave function? In the VB method, opposite spins are given to orbitals bonded together; we have three such pairs of orbitals, and two ways to give opposite spins to the electrons of each bonding pair of AO's. Hence, there are $2^3 = 8$ possible Slater determinants that we can write. We begin with

$$D_1 = |1s_a \overline{1s_a} 2s_a \overline{2s_a} 1s_b \overline{1s_b} 2s_b \overline{2s_b} 2p_{xa} \overline{2p_{xb}} 2p_{ya} \overline{2p_{yb}} 2p_{za} \overline{2p_{zb}}|$$

In all 8 determinants, the first 8 columns will remain unchanged, and to save space we write D_1 as

$$D_1 = |\cdots 2p_{xa} \overline{2p_{xb}} 2p_{ya} \overline{2p_{yb}} 2p_{za} \overline{2p_{zb}}| \qquad (13.171)$$

Reversing the spins of the electrons in $2p_{xa}$ and $2p_{xb}$, we get

$$D_2 = |\cdots \overline{2p_{xa}} 2p_{xb} 2p_{ya} \overline{2p_{yb}} 2p_{za} \overline{2p_{zb}}| \qquad (13.172)$$

There are 6 other determinants formed by interchanges of spins within the 3 pairs of bonding orbitals, and the VB wave function is a linear combination of 8 determinants (Problem 13.29). The following rule (proved in *Pilar*, pp. 553–554) gives a VB wave function that is an eigenfunction of $\hat{S}^2$ with eigenvalue 0 (as is desired for the ground state): the coefficient of each determinant is $+1$ or -1 according to whether the number of spin interchanges required to generate the determinant from D_1 is even or odd, respectively. Thus D_2 has coefficient -1. [Compare also (13.165).] Clearly the single-determinant ground-state N_2 MO function is easier to handle than the 8-determinant VB function.

The VB method places great emphasis on pairing of electrons. In treating O_2, whose ground state is a triplet, the VB method runs into difficulties. It *is* possible to give a VB explanation of why O_2 has a triplet ground state, but the reasoning is involved, in contrast to the very natural explanation given by the MO method.

13.14 Excited States of H₂

We have concentrated mostly on the ground electronic states of diatomic molecules; in this section we consider some of the excited states of H_2. Figure 13.17 gives the potential-energy curves for some of the H_2 electronic energy levels.

FIGURE 13.17 *Potential-energy curves for some states of* H_2. *[See W. Kolos and L. Wolniewicz, J. Chem. Phys.,* **43**, *2429 (1965);* **45**, *509 (1966); J. Gerhauser and H. S. Taylor, ibid.* **42**, *3621 (1965).]*

The lowest MO configuration is $(\sigma_g 1s)^2$; this closed-subshell configuration gives only a nondegenerate $^1\Sigma_g^+$ level, designated $X^1\Sigma_g^+$. The LCAO-MO function is (13.89).

The next lowest MO configuration is $(\sigma_g 1s)(\sigma_u^* 1s)$, which gives rise to the terms $^1\Sigma_u^+$ and $^3\Sigma_u^+$ (Table 13.3). There is no axial electronic orbital angular momentum, so that each term corresponds to one level; spectroscopists have named these electronic levels $B^1\Sigma_u^+$ and $b^3\Sigma_u^+$. By Hund's rule, the $b^3\Sigma_u^+$ is the lower of the two levels. The LCAO-MO functions for these levels are [see Eqs. (10.42)–(10.45)]:

$$b^3\Sigma_u^+: \quad 2^{-1/2}[\sigma_g 1s(1)\,\sigma_u^* 1s(2) - \sigma_g 1s(2)\,\sigma_u^* 1s(1)] \begin{cases} \alpha(1)\,\alpha(2) \\ 2^{-1/2}[\alpha(1)\,\beta(2) + \alpha(2)\,\beta(1)] \\ \beta(1)\,\beta(2) \end{cases}$$

$$B^1\Sigma_u^+: \quad 2^{-1/2}[\sigma_g 1s(1)\,\sigma_u^* 1s(2) + \sigma_g 1s(2)\,\sigma_u^* 1s(1)]\,2^{-1/2}[\alpha(1)\,\beta(2) - \alpha(2)\,\beta(1)]$$

where $\sigma_g 1s \approx N(1s_a + 1s_b)$ and $\sigma_u^* 1s \approx N'(1s_a - 1s_b)$. The $b^3\Sigma_u^+$ level is triply degenerate; the $B^1\Sigma_u^+$ level is nondegenerate. [The Heitler–London wave functions for the $b^3\Sigma_u^+$ level are given by (13.108).] Both these levels have one bonding and one antibonding electron, and we would expect the potential-energy curves for both levels to be repulsive. However, the $B^1\Sigma_u^+$ level actually has a minimum in its $U(R)$ curve; the stability of this state should caution us against drawing too hasty conclusions from very approximate wave functions.

We expect the next lowest configuration to be $(\sigma_g 1s)(\sigma_g 2s)$, giving rise to $^1\Sigma_g^+$ and $^3\Sigma_g^+$ levels; these levels of H_2 are designated $E^1\Sigma_g^+$ and $a^3\Sigma_g^+$. By Hund's rule, the triplet lies lower. Both levels are expected to be stable, as is observed. The E state is especially interesting, as it shows two substantial minima in its $U(R)$ curve.

Although the $\sigma_u^* 2s$ MO fills before the two $\pi_u 2p$ MO's in going across the periodic table, the $\pi_u 2p$ MO's are much lower than the $\sigma_u^* 2s$ MO for H_2. The configuration $(\sigma_g 1s)(\pi_u 2p)$ gives rise to the terms $^1\Pi_u$ and $^3\Pi_u$, the triplet lying lower. These terms are designated $C^1\Pi_u$ and $c^3\Pi_u$. The c term has three levels associated with it: $c^3\Pi_{2u}$, $c^3\Pi_{1u}$, and $c^3\Pi_{0u}$; however, these levels lie so close together that they are generally not resolved in spectroscopic work. The C level shows a slight hump in the potential-energy curve at large R. Each level is twofold degenerate, giving a total of 8 electronic states arising from the $(\sigma_g 1s)(\pi_u 2p)$ configuration.

13.15 The Valence-Electron Approximation

Suppose we want to treat K_2, which has 38 electrons. In the MO method, we would start by writing down a 38×38 Slater determinant of molecular orbitals. We would then approximate the MO's by functions containing variational parameters and go on to minimize the variational integral. Clearly, the large number of electrons makes this a formidable task. One way to simplify the problem is to divide the electrons into two groups: the 36 *core* electrons, and the two $4s$ *valence* electrons, which provide bonding; we then attempt to treat the valence electrons separately from the core, taking the molecular energy as the sum of core- and valence-electron energies. This approach, introduced in the 1930's, is called the *valence-electron approximation.*

The simplest approach is to regard the core electrons as point charges coinciding with the nucleus. For K_2 this would give a Hamiltonian for the two valence electrons that is identical with the electronic Hamiltonian for H_2. If we then go ahead and minimize the variational integral for the valence electrons in K_2, with no restrictions on the valence-electron trial functions, we will clearly be in trouble; such a procedure will cause the valence-electrons' MO to "collapse" to the $\sigma_g 1s$ MO, since the core electrons are considered absent. To avoid this collapse one can impose the constraint that the variational functions used for the valence electrons be orthogonal to the orbitals of the core electrons. Of course, the task of keeping the valence orbitals orthogonal to the core orbitals means more work. A somewhat different approach is to drop the approximation of treating the core electrons as coinciding with the nucleus, and to treat them as a charge distribution that provides some sort of effective repulsive potential for the motion of the valence electrons. This leads to an effective Hamiltonian for the valence electrons, which is then used in the variational integral. The valence-electron approximation is widely used in approximate treatments of polyatomic molecules (Sections 15.8 and 15.9).

13.16 SCF Wave Functions for Diatomic Molecules

A very important development in quantum chemistry has been the computation of accurate self-consistent-field wave functions for many diatomic and
polyatomic molecules.[19] The principles of molecular SCF calculations are essentially
the same as for atomic SCF calculations (Section 11.1). We shall restrict ourselves
to consideration of closed-subshell configurations; for open subshells, the formulas
are more complicated.

The molecular wave function is written as an antisymmetrized product
(Slater determinant) of spin-orbitals, each spin-orbital being a product of a spatial
orbital φ_i and a spin function (either α or β). The spatial orbitals that minimize the
variational integral are found by solving the Hartree–Fock differential equations,
which are[20]

$$\hat{H}^{\text{eff}}(1)\,\varphi_i(1) = \varepsilon_i\,\varphi_i(1) \tag{13.173}$$

where ε_i is the orbital energy and where the effective Hartree–Fock Hamiltonian
operator is (in atomic units)

$$\hat{H}^{\text{eff}}(1) = -\tfrac{1}{2}\nabla_1^2 - \sum_\alpha \frac{Z_\alpha}{r_{1\alpha}} + \sum_j [2\hat{J}_j(1) - \hat{K}_j(1)] \tag{13.174}$$

where the *Coulomb operator* $\hat{J}_j$ and the *exchange operator* $\hat{K}_j$ are defined by

$$\hat{J}_j(1)\,\varphi_i(1) = \varphi_i(1) \int |\varphi_j(2)|^2 \frac{1}{r_{12}}\,dv_2 \tag{13.175}$$

$$\hat{K}_j(1)\,\varphi_i(1) = \varphi_j(1) \int \frac{\varphi_j^*(2)\,\varphi_i(2)}{r_{12}}\,dv_2 \tag{13.176}$$

The first term on the right of (13.174) is the operator for the kinetic energy of one
electron; the second term is the potential-energy operators for the attractions
between one electron and the nuclei. (These two terms form the one-electron *core
Hamiltonian*; the core Hamiltonian omits interactions with all other electrons.)
The Coulomb operator $\hat{J}_j(1)$ is the potential energy of interaction between electron
one and a smeared-out electron with electronic density $-|\varphi_j(2)|^2$; the factor 2
occurs because there are 2 electrons in each spatial orbital. The exchange operator
has no simple physical interpretation, but arises from the requirement that the wave
function be antisymmetric with respect to electron exchange; the exchange operators
are absent from the Hartree equations (11.12). The summation in (13.174) is over
the $n/2$ occupied spatial orbitals of the n-electron molecule. Note the similarity
of (13.173) to the Schroedinger equation $\hat{H}\psi_i = E_i\psi_i$.

All the molecular orbitals φ_i are eigenfunctions of the *same* Hartree–Fock
Hamiltonian operator $\hat{H}^{\text{eff}}$; moreover, this operator is Hermitian (Problem 13.21).
Hence the molecular orbitals φ_i are (or can be chosen to be) orthogonal. This

---

[19] For a summary of the diatomic work, see A. C. Wahl, P. J. Bertoncini, G. Das, and T. L.
Gilbert, *Int. J. Quantum Chem.*, **1S**, 123 (1967); see also M. Yoshimine and A. D. McLean, *ibid.*,
1S, 313.

[20] For a derivation, see *Parr*, pp. 21–32, *Pilar*, Chapter 13.

orthogonality greatly simplifies MO calculations, causing many integrals to vanish. In contrast, the VB method uses atomic orbitals, and AO's centered on different atoms are not orthogonal. MO calculations are thus mathematically simpler than VB calculations, and the majority of molecular calculations are MO calculations.

The true Hamiltonian and wave function involve the coordinates of all n electrons; the Hartree–Fock Hamiltonian is a one-electron operator (i.e., it involves the coordinates of only one electron) and (13.173) is a one-electron differential equation. [This has been indicated in (13.173) by writing $\hat{H}^{\text{eff}}$ and φ_i as functions of the coordinates of electron 1; of course, the coordinates of any electron could have been used.] The operator $\hat{H}^{\text{eff}}$ is peculiar in that it depends on its own eigenfunctions, which are not known initially. Hence, the Hartree–Fock equations must be solved by an iterative process. The expression for the Hartree–Fock molecular energy E_{HF} involves Coulomb and exchange integrals [Eqs. (9.144) and (9.145)] in addition to the orbital energies ε_i:

$$E_{\text{HF}} = 2\sum_i \varepsilon_i - \sum_i \sum_j (2J_{ij} - K_{ij}) + V_{NN} \tag{13.177}$$

where the sums are over the $n/2$ occupied spatial orbitals. Since there are two electrons per MO, the quantity $2\sum \varepsilon_i$ is the sum of the orbital energies. Equation (13.177) is derived by substituting the Slater determinant of spin-orbitals into the variational integral.

In 1951 Roothaan proposed expanding the spatial orbitals as linear combinations of a complete set of basis functions f_k:

$$\varphi_i = \sum_k c_{ik} f_k \tag{13.178}$$

Substitution of this expression into (13.173) gives

$$\sum_k c_{ik} \hat{H}^{\text{eff}} f_k = \varepsilon_i \sum_k c_{ik} f_k$$

Multiplication by f_j^* and integration gives

$$\sum_k c_{ik}(H_{jk}^{\text{eff}} - \varepsilon_i S_{jk}) = 0, \qquad j = 1, 2, 3, \ldots \tag{13.179}$$

where

$$H_{jk}^{\text{eff}} = \langle f_j | \hat{H}^{\text{eff}} | f_k \rangle, \qquad S_{jk} = \langle f_j | f_k \rangle \tag{13.180}$$

The equations (13.179) are a set of simultaneous linear homogeneous equations in the unknowns c_{ik}; for a nontrivial solution, we must have

$$\det(H_{jk}^{\text{eff}} - \varepsilon_i S_{jk}) = 0 \tag{13.181}$$

This is a secular equation whose roots give the orbital energies. The Roothaan equations (13.179) must be solved by an iterative process, since the H_{jk}^{eff} integrals depend on the orbitals φ_i (through the dependence of $\hat{H}^{\text{eff}}$ on the φ_i), which in turn depend on the unknown coefficients c_{ik}.

One starts with guesses for the occupied-MO expressions as linear combinations of the basis functions, as in (13.178). This initial set of MO's is used to compute $\hat{H}^{\text{eff}}$ from (13.174)–(13.176). The matrix elements (13.180) are computed and the secular equation (13.181) solved to give an initial set of ε_i's; these ε_i's are used to solve (13.179) for an improved set of coefficients, giving an improved set of MO's, which are then used to compute an improved $\hat{H}^{\text{eff}}$, etc., etc. One keeps going until no further improvement in MO coefficients and energies occurs from one cycle to the next.

Now consider the basis functions used. Generally, each MO is written as a linear combination of one-electron functions (orbitals) centered on each atom. For diatomic molecules the functions most frequently used for the AO's are Slater functions, Eq. (11.16). To have a complete set of AO basis functions it is necessary to use an infinite number of Slater orbitals, but the true molecular Hartree–Fock wave function can be closely approximated with a reasonably small number of Slater orbitals, if these are carefully chosen. Molecular SCF calculations can be divided into two broad classes: those that use a minimal basis set of AO's, and those that use an extended basis set of AO's. A *minimal basis set* consists of only inner-shell and valence-shell AO's, while an *extended basis set* uses higher-shell AO's in addition to inner- and valence-shell AO's. Of course, minimal-basis-set SCF calculations are easier than extended-basis-set calculations, but the latter are more accurate.

We have used the terms SCF wave function and Hartree–Fock wave function interchangeably. In practice, the term "SCF wave function" is applied to any wave function obtained by iterative solution of the Roothaan equations, whether or not the basis set is large enough to give a really accurate approximation to the Hartree–Fock SCF wave function. There is only one true Hartree–Fock SCF wave function, which is the best possible wave function that can be written as a Slater determinant of spin-orbitals. Some of the extended-basis-set calculations are believed to approach the true Hartree–Fock wave function quite closely; such functions are called "near Hartree–Fock wave functions" or, less cautiously, "Hartree–Fock wave functions."

SCF wave functions using a minimal basis set were calculated by Ransil for several light diatomic molecules.[21] As an example, the SCF MO's for the ground state of Li_2 [MO configuration $(1\sigma_g)^2(1\sigma_u)^2(2\sigma_g)^2$] at $R = R_e$ are:

$$1\sigma_g = 0.706(1s_a + 1s_b) + 0.009(2s_{\perp a} + 2s_{\perp b}) + 0.0003(2p\sigma_a + 2p\sigma_b)$$

$$1\sigma_u = 0.709(1s_a - 1s_b) + 0.021(2s_{\perp a} - 2s_{\perp b}) + 0.003(2p\sigma_a - 2p\sigma_b) \qquad \text{(13.182)}$$

$$2\sigma_g = -0.059(1s_a + 1s_b) + 0.523(2s_{\perp a} + 2s_{\perp b}) + 0.114(2p\sigma_a + 2p\sigma_b)$$

The AO functions in these equations are STO's, except for $2s_\perp$. A Slater-type $2s$ AO has no radial nodes and is not orthogonal to a $1s$ STO. The Hartree–Fock $2s$ AO has one radial node ($n-l-1 = 1$) and is orthogonal to the $1s$ AO. We can form an orthogonalized $2s$ orbital with the proper number of nodes by taking the following normalized linear combination of $1s$ and $2s$ STO's of the same atom (Schmidt orthogonalization):

$$2s_\perp = (1-S^2)^{-1/2}(2s - S \cdot 1s) \qquad \text{(13.183)}$$

[21] B. J. Ransil, *Rev. Mod. Phys.*, **32**, 245 (1960).

where S is the overlap integral $\langle 1s|2s \rangle$. Ransil expressed the Li_2 orbitals using the (nonorthogonal) $2s$ STO, but since the orthogonalized $2s_\perp$ function gives a better representation of the $2s$ AO, we have rewritten the orbitals using $2s_\perp$. This changes the $1s$ and $2s$ coefficients, but the actual orbital is, of course, unchanged; see Problem 13.28. The notation $2p\sigma$ for an AO indicates that the p orbital points along the molecular axis; i.e., a $2p\sigma$ AO is a $2p_z$ AO. (The $2p_x$ and $2p_y$ AO's are called $2p\pi$ AO's.) The optimum orbital exponents for the orbitals in (13.182) are

$$\zeta_{1s} = 2.689, \qquad \zeta_{2s} = 0.634, \qquad \zeta_{2p\sigma} = 0.761$$

(Since 6 AO's were used as basis functions, the Roothaan equations yielded approximations for the 6 lowest MO's of ground-state Li_2; only 3 of these MO's are occupied. The expressions for the other 3 can be found in Ransil's paper.)

Our previous simple expressions for these MO's were

$$1\sigma_g = \sigma_g 1s = 2^{-1/2}(1s_a + 1s_b)$$
$$1\sigma_u = \sigma_u^* 1s = 2^{-1/2}(1s_a - 1s_b) \qquad \textbf{(13.184)}$$
$$2\sigma_g = \sigma_g 2s = 2^{-1/2}(2s_a + 2s_b)$$

Comparison of (13.184) with (13.182) shows the simple LCAO functions to be reasonable first approximations to the minimal-basis-set SCF MO's. The approximation is best for the $1\sigma_g$ and $1\sigma_u$ MO's, whereas the $2\sigma_g$ MO has a substantial $2p\sigma$ AO contribution in addition to the $2s$ AO contributions. For this reason, the notation of the third column of Table 13.1 is preferable to the separated-atoms MO notation. The substantial amount of $2s$–$2p\sigma$ hybridization is to be expected since the $2s$ and $2p$ AO's are close in energy [see Eq. (9.42)]; the hybridization allows for the polarization of the $2s$ AO's in forming the molecule.

Let us compare the $3\sigma_g$ MO of the F_2 ground state at R_e as calculated by Ransil using a minimal basis set and as calculated by Wahl[22] using an extended basis set:

$$3\sigma_{g,\,\text{min}} = 0.038(1s_a + 1s_b) - 0.184(2s_a + 2s_b) + 0.648(2p\sigma_a + 2p\sigma_b)$$

$$\zeta_{1s} = 8.65, \qquad \zeta_{2s} = 2.58, \qquad \zeta_{2p\sigma} = 2.49$$

$$3\sigma_{g,\,\text{ext}} = 0.048(1s_a + 1s_b) + 0.003(1s_a' + 1s_b') - 0.257(2s_a + 2s_b)$$
$$+ 0.582(2p\sigma_a + 2p\sigma_b) + 0.307(2p\sigma_a' + 2p\sigma_b') + 0.085(2p\sigma_a'' + 2p\sigma_b'')$$
$$- 0.056(3s_a + 3s_b) + 0.046(3d\sigma_a + 3d\sigma_b) + 0.014(4f\sigma_a + 4f\sigma_b)$$

$$\zeta_{1s} = 8.27, \qquad \zeta_{1s'} = 13.17, \qquad \zeta_{2s} = 2.26$$

$$\zeta_{2p\sigma} = 1.85, \qquad \zeta_{2p\sigma'} = 3.27, \qquad \zeta_{2p\sigma''} = 5.86$$

$$\zeta_{3s} = 4.91, \qquad \zeta_{3d\sigma} = 2.44, \qquad \zeta_{4f\sigma} = 2.83$$

Just as several STO's are needed to give an accurate representation of Hartree–Fock AO's (Section 11.1), one needs more than one STO of a given n and l in the linear

---

[22] A. C. Wahl, *J. Chem. Phys.*, **41**, 2600 (1964).

combination of STO's that is to accurately represent the Hartree–Fock MO. The primed and double-primed AO's in the extended-basis-set function are STO's with different orbital exponents. The $3d\sigma$ and $4f\sigma$ AO's are AO's with quantum number $m = 0$, i.e., the $3d_0$ and $4f_0$ AO's. The total energies found are -197.877 and -198.768 hartrees for the minimal and extended calculations, respectively. The experimental energy of F_2 at R_e is -199.670 hartrees, so that the error for the minimal calculation is twice that of the extended calculation. The extended-basis-set calculation is believed to give a wave function quite close to the true Hartree–Fock wave function; therefore the correlation energy in F_2 is about 24 eV.

In discussing H_2^+ and H_2, we saw how hybridization (i.e., the mixing of different AO's of the same atom) improves molecular wave functions. There is a tendency to think of hybridization as occurring only for certain molecular geometries. The SCF calculations make clear that *all* MO's are hybridized to some extent. Thus any diatomic-molecule σ MO is a linear combination of $1s, 2s, 2p_0, 3s, 3p_0, 3d_0, \ldots$ AO's of the separated atoms.

Wahl has plotted the contours of the near Hartree–Fock molecular orbitals of homonuclear diatomic molecules from H_2 through F_2. Figure 13.18 shows these plots for H_2 and Li_2.

Of course, Hartree–Fock wave functions are only approximations to the true wave functions. It is possible to prove that a Hartree–Fock wave function gives a very good approximation to the electron probability density $\rho(x, y, z)$. A

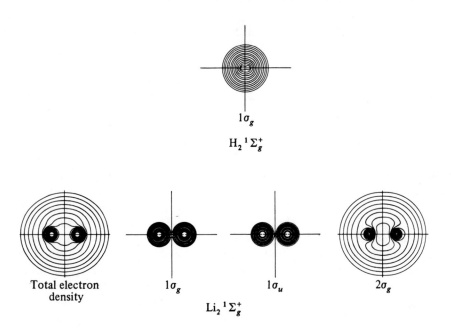

FIGURE 13.18   *Hartree–Fock* MO *electron-density contours for the ground states of* H_2 *and* Li_2, *as calculated by Wahl.* [*A. C. Wahl, Science,* **151**, *961* (*1966*); Scientific American, *April 1970, p. 54;* Atomic and Molecular Structure: *4 Wall Charts, McGraw-Hill* (*1970*).]

molecular property that involves only one-electron operators can be expressed as an integral involving ρ; consequently such properties are accurately calculated using Hartree–Fock wave functions. The prime example is the molecular dipole moment [Eq. (13.157)], for which the success of the near Hartree–Fock wave functions has been impressive. As an example, for LiH the dipole moment calculated[23] with a near-Hartree–Fock ψ is 6.00 D (debyes), compared to the experimental value 5.83 D. (One debye $= 10^{-18}$ statcoul cm.) For NaCl the calculated[24] and experimental d's are 9.18 and 9.02 D. An error of, say, 0.2 D is typical in such calculations, but where the dipole moment is small, the percent error can become large. An extreme example is CO. Here the experimental moment is 0.11 D with the polarity C^-O^+, but the near-Hartree–Fock moment is 0.27 D with the erroneous polarity C^+O^-. However, a wave function improved by configuration interaction gives[23] 0.12 D with the correct polarity.

Molecular Hartree–Fock calculations do not give good values for dissociation energies. For example, an extended-basis-set calculation[25] gives $D_e = 5.3$ eV for N_2, as compared to the true value 9.9 eV. (To calculate the Hartree–Fock D_e, the molecular energy at the minimum in the $U(R)$ Hartree–Fock curve is subtracted from the sum of the Hartree–Fock energies of the separated atoms.) For F_2, the true D_e is 1.65 eV, while the Hartree–Fock D_e is -1.4 eV; in other words, the Hartree–Fock calculation predicts the separated atoms to be more stable than the fluorine molecule. A related defect of Hartree–Fock molecular wave functions is that the energy approaches the wrong limit for large values of R; recall the MO discussion of H_2.

To overcome the two main defects of Hartree–Fock ψ's (improper behavior as $R \to \infty$ and incorrect D_e values due to a change in electron correlation energy on molecule formation), one must introduce configuration interaction, thus going beyond the Hartree–Fock MO approximation. Since there are unlimited numbers of configurations to consider, the task is a formidable one, but a number of successes have been achieved. In the ordinary CI approach, one takes the wave function as a linear combination of the ground-state Hartree–Fock ψ and a large number of excited configurations, as in (11.18), and varies the expansion coefficients to achieve a minimum energy. Because the excited configurations have much of their probability density at quite large distances from the nuclei, convergence is slow, and hundreds (or even thousands) of configurations must be included. To get faster convergence to the true ψ, one can vary not only the expansion coefficients c_i in (11.18), but also the forms of the orbitals in the excited configurations; the optimum orbitals are found by an iterative process, akin to the usual SCF iterative process used to find the (single-configuration) Hartree–Fock ψ; hence this method of CI is called the *multiconfiguration* SCF (MCSCF) method. By optimizing the orbitals, one can get good results with inclusion of relatively few configurations. Wahl, Das, and co-workers have developed an MCSCF approach to the calculation of diatomic-molecule D_e's, which they call the *optimized valence configuration* (OVC)

[23] S. Green, *J. Chem. Phys.*, **54**, 827 (1971).
[24] R. L. Matcha, *J. Chem. Phys.*, **48**, 335 (1968).
[25] P. E. Cade, K. D. Sales, and A. C. Wahl, *J. Chem. Phys.*, **44**, 1973 (1966).

method. Since the atomic cores remain relatively unchanged on molecule formation, the ovc method includes only configurations with valence electrons excited. To correctly take into account the changes that occur as the molecule forms, one must add those configurations needed to give proper dissociation of the molecule to Hartree–Fock atoms in their correct states, together with a few other configurations that make important contributions in the molecule near R_e. (The method does involve some trial and error to find the right configurations to include and has been criticized on this account.) Although the ovc CI ψ gives only a part (about 25% for F_2) of the molecular correlation energy (which is the error in the Hartree–Fock ψ; Section 11.3), it includes that part of the correlation energy that varies with R and hence gives a good $U(R)$ curve and a good D_e. As noted above, one of the outstanding failures of the Hartree–Fock method is the F_2 D_e. An ovc ψ for F_2 containing only 6 configurations gives $D_e = 1.82$ eV, and when contributions from further configurations are included by a perturbation calculation, the final result $D_e = 1.67$ eV is obtained[26]; this is in excellent agreement with the experimental value 1.65 eV. The ovc method has been applied with success to several other diatomics. For further discussion on CI in diatomics, see *Schaefer*, pp. 182–235.

13.17 MO Treatment of Heteronuclear Diatomic Molecules

The treatment of heteronuclear diatomic molecules is similar to that for homonuclear diatomic molecules. We first consider the MO description.

Suppose the two atoms have atomic numbers that differ only slightly; an example is CO. We could consider CO as being formed from the isoelectronic molecule N_2 by a gradual transfer of nuclear charge from one nucleus to the other. During this hypothetical transfer, the original N_2 MO's would slowly vary to give finally the CO MO's. We therefore expect the CO molecular orbitals to bear some resemblance to those of N_2. For a heteronuclear diatomic molecule like CO, the symbols used for the MO's are similar to those for homonuclear diatomics; however, for a heteronuclear diatomic, the electronic Hamiltonian (13.5) is not invariant with respect to inversion of the electronic coordinates (i.e., $\hat{H}_{el}$ doesn't commute with $\hat{\Pi}$) so that the g, u property of the MO's disappears. The correlation between the N_2 and CO subshell designations is:

N_2	$1\sigma_g$	$1\sigma_u$	$2\sigma_g$	$2\sigma_u$	$1\pi_u$	$3\sigma_g$	$1\pi_g$	$3\sigma_u$
CO	1σ	2σ	3σ	4σ	1π	5σ	2π	6σ

(13.185)

MO's of the same symmetry are numbered in order of increasing energy; because of the absence of the g, u property, the numbers of corresponding homonuclear and heteronuclear MO's differ. Figure 13.19 is a sketch of a contour of the CO $1\pi_{\pm 1}$ MO's, as determined by an extended basis-set SCF calculation.[27] Note its

---

[26] G. Das and A. C. Wahl, *J. Chem. Phys.*, **56**, 3532 (1972).
[27] W. M. Huo, *J. Chem. Phys.*, **43**, 624 (1965).

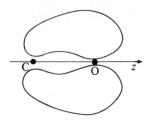

FIGURE 13.19 *Cross section of a contour of the* $1\pi_{\pm 1}$ *MO's in carbon monoxide.*

resemblance to the contour of Fig. 13.12, which is for the $1\pi_{u,\,\pm 1}$ MO's of a homonuclear diatomic molecule.

The ground-state configuration of CO is $1\sigma^2\,2\sigma^2\,3\sigma^2\,4\sigma^2\,1\pi^4\,5\sigma^2$ as compared to the N_2 configuration $(1\sigma_g)^2\,(1\sigma_u)^2\,(2\sigma_g)^2\,(2\sigma_u)^2\,(1\pi_u)^4\,(3\sigma_g)^2$.

As in homonuclear diatomics, the heteronuclear diatomic MO's are approximated as linear combinations of atomic orbitals. The coefficients are found by solving the Roothaan equations (13.179). For example, a minimal-basis-set SCF calculation[28] using Slater AO's (with nonoptimized exponents given by Slater's rules) gives for the CO 5σ, 1π, and 2π MO's at $R = R_e$:

$$5\sigma = 0.027\,(1s_C) + 0.011\,(1s_O) + 0.739\,(2s_{\perp C}) + 0.036\,(2s_{\perp O})$$

$$- 0.566\,(2p\sigma_C) - 0.438\,(2p\sigma_O)$$

$$1\pi = 0.469\,(2p\pi_C) + 0.771\,(2p\pi_O)$$

$$2\pi = 0.922\,(2p\pi_C) - 0.690\,(2p\pi_O)$$

(The expressions for the π MO's are simpler than those for the σ MO's because s and $p\sigma$ AO's cannot contribute to π MO's.) For comparison, the corresponding MO's in N_2 are found[28] to be (at $R = R_e$):

$$3\sigma_g = 0.030\,(1s_a + 1s_b) + 0.395\,(2s_{\perp a} + 2s_{\perp b}) - 0.603\,(2p\sigma_a + 2p\sigma_b)$$

$$1\pi_u = 0.624\,(2p\pi_a + 2p\pi_b)$$

$$1\pi_g = 0.835\,(2p\pi_a - 2p\pi_b)$$

The resemblance of CO and N_2 MO's is apparent. The 1σ MO in CO is found to be nearly the same as a $1s$ oxygen-atom AO; the 2σ MO in CO is essentially a carbon-atom $1s$ AO.

Accurate MO expressions like the above require the solution of the Roothaan equations for their determination. For qualitative discussion (but not quantitative work) it is useful to have simpler approximations for heteronuclear diatomic MO's. Just as the $2\sigma_g$ and $2\sigma_u$ MO's for homonuclear diatomics were approximated by the linear combinations (13.67), we can approximate the 3σ and 4σ MO's of a heteronuclear diatomic molecule having similar nuclei by the linear combinations:

$$3\sigma = c_1\,2s_a + c_2\,2s_b, \qquad 4\sigma = c_1'\,2s_a + c_2'\,2s_b$$

---

[28] B. J. Ransil, *Rev. Mod. Phys.*, **32**, 245 (1960).

In general, from two AO's φ_a and φ_b, we can form two MO's

$$c_1 \varphi_a + c_2 \varphi_b \quad \text{and} \quad c_1' \varphi_a + c_2' \varphi_b \tag{13.186}$$

The lack of symmetry in the heteronuclear diatomic causes the coefficients to be unequal in magnitude. The coefficients are determined by solving the secular equation [see Eq. (13.35)]:

$$\begin{vmatrix} H_{aa} - W & H_{ab} - WS_{ab} \\ H_{ab} - WS_{ab} & H_{bb} - W \end{vmatrix} = 0 \tag{13.187}$$

$$(H_{aa} - W)(H_{bb} - W) - (H_{ab} - WS_{ab})^2 = 0 \tag{13.188}$$

where $\hat{H}$ is some sort of effective one-electron Hamiltonian. Suppose that $H_{aa} > H_{bb}$, and let $f(W)$ be defined as the left side of (13.188). The overlap integral S_{ab} is less than 1 (except at $R = 0$). [A rigorous proof of this follows from the Schwarz inequality, Eq. (3-114) in *Margenau and Murphy*.] The coefficient of W^2 in $f(W)$ is $(1 - S_{ab}^2) > 0$; hence we have $f(\infty) = f(-\infty) = +\infty > 0$. For $W = H_{aa}$ or H_{bb}, the first product in (13.188) vanishes; hence, $f(H_{aa}) < 0$ and $f(H_{bb}) < 0$. The roots of (13.188) occur where $f(W)$ equals 0; hence, by continuity, one root must be between $+\infty$ and H_{aa} and the other between H_{bb} and $-\infty$. Therefore the orbital energy of one MO is less than both H_{aa} and H_{bb} (the energies of the two AO's), while the energy of the other MO is greater than both H_{aa} and H_{bb}. Thus, one bonding and one antibonding MO are formed from the two AO's. Figure 13.20 shows the formation of bonding and antibonding MO's from two AO's, for the homonuclear and heteronuclear cases. These figures are gross oversimplifications, since a given MO has contributions from many AO's, not just two.

For a molecule with similar nuclei (e.g., CO), the MO's are formed, in the first approximation, as linear combinations of corresponding AO's on each atom. For a molecule with quite different nuclei, this is not the case. Consider HF. The ground-state configurations of the atoms are: $H - 1s$; $F - 1s^2 2s^2 2p^5$. We expect the filled $1s$ and $2s$ F subshells to take little part in the bonding. The four $2p\pi$ fluorine electrons are nonbonding. To form a σ MO for the bonding electron pair, we take a linear combination of the hydrogen $1s$ AO and the fluorine $2p\sigma$ AO:

$$\varphi = c_1(1s_H) + c_2(2p\sigma_F) \tag{13.189}$$

FIGURE 13.20 *Formation of bonding and antibonding MO's from AO's in the homonuclear and heteronuclear cases. (See Problem 13.27.)*

The coefficients are found by solving the secular equation. Since fluorine is more electronegative than hydrogen, we expect that $c_2 > c_1$.

The picture of HF just given is only a crude qualitative approximation. A minimal-basis-set SCF calculation[29] using Slater orbitals with optimized exponents gives for the HF MO's:

$$1\sigma = 1.000(1s_F) + 0.012(2s_{\perp F}) + 0.002(2p\sigma_F) - 0.003(1s_H)$$

$$2\sigma = -0.018(1s_F) + 0.914(2s_{\perp F}) + 0.090(2p\sigma_F) + 0.154(1s_H)$$

$$3\sigma = -0.023(1s_F) - 0.411(2s_{\perp F}) + 0.711(2p\sigma_F) + 0.516(1s_H)$$

$$1\pi_{+1} = (2p\pi_{+1})_F$$

$$1\pi_{-1} = (2p\pi_{-1})_F \tag{13.190}$$

The ground-state MO configuration of HF is $1\sigma^2 2\sigma^2 3\sigma^2 1\pi^4$. The 1σ MO is virtually identical with the $1s$ fluorine AO. The 2σ MO is pretty close to the $2s$ fluorine AO. The 1π MO's are restricted by symmetry to be the same as the corresponding fluorine π AO's. The bonding 3σ MO has its largest contribution from the $2p\sigma$ fluorine and $1s$ hydrogen AO's, as would be expected from the discussion of the preceding paragraph; however, there is a substantial contribution to this MO from the $2s$ fluorine AO. (Since a single $2s$ function is only an approximation to the $2s$ AO of F, one cannot use (13.190) to say exactly how much $2s$ AO character the 3σ HF molecular orbital has.)

13.18 VB Treatment of Heteronuclear Diatomic Molecules

We will illustrate the valence-bond approach to the ground states of hetero-nuclear diatomic molecules by considering HF. Adopting the valence-electron approximation (Section 13.15), we will look at the wave function for the bonding electrons only. We expect a single bond to be formed by the pairing of the hydrogen $1s$ electron and the unpaired fluorine $2p\sigma$ electron. The Heitler–London function corresponding to this pairing is [Eq. (13.164)]

$$\varphi_{cov} = (2 + 2S^2)^{-1/2}\{|1s_H\,\overline{2p\sigma_F}| - |\overline{1s_H}\,2p\sigma_F|\} \tag{13.191}$$

This function is essentially covalent, the electrons being shared by the two atoms. However, the high electronegativity of fluorine leads us to include a contribution from an ionic structure as well. [Actually, the "covalent" function (13.191) does give some polarity to the bond for heteronuclear diatomic molecules; in the electron-density expression corresponding to (13.133), the AO's φ_a and φ_b are of different size.] An ionic valence-bond function has the form $\varphi_a(1)\varphi_a(2)$ [Eq. (13.123)]. Introduction of the required antisymmetric spin factor gives as the valence-bond function for an ionic structure in HF:

$$\varphi_{ion} = |2p\sigma_F\,\overline{2p\sigma_F}| \tag{13.192}$$

---

[29] B. J. Ransil, *Rev. Mod. Phys.*, **32**, 245 (1960).

The wave function for the bonding electrons is then written as

$$\varphi = c_1 \varphi_{cov} + c_2 \varphi_{ion} \qquad (13.193)$$

The optimum values of c_1 and c_2 are determined by the variation method, using an effective Hamiltonian; this leads to the usual secular equation. We have ionic-covalent "resonance," involving the structures H—F and H^+F^-; the true molecular structure is intermediate between the covalent and ionic structures. A term $c_3 |1s_H \bar{1s}_H|$ corresponding to the ionic structure H^-F^+ could also be included in the wave function, but this should make a negligible contribution for HF. For molecules that are less ionic, both ionic structures might well be included.

For a molecule like NaCl, which is highly ionic, we expect the valence-bond function to have $c_2 \gg c_1$. It might be thought that NaCl will dissociate to Na^+ and Cl^- ions, but this is not accurate. The ionization potential of Na is 5.1 eV, while the electron affinity of Cl is only 3.6 eV. Hence, in the gas phase, the neutral separated ground-state atoms Na+Cl are more stable than the ground-state separated ions $Na^+ + Cl^-$. (Of course, in aqueous solution, the ions are more stable due to the hydration energy, which makes the separated ions more stable than even the diatomic NaCl molecule.) If the nuclei are slowly pulled apart, a gas-phase NaCl molecule will dissociate to neutral atoms; this means that as R increases from R_e, the ratio c_2/c_1 in (13.193) must decrease, becoming zero at $R = \infty$. For intermediate values of R, the Coulombic attraction between the ions is greater than the 1.5 eV difference between the ionization potential and electron affinity, and the molecule is largely ionic; for very large R, the Coulombic attraction between the ions is less than 1.5 eV, and the molecule is largely covalent. However, if the nuclei in NaCl are pulled apart very rapidly, then the electrons won't have a chance to adjust their wave function from the ionic to the covalent wave function, and both bonding electrons will go with the chlorine nucleus, giving dissociation into ions.

Cesium has the lowest ionization potential, 3.9 eV. Chlorine has the highest electron affinity, 3.6 eV. (The electron affinity of fluorine is 3.45 eV.) Thus, even for CsCl and CsF, the separated ground-state neutral atoms are more stable than the separated ground-state ions. There are, however, cases of excited states of diatomic molecules whose potential-energy curves correspond to dissociation to ions.

PROBLEMS

13.1 Give the numerical value in atomic units of each of the following quantities: (a) proton mass; (b) electron charge; (c) Planck's constant; (d) He^+ ground-state energy, assuming infinite nuclear mass; (e) one second; (f) c (speed of light); (g) hydrogen-atom ground-state energy, taking internal nuclear motion into account; (h) one debye.

13.2 Use results of statistical mechanics to show that for the gas-phase reaction $A—B \rightarrow A + B$, the ΔE at 298°K is $RT/2$ greater than the ΔE at 0°K. Assume negligible population of excited vibrational and electronic states.

13.3 Derive Eqs. (13.26) and (13.27) from (13.25) and (13.21).

13.4 In confocal elliptic coordinates, what is the shape of surfaces of constant: (a) ξ; (b) η; (c) φ?

13.5 (a) From Fig. 13.2 show that

$$R\xi = [r^2 \sin^2 \theta + (z + \tfrac{1}{2}R)^2]^{1/2} + [r^2 \sin^2 \theta + (z - \tfrac{1}{2}R)^2]^{1/2}$$

and that η is given by a similar expression with the plus sign between the brackets replaced by a minus sign. (b) Verify the ranges given for the coordinates in Eq. (13.18).

13.6 Use the following procedure to show that the Born–Oppenheimer approximation is valid provided the electronic wave function is a slowly varying function of the nuclear coordinates: Substitute (13.12) into (13.3) and use (13.4) and Problem 5.7 to show that (13.10) holds if the derivatives of ψ_{el} with respect to the nuclear coordinates can be neglected.

13.7 Verify Eq. (13.58).

13.8 (a) Show that the variational integral W_1 for the ground state of H_2^+ [Eq. (13.59)] can be written as

$$W_1 = k^2 F(t) + k G(t)$$

where $t \equiv kR$, and F and G are certain functions of t. (b) Show that the minimization condition $\partial W_1 / \partial k = 0$ leads to

$$k = -\frac{G(t) + t G'(t)}{2F(t) + t F'(t)}$$

Using this equation, we can find k for a given value of t; we then use $R = t/k$ to find the value of R corresponding to our value of k.

13.9 Consider the trial function (13.48) for the first excited state of H_2^+. Find the limit of this function as R goes to zero. Compare the result to the $2p_z$ hydrogenlike function.

13.10 Calculate the energy at $R = 2.00$ bohrs for the H_2^+ trial function $e^{-k\xi}$. Calculate the percent error in: (a) the electronic energy including nuclear repulsion; (b) the purely electronic energy; (c) the dissociation energy.

13.11 Evaluate the geometric series

$$\sum_{n=0}^{\infty} R^4 e^{-Rn}$$

and show that the infinite sum behaves as R^3 for small values of R, even though each term in the sum behaves as R^4 for small R.

13.12 Write a computer program to calculate (at $R = R_e$) values of the H_2^+ MO's (13.47) and (13.48) at points in a plane containing the nuclei. Use the output to make contour plots of the MO's. Label the contours in units of electrons/bohr^3 (probability density).

13.13 Verify Eq. (13.75) for a σ_h reflection.

13.14 Which species of each pair has the greater D_e? (a) Li_2 or Li_2^+; (b) C_2 or C_2^+; (c) O_2 or O_2^+; (d) F_2 or F_2^+.

13.15 How many independent electronic wave functions correspond to each of the following diatomic-molecule terms? (a) $^1\Sigma^-$; (b) $^3\Sigma^+$; (c) $^3\Pi$; (d) $^1\Phi$; (e) $^6\Delta$.

13.16 Give the levels belonging to each of the terms in Problem 13.15.

13.17 The ground state of H_2 has $^1\Sigma_g^+$ symmetry. What restriction does this impose on the values of m, n, j, and k in (13.96)?

13.18 (a) Show that the simple MO wave function for the $b^3\Sigma_u^+$ level of H_2 is the same as the Heitler–London VB function for this level. (b) Show that the simple MO wave function for the $B^1\Sigma_u^+$ level of H_2 contains only ionic terms.

13.19 (a) Use (13.131) to find the electron probability density for the simple MO wave function of the $b^3\Sigma_u^+$ level of H_2. Verify that (13.136) holds for this case. (b) Verify Eq. (13.134).

13.20 Show that the dipole moment (13.137) of a system of charges is independent of the choice of the coordinate origin, *provided* the system has no net charge.

13.21 Prove that the one-electron Hartree-Fock Hamiltonian (13.174) is Hermitian.

13.22 Explain the origin of the extra terms in the Hartree-Fock molecular Hamiltonian (13.174) as compared to the Hartree atomic Hamiltonian of (11.12) and (11.10).

13.23 Verify that the Coulomb and exchange integrals J_{ij} and K_{ij} can be written in terms of the Coulomb and exchange operators of Section (13.16) as

$$J_{ij} = \langle\varphi_i(1)|\,\hat{J}_j(1)\,|\varphi_i(1)\rangle, \qquad K_{ij} = \langle\varphi_i(1)|\,\hat{K}_j(1)\,|\varphi_i(1)\rangle$$

13.24 True or false: (a) If $|\psi_1| = |\psi_2|$, then ψ_1 and ψ_2 must represent the same state. (b) The probability density for the wave function (13.193) is the sum of the probability densities for the functions $c_1\varphi_{\text{cov}}$ and $c_2\varphi_{\text{ion}}$.

13.25 Show that for a diatomic molecule $[\hat{L}_z, \hat{O}_{\sigma_v}] \neq 0$.

13.26 In applying quantum chemistry to chemical kinetics, which would be the more accurate approximation, the simple MO or the simple VB theory?

13.27 Use orthogonality (Section 8.5) to derive the expression given in Fig. 13.20 for the heteronuclear antibonding MO. Then do the same for the antibonding homonuclear MO.

13.28 (a) Verify that the $2s_\perp$ AO in (13.183) is orthogonal to the $1s$ AO and is normalized. (b) Let an MO φ have the form $\varphi = a(1s) + b(2s) + \cdots$ when expressed using a nonorthogonal $2s$ STO and the form $\varphi = c(1s) + d(2s_\perp) + \cdots$ when expressed using an orthogonalized $2s$ orbital. Show that $c = a + Sb$ and $d = b(1 - S^2)^{1/2}$, where $S = \langle 1s|2s\rangle$. (c) Let ζ_1 and ζ_2 be the orbital exponents of $1s$ and $2s$ STO's, respectively. Show that $S = 24\zeta_1^{3/2}\zeta_2^{5/2}/3^{1/2}(\zeta_1 + \zeta_2)^4$.

13.29 Write down abbreviated expressions for the remaining 6 determinants of the N_2 VB function of Section 13.13. Use the rule given in that section to find the coefficient of each determinant in the wave function.

13.30 (a) Explain why the permanent dipole moment of a many-electron atom is always zero. (b) Explain why the permanent electric dipole moment of H can be nonzero for certain excited states. (c) Show qualitatively that two of the four correct zeroth-order functions of Problem 9.11 give nonzero permanent dipole moments.

13.31 Show that the 4 functions of (13.86) have the indicated eigenvalues with respect to a $\sigma_v(xz)$ reflection of electronic coordinates. (Start by showing that this reflection converts φ to $-\varphi$ and leaves r_a and r_b unchanged.)

The Virial Theorem and the Hellmann–Feynman Theorem

14.1 The Virial Theorem

In this chapter we discuss two theorems that aid in understanding chemical bonding. We begin with the virial theorem.

Consider a system in the stationary state ψ and let $\hat{H}$ be its time-independent Hamiltonian:

$$\hat{H}\psi = E\psi \tag{14.1}$$

Let $\hat{A}$ be a linear operator that does not involve the time. We consider the following integral:

$$\int \psi^*[\hat{H}, \hat{A}]\psi \, d\tau \tag{14.2}$$

$$= \int \psi^*(\hat{H}\hat{A} - \hat{A}\hat{H})\psi \, d\tau = \int \psi^*\hat{H}\hat{A}\psi \, d\tau - E\int \psi^*\hat{A}\psi \, d\tau \tag{14.3}$$

Since $\hat{H}$ is Hermitian, we have

$$\langle \psi | \hat{H} | \hat{A}\psi \rangle = \langle \hat{A}\psi | \hat{H} | \psi \rangle^* \tag{14.4}$$

Using (14.4) and (14.1) in (14.3), we get

$$\int \psi^*[\hat{H}, \hat{A}]\psi \, d\tau = E\int (\hat{A}\psi)\psi^* \, d\tau - E\int \psi^*\hat{A}\psi \, d\tau$$

$$\int \psi^*[\hat{H}, \hat{A}]\psi \, d\tau = 0 \tag{14.5}$$

Equation (14.5) has been christened the *hypervirial theorem.*[1]

We now derive the virial theorem from (14.5). We choose $\hat{A}$ to be:

$$\sum_i \hat{q}_i \hat{p}_i = -i\hbar \sum_i q_i \frac{\partial}{\partial q_i} \tag{14.6}$$

where the sum runs over the $3n$ Cartesian coordinates of the n particles. (Particle 1 has Cartesian coordinates q_1, q_2, q_3 and corresponding linear-momentum components p_1, p_2, p_3. Throughout this chapter, the symbol q will indicate a *Cartesian* coordinate.) We want to evaluate $[\hat{H}, \hat{A}]$. Using (5.5), (5.7), (5.12), and (5.13), we get

$$\left[\hat{H}, \sum_i \hat{q}_i \hat{p}_i \right] = \sum_i [\hat{H}, \hat{q}_i \hat{p}_i] = \sum_i \hat{q}_i [\hat{H}, \hat{p}_i] + \sum_i [\hat{H}, \hat{q}_i] \hat{p}_i$$

$$= i\hbar \sum_i q_i \frac{\partial V}{\partial q_i} - i\hbar \sum_i \frac{1}{m_i} \hat{p}_i^2 = i\hbar \sum_i q_i \frac{\partial V}{\partial q_i} - 2i\hbar \hat{T}$$

where $\hat{T}$ and $\hat{V}$ are the kinetic- and potential-energy operators for the system. Application of (14.5) gives

$$\left\langle \psi \left| \sum_i q_i \frac{\partial V}{\partial q_i} \right| \psi \right\rangle = 2 \langle \psi | \hat{T} | \psi \rangle \tag{14.7}$$

Using $\langle B \rangle$ for the quantum-mechanical average value of the quantity B, we write (14.7) as

$$\left\langle \sum_i q_i \frac{\partial V}{\partial q_i} \right\rangle = 2 \langle T \rangle \tag{14.8}$$

Equation (14.8) is the quantum-mechanical *virial theorem.* Note that its validity is restricted to stationary states. [The name of the theorem comes from a similar theorem in classical mechanics, which has the same form as (14.8), except that the averages are time averages. The word *vires* is Latin for "forces"; the derivatives of the potential energy give the negatives of the force components.]

For certain systems, the form of V causes the virial theorem to take on a particularly simple form. To discuss these systems, we introduce the idea of a homogeneous function. A function $f(x_1, x_2, ..., x_j)$ of several variables is said to be *homogeneous of degree n* if it satisfies

$$f(sx_1, sx_2, ..., sx_j) = s^n f(x_1, x_2, ..., x_j) \tag{14.9}$$

where s is an arbitrary parameter. For example, the function

$$g = \frac{1}{x^3} + \frac{1}{y^3} + \frac{1}{z^3} + \frac{x}{y^2 z^2} \tag{14.10}$$

[1] For some of its applications, see J. O. Hirschfelder, *J. Chem. Phys.*, **33**, 1462 (1960); J. H. Epstein and S. T. Epstein, *Am. J. Phys.*, **30**, 266 (1962).

is homogeneous of degree -3, since

$$g(sx, sy, sz) = \frac{1}{s^3 x^3} + \frac{1}{s^3 y^3} + \frac{1}{s^3 z^3} + \frac{sx}{s^2 y^2 s^2 z^2} = s^{-3} g(x, y, z)$$

Euler's theorem on homogeneous functions states that if $f(x_1, ..., x_j)$ is homogeneous of degree n, then

$$\sum_{k=1}^{j} x_k \frac{\partial f}{\partial x_k} = nf \tag{14.11}$$

The theorem is proved as follows. Let

$$u_1 = sx_1, \quad u_2 = sx_2, \quad ..., \quad u_j = sx_j \tag{14.12}$$

From the chain rule, the derivative of the left side of (14.9) is:

$$\frac{\partial f(u_1, ..., u_j)}{\partial s} = \frac{\partial f}{\partial u_1}\frac{\partial u_1}{\partial s} + \frac{\partial f}{\partial u_2}\frac{\partial u_2}{\partial s} + \cdots + \frac{\partial f}{\partial u_j}\frac{\partial u_j}{\partial s}$$

$$= x_1 \frac{\partial f}{\partial u_1} + x_2 \frac{\partial f}{\partial u_2} + \cdots + x_j \frac{\partial f}{\partial u_j} \tag{14.13}$$

For the partial derivative of (14.9) with respect to s, we then have

$$\sum_{k=1}^{j} x_k \frac{\partial f(u_1, ..., u_j)}{\partial u_k} = ns^{n-1} f(x_1, ..., x_j) \tag{14.14}$$

Now let $s = 1$, so that $u_i = x_i$; Eq. (14.14) then gives (14.11). Q.E.D. As an example of Euler's theorem, let $f = x^2 + y^2 + z^2$. We have

$$\sum_k x_k \frac{\partial f}{\partial x_k} = x \cdot 2x + y \cdot 2y + z \cdot 2z = 2f \tag{14.15}$$

Now we return to the virial theorem (14.8). If V happens to be a homogeneous function of degree n when expressed in Cartesian coordinates, then Euler's theorem gives

$$\sum_i q_i \frac{\partial V}{\partial q_i} = nV \tag{14.16}$$

and the virial theorem (14.8) simplifies to

$$2\langle T \rangle = n\langle V \rangle \tag{14.17}$$

Since (Problem 6.7)

$$\langle T \rangle + \langle V \rangle = E \tag{14.18}$$

we can write (14.17) in two other forms:

$$\langle V \rangle = \frac{2E}{n+2} \tag{14.19}$$

$$\langle T \rangle = \frac{nE}{n+2} \tag{14.20}$$

Consider some examples. For the one-dimensional harmonic oscillator we have $V = kx^2/2$, which is homogeneous of degree 2. Hence

$$\langle T \rangle = \langle V \rangle = E/2 = \tfrac{1}{2}h\nu(v+\tfrac{1}{2}) \tag{14.21}$$

This was verified for the ground state in Problem 4.1.

For the hydrogen atom, V in Cartesian coordinates is

$$V = -\frac{e^2}{(x^2+y^2+z^2)^{1/2}} \tag{14.22}$$

which is a homogeneous function of degree -1. Hence

$$2\langle T \rangle = -\langle V \rangle \tag{14.23}$$

a relation verified for the ground state in Problem 6.8. For any hydrogen-atom stationary state, we have

$$\langle V \rangle = 2E \tag{14.24}$$

$$\langle T \rangle = -E \tag{14.25}$$

For a many-electron atom, the potential energy is

$$V = -Ze^2 \sum_{i=1}^{n} \frac{1}{(x_i^2 + y_i^2 + z_i^2)^{1/2}} + {\sum_{i}}{\sum_{j>i}} \frac{e^2}{[(x_i-x_j)^2 + (y_i-y_j)^2 + (z_i-z_j)^2]^{1/2}} \tag{14.26}$$

Replacing each of the $3n$ coordinates by s times the coordinate, we find that V is homogeneous of degree -1. Hence the relations (14.23)–(14.25) are valid for any atom.

Now consider molecules. We shall assume the validity of the Born–Oppenheimer approximation and write the molecular wave function ψ as [Eq. (13.12)]

$$\psi = \psi_{\text{el}}(q_i; q_\alpha)\psi_N(q_\alpha) \tag{14.27}$$

where q_i and q_α symbolize the electronic and nuclear coordinates, respectively. The electronic wave function is found by solving the electronic Schroedinger equation (13.7):

$$\hat{H}_{\text{el}}\psi_{\text{el}}(q_i; q_\alpha) = E_{\text{el}}(q_\alpha)\psi_{\text{el}}(q_i; q_\alpha) \tag{14.28}$$

where E_{el} is the electronic energy, and

$$\hat{H}_{\text{el}} = \hat{T}_{\text{el}} + \hat{V}_{\text{el}} \tag{14.29}$$

$$\hat{T}_{\text{el}} = -\frac{\hbar^2}{2m} \sum_{i} \left(\frac{\partial^2}{\partial x_i^2} + \frac{\partial^2}{\partial y_i^2} + \frac{\partial^2}{\partial z_i^2} \right) \tag{14.30}$$

$$\hat{V}_{\text{el}} = -{\sum_{\alpha}}{\sum_{i}} \frac{Z_\alpha e^2}{[(x_i-x_\alpha)^2 + (y_i-y_\alpha)^2 + (z_i-z_\alpha)^2]^{1/2}}$$

$$+ {\sum_{i}}{\sum_{j>i}} \frac{e^2}{[(x_i-x_j)^2 + (y_i-y_j)^2 + (z_i-z_j)^2]^{1/2}} \tag{14.31}$$

Let the system be in the electronic stationary state ψ_{el}. If we put the subscript "el" on $\hat{H}$ and ψ in (14.1), and regard the variables of ψ_{el} to be the electronic coordinates q_i (with the nuclear coordinates q_α being parameters), then the derivation of the virial theorem (14.8) is seen to be valid for the electronic kinetic- and potential-energy operators, and we have

$$2\langle\psi_{el}|\hat{T}_{el}|\psi_{el}\rangle = \left\langle\psi_{el}\left|\sum_i q_i\frac{\partial V_{el}}{\partial q_i}\right|\psi_{el}\right\rangle \tag{14.32}$$

Viewed as a function of the electronic coordinates, V_{el} is *not* a homogeneous function, since

$$[(sx_i-x_\alpha)^2 + (sy_i-y_\alpha)^2 + (sz_i-z_\alpha)^2]^{-1/2}$$
$$\neq s^{-1}[(x_i-x_\alpha)^2 + (y_i-y_\alpha)^2 + (z_i-z_\alpha)^2]^{-1/2}$$

Thus the virial theorem for the average electronic kinetic and potential energies of a molecule will not have the simple form (14.23), which holds for atoms. We can, however, view V_{el} as a function of both the electronic and the nuclear Cartesian coordinates; from this viewpoint, V_{el} *is* a homogeneous function of degree -1, since

$$\frac{1}{[(sx_i-sx_\alpha)^2 + (sy_i-sy_\alpha)^2 + (sz_i-sz_\alpha)^2]^{1/2}} = \frac{1}{s[(x_i-x_\alpha)^2 + (y_i-y_\alpha)^2 + (z_i-z_\alpha)^2]^{1/2}}$$

Therefore, considering V_{el} as a function of both electronic and nuclear coordinates and applying Euler's theorem (14.11), we have

$$\sum_i q_i\frac{\partial V_{el}}{\partial q_i} + \sum_\alpha q_\alpha\frac{\partial V_{el}}{\partial q_\alpha} = -V_{el} \tag{14.33}$$

Using (14.33) in (14.32), we get

$$2\langle\psi_{el}|\hat{T}_{el}|\psi_{el}\rangle = -\langle\psi_{el}|\hat{V}_{el}|\psi_{el}\rangle - \left\langle\psi_{el}\left|\sum_\alpha q_\alpha\frac{\partial V_{el}}{\partial q_\alpha}\right|\psi_{el}\right\rangle \tag{14.34}$$

which contains an additional term as compared to the atomic virial theorem (14.23). Consider this extra term. We have

$$\left\langle\psi_{el}\left|\sum_\alpha q_\alpha\frac{\partial V_{el}}{\partial q_\alpha}\right|\psi_{el}\right\rangle = \sum_\alpha q_\alpha\int\psi_{el}^*\frac{\partial V_{el}}{\partial q_\alpha}\psi_{el}\,d\tau_{el} \tag{14.35}$$

where the nuclear coordinate q_α has been taken outside the integral over electronic coordinates. In Section 14.3 we will show that

$$\int\psi_{el}^*\frac{\partial V_{el}}{\partial q_\alpha}\psi_{el}\,d\tau_{el} = \frac{\partial E_{el}}{\partial q_\alpha} \tag{14.36}$$

[Equation (14.36) is an example of the Hellmann–Feynman theorem.] Using these last two equations in the molecular electronic virial theorem (14.34), we get

$$2\langle\psi_{el}|\hat{T}_{el}|\psi_{el}\rangle = -\langle\psi_{el}|\hat{V}_{el}|\psi_{el}\rangle - \sum_\alpha q_\alpha\frac{\partial E_{el}}{\partial q_\alpha} \tag{14.37}$$

where the q_α are the nuclear *Cartesian* coordinates. We abbreviate (14.37) as

$$2\langle T_{el} \rangle = -\langle V_{el} \rangle - \sum_\alpha q_\alpha \frac{\partial E_{el}}{\partial q_\alpha} \tag{14.38}$$

Using

$$\langle T_{el} \rangle + \langle V_{el} \rangle = E_{el} \tag{14.39}$$

we can eliminate either $\langle T_{el} \rangle$ or $\langle V_{el} \rangle$ from (14.38).

Now consider a diatomic molecule. The electronic energy is a function of the internuclear distance R: $E_{el} = E_{el}(R)$. The summation in (14.38) is over the nuclear Cartesian coordinates: $x_a, y_a, z_a, x_b, y_b, z_b$. We have

$$\frac{\partial E_{el}}{\partial x_a} = \frac{dE_{el}}{dR} \frac{\partial R}{\partial x_a}, \qquad \frac{\partial E_{el}}{\partial x_b} = \frac{dE_{el}}{dR} \frac{\partial R}{\partial x_b} \tag{14.40}$$

$$R = [(x_a - x_b)^2 + (y_a - y_b)^2 + (z_a - z_b)^2]^{1/2} \tag{14.41}$$

$$\frac{\partial R}{\partial x_a} = \frac{x_a - x_b}{R}, \qquad \frac{\partial R}{\partial x_b} = \frac{x_b - x_a}{R} \tag{14.42}$$

with similar equations for the y and z coordinates. The sum in (14.38) becomes

$$\sum_\alpha q_\alpha \frac{\partial E_{el}}{\partial q_\alpha} = \frac{1}{R} \frac{dE_{el}}{dR} [x_a(x_a - x_b) + x_b(x_b - x_a) + y_a(y_a - y_b)$$

$$+ y_b(y_b - y_a) + z_a(z_a - z_b) + z_b(z_b - z_a)]$$

$$\sum_\alpha q_\alpha \frac{\partial E_{el}}{\partial q_\alpha} = R \frac{dE_{el}}{dR} \tag{14.43}$$

The virial theorem (14.38) for a diatomic molecule reads

$$2\langle T_{el} \rangle = -\langle V_{el} \rangle - R \frac{dE_{el}}{dR} \tag{14.44}$$

Using (14.39), we have the two alternative forms

$$\langle T_{el} \rangle = -E_{el} - R \frac{dE_{el}}{dR} \tag{14.45}$$

$$\langle V_{el} \rangle = 2E_{el} + R \frac{dE_{el}}{dR} \tag{14.46}$$

In deriving the molecular electronic virial theorem, we omitted the internuclear repulsion

$$V_{NN} = \sum_\beta \sum_{\alpha > \beta} \frac{Z_\alpha Z_\beta e^2}{[(x_\alpha - x_\beta)^2 + (y_\alpha - y_\beta)^2 + (z_\alpha - z_\beta)^2]^{1/2}} \tag{14.47}$$

from the electronic Hamiltonian (14.29)–(14.31). Let

$$V = V_{el} + V_{NN} \tag{14.48}$$

where V_{el} is given by (14.31). We can rewrite the electronic Schroedinger equation (14.28) as [Eq. (13.4)]

$$(\hat{T}_{el} + \hat{V})\psi_{el} = U(q_\alpha)\psi_{el} \tag{14.49}$$

where

$$U(q_\alpha) = E_{el}(q_\alpha) + V_{NN} \tag{14.50}$$

$U(q_\alpha)$ is the potential-energy function for nuclear motion. Now consider what happens to the right side of Eq. (14.37) when we add in V_{NN} to V_{el} and E_{el}. We have

$$-\int \psi_{el}^*(\hat{V}_{el} + V_{NN})\psi_{el}\, d\tau_{el} - \sum_\alpha q_\alpha \frac{\partial U}{\partial q_\alpha}$$

$$= -\langle \psi_{el} | \hat{V}_{el} | \psi_{el} \rangle - V_{NN} - \sum_\alpha q_\alpha \frac{\partial E_{el}}{\partial q_\alpha} - \sum_\alpha q_\alpha \frac{\partial V_{NN}}{\partial q_\alpha} \tag{14.51}$$

V_{NN} is a homogeneous function of the nuclear Cartesian coordinates of degree -1, so that (Euler's theorem)

$$\sum_\alpha q_\alpha \frac{\partial V_{NN}}{\partial q_\alpha} = -V_{NN} \tag{14.52}$$

and (14.51) becomes

$$-\langle \psi_{el} | \hat{V}_{el} + V_{NN} | \psi_{el} \rangle - \sum_\alpha q_\alpha \frac{\partial U}{\partial q_\alpha} = -\langle \psi_{el} | \hat{V}_{el} | \psi_{el} \rangle - \sum_\alpha q_\alpha \frac{\partial E_{el}}{\partial q_\alpha} \tag{14.53}$$

Substitution of (14.53) into (14.37) gives

$$2\langle \psi_{el} | \hat{T}_{el} | \psi_{el} \rangle = -\langle \psi_{el} | \hat{V}_{el} + V_{NN} | \psi_{el} \rangle - \sum_\alpha q_\alpha \frac{\partial U}{\partial q_\alpha}$$

$$2\langle T_{el} \rangle = -\langle V \rangle - \sum_\alpha q_\alpha \frac{\partial U}{\partial q_\alpha} \tag{14.54}$$

so that the molecular electronic virial theorem holds whether or not we include the internuclear repulsion. Corresponding to Eqs. (14.44)–(14.46) for diatomic molecules, we have

$$2\langle T_{el} \rangle = -\langle V \rangle - R(dU/dR) \tag{14.55}$$

$$\langle T_{el} \rangle = -U - R(dU/dR) \tag{14.56}$$

$$\langle V \rangle = 2U + R(dU/dR) \tag{14.57}$$

The potential energy V is given by Eqs. (14.48), (14.47), and (14.31); we see that the zero of energy is taken with all particles (electrons and nuclei) at infinite separation from each other. Thus the function $U(R)$ in (14.55)–(14.57) does not go to zero at $R = \infty$, but goes to the sum of the energies of the separated atoms, which is negative.

The molecular electronic virial theorem was first derived by Slater.

For polyatomic molecules, (14.54) can be written as

$$2\langle T_{el} \rangle = -\langle V \rangle - \sum_\alpha \sum_{\beta > \alpha} R_{\alpha\beta}(\partial U/\partial R_{\alpha\beta})$$

where the sum runs over either all internuclear distances or the bond lengths only; proofs are given in R. G. Parr and J. E. Brown, *J. Chem. Phys.*, **49**, 4849 (1968) and B. Nelander, *ibid.*, **51**, 469 (1969).

The true wave functions for a system with V a homogeneous function of the coordinates must satisfy the form of the virial theorem (14.17); we now ask, what determines whether an *approximate* wave function for such a system satisfies (14.17)? The answer is that by inserting a variational parameter as a multiplier of each Cartesian coordinate and choosing this parameter to minimize the variational integral, we can make any trial variation function satisfy the virial theorem. (For the proof, see *Kauzmann*, p. 229.) This process is called *scaling*, and the variational parameter multiplying each coordinate is called a *scale factor*. For a molecular trial function, the scaling parameter must be inserted in front of the nuclear Cartesian coordinates, as well as in front of the electronic coordinates.

Consider some examples. The zeroth-order perturbation wave function (9.60) for the heliumlike atom has no scale factor and so does not satisfy the virial theorem. If we were to calculate $\langle T \rangle$ and $\langle V \rangle$ for (9.60), we would find $2\langle T \rangle \neq -\langle V \rangle$; see Problem 14.7. The Heitler–London trial function for H_2, Eq. (13.107), has no scale factor and does not satisfy the virial theorem. The Heitler–London–Wang function, which uses a variationally determined orbital exponent satisfies the virial theorem. Hartree–Fock wave functions satisfy the virial theorem—note the scale factor in the Slater basis functions (11.16).

14.2 The Virial Theorem and Chemical Bonding

We now use the virial theorem to examine the changes in electronic kinetic and potential energy that occur when a covalent chemical bond is formed in a diatomic molecule. The prime requisite for formation of a stable bond is that the $U(R)$ curve have a substantial minimum. At this minimum, we have

$$\frac{dU}{dR}\bigg|_{R_e} = 0 \qquad (14.58)$$

and Eqs. (14.55)–(14.57) become

$$2\langle T_{el} \rangle|_{R_e} = -\langle V \rangle|_{R_e} \qquad (14.59)$$

$$\langle T_{el} \rangle|_{R_e} = -U(R_e) \qquad (14.60)$$

$$\langle V \rangle|_{R_e} = 2U(R_e) \qquad (14.61)$$

These equations resemble those for atoms [Eqs. (14.23)–(14.25)]. At $R = \infty$ we have the separated atoms, and the atomic virial theorem gives

$$2\langle T_{el} \rangle|_{\infty} = -\langle V \rangle|_{\infty} \qquad (14.62)$$

$$\langle T_{el} \rangle|_{\infty} = -U(\infty) \qquad (14.63)$$

$$\langle V \rangle|_{\infty} = 2U(\infty) \qquad (14.64)$$

$U(\infty)$ is the sum of the energies of the two separated atoms. Therefore

$$\langle T_{el}\rangle|_{R_e} - \langle T_{el}\rangle|_\infty = U(\infty) - U(R_e) \tag{14.65}$$

$$\langle V\rangle|_{R_e} - \langle V\rangle|_\infty = 2[U(R_e) - U(\infty)] \tag{14.66}$$

For bonding we have

$$U(R_e) < U(\infty)$$

Thus the average molecular potential energy at R_e is *less* than the sum of the potential energies of the separated atoms, while the average molecular kinetic energy is *greater* at R_e than at ∞. The decrease in potential energy is twice the increase in kinetic energy, and results from allowing the electrons to feel the attractions of both nuclei and from the increase in orbital exponents in the molecule (Section 13.4). The dissociation energy (13.9) is

$$D_e = \tfrac{1}{2}[\langle V\rangle|_\infty - \langle V\rangle|_{R_e}] \tag{14.67}$$

Consider the behavior of the average potential and kinetic energies for large R. The interactions between atoms at large distances are called *van der Waals forces*. For two neutral atoms, at least one of which is in an S state, quantum-mechanical perturbation theory shows[2] that the van der Waals force of attraction is proportional to $1/R^7$, and the potential energy behaves like

$$U(R) \approx U(\infty) - \frac{A}{R^6} \qquad R \text{ large} \tag{14.68}$$

where A is a positive constant. This expression was first derived by London, and van der Waals forces between neutral atoms are called *London forces* (or dispersion forces); London forces can be viewed as due to the polarization of one atom by the instantaneous dipole moment of the other. [This van der Waals interaction introduces a slight minimum at a large value of R in the $U(R)$ curve of a repulsive state. For the lowest excited state of H_2, the $(\sigma_g 1s)(\sigma_u^* 1s)\,{}^3\Sigma_u^+$ repulsive state, the van der Waals minimum has been calculated[3] to occur at about 4 Å and to be about 0.0005 eV deep.]

Using (14.68), (14.56), (14.57), (14.63), and (14.64), we have

$$\langle V\rangle \approx \langle V\rangle|_\infty + \frac{4A}{R^6}, \qquad R \text{ large} \tag{14.69}$$

$$\langle T_{el}\rangle \approx \langle T_{el}\rangle|_\infty - \frac{5A}{R^6}, \qquad R \text{ large} \tag{14.70}$$

Hence, as R decreases from infinity, the average potential energy at first increases, while the average kinetic energy at first decreases. The combination of these conclusions with our conclusions about $\langle V\rangle|_{R_e}$ and $\langle T_{el}\rangle|_{R_e}$ shows that $\langle V\rangle$ must go through a maximum somewhere between R_e and infinity and $\langle T_{el}\rangle$ must go through a minimum in this region.

---

[2] See *Landau and Lifshitz*, Section 89; *Kauzmann*, Chapter 13.
[3] W. Kolos and L. Wolniewicz, *J. Chem. Phys.*, **43**, 2429 (1965).

For R much less than R_e, we can use (13.80) and (13.8) to write

$$U(R) \approx \frac{Z_a Z_b e^2}{R} + E_{UA} + aR^2, \qquad R \text{ small} \qquad (14.71)$$

where E_{UA} is the united-atom energy. The virial theorem then gives

$$\langle T_{el} \rangle \approx -E_{UA} - 3aR^2, \qquad R \text{ small} \qquad (14.72)$$

$$\langle V \rangle \approx \frac{Z_a Z_b e^2}{R} + 2E_{UA} + 4aR^2, \qquad R \text{ small} \qquad (14.73)$$

The virial theorem holds for the united atom:

$$\langle T_{el} \rangle|_0 = -E_{UA}, \qquad \langle V_{el} \rangle|_0 = 2E_{UA} \qquad (14.74)$$

and we have

$$\langle T_{el} \rangle \approx \langle T_{el} \rangle|_0 - 3aR^2, \qquad R \text{ small} \qquad (14.75)$$

$$\langle V \rangle \approx \frac{Z_a Z_b e^2}{R} + \langle V_{el} \rangle|_0 + 4aR^2, \qquad R \text{ small} \qquad (14.76)$$

The average value of $\langle V \rangle$ goes to infinity as R goes to zero, due to the internuclear repulsion.

Having found the general behavior of $\langle V \rangle$ and $\langle T_{el} \rangle$ as functions of R, we now draw Fig. 14.1. This figure is not for any particular molecule, but resembles the known curves[4] for H_2 and H_2^+.

What explanation can we give for the change in average kinetic and potential energy with R? Consider H_2^+. The electronic potential-energy function is

$$V_{el} = -\frac{e^2}{r_a} - \frac{e^2}{r_b} \qquad (14.77)$$

If we plot the values of V_{el} for points on the molecular axis for a large value of R, we get a curve like Fig. 14.2, which resembles two hydrogen-atom potential-energy curves (Fig. 6.5) placed side by side. We have seen that the overlapping of the $1s$ AO's occurring in molecule formation leads to a buildup of charge probability density between the nuclei for the ground state. However, Fig. 14.2 shows that the potential energy is relatively *high* in the region midway between the nuclei when R is large. Thus we get an initial increase in $\langle V \rangle$ as R decreases from infinity. Now consider the kinetic energy. The uncertainty principle (5.18) gives $(\Delta x)^2 (\Delta p_x)^2 \geq \hbar^2/4$. For a stationary state, $\langle p_x \rangle$ is zero [see for example (3.125)] and (5.15) gives $(\Delta p_x)^2 = \langle p_x^2 \rangle$. Hence a small value of $(\Delta x)^2$ means a large value of $\langle p_x^2 \rangle$ and hence a large value of the average kinetic energy (which equals $\langle p^2 \rangle/2m$). Thus a compact ψ_{el} corresponds to a large electronic kinetic energy. In the separated atoms, the wave function is concentrated in two rather small regions about each nucleus (Fig. 6.6). In the initial stages of molecule formation, the buildup of probability density between the nuclei corresponds to having a wave function that is less compact

---

[4] W. Kolos and L. Wolniewicz, *J. Chem. Phys.*, **41**, 3663 (1964); *Slater, Quantum Theory of Molecules and Solids*, vol. 1, p. 36.

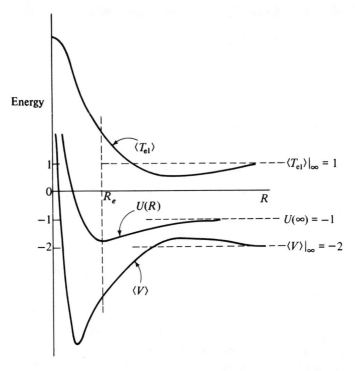

FIGURE 14.1 *Variation of the average potential and kinetic energies of a diatomic molecule. The unit of energy is taken as the electronic kinetic energy of the separated atoms.*

than in the separated atoms. Thus as R decreases from infinity, the electronic kinetic energy initially decreases. The energies E_{el} of the two lowest H_2^+ states have been indicated in Fig. 14.2. For large R, the region between the nuclei is classically forbidden, but is accessible according to quantum mechanics (tunneling).

Now consider what happens as R decreases further. Plotting (14.77) for an intermediate value of R, we find that now the region between the nuclei is a region

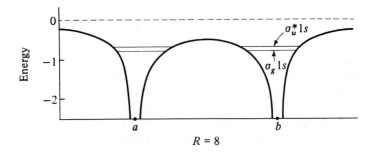

FIGURE 14.2 *Potential energy along the internuclear axis for electronic motion in H_2^+ for large internuclear separation. Atomic units are used.*

of *low* potential energy, since an electron in this region feels substantial attractions from both nuclei. (See Fig. 14.3.) Hence, at intermediate values of R, the overlap charge buildup between the nuclei (and the increase in orbital exponents) lower the potential energy. For intermediate values of R, the wave function has become more compact as compared to large R (due in part to the increase in orbital exponents), which gives an increase in $\langle T_{el} \rangle$ as R is reduced. In fact, we see from Fig. 14.1 and Eq. (14.65) that $\langle T_{el} \rangle$ is *greater* at R_e in the molecule than in the separated atoms; hence, the molecular wave function at R_e is more compact than the separated-atom wave functions.

FIGURE 14.3 *Potential energy along the internuclear axis for electronic motion in* $H_2{}^+$ *for intermediate internuclear distance.*

For very small R the average potential energy goes to infinity, due to the internuclear repulsion. *However, for* $R = R_e$ Fig. 14.1 shows that $\langle V \rangle$ is still decreasing sharply with decreasing R, and it is the increase in $\langle T_{el} \rangle$, and not the nuclear repulsion, that causes the $U(R)$ curve to turn up as R becomes less than R_e. The squeezing of the molecular wave function into a smaller region with the associated increase in $\langle T_{el} \rangle$ is more important than the internuclear repulsion in causing the initial repulsion between the atoms.

14.3 The Hellmann–Feynman Theorem

Consider a system with a time-independent Hamiltonian $\hat{H}$ that involves parameters. An obvious example is the molecular electronic Hamiltonian (13.5), which depends parametrically on the nuclear coordinates. However, the Hamiltonian of any system contains parameters. For example, the one-dimensional harmonic-oscillator Hamiltonian is

$$-\frac{\hbar^2}{2m}\frac{d^2}{dx^2} + \tfrac{1}{2}kx^2 \tag{14.78}$$

The force constant k is a parameter, as is the mass m. Although $\hbar$ is a constant, there is nothing to prevent us from considering it as a parameter also. The stationary-state energies E_n are functions of the same parameters as $\hat{H}$. For example, for the harmonic oscillator:

$$E_n = (v + \tfrac{1}{2})hv = (v + \tfrac{1}{2})\hbar (k/m)^{1/2} \tag{14.79}$$

The stationary-state wave functions also depend on the parameters in $\hat{H}$. We now investigate how E_n varies with each of the parameters. More specifically, let λ be one of the parameters; we ask for $\partial E_n/\partial\lambda$, where the partial derivative is taken with all other parameters held constant.

We begin with the Schroedinger equation

$$\hat{H}\psi_n = E_n\psi_n \tag{14.80}$$

where the ψ_n are the normalized stationary-state eigenfunctions. Because of normalization, we have

$$E_n = \int \psi_n^*\hat{H}\psi_n\,d\tau \tag{14.81}$$

$$\frac{\partial E_n}{\partial\lambda} = \frac{\partial}{\partial\lambda}\int \psi_n^*\hat{H}\psi_n\,d\tau \tag{14.82}$$

The integral in (14.81) is a definite integral over all space, and its value depends parametrically on λ, since $\hat{H}$ and ψ_n depend on λ. Provided the integrand is well behaved, we can evaluate the integral's derivative with respect to a parameter by differentiating under the integral sign. (We used this procedure in Problems 7.18 and 8.2.) Therefore

$$\frac{\partial E_n}{\partial\lambda} = \int \frac{\partial}{\partial\lambda}(\psi_n^*\hat{H}\psi_n)\,d\tau \tag{14.83}$$

$$\frac{\partial E_n}{\partial\lambda} = \int \frac{\partial\psi_n^*}{\partial\lambda}\hat{H}\psi_n\,d\tau + \int \psi_n^*\frac{\partial}{\partial\lambda}(\hat{H}\psi_n)\,d\tau \tag{14.84}$$

We have

$$\frac{\partial}{\partial\lambda}(\hat{H}\psi_n) = \frac{\partial}{\partial\lambda}(\hat{T}\psi_n) + \frac{\partial}{\partial\lambda}(\hat{V}\psi_n) \tag{14.85}$$

The potential-energy operator is just multiplication by V, so that

$$\frac{\partial}{\partial\lambda}(\hat{V}\psi_n) = \frac{\partial V}{\partial\lambda}\psi_n + V\frac{\partial\psi_n}{\partial\lambda} \tag{14.86}$$

The parameter λ will occur in the kinetic-energy operator as part of the factor multiplying one or more of the derivatives with respect to the coordinates. For example, taking λ as the mass of the particle, we have for a one-particle problem:

$$\hat{T} = -\frac{\hbar^2}{2\lambda}\left(\frac{\partial^2}{\partial x^2} + \frac{\partial^2}{\partial y^2} + \frac{\partial^2}{\partial z^2}\right) \tag{14.87}$$

$$\frac{\partial}{\partial\lambda}(\hat{T}\psi) = -\frac{\hbar^2}{2}\frac{\partial}{\partial\lambda}\left[\frac{1}{\lambda}\left(\frac{\partial^2\psi}{\partial x^2} + \frac{\partial^2\psi}{\partial y^2} + \frac{\partial^2\psi}{\partial z^2}\right)\right]$$

$$= \frac{\hbar^2}{2\lambda^2}\left(\frac{\partial^2\psi}{\partial x^2} + \frac{\partial^2\psi}{\partial y^2} + \frac{\partial^2\psi}{\partial z^2}\right) - \frac{\hbar^2}{2\lambda}\left(\frac{\partial^2}{\partial x^2} + \frac{\partial^2}{\partial y^2} + \frac{\partial^2}{\partial z^2}\right)\left(\frac{\partial\psi}{\partial\lambda}\right)$$

since we can change the order of the partial differentiations without affecting the result. We can write this last equation as

$$\frac{\partial}{\partial \lambda}(\hat{T}\psi_n) = \left(\frac{\partial \hat{T}}{\partial \lambda}\right)\psi_n + \hat{T}\left(\frac{\partial \psi_n}{\partial \lambda}\right) \tag{14.88}$$

where $(\partial \hat{T}/\partial \lambda)$ is found by differentiating $\hat{T}$ with respect to λ just as if it were a function instead of an operator. Although we got (14.88) by considering a specific $\hat{T}$ and λ, the same arguments show it to be generally valid. Combining (14.88) and (14.86), we write

$$\frac{\partial}{\partial \lambda}(\hat{H}\psi_n) = \left(\frac{\partial \hat{H}}{\partial \lambda}\right)\psi_n + \hat{H}\left(\frac{\partial \psi_n}{\partial \lambda}\right) \tag{14.89}$$

Equation (14.84) becomes

$$\frac{\partial E_n}{\partial \lambda} = \int \frac{\partial \psi_n^*}{\partial \lambda} \hat{H}\psi_n \, d\tau + \int \psi_n^* \frac{\partial \hat{H}}{\partial \lambda}\psi_n \, d\tau + \int \psi_n^* \hat{H} \frac{\partial \psi_n}{\partial \lambda} \, d\tau \tag{14.90}$$

For the first integral in (14.90), we have

$$\int \frac{\partial \psi_n^*}{\partial \lambda} \hat{H}\psi_n \, d\tau = E_n \int \frac{\partial \psi_n^*}{\partial \lambda}\psi_n \, d\tau \tag{14.91}$$

The Hermitian property of $\hat{H}$ and (14.80) give for the last integral in (14.90):

$$\int \psi_n^* \hat{H} \frac{\partial \psi_n}{\partial \lambda} \, d\tau = \int \frac{\partial \psi_n}{\partial \lambda}(\hat{H}\psi_n)^* \, d\tau = E_n \int \psi_n^* \frac{\partial \psi_n}{\partial \lambda} \, d\tau$$

Therefore

$$\frac{\partial E_n}{\partial \lambda} = \int \psi_n^* \frac{\partial \hat{H}}{\partial \lambda}\psi_n \, d\tau + E_n \int \frac{\partial \psi_n^*}{\partial \lambda}\psi_n \, d\tau + E_n \int \psi_n^* \frac{\partial \psi_n}{\partial \lambda} \, d\tau \tag{14.92}$$

The wave function is normalized; hence

$$\int \psi_n^* \psi_n \, d\tau = 1$$

$$\frac{\partial}{\partial \lambda} \int \psi_n^* \psi_n \, d\tau = 0$$

$$\int \frac{\partial \psi_n^*}{\partial \lambda}\psi_n \, d\tau + \int \psi_n^* \frac{\partial \psi_n}{\partial \lambda} \, d\tau = 0 \tag{14.93}$$

Using (14.93) in (14.92), we obtain

$$\frac{\partial E_n}{\partial \lambda} = \int \psi_n^* \frac{\partial \hat{H}}{\partial \lambda}\psi_n \, d\tau \tag{14.94}$$

Equation (14.94) is called the *generalized Hellmann–Feynman theorem*, although it seems to have first been given by Pauli.[5]

---

[5] For a discussion of the origin of the Hellmann–Feynman and related theorems, see J. I. Musher, *Am. J. Phys.*, **34**, 267 (1966).

Consider some examples. If we take λ to be the force constant k in the harmonic-oscillator Hamiltonian (14.78), then (14.94) gives

$$\frac{\partial}{\partial k}\left[(v+\tfrac{1}{2})\hbar\left(\frac{k}{m}\right)^{1/2}\right] = \int \psi_n^*(\tfrac{1}{2}x^2)\psi_n \, d\tau$$

$$\int \psi_n^* x^2 \psi_n \, d\tau = (v+\tfrac{1}{2})\frac{\hbar v}{k} \tag{14.95}$$

We have found an expression for the average value of x^2 for any harmonic-oscillator stationary state, without evaluating any integrals. This result was also obtained from the virial theorem; see Eq. (14.21). For a third derivation, see *Eyring, Walter, and Kimball*, p. 79.

Application of the Hellmann–Feynman theorem to the hydrogenlike atom, with Z as the parameter, gives (Problem 14.6a):

$$\int r^{-1}|\psi|^2 \, d\tau = \left\langle \frac{1}{r} \right\rangle = \frac{Z}{n^2}\left(\frac{1}{a_0}\right) \tag{14.96}$$

This result was also gotten from the virial theorem; see Eq. (14.24).

The first-order perturbation theory result Eq. (9.30) is a special case of the Hellmann–Feynman theorem: Differentiation of Eqs. (9.7) and (9.18) gives

$$\frac{\partial E_n}{\partial \lambda} = E_n^{(1)} + 2\lambda E_n^{(2)} + \cdots \tag{14.97}$$

$$\frac{\partial \hat{H}}{\partial \lambda} = \hat{H}' \tag{14.98}$$

The Hellmann–Feynman theorem (14.94) gives

$$E_n^{(1)} + 2\lambda E_n^{(2)} + \cdots = \int \psi_n^* \hat{H}' \psi_n \, d\tau \tag{14.99}$$

If we set λ equal to zero, then ψ_n goes over to $\psi_n^{(0)}$ [Eq. (9.17)] and we get the result (9.30).[6]

The Hellmann–Feynman theorem (with E_n being the Hartree–Fock energy) is obeyed by Hartree–Fock (as well as exact) wave functions.[7]

14.4 The Electrostatic Theorem

Hellmann and Feynman independently applied Eq. (14.94) to molecules, taking λ as a nuclear Cartesian coordinate. We now consider their results.

[Hellmann was a German physical chemist. The Nazis had him dismissed from his position, and he then settled in Russia. He was executed as a "German spy" in the Stalinist purges of the late 1930's. His results appear in his textbook

---

[6] For further discussion of the relation between perturbation theory and the Hellmann–Feynman theorem, see S. T. Epstein, *Am. J. Phys.*, **22**, 613 (1954).

[7] For a proof, see R. E. Stanton, *J. Chem. Phys.*, **36**, 1298 (1962).

Einführung in die Quantenchemie, Deuticke, Leipzig, 1937, p. 285. The American physicist Richard Feynman is noted for his contributions to quantum field theory. His paper "Forces in Molecules"—*Phys. Rev.*, **56**, 340 (1939)—consists of work he did as an undergraduate at MIT.]

As usual, we are using the Born–Oppenheimer approximation, solving the electronic Schroedinger equation for a fixed nuclear configuration [Eq. (14.49)]:

$$\hat{H}\psi_{el} = (\hat{T}_{el}+\hat{V})\,\psi_{el} = U\psi_{el} \tag{14.100}$$

The potential energy V is

$$\hat{V} = \hat{V}_{el} + \hat{V}_{NN} \tag{14.101}$$

The operators $\hat{T}_{el}$, $\hat{V}_{el}$, and $\hat{V}_{NN}$ are given by (14.30), (14.31), and (14.47). The Hamiltonian $\hat{H}$ depends on the nuclear Cartesian coordinates as parameters. If x_δ is the x coordinate of nucleus δ, the generalized Hellmann–Feynman theorem (14.94) gives

$$\frac{\partial U}{\partial x_\delta} = \int \psi_{el}^* \frac{\partial \hat{H}}{\partial x_\delta} \psi_{el}\, d\tau_{el} \tag{14.102}$$

The kinetic-energy part of $\hat{H}$ is independent of the nuclear Cartesian coordinates, as can be seen from (14.30). Hence

$$\frac{\partial U}{\partial x_\delta} = \int \psi_{el}^* \frac{\partial V}{\partial x_\delta} \psi_{el}\, d\tau_{el} \tag{14.103}$$

[If we had omitted the internuclear repulsion V_{NN} from V, we would have obtained Eq. (14.36), which was used in deriving the molecular electronic virial theorem.] We have

$$\frac{\partial V}{\partial x_\delta} = \frac{\partial V_{el}}{\partial x_\delta} + \frac{\partial V_{NN}}{\partial x_\delta} \tag{14.104}$$

From (14.31) we get

$$\frac{\partial V_{el}}{\partial x_\delta} = -\sum_i \frac{Z_\delta (x_i - x_\delta) e^2}{r_{i\delta}^3} \tag{14.105}$$

where $r_{i\delta}$ is the distance from electron i to nucleus δ. To evaluate $\partial V_{NN}/\partial x_\delta$, we need only consider those internuclear repulsion terms that involve nucleus δ; hence

$$\frac{\partial V_{NN}}{\partial x_\delta} = \frac{\partial}{\partial x_\delta} \sum_{\alpha \neq \delta} \frac{Z_\alpha Z_\delta e^2}{[(x_\alpha - x_\delta)^2 + (y_\alpha - y_\delta)^2 + (z_\alpha - z_\delta)^2]^{1/2}}$$

$$= \sum_{\alpha \neq \delta} Z_\alpha Z_\delta e^2 \frac{(x_\alpha - x_\delta)}{R_{\alpha\delta}^3} \tag{14.106}$$

where $R_{\alpha\delta}$ is the distance between nuclei α and δ. Noting that (14.106) does not involve the electronic coordinates and that ψ_{el} is normalized, we see that (14.103) becomes

$$\frac{\partial U}{\partial x_\delta} = -\sum_i Z_\delta e^2 \int |\psi_{el}|^2 \frac{(x_i - x_\delta)}{r_{i\delta}^3}\, d\tau_{el} + \sum_{\alpha \neq \delta} Z_\alpha Z_\delta e^2 \frac{(x_\alpha - x_\delta)}{R_{\alpha\delta}^3} \tag{14.107}$$

Consider the integral in (14.107). The factor multiplying $|\psi_{el}|^2$ depends only on the coordinates of electron i, and this integral equals (recall that $\int d\tau$ implies a summation over all spin variables, as well as integration over all space coordinates):

$$\int_{-\infty}^{\infty}\int_{-\infty}^{\infty}\int_{-\infty}^{\infty}\left[\sum_{\text{all } m_s}\int' |\psi_{el}|^2 \, dv'_{el}\right]\frac{(x_i - x_\delta)}{r_{i\delta}^3} \, dx_i \, dy_i \, dz_i$$

where by $\int' dv'_{el}$ we mean an integration over the $3n-3$ spatial coordinates of all electrons except electron i. From Eq. (13.131) we see that the quantity in brackets is equal to ρ/n, where ρ is the electron probability density of the n-electron molecule. Hence (14.107) simplifies to[8]

$$\frac{\partial U}{\partial x_\delta} = -\frac{1}{n}\sum_{i=1}^{n} Z_\delta e^2 \int \rho(x_i, y_i, z_i)\frac{(x_i - x_\delta)}{r_{i\delta}^3} \, dv_i + \sum_{\alpha \neq \delta} Z_\alpha Z_\delta e^2 \frac{(x_\alpha - x_\delta)}{R_{\alpha\delta}^3}$$

(14.108)

The integration variables in each of the n definite integrals in (14.108) are dummy variables, and the integrals have the same value no matter what the value of i is. Thus each term in the first sum in (14.108) has the same value, and since there are n terms in this sum, we get

$$\frac{\partial U}{\partial x_\delta} = -Z_\delta e^2 \iiint \rho(x, y, z)\frac{(x - x_\delta)}{r_\delta^3} \, dx \, dy \, dz + \sum_{\alpha \neq \delta} Z_\alpha Z_\delta e^2 \frac{(x_\alpha - x_\delta)}{R_{\alpha\delta}^3}$$

(14.109)

where we have dropped the superfluous subscript i. The variable r_δ is the distance between nucleus δ and point (x, y, z) in space:

$$r_\delta = [(x - x_\delta)^2 + (y - y_\delta)^2 + (z - z_\delta)^2]^{1/2}$$

What is the significance of (14.109)? In the Born–Oppenheimer approximation, the function $U(x_\alpha, y_\alpha, z_\alpha, x_\beta, \ldots)$ is the potential-energy function for nuclear motion, the nuclear Schroedinger equation being

$$\left[-\frac{\hbar^2}{2}\sum_\alpha \frac{1}{m_\alpha}\nabla_\alpha^2 + U\right]\psi_N = E\psi_N$$

(14.110)

The quantity $-\partial U/\partial x_\delta$ can thus be viewed [see Eq. (5.46)] as the x component of the effective force on nucleus δ due to the other nuclei and the electrons. In addition to (14.109), we have two corresponding equations for $\partial U/\partial y_\delta$ and $\partial U/\partial z_\delta$; if $\mathbf{F}_\delta$ is the effective force on nucleus δ, we have

$$\mathbf{F}_\delta = -\mathbf{i}\frac{\partial U}{\partial x_\delta} - \mathbf{j}\frac{\partial U}{\partial y_\delta} - \mathbf{k}\frac{\partial U}{\partial z_\delta}$$

(14.111)

$$\mathbf{F}_\delta = -Z_\delta e^2 \iiint \rho(x, y, z)\frac{\mathbf{r}_\delta}{r_\delta^3} \, dx \, dy \, dz + e^2 \sum_{\alpha \neq \delta} Z_\alpha Z_\delta \frac{\mathbf{R}_{\alpha\delta}}{R_{\alpha\delta}^3}$$

(14.112)

---

[8] Recall that we used this kind of simplification in Section 13.12 on dipole moments.

where $\mathbf{r}_\delta$ is the vector from point (x, y, z) to nucleus δ:

$$\mathbf{r}_\delta = \mathbf{i}(x_\delta - x) + \mathbf{j}(y_\delta - y) + \mathbf{k}(z_\delta - z) \qquad (14.113)$$

and where $\mathbf{R}_{\alpha\delta}$ is the vector from nucleus α to nucleus δ:

$$\mathbf{R}_{\alpha\delta} = \mathbf{i}(x_\delta - x_\alpha) + \mathbf{j}(y_\delta - y_\alpha) + \mathbf{k}(z_\delta - z_\alpha) \qquad (14.114)$$

Equation (14.112) has a simple physical interpretation. Let us imagine the electrons smeared out into a charge distribution whose density is $-e\rho(x, y, z)$. The force on nucleus δ exerted by the infinitesimal element of electronic charge $-e\rho \, dx \, dy \, dz$ is [Eq. (6.64)]:

$$-Z_\delta e^2 \frac{\mathbf{r}_\delta}{r_\delta^3} \rho \, dx \, dy \, dz \qquad (14.115)$$

and integration of (14.115) shows that the total force exerted on δ by this hypothetical electron smear is given by the first term on the right of (14.112). The second term on the right of (14.112) is clearly the Coulomb's law force on nucleus δ due to the electrostatic repulsions of the other nuclei.

Thus the effective force acting on a nucleus in a molecule can be calculated by simple electrostatics as the sum of the Coulombic forces exerted by the other nuclei and by a hypothetical electron cloud whose charge density $-e\rho(x, y, z)$ is found by solving the electronic Schroedinger equation. This statement is called the *electrostatic theorem*. It is frequently called the Hellmann–Feynman theorem, but to avoid confusion with the generalized Hellmann–Feynman theorem (of which it is a special case), the term "electrostatic theorem" is widely used. The electron probability density depends on the parameters defining the nuclear configuration:

$$\rho = \rho(x, y, z; x_\alpha, y_\alpha, z_\alpha, x_\beta, \dots)$$

It is quite reasonable that the electrostatic theorem follows from the Born–Oppenheimer approximation, since the rapid motion of the electrons allows the electronic wave function and probability density to adjust immediately to changes in nuclear configuration; the rapid motion of the electrons causes the sluggish nuclei to "see" the electrons as a charge cloud, rather than as discrete particles. The fact that the effective forces on the nuclei are electrostatic affirms that there are no "mysterious quantum-mechanical forces" acting in molecules.

Let us consider the implications of the electrostatic theorem for chemical bonding in diatomic molecules. We take the internuclear axis as the z axis (Fig. 14.4). By symmetry, the x and y components of the effective forces on the two nuclei are zero. For the z force component on nucleus a, we have [Eq. (14.112)]:

$$F_{z,a} = -Z_a e^2 \int\int\int \rho \frac{(z_a - z)}{r_a^3} \, dx \, dy \, dz - \frac{Z_a Z_b e^2}{R^2} \qquad (14.116)$$

where R is the internuclear distance. From Fig. 14.4, we see that (z_a is negative): $r_a \cos\theta_a = -z_a + z$. Hence

$$F_{z,a} = Z_a e^2 \int\int\int \rho \frac{\cos\theta_a}{r_a^2} \, dx \, dy \, dz - \frac{Z_a Z_b e^2}{R^2} \qquad (14.117)$$

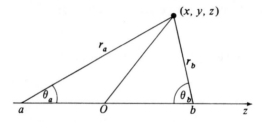

FIGURE 14.4 *Coordinate system for a diatomic molecule. The origin is at O.*

Similarly, we find

$$F_{z,b} = -Z_b e^2 \iiint \rho \frac{\cos \theta_b}{r_b^2} \, dx \, dy \, dz + \frac{Z_a Z_b e^2}{R^2} \qquad (14.118)$$

Using Eq. (14.42), we have

$$F_{z,a} = -\frac{dU(R)}{dR} \frac{\partial R}{\partial z_a} = -\frac{dU}{dR} \frac{(z_a - z_b)}{R} = \frac{dU}{dR} \frac{\partial R}{\partial z_b} = -F_{z,b} \qquad (14.119)$$

so that the effective forces on nuclei a and b are equal in magnitude and opposite in direction. From (14.117), (14.118), and (14.119), we get

$$Z_a e^2 \iiint \rho \frac{\cos \theta_a}{r_a^2} \, dx \, dy \, dz = Z_b e^2 \iiint \rho \frac{\cos \theta_b}{r_b^2} \, dx \, dy \, dz \qquad (14.120)$$

and we can write the effective force on nucleus a as

$$F_{z,a} = \frac{e^2}{2} \iiint \rho \left(\frac{Z_a \cos \theta_a}{r_a^2} + \frac{Z_b \cos \theta_b}{r_b^2} \right) dx \, dy \, dz - \frac{Z_a Z_b e^2}{R^2} \qquad (14.121)$$

From (14.117), the z component of the effective force on nucleus a due to the element of electronic charge in the region about (x, y, z) is

$$e^2 Z_a \rho \frac{\cos \theta_a}{r_a^2} \, dx \, dy \, dz \qquad (14.122)$$

Similarly, the z component of force on nucleus b due to this charge is

$$-e^2 Z_b \rho \frac{\cos \theta_b}{r_b^2} \, dx \, dy \, dz \qquad (14.123)$$

A positive value of (14.122) or (14.123) corresponds to a force in the $+z$ direction, i.e., to the right in Fig. 14.4. When the force on nucleus a is algebraically greater than the force on nucleus b, then the element of electronic charge tends to draw a toward b; hence electronic charge that is binding is located in the region where

$$e^2 Z_a \rho \frac{\cos \theta_a}{r_a^2} \, dx \, dy \, dz > -e^2 Z_b \rho \frac{\cos \theta_b}{r_b^2} \, dx \, dy \, dz \qquad (14.124)$$

Since the probability density ρ is nonnegative, division by ρ preserves the direction of the inequality sign, and the binding region of space is where

$$Z_a \frac{\cos \theta_a}{r_a^2} + Z_b \frac{\cos \theta_b}{r_b^2} > 0 \qquad (14.125)$$

When the force on b is algebraically greater than that on a, the electronic charge element tends to draw b away from a; the antibinding region of space is thus characterized by having the left side of (14.125) negative. The surfaces for which the left side of (14.125) equals zero divide space into the binding and antibinding regions. (This concept of *binding* and *antibinding* regions was proposed[9] by Berlin.) Figures 14.5 and 14.6 show this division for a homonuclear and a heteronuclear diatomic molecule. As might be expected, the binding region for a homonuclear diatomic molecule lies between the nuclei. Charge in this region tends to draw the nuclei together. We have seen time and again that bonding leads to a transfer of charge probability density into the region between the nuclei, due to the overlap between the bonding AO's. Electronic charge that is "behind" the nuclei (to the left of nucleus a or to the right of nucleus b in Fig. 14.5) exerts a greater attraction on the nucleus that is nearer to it than on the other nucleus and thus tends to pull the nuclei apart.

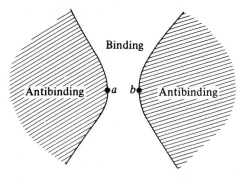

FIGURE 14.5 *Cross section of binding and antibinding regions in a homonuclear diatomic molecule. To obtain the three-dimensional regions, rotate the figure about the internuclear axis.*

Bader, Henneker, and Cade have[10] taken the electron probability densities for homonuclear diatomic molecules as calculated from Hartree–Fock functions, and subtracted off the probability densities for the corresponding separated atoms, as calculated from atomic SCF wave functions. They then plotted contours of this *density difference* $\Delta\rho$ for Li_2 through F_2. A contour with positive $\Delta\rho$ corresponds to a charge buildup as compared to the separated atoms. Not surprisingly, they found a charge buildup in the central part of the binding region, between the nuclei. However, they also found that molecule formation is accompanied by a charge buildup in most of the volume of the antibinding regions also. (The buildup is at

[9] T. Berlin, *J. Chem. Phys.*, **19**, 208 (1951).
[10] R. F. W. Bader, W. H. Henneker, and P. E. Cade, *J. Chem. Phys.*, **46**, 3341 (1967).

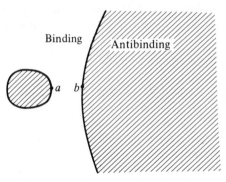

FIGURE 14.6 *Binding and antibinding regions for a heteronuclear diatomic molecule with $Z_b > Z_a$.*

the expense of charge probability density in the regions near the nuclei and containing the boundaries between binding and antibinding regions; see Fig. 3 of the paper.) Of course, the charge buildup between the nuclei is such that its contribution to the attractive force between the nuclei exceeds the Hellmann–Feynman repulsive force due to the charge buildup in the antibinding region. At $R = R_e$, the effective force on each nucleus is zero ($\partial U/\partial R|_{R_e} = 0$), and the hypothetical electron smear must exert a net attractive Hellmann–Feynman force to counterbalance the internuclear repulsion. As mentioned (Section 13.16), Hartree–Fock wave functions provide accurate electron probability-density functions. However, the difference between the molecular and atomic ρ's is sensitive to small errors in the ρ's, and one might therefore question the accuracy of Hartree–Fock $\Delta\rho$ maps. For H_2 and for Li_2, when a configuration-interaction wave function is used in place of the Hartree–Fock ψ, one finds little change in the $\Delta\rho$ maps, indicating that the Hartree–Fock functions probably give accurate $\Delta\rho$'s [R. F. W. Bader and A. K. Chandra, *Can. J. Chem.*, **46**, 953 (1968)].

In discussing things from the Hellmann–Feynman viewpoint, we seem to be considering chemical bonding solely in terms of potential energy, whereas the virial-theorem discussion talked about both potential and kinetic energy. For the purposes of the Hellmann–Feynman discussion, we are imagining the electrons to be smeared out into a continuous charge distribution; hence we make no reference to electronic kinetic energy. The use of the electrostatic theorem to explain chemical bonding has been criticized by some quantum chemists on the grounds that it hides the important role of kinetic energy in bonding. [See the references cited after Eq. (13.62).]

PROBLEMS

14.1 Which of the following functions are homogeneous? Give the degree of homogeneity. (a) $x + 3yz$; (b) 179; (c) x^2/yz^3; (d) $(ax^3 + bxy^2)^{1/2}$.

14.2 Let 1 and 2 be two states of an atom, with $E_2 > E_1$. For which state is the average electronic kinetic energy larger?

14.3 Show that the hypervirial theorem follows from Eq. (7.151).

14.4 The $U(R)$ curve for a repulsive state can be roughly approximated by the function $ae^{-bR} - c$, where a, b, and c are positive constants with $a > c$. (This function omits the van der Waals minimum and fails to go to infinity at $R = 0$.) Sketch U, $\langle T_{el}\rangle$, and $\langle V\rangle$ as functions of R for this function.

14.5 Prove that $\partial\langle V\rangle/\partial R$ must be nonnegative at $R = R_e$, i.e., that $\langle V\rangle$ cannot be increasing with decreasing R as we go through the minimum in the $U(R)$ curve (Fig. 14.1). State and prove the corresponding theorem for $\langle T_{el}\rangle$.

14.6 (a) Use the generalized Hellmann–Feynman theorem to calculate $\langle 1/r\rangle$ for the hydrogen-atom bound states. (b) We now want an expression for $\langle 1/r^2\rangle$, and we proceed as follows. Equation (6.70) can be written as $\hat{H}_r R(r) = ER(r)$, where the "radial Hamiltonian" is given by deleting the function R from the left side of (6.70). Since $\hat{H}_r$ doesn't affect the angles θ and φ, we can multiply the above equation by Y_l^m to get $\hat{H}_r \psi = E\psi$. If we view the quantum number l as a parameter in $\hat{H}_r$, then the generalized Hellmann–Feynman theorem gives

$$\left\langle \psi \left| \frac{\partial \hat{H}_r}{\partial l} \right| \psi \right\rangle = \frac{\partial E}{\partial l}$$

Use this equation and Eq. (6.104) to show that for hydrogen-atom bound states:

$$\left\langle \frac{1}{r^2} \right\rangle = \frac{2Z^2}{(2l+1)n^3}\left(\frac{1}{a_0^2}\right)$$

14.7 (a) Calculate $\langle T\rangle$ and $\langle V\rangle$ for the helium-atom trial function (9.77). All the needed integrals were evaluated in Chapter 9. (b) Verify that the virial theorem is satisfied for $\zeta = Z - 5/16$ but not for $\zeta = Z$.

14.8 A particle is subject to the potential energy $V = ax^4 + by^4 + cz^4$. If its ground-state energy is 10 eV, calculate $\langle T\rangle$ and $\langle V\rangle$ for the ground state.

14.9 Let ψ be the complete wave function for a molecule, with the Born–Oppenheimer approximation of writing $\psi = \psi_{el}\psi_N$ not necessarily being made. Is it true that

$$2\langle \psi| \hat{T}_{el} + \hat{T}_N |\psi\rangle = -\langle \psi| \hat{V} |\psi\rangle$$

where $\hat{T}_{el}$ and $\hat{T}_N$ are the kinetic-energy operators for the electrons and nuclei and $\hat{V}$ is the complete potential-energy operator? Justify your answer.

14.10 The R_e values for the ground electronic states of HF, HCl, HBr, and HI are 0.9, 1.3, 1.4, and 1.6 Å. The surface enclosing the antibinding region "behind" the proton in these molecules intersects the internuclear axis in two points, one of which is the proton location. Calculate the distance between these two points of intersection for each of the hydrogen halides.

Electronic Structure
of Polyatomic Molecules

15.1 Introduction

The search for accurate electronic wave functions of polyatomic molecules uses mainly the MO method. The presence of several nuclei causes greater computational difficulties than for diatomic molecules. Moreover, the electronic wave function of a diatomic molecule is a function of only one parameter—the internuclear distance; in contrast, the electronic wave function of a polyatomic molecule depends simultaneously on several parameters—the bond distances and bond angles. A full theoretical treatment of a polyatomic molecule involves calculation of the electronic wave function for a wide range of each of these parameters; the equilibrium bond distances and angles are then found as those values that minimize the electronic energy (including nuclear repulsion). Such a calculation is a formidable task, and the majority of polyatomic-molecule calculations have calculated ψ_{el} for only the experimentally determined bond distances and angles.

Molecular quantum-mechanical calculations can be divided into two classes: *ab initio* and *semiempirical*. Semiempirical calculations generally use a simpler Hamiltonian than the correct molecular Hamiltonian and incorporate into the calculation experimental data or parameters which can be adjusted to fit experimental data. The prime example of a semiempirical method is the Hückel MO treatment of conjugated hydrocarbons (Section 15.8), which uses a one-electron Hamiltonian and takes the bond integrals as adjustable parameters rather than quantities to be calculated theoretically. In contrast, an *ab initio* calculation uses the correct Hamiltonian for the system and attempts a solution without the use of experimental data. A Hartree–Fock SCF calculation seeks the antisymmetrized product φ of one-electron functions that minimizes $\int \varphi^* \hat{H} \varphi \, d\tau$, where $\hat{H}$ is the true Hamiltonian, and is thus an *ab initio* calculation.

15.2 Classification of Electronic Terms of Polyatomic Molecules

For polyatomic molecules, the operator $\hat{S}^2$ for the square of the total electronic spin angular momentum commutes with the electronic Hamiltonian, and, as for diatomic molecules, the electronic terms of polyatomic molecules are classified as singlets, doublets, triplets, etc., according to the value of $2S + 1$. (The commutation of $\hat{S}^2$ and $\hat{H}_{el}$ holds provided spin-orbit interaction is omitted from the Hamiltonian; for molecules containing heavy atoms, spin-orbit interaction is considerable, and S is not a good quantum number.)

For linear polyatomic molecules, the operator $\hat{L}_z$ for the axial component of the total electronic orbital angular momentum commutes with the electronic Hamiltonian, and the same term classifications are used as for diatomic molecules; we have such possibilities as $^1\Sigma^+$, $^1\Sigma^-$, $^3\Sigma^+$, $^1\Pi$, etc. For linear polyatomic molecules with a center of symmetry, the g, u classification is added.

For nonlinear polyatomic molecules, there is no orbital angular-momentum operator that commutes with the electronic Hamiltonian, and the angular-momentum classification of electronic terms cannot be used. Operators that do commute with the electronic Hamiltonian are the symmetry operators $\hat{O}_R$ of the molecule (Section 12.1), and the electronic states of polyatomic molecules are classified according to the behavior of the electronic wave function on application of these operators. Consider H_2O as an example.

In its equilibrium configuration, water belongs to group $\mathscr{C}_{2v}$ with the symmetry operations

$$\hat{E} \qquad \hat{C}_2(z) \qquad \hat{\sigma}_v(xz) \qquad \hat{\sigma}_v(yz) \qquad \text{(15.1)}$$

We follow the standard convention[1] and take the molecular plane as the yz plane (Fig. 15.1). We readily find that each of the symmetry operations commutes with the other three, so that the electronic wave functions can be chosen as simultaneous eigenfunctions of all four symmetry operators. Since $\hat{O}_E$ is the unit operator, we have $\hat{O}_E \psi_{el} = \psi_{el}$. Each of the remaining symmetry operators satisfies $\hat{O}_R^2 = \hat{1}$, so that each has as its eigenvalues $+1$ and -1 (Eq. 7.87). Therefore each electronic wave function of water is an eigenfunction of $\hat{O}_E$ with eigenvalue $+1$, and an eigenfunction of each of the other three symmetry operators with the eigenvalues $+1$ or -1.

How many different combinations of these symmetry eigenvalues are there for water? At first sight, we might think there are $(1)(2)(2)(2) = 8$ possible sets. However, certain sets can be ruled out, as we now show. Let the product of the symmetry operations $\hat{R}$ and $\hat{S}$ be the symmetry operation $\hat{T}$:

$$\hat{R}\hat{S} = \hat{T} \qquad \text{(15.2)}$$

---

[1] R. S. Mulliken, *J. Chem. Phys.*, **23**, 1997 (1955).

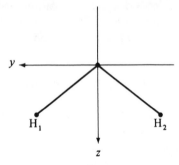

y ←

z

FIGURE 15.1 *Coordinate axes for the water molecule. The x axis is perpendicular to the molecular plane.*

Let ψ_{el} be an eigenfunction of $\hat{O}_R$, $\hat{O}_S$, and $\hat{O}_T$ with eigenvalues r, s, and t, respectively. Since the symmetry operators multiply the same way the symmetry operations do, we have

$$t\psi_{el} = \hat{O}_T\psi_{el} = \hat{O}_R[\hat{O}_S\psi_{el}] = s\hat{O}_R\psi_{el} = rs\psi_{el} \qquad (15.3)$$

Dividing by ψ_{el} we have $rs = t$. Hence the eigenvalues of the symmetry operators must multiply in the same way the symmetry operators do. Now consider water. Let us examine the set of symmetry eigenvalues

$$1 \qquad -1 \qquad -1 \qquad -1 \qquad\qquad (15.4)$$

where the eigenvalues are listed in the order corresponding to (15.1). We have $\hat{C}_2(z)\hat{\sigma}_v(xz) = \hat{\sigma}_v(yz)$; the set (15.4), however, has the product of the $\hat{O}_{C_2}$ and $\hat{O}_{\sigma_v(xz)}$ eigenvalues as $(-1)(-1) = 1$, which differs from the $\hat{O}_{\sigma_v(yz)}$ eigenvalue in (15.4). The set (15.4) must be discarded. Of the eight possible symmetry-eigenvalue combinations, only four are found to multiply properly; these four sets are (Problem 15.3):

	$\hat{E}$	$\hat{C}_2(z)$	$\hat{\sigma}_v(xz)$	$\hat{\sigma}_v(yz)$
A_1	1	1	1	1
A_2	1	1	-1	-1
B_1	1	-1	1	-1
B_2	1	-1	-1	1

$$(15.5)$$

In this table, the sets have been labeled A_1, A_2, B_1, and B_2. The letter A or B indicates whether the symmetry eigenvalue for the highest-order $\hat{C}_n$ or $\hat{S}_n$ operation of the molecule [$\hat{C}_2(z)$ for water] is $+1$ or -1, respectively. The subscripts 1 and 2 distinguish sets having the same letter label. Each possible set of symmetry eigenvalues in (15.5) is called a *symmetry species* (or *symmetry type*). (The group-theory term is *irreducible representation*.) The symmetry species with all symmetry eigenvalues $+1$ (A_1 for H_2O) is called the *totally symmetric* species.

Each molecular electronic term of H_2O is designated by giving the symmetry species of the electronic wave functions of the term, with the spin multiplicity

$(2S+1)$ as a left superscript. For example, an electronic state of water with two electrons unpaired and with the electronic wave function unchanged by all four symmetry operators belongs to a $^3A_1$ term. (The subscript "1" is not an angular-momentum eigenvalue, but is part of the symmetry-species label.)

We now consider the *orbital degeneracy* of molecular electronic terms; this is degeneracy connected with the electrons' spatial (orbital) motion, as distinguished from spin degeneracy. Thus $^1\Pi$ and $^3\Pi$ terms of linear molecules are orbitally degenerate, while $^1\Sigma$ and $^3\Sigma$ terms are orbitally nondegenerate. Consider an operator $\hat{F}$ that commutes with the molecular electronic Hamiltonian and that does not involve spin; we have

$$\hat{F}\hat{H}_{el}\psi_{el,i} = \hat{F}E_{el}\psi_{el,i}$$

$$\hat{H}_{el}[\hat{F}\psi_{el,i}] = E_{el}[\hat{F}\psi_{el,i}] \tag{15.6}$$

so that $\hat{F}\psi_{el,i}$ is an eigenfunction of $\hat{H}_{el}$ with eigenvalue E_{el}. Let the orbital degeneracy of the term to which $\psi_{el,i}$ belongs be n. It follows from (15.6) that $\hat{F}\psi_{el,i}$ must be some linear combination of the n orbitally degenerate wave functions of the term that have the same value of S_z as $\psi_{el,i}$:

$$\hat{F}\psi_{el,i} = \sum_{j=1}^{n} c_{ij,F}\psi_{el,j} \tag{15.7}$$

where the c's are certain constants. (These arguments were previously given in Section 7.4.) For a level that is not orbitally degenerate ($n=1$), Eq. (15.7) reduces to

$$\hat{F}\psi_{el,i} = c_F\psi_{el,i} \tag{15.8}$$

so that here $\psi_{el,i}$ *must* be an eigenfunction of $\hat{F}$. For $n > 1$, we can *choose* n linear combinations of the $\psi_{el,j}$'s that are eigenfunctions of $\hat{F}$, but there is no *necessity* for the eigenfunctions of a degenerate level to be eigenfunctions of $\hat{F}$. If we have two operators $\hat{F}$ and $\hat{G}$ that commute with $\hat{H}_{el}$, but not with each other, we can pick the linear combinations to be eigenfunctions of $\hat{F}$ or of $\hat{G}$, but not in general of both $\hat{F}$ and $\hat{G}$ simultaneously.

Now consider symmetry operators. For water, all the symmetry operators commute among themselves, so that each electronic wave function is simultaneously an eigenfunction of all the symmetry operators. If all the electronic wave functions were orbitally nondegenerate, then it would automatically follow from (15.8) that they were simultaneously eigenfunctions of all the symmetry operators. We therefore suspect (but have not proved) that the electronic wave functions of water are all orbitally nondegenerate. This statement is in fact correct. The letters A and B designate symmetry species of orbitally nondegenerate electronic terms. For any molecule all of whose symmetry operators commute with one another, the electronic wave functions are each simultaneous eigenfunctions of all symmetry operators, and the only symmetry species are nondegenerate A and B species.

For some point groups, the symmetry operators do not all commute; an example is $\mathcal{O}_h$ (Fig. 12.9). When the symmetry operators do not all commute, some of the electronic terms are orbitally degenerate; a symmetry operator applied to an electronic wave function of an orbitally degenerate term converts it to a linear combination of the wave functions of the term [Eq. (15.7)]. The effects of the symmetry operator $\hat{O}_R$ on the wave functions of an n-fold orbitally degenerate electronic term are specified by the n^2 numbers

$$c_{ij,R}, \qquad i = 1, \ldots, n, \qquad j = 1, \ldots, n \qquad (15.9)$$

The n^2 numbers (15.9) when arranged in an $n \times n$ square array form a *matrix*. If there are h symmetry operations in the molecular point group, then the h matrices of coefficients in (15.7) constitute the *symmetry species* (or *symmetry type*) of the degenerate-term wave functions in (15.7). The following letter labels are used for the symmetry species, according to the orbital degeneracy n:

n	1	2	3	4	5
Letter	A, B	E	T	G	H

(15.10)

Numerical subscripts distinguish different symmetry species having the same letter designation. For molecules with a center of symmetry, a g or u subscript is added, depending on whether the wave function has the eigenvalue $+1$ or -1 for inversion of all electronic spatial coordinates. The possible symmetry species can be found in a systematic way using group theory (see *Schonland*). As an example, group theory shows the possible symmetry species of a $\mathscr{D}_{6h}$ molecule to be

$$\begin{array}{cccccc} A_{1g} & A_{2g} & B_{1g} & B_{2g} & E_{1g} & E_{2g} \\ A_{1u} & A_{2u} & B_{1u} & B_{2u} & E_{1u} & E_{2u} \end{array} \qquad (15.11)$$

We shall not give the numbers $c_{ij,R}$ that specify these symmetry species, except to note that A_{1g} is the totally symmetric symmetry species, with all c's equal to 1.

It is an empirical fact that for most molecules in their electronic ground states, the wave function belongs to the (nondegenerate) totally symmetric species; also the electronic spins are usually all paired in the ground state, so that the ground state is a singlet. For water, the ground electronic state is $^1A_1$; for benzene it is $^1A_{1g}$.

We have been using the equilibrium-geometry point groups of H_2O and C_6H_6. For nonequilibrium nuclear configurations, the symmetry is in general less than that of $\mathscr{C}_{2v}$ or $\mathscr{D}_{6h}$; for reasonably small departures from equilibrium, however, the symmetry behavior should be given to a good approximation by the symmetry species of the equilibrium-geometry point group. We also note that excited states sometimes differ in their equilibrium point group from the ground electronic state. For example, the point group of NH_3 is $\mathscr{D}_{3h}$ for several excited electronic states.[2]

Corresponding to a given molecular electronic term, there are in general several electronic states. The interactions between electronic spin and electronic orbital motion and between electronic and nuclear motions split the energies of these states. These splittings are usually small.

---

[2] For properties of molecular electronic states, see G. Herzberg, *Electronic Spectra of Polyatomic Molecules*, Van Nostrand, 1966, Appendix VI.

15.3 The SCF MO Treatment of Polyatomic Molecules

The purely electronic nonrelativistic Hamiltonian for a polyatomic molecule is (in atomic units):

$$\hat{H}_{el} = -\tfrac{1}{2} \sum_i \nabla_i^2 - \sum_i \sum_\alpha \frac{Z_\alpha}{r_{i\alpha}} + \sum_i \sum_{j>i} \frac{1}{r_{ij}} \qquad (15.12)$$

If interelectronic repulsions are neglected, the zeroth-order wave function is the product of one-electron spatial functions (molecular orbitals). Allowance for electron spin and the Pauli principle gives a zeroth-order wave function that is an antisymmetrized product of molecular spin-orbitals, each spin-orbital being a product of a spatial MO and a spin function. The best possible variation function that has the form of an antisymmetrized product of spin-orbitals is the Hartree–Fock SCF function. [Improvements beyond the Hartree–Fock stage require configuration interaction (CI).] The MO's are usually expressed as linear combinations of basis functions, the coefficients being found by solution of the Roothaan equations (Section 13.16). If a sufficiently large basis set is used, the MO's are accurate approximations to the Hartree–Fock MO's. If a minimal basis set is used, the MO's are only rough approximations to the Hartree–Fock MO's, but are still referred to as SCF molecular orbitals.

How are polyatomic MO's classified? As might be expected, the MO's of a polyatomic molecule show the same kinds of possible symmetry behavior as the over-all electronic wave function does[3] (Section 15.2); the MO's are therefore classified according to the symmetry species of the molecular point group. For example, the MO's of H_2O have the possible symmetry species a_1, a_2, b_1, and b_2 of (15.5). (Lower-case letters are used for MO symmetry species.) MO's of the same symmetry species are distinguished by numbering them in order of increasing energy. Thus the lowest three a_1 MO's of water are called $1a_1$, $2a_1$, and $3a_1$. (This nomenclature is similar to that of the third column in Table 13.1.)

Each MO holds two electrons of opposite spin. MO's having the same energy constitute a *subshell* (often simply called a *shell*). A subshell that consists of a single MO of symmetry species a or b holds two electrons; a subshell that consists of two e MO's having the same energy holds four electrons; and so on. For water, there are no degenerate symmetry species, and each subshell holds two electrons. For benzene, there are some doubly degenerate symmetry species [see (15.11)], so that some of the benzene MO's occur in pairs having the same energy. Specification of the number of electrons in each subshell specifies the molecular electronic *configuration*. As for atoms and diatomic molecules, a given electron configuration of a polyatomic molecule gives rise in general to several electronic terms. The systematic method for finding the possible terms uses group theory and will not be discussed here.[4] [As an example, an $(e_{1g})^2$ configuration of a $\mathscr{D}_{6h}$ molecule gives the terms $^1A_{1g}$, $^1E_{2g}$, and $^3A_{2g}$.] *A closed-subshell configuration gives rise to a*

---

[3] For the proof, see C. C. J. Roothaan, *Rev. Mod. Phys.*, **23**, 161 (1951).

[4] For tables of the possible terms arising from various configurations, see G. Herzberg, *Electronic Spectra of Polyatomic Molecules*, pp. 330–334, 570–573.

single nondegenerate term, whose multiplicity is 1, and whose symmetry species is the totally symmetric one. Most polyatomic molecules have a closed-subshell ground state; here, the MO wave function is a single Slater determinant. For states arising from open-subshell configurations, the MO wave function may require a linear combination of several Slater determinants.

We now consider the kinds of basis functions used in molecular SCF calculations. For diatomic molecules, the basis functions are usually taken as atomic orbitals, some centered on one atom, the remainder being centered on the other atom, with each AO being represented as a *linear combination* of one or more Slater-type orbitals (11.16); the real form of the STO's is used for nonlinear molecules. We have an LC-STO MO. For polyatomic molecules, the LC-STO method involves one or more STO's centered on each of the atoms. The presence of more than two atoms causes difficulties in evaluating the needed integrals. For a triatomic molecule, one must deal with three-center as well as one- and two-center integrals. For a molecule with four or more atoms, one has four-center integrals as well, but the number of centers occurring in any one integral does not exceed four, as we now demonstrate. We shall use $\alpha, \beta, ..., \varepsilon$ for the nuclei and $\varphi_1, \varphi_2, ..., \varphi_n$ for the spatial MO's of electrons $1, 2, ..., n$. The Hamiltonian (15.12) contains only one-electron and two-electron terms. A typical two-electron integral is

$$\int\int \cdots \int \varphi_1^* \varphi_2^* \cdots \varphi_n^* \frac{1}{r_{12}} \varphi_1 \varphi_2 \cdots \varphi_n \, dv_1 \, dv_2 \cdots dv_n = \int\int |\varphi_1|^2 |\varphi_2|^2 \frac{1}{r_{12}} \, dv_1 \, dv_2$$

(15.13)

Let $f_\alpha(1)$ be a Slater-type function of the coordinates of electron 1 centered on nucleus α. For example, for a $1s$ STO, $f_\alpha = \zeta^{3/2} \pi^{-1/2} e^{-\zeta r_{\alpha 1}}$. Each MO is a linear combination of the STO's:

$$\varphi_1 = c_\alpha f_\alpha(1) + c_\beta f_\beta(1) + \cdots + c_\varepsilon f_\varepsilon(1) \tag{15.14}$$

$$\varphi_2 = d_\alpha f_\alpha(2) + d_\beta f_\beta(2) + \cdots + d_\varepsilon f_\varepsilon(2) \tag{15.15}$$

where the c's and d's are certain coefficients. [In these equations, we have used only one STO for each atom, but in general one would use several STO's per atom.] Substituting into the integral (15.13), we see that several integrals are obtained, each involving at most four centers. A typical four-center integral that occurs is

$$c_\alpha^* c_\beta d_\gamma^* d_\delta \int\int f_\alpha^*(1) f_\beta(1) f_\gamma^*(2) f_\delta(2) \frac{1}{r_{12}} \, dv_1 \, dv_2 \tag{15.16}$$

Two other choices of basis functions are used to avoid the difficult three- and four-center integrals that arise in the LC-STO MO method. These are the one-center expansion method and the Gaussian-orbital method.

The *one-center expansion* (OCE) *method* takes each MO as a linear combination of functions (usually STO's) *all* of which are centered at the same point in space. For example, a one-center MO calculation of CH_4 takes each MO as a linear combination of functions all of which are centered on the carbon atom. With the OCE method, all integrals are one-center, but the method has drawbacks. The presence of a nucleus at a point in space introduces a cusp (Fig. 6.6) into the electronic wave function at that point. The representation of an MO as a linear combination of orbitals all centered at a single nucleus makes it difficult to get the proper cusp behavior at the other nuclei. A one-center wave function for CH_4 is inaccurate in the regions near the hydrogen nuclei, unless very many basis functions are used. The OCE method is clearly most applicable to molecules with the formula AH_n; here, most of the electron probability density is located near atom A and the hydrogen atoms introduce only small cusps into the wave function. The OCE method is related to the united-atom viewpoint; the corresponding united atom for CH_4 is Ne, and a united-atom perturbation treatment would express the methane wave function as an expansion of neon ground-state and excited-state (one-center) wave functions. Because of generally discouraging results and the limited applicability of the method, there is currently not much interest in the OCE method.

To simplify molecular integral evaluation, Boys proposed in 1950 the use of *Gaussian-type orbitals* (GTO's) instead of STO's for the atomic orbitals in an LCAO wave function. A *Gaussian function* centered on nucleus a has the form

$$Nr^l e^{-\zeta r_a^2} Y_l^m(\theta, \varphi) \tag{15.17}$$

which is in contrast to hydrogenlike and Slater functions, whose exponential factor is $\exp(-\zeta r_a)$. As with Slater orbitals, the real form of the spherical harmonics (Problem 15.31) is used in molecular calculations. Thus any s AO (whether $1s$ or $2s$ or ...) is represented by a linear combination of several Gaussians with different orbital exponents, each Gaussian having the form $\exp(-\zeta r_a^2)$; any atomic p_x orbital is represented by a linear combination of Gaussians, each of the form $x \exp(-\zeta r_a^2)$; and so on. [It is possible to use higher powers of r in (15.17), but this has been found to be of no advantage.] The behavior of the Gaussian exponential factor is shown in Fig. 4.1a, where the origin is at nucleus a. A Gaussian function does not have the desired cusp at the nucleus and hence gives a poor representation of an AO for small values of r_a. To get an accurate representation of an AO, we must therefore use a linear combination of several Gaussians. Therefore an LC-GTO SCF MO calculation involves evaluation of many more integrals than the corresponding LC-STO SCF MO calculation. [The number of two-electron integrals is proportional to the fourth power of the number of basis functions, as can be seen from (15.16).] However, Gaussian integral evaluation takes much less computer time than Slater integral evaluation. This is because the product of two Gaussian functions centered at two different points is equal to a single Gaussian centered at a third point. Thus all three- and four-center two-electron repulsion integrals are reduced to two-center integrals. [A modification of the LC-GTO method is the *Gaussian-lobe method*, which uses $1s$ Gaussian functions placed at points in space to simulate s, p, d, etc., orbitals; for example, a p_x orbital (which has two lobes) can be simulated by two Gaussians centered on the x axis, one on each side of the nucleus.]

A device widely used with GTO basis functions is that of a *contracted* Gaussian set. Here, not all the coefficients of the basis functions are independently varied; rather, the coefficient ratios between certain basis functions are kept fixed at predetermined values. This gives substantial savings in computation time with but little loss in accuracy.

Whether Gaussian or Slater basis sets will ultimately prove to be the method of choice for polyatomic molecules is an open question. For calculations on atoms, Slater functions are the obvious choice since atomic (one-center) integrals are no more difficult for STO's than for GTO's. Most SCF calculations on linear molecules have used STO's since linear geometry allows special numerical methods to be used. The most accurate nonlinear polyatomic-molecule SCF calculations to date have been done using Gaussians.

15.4 The SCF MO Treatment of Water

For a minimal-basis-set MO treatment of H_2O (Fig. 15.1), we start with the $O1s$, $O2s$, $O2p_x$, $O2p_y$, and $O2p_z$ inner-shell and valence oxygen AO's and the $H_1 1s$ and $H_2 1s$ valence AO's of the hydrogen atoms. Linear combinations of these 7 basis AO's give LCAO approximations to the 7 lowest MO's of water. As stated in the last section, the MO's can be chosen so that upon application of the molecular symmetry operators each MO transforms according to one of the symmetry species of the molecular point group. To aid in choosing the right linear combinations of AO's, we examine the symmetry behavior of the AO's.

The $1s$ and $2s$ oxygen AO's are spherically symmetric; rotation about the $C_2(z)$ axis and reflection in the xz or yz plane has no effect on them; they thus belong to the totally symmetric symmetry species a_1 of (15.5). The effect of a $\hat{C}_2(z)$ rotation on the oxygen $2p_y$ AO is shown in Fig. 15.2; this rotation sends $O2p_y$ into its negative [see also Fig. 12.8]. Reflection in the molecular plane sends $O2p_y$ into itself, while reflection in the xz plane sends it into its negative. The symmetry eigenvalues of $O2p_y$ are 1, -1, -1, and 1; the symmetry species of this AO is b_2. Similarly, the symmetry species of $O2p_x$ and $O2p_z$ are found to be b_1 and a_1, respectively.

Now for the hydrogen $1s$ AO's. Reflection in the yz plane leaves each of them unchanged. However, rotation by $180°$ about the z axis sends $H_1 1s$ into $H_2 1s$ and vice versa (Fig. 15.3); similarly for reflection in the xz plane. The $H_1 1s$ and $H_2 1s$ functions are *not* eigenfunctions of $\hat{O}_{C_2(z)}$ and $\hat{O}_{\sigma_v(xz)}$ and they therefore do not transform according to any of the symmetry species of water.

As a preliminary step in finding the MO's of a molecule, it is helpful (but not essential) to construct linear combinations of the original basis AO's such that

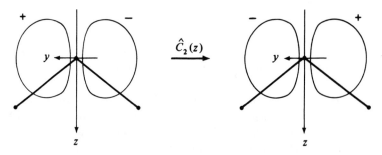

FIGURE 15.2 *The effect of $\hat{C}_2(z)$ on the $2p_y$ oxygen AO in water.*

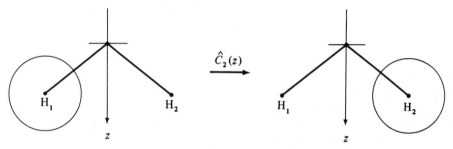

FIGURE 15.3 *The effect of a $\hat{C}_2(z)$ rotation on the H_1 1s AO in water.*

each linear combination does transform according to one of the molecular symmetry species. Such linear combinations are called *symmetry orbitals*. (Synonyms are *symmetry-adapted orbitals* and *group orbitals*.[5]) The symmetry orbitals are used as the basis functions f_k in the expansion (13.178). *The use of basis functions that transform according to the molecular symmetry species simplifies the calculation by putting the secular determinant in block-diagonal form*; this will be illustrated below.

Each oxygen AO transforms according to one of the symmetry species of water, and can serve as a symmetry orbital. We must, however, construct two symmetry orbitals from the two hydrogen 1s AO's, neither of which belongs to a symmetry species of water. Consider the following linear combinations:

$$H_1 1s + H_2 1s \qquad (15.18)$$

$$H_1 1s - H_2 1s \qquad (15.19)$$

We have

$$\hat{O}_{C_2(z)}(H_1 1s + H_2 1s) = H_2 1s + H_1 1s \qquad (15.20)$$

$$\hat{O}_{C_2(z)}(H_1 1s - H_2 1s) = H_2 1s - H_1 1s \qquad (15.21)$$

Thus (15.18) and (15.19) are eigenfunctions of $\hat{O}_{C_2(z)}$ with eigenvalues $+1$ and -1, respectively. Examination of the effects of the other three symmetry operators shows (15.18) and (15.19) to belong to the symmetry species a_1 and b_2, respectively. We shall not bother to normalize the symmetry orbitals (15.18) and (15.19). The 7 basis symmetry orbitals are then:

Symmetry Orbital	Symmetry Species	
$f_1 = H_1 1s + H_2 1s$	a_1	
$f_2 = O1s$	a_1	
$f_3 = O2s$	a_1	
$f_4 = O2p_z$	a_1	(15.22)
$f_5 = H_1 1s - H_2 1s$	b_2	
$f_6 = O2p_y$	b_2	
$f_7 = O2p_x$	b_1	

[5] The term "group orbital" is also applied to an orbital having the local symmetry of a group of atoms in the molecule, rather than the symmetry of the molecule. For example, in toluene one can take linear combinations of the three methyl hydrogen 1s orbitals to form three group orbitals each belonging to a $\mathscr{C}_{3v}$ symmetry species.

Now consider the secular determinant in (13.181). We assert that

$$H_{jk}^{\text{eff}} = 0 \qquad (15.23)$$

whenever f_j and f_k belong to different symmetry species. This result follows from the theorem (Section 7.4) that $\langle f_j | \hat{B} | f_k \rangle = 0$ if f_j and f_k are eigenfunctions of a Hermitian operator $\hat{A}$ with different eigenvalues, where $\hat{A}$ commutes with $\hat{B}$. The symmetry orbitals of water are eigenfunctions of the symmetry operators, each of which commutes with the electronic Hamiltonian and with the effective electronic Hamiltonian $\hat{H}^{\text{eff}}$. Symmetry orbitals f_j and f_k that belong to different symmetry species differ in at least one symmetry eigenvalue. Hence (15.23) follows. Moreover, since two eigenfunctions of a Hermitian operator that correspond to different eigenvalues are orthogonal, we have

$$S_{jk} = 0 \qquad (15.24)$$

whenever f_j and f_k belong to different symmetry species. From (15.23) and (15.24) it follows that using symmetry orbitals as basis functions puts the secular determinant of water in block-diagonal form, each block corresponding to a different symmetry species; the blocks are 4×4, 2×2, and 1×1. [For molecules with degenerate symmetry species (E, T, etc.), the symmetry orbitals of the degenerate species are not necessarily eigenfunctions of the symmetry operators; nevertheless, the symmetry orbitals still put the secular determinant in block-diagonal form as can be shown using group theory.]

The set of simultaneous equations (13.179) then breaks up into one set of four simultaneous equations, one set of two simultaneous equations, and one set of one "simultaneous" equation (Section 9.6). The first set contains matrix elements involving only the four a_1 symmetry orbitals. Therefore four of the lowest seven water MO's are linear combinations of the four a_1 symmetry orbitals; these four MO's must have a_1 symmetry. Similarly, we have two MO's of b_2 symmetry and one MO of b_1 symmetry. The symmetry orbitals are *not* (in general) the MO's, but each MO must be a linear combination of those symmetry orbitals having the same symmetry species as the MO. The forms of the lowest MO's of water are then:

$$\varphi_1 = c_{11} f_1 + c_{12} f_2 + c_{13} f_3 + c_{14} f_4$$
$$\varphi_2 = c_{21} f_1 + c_{22} f_2 + c_{23} f_3 + c_{24} f_4$$
$$\varphi_3 = c_{31} f_1 + c_{32} f_2 + c_{33} f_3 + c_{34} f_4$$
$$\varphi_4 = c_{41} f_1 + c_{42} f_2 + c_{43} f_3 + c_{44} f_4 \qquad (15.25)$$
$$\varphi_5 = c_{55} f_5 + c_{56} f_6$$
$$\varphi_6 = c_{65} f_5 + c_{66} f_6$$
$$\varphi_7 = f_7$$

The next step in the SCF MO calculation is to choose explicit forms for the seven AO's. The orbital energies and the coefficients of the symmetry orbitals are then found using Roothaan's equations.

Pitzer and Merrifield[6] did an H_2O minimal-basis-set calculation, representing each AO by a single STO. They optimized the orbital exponents, finding 1.27 for H1s, 7.66 for O1s, 2.25 for O2s, 2.21 for O2p. (To optimize the exponents, one must repeat the entire SCF iterative calculation for several different sets of orbital exponents to locate the set that gives the minimum energy.) The orbital energies in hartrees are found to be: $1a_1$, -20.56; $2a_1$, -1.28; $1b_2$, -0.62; $3a_1$, -0.47; $1b_1$, -0.40. The ground-state electronic configuration of this ten-electron molecule is

$$(1a_1)^2 (2a_1)^2 (1b_2)^2 (3a_1)^2 (1b_1)^2 \qquad (15.26)$$

The ground state has a closed-subshell configuration and is a $^1A_1$ state.

The five lowest SCF MO's found by Pitzer and Merrifield at the experimental geometry are

$$1a_1 = 1.00(O1s) + 0.01(O2s_\perp) + 0.003(O2p_z) - 0.004(H_1 1s + H_2 1s)$$

$$2a_1 = -0.03(O1s) + 0.82(O2s_\perp) + 0.13(O2p_z) + 0.15(H_1 1s + H_2 1s)$$

$$1b_2 = 0.62(O2p_y) + 0.42(H_1 1s - H_2 1s)$$

$$3a_1 = -0.03(O1s) - 0.50(O2s_\perp) + 0.79(O2p_z) + 0.26(H_1 1s + H_2 1s)$$

$$1b_1 = O2p_x \qquad (15.27)$$

The $O2s_\perp$ orbital in (15.27) is an orthogonalized orbital [Eq. (13.183)]:

$$O2s_\perp = (0.973)^{-1}[O2s - 0.231(O1s)] \qquad (15.28)$$

where O2s is the ordinary $2s$ STO:

$$O2s = 2.25^{5/2}\pi^{-1/2}3^{-1/2}r_O \exp(-2.25r_O) \qquad (15.29)$$

where r_O is the distance to the oxygen nucleus. The MO approximation to the ground-state wave function of H_2O is the 10×10 Slater determinant

$$|1a_1 \overline{1a_1} 2a_1 \overline{2a_1} 1b_2 \overline{1b_2} 3a_1 \overline{3a_1} 1b_1 \overline{1b_1}| \qquad (15.30)$$

Consider the nature of the MO's. The lowest MO, $1a_1$, is essentially a pure nonbonding 1s oxygen AO, which is hardly surprising.

The oxygen part of the $2a_1$ MO is mostly O2s with some $O2p_z$ mixed in. This mixing in (hybridization) of $O2p_z$ adds to the value of the O2s AO along the positive z axis (which points towards the hydrogens—Fig. 15.1) and subtracts from O2s along the negative z axis. The combination of the hybridized O2s and $O2p_z$ orbitals with the $H_1 1s$ and $H_2 1s$ orbitals in the $2a_1$ MO then gives electron probability-density buildup in the region enclosed by the three nuclei. Therefore the $2a_1$ MO contributes to the bonding in water.

Consider the $1b_2$ MO. The $2p_y$ oxygen AO has its positive lobe on the H_1 side of the molecule, so that the positive lobe of $O2p_y$ adds to $H_1 1s$ in the $1b_2$ MO, giving electron charge buildup between the H_1 and O nuclei. Similarly, the negative lobe

[6] R. M. Pitzer and D. P. Merrifield, *J. Chem. Phys.*, **52**, 4782 (1970); S. Aung, R. M. Pitzer, and S. I. Chan, *ibid.*, **49**, 2071 (1968).

of $O2p_y$ adds to $-H_2 1s$, giving charge buildup between O and H_2 in this MO. Hence $1b_2$ is a bonding MO. Comparing $1b_2$ and $2a_1$, we see that the rather small value of the H_1 and H_2 AO coefficients in $2a_1$ indicates that its contribution to the bonding is not as great as that of the $1b_2$ MO.

The hybridization of the $2s$ and $2p_z$ oxygen AO's in $3a_1$ concentrates electron probability density along the negative z axis, away from the hydrogens; hence, this MO contributes only modestly to the bonding, and is best described as mainly a lone-pair MO with some bonding character. (It is sometimes erroneously stated that the $3a_1$ and $1b_2$ MO's are the main bonding MO's in water.)

The $1b_1$ MO is a nonbonding lone-pair $2p_x$ oxygen AO.

The shapes of the bonding MO's $2a_1$ and $1b_2$ are shown in Fig. 15.4. Note that their symmetry eigenvalues are as given by (15.5).

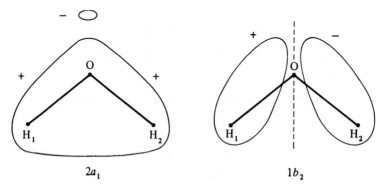

FIGURE 15.4 Sketches of the two main bonding MO's of water.

Each of the SCF bonding MO's in (15.27) is delocalized over the entire molecule and does not resemble a chemical bond. Hence the reader may be wondering about the relation of these MO's to the picture presented in most freshman-chemistry books, where one bonding MO points along the O—H_1 bond, and the other points along the O—H_2 bond. We shall discuss this point in Section 15.5.

The unoccupied $4a_1$ and $2b_2$ MO's of water calculated by Pitzer and Merrifield (for nonoptimized, Slater-rule exponents) are:

$$4a_1 = 0.08(O1s) + 0.84(O2s_\perp) + 0.70(O2p_z) - 0.75(H_1 1s + H_2 1s)$$

$$2b_2 = 0.99(O2p_y) - 0.89(H_1 1s - H_2 1s) \tag{15.31}$$

For these two MO's the opposite signs of the oxygen and hydrogen AO coefficients give charge depletion between the nuclei. These MO's are antibonding.

The unoccupied orbitals (15.31) are called *virtual orbitals*. Because they were calculated for the electron configuration (15.26), they are not accurate representations of the SCF orbitals actually occupied in H_2O excited electronic states. When the electron configuration changes, the interorbital electronic interactions change, thereby changing the forms of all the SCF orbitals. We can, however, use the virtual orbitals and their calculated energies as rough approximations to the higher SCF orbitals and energies.

The formation of the H_2O MO's from the separated-atom AO's is illustrated schematically in Fig. 15.5; the dotted lines indicate which AO's contribute significantly to each MO. Note that only AO's of roughly the same energy combine to a significant degree in a given MO. [This fact is explained by the $1/(E_n^{(0)} - E_m^{(0)})$ term in Eq. (9.36).] We can thus get a qualitative idea of the MO's without doing any calculations by using the rules that only symmetry orbitals of the same symmetry species combine and that only AO's of comparable energy (Fig. 11.2) contribute significantly to a given MO.

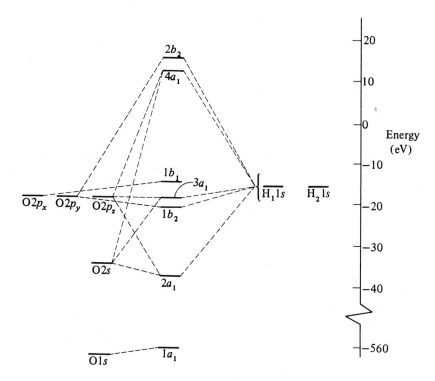

FIGURE 15.5   *Formation of the H_2O MO's from the minimal basis AO's. The 5 lowest MO's are filled in the ground state. (Note the break in the scale.)*

Table 15.1 lists some of the many calculations on the H_2O ground state. The experimental electronic energy of H_2O is -76.481 hartrees. All the calculations listed are nonrelativistic. The only significant relativistic correction will occur in the $1s$ inner-shell electrons of oxygen (see Section 11.7); since this shell remains essentially unchanged on molecule formation, one can use the relativistic energy correction for the O atom (which has been calculated to be -0.04_9 hartree) as the relativistic correction for H_2O. Thus we can add -0.04_9 to all the calculated energies listed, or, alternatively, we can compare the nonrelativistic calculated energies with the exact nonrelativistic H_2O energy $-76.481 + 0.04_9 = -76.43_2$ hartrees.

Table 15.1 Calculations for H_2O

Reference[1]	Method	Total Energy[2] (hartrees)	Dipole Moment	Predicted Bond Angle	Predicted Bond Length
Pitzer, Merrifield	SCF Multicenter STO	−75.70 (7)	1.92 D	100°	0.990 Å
Moccia	SCF One-center STO	−75.92 (28)	2.08 D	107°	0.960 Å
Aung, Pitzer, Chan	SCF Multicenter STO	−76.00 (26)	2.03 D	—	—
Ermler, Kern	SCF Multicenter GTO	−76.051 (46; 28)	2.00 D	106.1°	0.941 Å
Neumann, Moskowitz	SCF Multicenter GTO	−76.059 (56)	1.99 D	—	—
Dunning, Pitzer, Aung	SCF Multicenter GTO	−76.062 (56; 41)	2.08 D	106.6°	0.941 Å
Dunning, Pitzer, Aung	SCF Multicenter STO	−76.063 (33)	2.05 D	—	—
Clementi, Popkie	SCF Multicenter GTO	−76.066	—	—	—
Estimated Hartree-Fock energy		−76.068			
Montgomery, Bruner, Knight	Varn.-Pert.	−75.99	—	—	—
Peterson, Pfeiffer	*Ab initio* VB	−76.02	—	106.5°	0.968 Å
Schaefer, Bender	CI, GTO	−76.24	—	—	—
Meyer	CI, GTO	−76.37	—	—	—
Miller, Kelly	MBPT	−76.48 ± 0.07	—	—	—
Experimental Values		−76.48	1.85 D	104.5°	0.957 Å

[1] R. M. Pitzer and D. P. Merrifield, *J. Chem. Phys.*, **52**, 4782 (1970); R. Moccia, *ibid.*, **40**, 2186 (1964); S. Aung, R. M. Pitzer, and S. I. Chan, *ibid.*, **49**, 2071 (1968); W. C. Ermler and C. W. Kern, *ibid.*, **55**, 4851 (1971); D. Neumann and J. W. Moskowitz, *ibid.*, **49**, 2056 (1968); T. H. Dunning, R. M. Pitzer, and S. Aung, *ibid.*, **57**, 5044 (1972); E. Clementi and H. Popkie, *ibid.*, **57**, 1077 (1972); H. E. Montgomery, B. L. Bruner, and R. E. Knight, *ibid.* **52**, 4407 (1970); C. Peterson and G. V. Pfeiffer, *Theor. Chim. Acta*, **26**, 321 (1972); H. F. Schaefer and C. F. Bender, *J. Chem. Phys.*, **55**, 1720 (1971); W. Meyer, *Int. J. Quantum Chem.*, **5S**, 341 (1971); J. H. Miller and H. P. Kelly, *Phys. Rev. A*, **4**, 480 (1971).

[2] This is the total electronic energy (including nuclear repulsion) calculated at or near the true structural values. Number of basis functions in parentheses; the notation (46; 28) means 46 Gaussians contracted to 28.

The first 8 calculations listed are SCF MO calculations. The size and quality of the basis set used determines how closely the Hartree–Fock limit is approached. Ermler and Kern did calculations at 45 different geometries to generate the potential-energy surface in the region of the equilibrium geometry. They then calculated zero-point vibrational corrections to properties like the dipole moment; these corrections generally turned out to be small. Montgomery, Bruner, and Knight used the variational perturbation method discussed at the end of Section 9.3, taking the unperturbed problem as an O^{-2} ion with (10) noninteracting electrons; the perturbation is then the sum of interelectronic repulsions and electron-proton attractions; the energy was calculated through second order. Schaefer and Bender included 1027 configurations in their CI calculation. Meyer used only 237 configurations, but because of special techniques employed, he was able to get 82% of the correlation energy. The other two calculations will be discussed later in this chapter.

Although the SCF MO calculations give good geometries and dipole moments, they give poor binding energies. For the minimal-basis Pitzer–Merrifield calculation, the difference between the energy of two isolated hydrogen atoms and one oxygen atom (as calculated with the minimal basis set) and the calculated H_2O energy gives a binding energy of only 4.5 eV, compared to the experimental value 10.1 eV. (With nonoptimized exponents, the minimal basis set gives 3.4 eV.) The near-Hartree–Fock calculations of Dunning, Pitzer, and Aung give a binding energy of 6.9 eV. This rather large error in dissociation energy is typical of Hartree–Fock calculations, as we saw for diatomics. When H_2O is formed from $2H + O$, two new electron pairs are formed. Two electrons paired in the same MO move through the same region of space and hence the correlation energy of such a pair is high. The Hartree–Fock calculation does not take into account this extra correlation in the molecule (as compared to the separated atoms) and hence gives too low a binding energy.

15.5 Localized MO's

The idea of a chemical *bond* between a pair of atoms in a molecule is fundamental to chemistry. The experimental evidence supporting this concept is substantial. One can assign bond energies to various kinds of bonds and obtain good estimates for the heats of formation of most molecules by adding the energies of the individual bonds. Other molecular properties (e.g., magnetic susceptibility, dipole moment) can also be analyzed as the sum of contributions from individual bonds (and lone pairs). Examination of the infrared spectrum of a compound containing an —O—H group shows a characteristic band near 3600 cm^{-1}; this O—H stretching vibrational band occurs at nearly the same frequency no matter whether it is HOH or HOCl or CH_3OH which is observed. The length of an O—H bond is nearly constant from molecule to molecule, about 0.96 Å.

The MO picture of water presented in the last section appears to be gravely deficient, in that it is seemingly inconsistent with the existence of individual bonds in the molecule. Each of the bonding MO's in (15.27) is delocalized over the entire molecule; if one were to compare the bonding MO's for HOH and HOCl, one would find them to be quite different. Yet we know that the OH parts of these two molecules are similar. Actually, MO theory *can* explain the observed near invariance of a given kind of chemical bond, as we now show.

The MO approximation to the ground state of water is a Slater determinant of the form:

$$|\varphi_1 \overline{\varphi_1} \varphi_2 \overline{\varphi_2} \varphi_3 \overline{\varphi_3} \varphi_4 \overline{\varphi_4} \varphi_5 \overline{\varphi_5}| \tag{15.32}$$

Putting (15.32) into words, we say that two electrons are in each of the orthonormal MO's φ_1, φ_2, φ_3, φ_4, and φ_5. However, this MO description is not unique. The addition of a multiple of one column of a determinant to another column leaves the determinant unchanged in value. Adding column 7 to column 9 and column 8 to column 10 in (15.32), we get

$$|\varphi_1 \overline{\varphi_1} \varphi_2 \overline{\varphi_2} \varphi_3 \overline{\varphi_3} \varphi_4 \overline{\varphi_4} (\varphi_4 + \varphi_5) \overline{(\varphi_4 + \varphi_5)}| \tag{15.33}$$

This determinant leads to the description of the molecule as having the MO's φ_1, φ_2, φ_3, φ_4, and $(\varphi_4 + \varphi_5)$ each doubly occupied. Despite the different verbal descriptions, the wave functions (15.32) and (15.33) are identical.

[In discussing SCF calculations, we used an orthogonalized 2s AO of the form $a(1s) + b(2s)$, where 2s is a (nodeless) 2s Slater-type orbital. This procedure is justified by use of the freedom of adding a multiple of one column of a determinant to another; the determinantal wave function for the oxygen atom is the same whether it is the 2s or the orthogonalized $2s_\perp$ AO that is used.]

An objection that can be raised to (15.33) is that the MO $(\varphi_4 + \varphi_5)$ is neither normalized, nor orthogonal to φ_4. Consider, however, the Slater determinant

$$|\varphi_1 \overline{\varphi_1} \varphi_2 \overline{\varphi_2} \varphi_3 \overline{\varphi_3} (b\varphi_4 + c\varphi_5) \overline{(b\varphi_4 + c\varphi_5)} (c\varphi_4 - b\varphi_5) \overline{(c\varphi_4 - b\varphi_5)}| \tag{15.34}$$

where b and c are any two real constants such that

$$b^2 + c^2 = 1 \tag{15.35}$$

We now show (15.34) and (15.32) to be the same wave function. Multiplication of columns 7 and 8 of (15.32) by b and columns 9 and 10 by $-b^{-1}$ gives

$$|\cdots b\varphi_4 \overline{(b\varphi_4)} (-b^{-1}\varphi_5) \overline{(-b^{-1}\varphi_5)}| \tag{15.36}$$

This step multiplies (15.32) by $b^2(-b^{-1})^2 = 1$. Next, $-bc$ times column 9 is added to column 7 and $-bc$ times column 10 is added to column 8 to give:

$$|\cdots (b\varphi_4 + c\varphi_5) \overline{(b\varphi_4 + c\varphi_5)} (-b^{-1}\varphi_5) \overline{(-b^{-1}\varphi_5)}| \tag{15.37}$$

Finally, c/b times column 7 is added to column 9 and c/b times column 8 is added to column 10, and (15.35) is used, which gives

$$|\cdots (b\varphi_4 + c\varphi_5) \overline{(b\varphi_4 + c\varphi_5)} (c\varphi_4 - b\varphi_5) \overline{(c\varphi_4 - b\varphi_5)}| \tag{15.38}$$

This completes the proof. The orthonormality of the MO's $(c\varphi_4 - b\varphi_5)$ and $(b\varphi_4 + c\varphi_5)$ readily follows from (15.35) and the orthonormality of φ_4 and φ_5.

Thus we can describe the molecule as having the orthonormal MO's

$$\varphi_1, \varphi_2, \varphi_3, b\varphi_4 + c\varphi_5, c\varphi_4 - b\varphi_5 \qquad (15.39)$$

each doubly occupied.

There are an infinite number of other MO descriptions consistent with (15.32): Let d and e be any two real constants such that $d^2 + e^2 = 1$. If the procedure used to go from (15.32) to (15.34) is applied to columns 5, 6, 7, and 8 of (15.34), we end up with

$$|\varphi_1 \overline{\varphi_1} \varphi_2 \overline{\varphi_2} (d\varphi_3 + be\varphi_4 + ce\varphi_5) \overline{(d\varphi_3 + be\varphi_4 + ce\varphi_5)}$$
$$\times (e\varphi_3 - bd\varphi_4 - cd\varphi_5) \overline{(e\varphi_3 - bd\varphi_4 - cd\varphi_5)} (c\varphi_4 - b\varphi_5) \overline{(c\varphi_4 - b\varphi_5)}|$$

We can thus describe the electronic configuration as having the orthonormal MO's

$$\varphi_1, \varphi_2, (d\varphi_3 + be\varphi_4 + ce\varphi_5), (e\varphi_3 - bd\varphi_4 - cd\varphi_5), (c\varphi_4 - b\varphi_5)$$

each doubly occupied. Continuing on in this manner, we can derive MO's each of which is a linear combination of all the original MO's $\varphi_1, \varphi_2, \varphi_3, \varphi_4, \varphi_5$. [For the general conditions that must be satisfied by the coefficients in these linear combinations, see *Pilar*, p. 345.]

Thus, for a given closed-subshell electronic state of a molecule, there are many possible MO descriptions. The delocalized MO's (15.27) of water are uniquely determined as the solutions of the SCF equations [Eq. (13.173)]:

$$\hat{H}^{\text{eff}}\varphi_i = \varepsilon_i \varphi_i, \qquad i = 1, 2, \dots \qquad (15.40)$$

Hence the reader may be wondering how we can have other sets of MO's that also minimize the variational integral. Actually, Eq. (15.40) is not the most general equation satisfied by the MO's that minimize the variational integral; instead, one finds in deriving the SCF equations that the Hartree–Fock MO's must satisfy[7]

$$\hat{H}^{\text{eff}}\varphi_i = \sum_{j=1}^{N} \lambda_{ji} \varphi_j, \qquad i = 1, \dots, N \qquad (15.41)$$

where the sum runs over the occupied MO's. The λ_{ji}'s are certain constants (Lagrangian multipliers) which can be chosen arbitrarily, subject to the MO orthonormality requirement. Different choices of the λ_{ji}'s give different sets of MO's, but each such set minimizes the variational integral. For a closed-subshell configuration, one possible choice of the λ_{ji}'s can be shown to be

$$\lambda_{ji} = \varepsilon_i \delta_{ij} \qquad (15.42)$$

This choice reduces (15.41) to (15.40). The delocalized MO's [(15.27) for water] that satisfy (15.40) are called the *canonical* SCF MO's. The canonical MO's are eigenfunctions of the effective Hartree–Fock Hamiltonian, which commutes with the molecular symmetry operators, and hence the canonical MO's each transform according to one of the possible molecular symmetry species. A set of MO's like (15.39) satisfies (15.41) but not (15.40), and does not necessarily transform according to the molecular symmetry species.

---

[7] For the proof of (15.41) and (15.42), see e.g., S. M. Blinder, *Am. J. Phys.*, **33**, 431 (1965), Appendix D; *Pilar*, Chapter 13.

For an open-subshell configuration, one can also find canonical delocalized MO's that satisfy (15.40) and that transform according to the molecular symmetry species; however, the form of $\hat{H}^{\text{eff}}$ is more complicated than for the closed-subshell case. [See C. C. J. Roothaan, *Rev. Mod. Phys.*, **32**, 179 (1960).]

Of the possible MO sets formed as linear combinations of the delocalized canonical MO's of water, a set that would appeal to a chemist is one for which the charge probability density of each bonding MO is localized in the region of one of the O—H bonds. There are many ways of taking linear combinations of the delocalized MO's to get such *localized* MO's. A natural requirement that the two localized bonding MO's in water should satisfy is that they be equivalent to each other; i.e., each localized bonding MO of water should be transformed into the other by the $\hat{C}_2(z)$ symmetry operation (Fig. 15.7). Localized MO's that are permuted among one another by a symmetry operation that permutes equivalent chemical bonds are called *equivalent orbitals*. The concept of localized equivalent orbitals goes back to papers by Hund (1932) and Coulson (1942), but the systematic procedure for deriving equivalent MO's from the canonical MO's was given by Lennard-Jones in 1949.[8] As we shall see, equivalent MO's reconcile MO theory with the chemist's intuitive picture of chemical bonding.

For water, chemical intuition (H—Ö—H) suggests the equivalent MO's to be: a pair of equivalent bonding orbitals $b(\text{OH}_1)$ and $b(\text{OH}_2)$, an inner-shell $1s$ oxygen orbital $i(\text{O})$ (which is equivalent to itself), and two lone-pair equivalent MO's $l_1(\text{O})$ and $l_2(\text{O})$ on oxygen. Actually, the symmetry requirement that the MO's be equivalent is not sufficient to determine the equivalent MO's of water uniquely, and many possible equivalent MO's can be constructed.

The concept of equivalent orbitals has two shortcomings. First, it cannot be used to define localized MO's in molecules having no equivalent chemical bonds. For HOCl, the O—H and O—Cl bonds are not equivalent, and the localized bonding MO's cannot be expected to be equivalent. Second, even for symmetric molecules, the choice of equivalent MO's is not unique in many cases (e.g., HOH). Hence we want a definition that will specify a unique set of localized MO's for any molecule.

The most "localized" MO's are those that are most separated from one another; by this we mean that set of MO's for which the interelectronic repulsions between the different MO's viewed as "charge clouds" is a minimum. The energy of repulsion between the charge clouds of electron 1 in the MO φ_i and electron 2 in the MO φ_j is a Coulomb integral of the form (9.144). The total interorbital charge-cloud repulsion energy is then

$$4 \sum_{i} \sum_{j>i} \int\int |\varphi_i(1)|^2 |\varphi_j(2)|^2 \frac{1}{r_{12}} \, dv_1 \, dv_2 \qquad (15.43)$$

where the sums run over the occupied MO's. (The factor 4 comes from the 4 inter-orbital repulsions of the electrons in each MO pair.) We define the localized MO's as those orthonormal MO's that minimize (15.43). [It turns out that minimization of (15.43) implies the maximization of the total *intra*orbital electron repulsion and

---

[8] J. E. Lennard-Jones, *Proc. Roy. Soc.*, **A198**, 1, 14 (1949); G. G. Hall and J. E. Lennard-Jones, *ibid.*, **A202**, 155 (1950); J. E. Lennard-Jones and J. A. Pople, *ibid.*, **A202**, 166 (1950).

the minimization of the magnitude of the (interorbital) exchange energy.] This definition was originally suggested by Lennard-Jones and Pople and has been applied to many molecules by Edmiston and Ruedenberg.[9] We shall call these MO's the *energy-localized* MO's. For molecules with symmetry, we expect that the energy-localized MO's will also be equivalent MO's. (An apparent exception has been found by Edmiston and Ruedenberg for C_2, but inasmuch as their calculation is based on minimal-basis-set MO's with nonoptimized orbital exponents, their conclusion cannot be regarded as final.) Energy-localized MO's are thus a generalization of equivalent MO's.

Liang and Taylor calculated the energy-localized MO's for water, starting with the canonical MO's (15.27) of Pitzer and Merrifield. In terms of the canonical (delocalized) MO's, Liang and Taylor find[10]:

$$i(O) = 0.99(1a_1) - 0.12(2a_1) \qquad\qquad + 0.06(3a_1)$$
$$b(OH_1) = 0.05(1a_1) + 0.57(2a_1) + 0.71(1b_2) + 0.42(3a_1)$$
$$b(OH_2) = 0.05(1a_1) + 0.57(2a_1) - 0.71(1b_2) + 0.42(3a_1) \qquad\text{(15.44)}$$
$$l_1(O) = 0.08(1a_1) + 0.42(2a_1) \qquad\qquad - 0.57(3a_1) - 0.71(1b_1)$$
$$l_2(O) = 0.08(1a_1) + 0.42(2a_1) \qquad\qquad - 0.57(3a_1) + 0.71(1b_1)$$

The lone-pair $1b_1$ MO $(2p_{xO})$ is equally divided between the equivalent lone-pair localized orbitals. $(\sqrt{\tfrac{1}{2}} = 0.71.)$ The inner-shell $1a_1$ MO contributes substantially to only the $i(O)$ MO. The strongly bonding $1b_2$ MO is equally divided between the two bonding localized MO's. The less strongly bonding $2a_1$ MO makes substantial contributions to the two bonding localized MO's and smaller, but still substantial, contributions to the lone-pair localized MO's. The largely lone-pair, weakly bonding $3a_1$ MO makes substantial contributions to the lone-pair localized MO's and lesser contributions to the bonding localized MO's.

In terms of the AO's, the energy-localized MO's of water are:

$$i(O) = -0.007(H_1 1s) - 0.007(H_2 1s) + 0.99(O1s) - 0.12(O2s_{\perp})$$
$$+ 0.03(O2p_z)$$
$$b(OH_1) = \quad 0.50(H_1 1s) \ - 0.10(H_2 1s) \ + 0.02(O1s) + 0.25(O2s_{\perp})$$
$$+ 0.407(O2p_z) + 0.441(O2p_y)$$
$$b(OH_2) = -0.10(H_1 1s) \ + 0.50(H_2 1s) \ + 0.02(O1s) + 0.25(O2s_{\perp})$$
$$+ 0.407(O2p_z) - 0.441(O2p_y) \qquad\text{(15.45)}$$
$$l_1(O) = -0.09(H_1 1s) \ - 0.09(H_2 1s) \ + 0.09(O1s) + 0.63(O2s_{\perp})$$
$$- 0.39(O2p_z) - 0.71(O2p_x)$$
$$l_2(O) = -0.09(H_1 1s) \ - 0.09(H_2 1s) \ + 0.09(O1s) + 0.63(O2s_{\perp})$$
$$- 0.39(O2p_z) + 0.71(O2p_x)$$

[9] C. Edmiston and K. Ruedenberg, *Rev. Mod. Phys.*, **35**, 457 (1963); *J. Chem. Phys.*, **43**, S97 (1965); P.-O. Löwdin, ed., *Quantum Theory of Atoms, Molecules, and the Solid State*, Academic Press, New York, 1966, pp. 263–280.

[10] J. H. Liang, Ph.D. thesis, Ohio State U., 1970. I am grateful to Professor William J. Taylor for making this work available to me. See also F. Franks, ed., *Water*, Vol. 1, Plenum, 1972, p. 42.

The MO wave function

$$|i(O)\overline{i(O)}\,b(OH_1)\overline{b(OH_1)}\,b(OH_2)\overline{b(OH_2)}\,l_1(O)\overline{l_1(O)}\,l_2(O)\overline{l_2(O)}| \quad \text{(15.46)}$$

is identical to (15.30).

Let us analyze these equivalent MO's for water. The $i(O)$ MO is nearly a pure $1s$ inner-shell oxygen AO.

The directional character of the two bonding localized MO's is determined by the oxygen $2p_y$ and $2p_z$ AO contributions. For $b(OH_1)$, this contribution contains the factor $0.407z_O + 0.441y_O$. Let us carry out a rotation of coordinates in the zy plane by an angle $\alpha = \arctan(0.441/0.407) = 47\tfrac{1}{2}°$, as in Fig. 15.6. The relation between coordinates in the unrotated system and the rotated $z'y'$ system is given by the well-known formulas:

$$z' = z\cos\alpha + y\sin\alpha$$
$$y' = -z\sin\alpha + y\cos\alpha \quad \text{(15.47)}$$

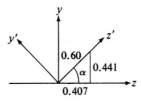

FIGURE 15.6   *A coordinate rotation in the yz plane.*

From (15.47) we have

$$0.407z_O + 0.441y_O = 0.600z'_O \quad \text{(15.48)}$$

Multiplication by the exponential factor of the $2p$ oxygen AO then gives

$$0.407\,(O2p_z) + 0.441\,(O2p_y) = 0.60\,(O2p_{z'}) \quad \text{(15.49)}$$

In other words, the hybridized $2p_z\,2p_y$ AO on the left of (15.49) is the same function as 0.60 times a $2p$ AO inclined at an angle of $47\tfrac{1}{2}°$ with the z axis. Thus the bonding $2p_z\,2p_y$ hybrid AO's of oxygen in $b(OH_1)$ and $b(OH_2)$ point in the general direction of the hydrogen atoms. The contribution from the hydrogen atoms to $b(OH_1)$ is mostly from $H_1 1s$, and the overlap between $H_1 1s$ and the $2p_z\,2p_y$ oxygen hybrid then forms the O—H_1 chemical bond. The angle between the two hybrid oxygen AO's in $b(OH_1)$ and $b(OH_2)$ is 95°, and, in the vicinity of the O atom, this is essentially the angle between the localized bonding MO's. This angle is less than the $104\tfrac{1}{2}°$ molecular bond angle. The localized bonding MO's do not point exactly along the O—H internuclear line, but are apparently bent inward by up to 5°. (For accurately plotted contours, see F. Franks, ed., *Water*, Vol. 1, Plenum, 1972, p. 46.)

There is a small but significant contribution to $b(OH_1)$ from the $H_2 1s$ AO. (The ratio of the contributions of two AO's to an MO is given essentially by the square of the ratio of their coefficients.) The $b(OH_1)$ MO is not completely localized in the

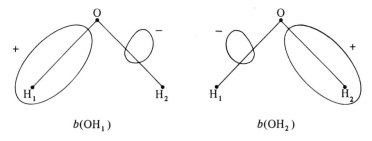

$$b(OH_1)$$ $$b(OH_2)$$

FIGURE 15.7 *Rough sketches of the localized equivalent bonding* MO's *in water.*

region of the O—H$_1$ bond, but contains a small amount of electron probability density on the OH$_2$ side of the molecule (Fig. 15.7); even so, this MO is far more localized than any of the bonding canonical MO's in (15.27). Because $b(OH_1)$ is mostly localized in the OH$_1$ region, we expect but a small change in its form on going from HOH to, say, HOCl. The observed near invariance of the O—H bond from molecule to molecule is explained by MO theory using localized bonding MO's. (Neglect of the contribution of H$_2$ $1s$ to the $b(OH_1)$ localized MO gives a two-center orbital called a *bond orbital.*)

Finally, consider the two lone-pair MO's $l_1(O)$ and $l_2(O)$. These two MO's are mainly localized on the oxygen atom and are equivalent to each other. They are directed away from the hydrogen atoms and project above and below the molecular (yz) plane (Fig. 15.8). The $\hat{\sigma}_v(yz)$ operation converts x to $-x$ and hence interchanges the lone-pair MO's. The angle between them is

$$2 \arctan(0.71/0.39) = 122°$$

Edmiston and Ruedenberg calculated energy-localized MO's for several diatomic molecules. Consider Li$_2$. Chemical intuition (Li—Li) suggests the localized MO's to be: an inner-shell $1s$ AO on Li$_a$, an equivalent inner-shell AO on Li$_b$, and a bonding MO extending over the molecule. In terms of Ransil's minimal-basis-set SCF MO's with optimized orbital exponents (Section 13.16), Edmiston and

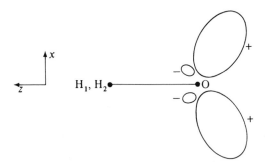

FIGURE 15.8 *Rough sketches of the localized equivalent lone-pair* MO's *of water.*

Ruedenberg found the energy-localized MO's of Li_2 to be:

$$i(Li_a) = 0.703(1\sigma_g) + 0.707(1\sigma_u) - 0.074(2\sigma_g)$$

$$i(Li_b) = 0.703(1\sigma_g) - 0.707(1\sigma_u) - 0.074(2\sigma_g)$$

$$b(Li_aLi_b) = 0.105(1\sigma_g) \qquad\qquad + 0.995(2\sigma_g)$$

In terms of AO's, we have

$$i(Li_a) = \quad 1.00(1s_a) - 0.02(2s_{\perp a}) - 0.006(2p\sigma_a) - 0.0001(1s_b)$$
$$- 0.05(2s_{\perp b}) - 0.01(2p\sigma_b)$$

$$i(Li_b) = -0.0001(1s_a) - 0.05(2s_{\perp a}) - 0.01(2p\sigma_a) + 1.00(1s_b)$$
$$- 0.02(2s_{\perp b}) - 0.006(2p\sigma_b)$$

$$b(Li_aLi_b) = \quad 0.02(1s_a) + 0.52(2s_{\perp a}) + 0.11(2p\sigma_a) + 0.02(1s_b)$$
$$+ 0.52(2s_{\perp b}) + 0.11(2p\sigma_b) \qquad \textbf{(15.50)}$$

The bonding MO is very nearly the same as the $2\sigma_g$ MO; the lone-pair MO's are very nearly $1s$ AO's on each atom.

For N_2, we expect $(:N\equiv N:)$ the localized MO's to be: an inner-shell $1s$ AO on each atom, a lone-pair $2s$ AO on each atom, and three bonding MO's spread over the two atoms. The canonical-MO picture is that the triple bond consists of one σ bond and two π bonds, as in Section 13.6. The energy-localized bonding MO's were found by Edmiston and Ruedenberg to be three equivalent banana-shaped bond orbitals spaced 120° apart from one another; the AO's that make significant contributions to the localized bonding MO's are the $2s$, $2p\sigma$, $2p\pi_x$, and $2p\pi_y$ orbitals of each atom. The $i(N_a)$ and $i(N_b)$ localized MO's were found to be nearly pure $1s$ nitrogen AO's. Each of the $l(N_a)$ and $l(N_b)$ localized MO's is a hybrid of the $2s$ and $2p\sigma$ AO's of the relevant nitrogen atom, with the $2s$ AO making the larger contribution to the MO; each lone-pair localized MO is directed away from the other nitrogen atom.

The concept of localized MO's is not as widely applicable as that of delocalized canonical MO's. Delocalized MO's are valid for any molecule. However (as noted in Section 11.5), the Hartree–Fock wave functions of nonclosed-subshell electronic states are, in most cases, linear combinations of *several* Slater determinants [e.g., see (10.62) and (10.63)], and the above localization procedure is not applicable to the open-subshell orbitals in these wave functions. Thus, in a molecule in an excited electronic state with an open-subshell configuration, the electrons in the incompletely filled MO's are delocalized over much of the molecule.

The great success of the concept of chemical bonds between pairs of atoms is a reflection of the fact that the electronic ground states of most molecules have closed-subshell configurations, for which the localized MO description is just as valid as the delocalized MO description.

For a closed-subshell ground-state molecule, those properties that involve only the ground-state wave function can be calculated just as well with either the localized or the delocalized MO description. Such properties include electron probability density, dipole moment, geometry, heat of formation, etc. Properties of a molecule that involve the wave function of the ground state and also the wave function of an open-subshell excited state or the wave function of an open-subshell ion, cannot be calculated using a localized MO description. Such properties include the ultraviolet absorption spectrum and molecular ionization energies. (For the special case of conjugated and aromatic molecules, see Section 15.8.)

Aside from justifying chemists' intuitive picture of bonding, the concept of localized MO's is significant in that localized MO's should be approximately transferable from molecule to molecule (which is not true of course for delocalized MO's). Having calculated the localized MO for the C—H bond in, say, methane, we expect to find this localized $b(CH)$ MO to be about the same in any hydrocarbon. Rothenberg calculated energy-localized $b(CH)$ MO's in CH_4, staggered and eclipsed C_2H_6, and staggered and eclipsed CH_3OH, and found them to have essentially the same contour shape (which resembles Fig. 15.22); the overlap integrals (calculated for coincident carbon atoms and coincident C—H axes) between pairs of these localized MO's all exceeded 0.996; properties such as the bond dipole moment of the $b(CH)$ MO were found to be nearly the same in all three molecules. Similar results were found for the energy-localized $b(CH)$ MO's in ethylene and acetylene. [See S. Rothenberg, *J. Chem. Phys.*, **51**, 3389 (1969); *J. Am. Chem. Soc.*, **93**, 68 (1971).]

The labor in calculating a wave function increases steeply with increasing numbers of electrons and nuclei. The approximate transferability of localized MO's raises the exciting possibility of building up the MO wave function of a large molecule using localized MO's found from calculations on smaller molecules. Unfortunately, calculation of energy-localized MO's from canonical MO's is quite time-consuming, and most such calculations have been done with minimal (rather than extended) basis sets.

15.6 The SCF MO Treatment of Methane, Ethane, and Ethylene

The AO's for a minimal-basis-set SCF calculation of CH_4 are the carbon $1s$, $2s$, $2p_x$, $2p_y$, and $2p_z$ AO's and a $1s$ AO on each hydrogen atom. The point group of methane is $\mathcal{T}_d$; group theory (see *Cotton* or *Schonland*) gives the possible symmetry species as A_1, A_2, E, T_1, and T_2. We shall not worry about specifying the symmetry behavior that corresponds to each symmetry species, but shall use the species mainly as labels for the MO's. As usual, we set up the coordinate system with the z axis coinciding with the highest-order C_n or S_n axis; for methane, this is an S_4 axis. The coordinates of the hydrogen atoms are: (q,q,q), $(q, -q, -q)$, $(-q,q, -q)$, and $(-q, -q,q)$, where $2q$ is the edge of the cube in which the molecule is inscribed (Fig. 15.9). Note the equivalence of the x, y, and z axes.

The carbon atom is at the center of the molecule and the carbon $1s$ and $2s$ AO's are each sent into themselves by every symmetry operation; these AO's transform according to the totally symmetric species A_1. The carbon $2p_x$, $2p_y$, and $2p_z$ AO's are given by x, y, or z times a radial function; their symmetry behavior is the same as that of the functions x, y, and z, respectively. From the formulas for rotation of coordinates [Eq. (15.63)], we see that any proper rotation sends each of the functions x, y, and z into some linear combination of x, y, and z. Any improper

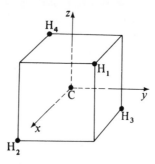

FIGURE 15.9   *Coordinate axes for methane.   The origin is at the center of the cube.*

rotation is the product of some proper rotation and an inversion (Problem 12.23); the inversion simply converts each coordinate to its negative.   Hence, the three carbon 2*p* orbitals are sent into linear combinations of one another by each symmetry operation; they must therefore transform according to one of the triply degenerate symmetry species.   Further investigation (which we omit) shows the symmetry species of the 2*p* AO's to be T_2.

Just as in water, each 1*s* hydrogen AO in methane does not transform according to any of the molecular symmetry species, and it is convenient to form symmetry orbitals by taking linear combinations of the 1*s* AO's.   One obvious symmetry orbital is

$$f_1 = H_1 1s + H_2 1s + H_3 1s + H_4 1s \tag{15.51}$$

Since each methane symmetry operator permutes the hydrogen 1*s* orbitals among themselves, (15.51) is sent into itself by each symmetry operation and belongs to the totally symmetric species A_1.   We need three more symmetry orbitals.   The construction of these is not obvious without the use of group theory, and we shall simply write down the results.   The remaining three orthogonal (unnormalized) symmetry orbitals can be taken as:

$$f_2 = H_1 1s + H_2 1s - H_3 1s - H_4 1s \tag{15.52}$$

$$f_3 = H_1 1s - H_2 1s + H_3 1s - H_4 1s \tag{15.53}$$

$$f_4 = H_1 1s - H_2 1s - H_3 1s + H_4 1s \tag{15.54}$$

Each of these three functions is transformed into some linear combination of the three functions by each symmetry operation.   For example, a $\hat{C}_3$ rotation about the CH_1 bond causes the following permutation of hydrogen atoms:

$$1 \to 1,\, 2 \to 3,\, 3 \to 4,\, 4 \to 2$$

The corresponding $\hat{O}_{C_3}$ operator transforms f_2, f_3, and f_4 into f_3, f_4, and f_2, respectively.   These three symmetry orbitals therefore transform according to one of the triply degenerate symmetry species.   The function f_2 has positive signs for the hydrogen AO's with a positive x coordinate and negative signs for the hydrogen AO's with a negative x coordinate; we thus expect f_2 to have the same symmetry behavior as the function x. Similarly, f_3 and f_4 behave as y and z, respectively. (As an example, note that a 120° counterclockwise rotation about the CH_1 bond has the following effect on the three unit vectors: $\mathbf{i} \to \mathbf{j}, \mathbf{j} \to \mathbf{k}, \mathbf{k} \to \mathbf{i}$; this is the same behavior shown by the functions f_2, f_3, and f_4 for this rotation.) These three symmetry orbitals thus transform according to the species T_2.

The symmetry orbitals are then:

Symmetry Orbital	f_1	f_2	f_3	f_4	C1s	C2s	$C2p_x$	$C2p_y$	$C2p_z$
Symmetry Species	a_1	t_2	t_2	t_2	a_1	a_1	t_2	t_2	t_2

The nine lowest MO's therefore consist of three a_1 and six t_2 MO's. The six t_2 MO's belong to triply degenerate levels and thus fall into two different subshells $1t_2$ and $2t_2$; each such subshell contains three MO's of equal orbital energy and each subshell holds six electrons. SCF calculations give the three lowest subshells as $1a_1$, $2a_1$, and $1t_2$, with energies -11.20, -0.93, and -0.54 hartrees, respectively. The ground state of methane has the closed-subshell configuration

$$(1a_1)^2 (2a_1)^2 (1t_2)^6 \tag{15.55}$$

and is a $^1A_1$ state.

Pitzer[11] did SCF calculations for methane at several CH distances, representing each basis AO by a single STO and optimizing the orbital exponents. He found a minimum in energy for a bond distance of 1.089 Å as compared to the experimental value 1.085 Å. The MO's found by Pitzer at the experimental equilibrium bond distance are:

$$1a_1 = -0.005(H_1 1s + H_2 1s + H_3 1s + H_4 1s) + 1.001(C1s) + 0.025(C2s_\perp)$$

$$2a_1 = 0.186(H_1 1s + H_2 1s + H_3 1s + H_4 1s) - 0.064(C1s) + 0.584(C2s_\perp)$$

$$1t_{2x} = 0.318(H_1 1s + H_2 1s - H_3 1s - H_4 1s) + 0.554(C2p_x) \tag{15.56}$$

$$1t_{2y} = 0.318(H_1 1s - H_2 1s + H_3 1s - H_4 1s) + 0.554(C2p_y)$$

$$1t_{2z} = 0.318(H_1 1s - H_2 1s - H_3 1s + H_4 1s) + 0.554(C2p_z)$$

The $1a_1$ MO is essentially the carbon $1s$ AO. The $2a_1$ MO is a bonding combination of the carbon $2s$ AO and the symmetry orbital (15.51); this MO has charge buildup between the carbon atom and each of the four hydrogen atoms. The $1t_{2x}$ MO is a bonding MO; the function (15.52) is positive on the positive half of the x axis and negative on the negative half of the x axis, and its overlap with $C2p_x$ gives charge buildup in the regions about the x axis. Similarly, the bonding $1t_{2y}$ and $1t_{2z}$ MO's have charge buildup in the regions about the y and z axes, respectively.

We now consider the four localized (equivalent) bonding MO's of methane. Because of the tetrahedral symmetry, each of these orbitals *must* point along a CH bond, since otherwise they would not be equivalent to one another. (This is

---

[11] R. M. Pitzer, *J. Chem. Phys.*, **46**, 4871 (1967).

not true for water, where the equivalence requirement is satisfied by any two bonding MO's that make the same angle with the C_2 axis.) Each localized bonding MO is some linear combination of the five canonical occupied MO's:

$$b(CH_1) = a(1a_1) + b(2a_1) + d(1t_{2x}) + e(1t_{2y}) + f(1t_{2z}) \qquad (15.57)$$

with similar expressions for $b(CH_2)$, $b(CH_3)$, and $b(CH_4)$. (Since $1a_1$ is a non-bonding low-energy inner-shell orbital, we expect $|a| \ll |b|$.) The $1a_1$ and $2a_1$ canonical MO's are directed equally to all four hydrogens, so that varying a or b in (15.57) does not direct $b(CH_1)$ preferentially to any one hydrogen. The $1t_{2x}$, $1t_{2y}$, and $1t_{2z}$ MO's are directed along the x, y, and z axes, respectively, so that by adjusting d, e, and f appropriately, we can get $b(CH_1)$ to be localized mainly in the region of the CH_1 bond. To fix d, e, and f, we use some properties of direction cosines.

If line L passes through the origin and makes the angles α, β, and γ with the x, y, and z axes, respectively, then the quantities

$$l \equiv \cos\alpha, \qquad m \equiv \cos\beta, \qquad n \equiv \cos\gamma \qquad (15.58)$$

are the *direction cosines* of L. If (x_L, y_L, z_L) is a point on L, then clearly

$$x_L = r\cos\alpha, \qquad y_L = r\cos\beta, \qquad z_L = r\cos\gamma \qquad (15.59)$$

where r is the distance from the origin. From $x^2 + y^2 + z^2 = r^2$, it follows that

$$l^2 + m^2 + n^2 = 1 \qquad (15.60)$$

Let the lines L_1 and L_2 go from the origin to (x_1, y_1, z_1) and (x_2, y_2, z_2), respectively; if θ_{12} is the angle between L_1 and L_2, then [Eq. (5.29)]:

$$\cos\theta_{12} = \frac{x_1 x_2 + y_1 y_2 + z_1 z_2}{r_1 r_2} \qquad (15.61)$$

$$\cos\theta_{12} = l_1 l_2 + m_1 m_2 + n_1 n_2 \qquad (15.62)$$

Direction cosines are useful in discussing changes in coordinate axes. Let the $x'y'z'$ and the xyz Cartesian coordinate systems have a common origin, and let the $x'y'z'$ axes be obtained from the xyz axes by rotation, or reflection, or inversion, or some combination of these operations. Let the direction cosines of the x' axis with respect to the xyz system be l_1, m_1, n_1; let l_2, m_2, n_2 and l_3, m_3, n_3 be the direction cosines of the y' and z' axes, respectively. Let the vector $\mathbf{s}$ have coordinates (x, y, z) and (x', y', z') in the unrotated and rotated coordinate systems. We have $x' = \mathbf{s} \cdot \mathbf{i}'$, where $\mathbf{i}'$ is a unit vector along the x' axis; since $\mathbf{i}'$ is of unit length, it follows from (15.59) and (15.58) that the coordinates of $\mathbf{i}'$ in the xyz system are l_1, m_1, and n_1. Hence

$$x' = l_1 x + m_1 y + n_1 z$$
$$y' = l_2 x + m_2 y + n_2 z \qquad (15.63)$$
$$z' = l_3 x + m_3 y + n_3 z$$

where the y' and z' equations follow from $y' = \mathbf{s} \cdot \mathbf{j}'$, $z' = \mathbf{s} \cdot \mathbf{k}'$. [Equation (15.47) is a special case of (15.63).] Since the angle between any pair of the x', y', and z'

axes is 90°, it follows from (15.62) that

$$l_1 l_2 + m_1 m_2 + n_1 n_2 = 0$$

$$l_1 l_3 + m_1 m_3 + n_1 n_3 = 0 \qquad \text{(15.64)}$$

$$l_2 l_3 + m_2 m_3 + n_2 n_3 = 0$$

Now we return to the determination of d, e, and f. The MO's t_{2x}, t_{2y}, and t_{2z} are directed along the x, y, and z axes, respectively, and the contributions of the carbon $2p_x$, $2p_y$, and $2p_z$ AO's to these MO's are

$$xe^{-\zeta r}, \qquad ye^{-\zeta r}, \qquad ze^{-\zeta r} \qquad \text{(15.65)}$$

The contribution of the hydrogen AO's to the t_2 MO's has a more complicated form (the hydrogens are not at the coordinate origin), but we need not explicitly consider the hydrogen part of the MO's; this is because the hydrogen symmetry orbitals (15.52)–(15.54) have the same directional properties as the corresponding carbon $2p$ AO's (15.65) with which each is combined in the $1t_2$ MO's [Eq. (15.56)]. The linear combination (15.57) has as its carbon $2p$ contribution

$$(dx + ey + fz)e^{-\zeta r} \qquad \text{(15.66)}$$

Let l_1, m_1, and n_1 be the direction cosines of the CH$_1$ line. We assert that if d, e, and f are chosen as proportional to these direction cosines, then $b(\text{CH}_1)$ will be directed toward H$_1$. To verify this, we set $d:e:f = l_1:m_1:n_1$ in (15.66) to get

$$c(l_1 x + m_1 y + n_1 z)e^{-\zeta r} = cx'e^{-\zeta r} \qquad \text{(15.67)}$$

where c is some constant, and the x' axis runs from C to H$_1$.

Similarly, by picking d, e, and f proportional to the direction cosines of the other CH lines, we form localized orbitals along these bonds. From (15.59), the direction cosines of the CH lines are:

$$
\begin{array}{ll}
\text{CH}_1: 3^{-1/2}, 3^{-1/2}, 3^{-1/2} & \text{CH}_2: 3^{-1/2}, -3^{-1/2}, -3^{-1/2} \\
\text{CH}_3: -3^{-1/2}, 3^{-1/2}, -3^{-1/2} & \text{CH}_4: -3^{-1/2}, -3^{-1/2}, 3^{-1/2}
\end{array}
\qquad \text{(15.68)}
$$

To satisfy the equivalence requirement, the values of a and b in (15.57) must be the same for each bonding localized MO. The equivalent localized MO's for methane thus have the forms:

$$b(\text{CH}_1) = a(1a_1) + b(2a_1) + 3^{-1/2}c(1t_{2x} + 1t_{2y} + 1t_{2z})$$

$$b(\text{CH}_2) = a(1a_1) + b(2a_1) + 3^{-1/2}c(1t_{2x} - 1t_{2y} - 1t_{2z})$$

$$b(\text{CH}_3) = a(1a_1) + b(2a_1) + 3^{-1/2}c(-1t_{2x} + 1t_{2y} - 1t_{2z}) \qquad \text{(15.69)}$$

$$b(\text{CH}_4) = a(1a_1) + b(2a_1) + 3^{-1/2}c(-1t_{2x} - 1t_{2y} + 1t_{2z})$$

Orthonormality of the bonding localized MO's (15.69) requires that

$$a^2 + b^2 + c^2 = 1 \qquad \text{(15.70)}$$

$$a^2 + b^2 - \tfrac{1}{3}c^2 = 0 \qquad \text{(15.71)}$$

Hence

$$c = \tfrac{1}{2}\sqrt{3}, \qquad (a^2 + b^2)^{1/2} = \tfrac{1}{2} \tag{15.72}$$

The equivalence, directional, and orthonormality requirements have fixed all but one parameter (the ratio a/b) in the localized bonding MO's of methane.

The $1t_{2x}$ MO points equally in the $+x$ and $-x$ directions. Similarly, the $1t_{2y}$ and $1t_{2z}$ MO's point equally on both sides of the carbon atom. This is not true of the bonding localized MO's: The $2a_1$ MO is positive in most of the bonding region between the carbon atom and the hydrogen atoms. [It is negative in the region very near the carbon atom, due to the $-0.06(C1s)$ term and to the negative portion of the orthogonalized C2s AO—see Eq. (15.28).] The linear combination $(1t_{2x} + 1t_{2y} + 1t_{2z})$ points equally in the $(1, 1, 1)/\sqrt{3}$ and the $(-1, -1, -1)/\sqrt{3}$ directions; if b in (15.69) is taken as positive (as we have taken c), then the $2a_1$ MO adds to the positive half of this linear combination of the $1t_2$ MO's and cancels much of the negative half of this linear combination. With b and c having the same sign, the $b(CH_1)$ MO points mostly in the $(1, 1, 1)/\sqrt{3}$ direction, with only a small "tail" in the $(-1, -1, -1)/\sqrt{3}$ direction.

Pitzer's SCF calculation gives the energy-localized bonding and inner-shell methane MO's as

$$b(CH_1) = 0.055(1a_1) + 0.497(2a_1) + \tfrac{1}{2}(1t_{2x} + 1t_{2y} + 1t_{2z})$$

$$b(CH_2) = 0.055(1a_1) + 0.497(2a_1) + \tfrac{1}{2}(1t_{2x} - 1t_{2y} - 1t_{2z})$$

$$b(CH_3) = 0.055(1a_1) + 0.497(2a_1) + \tfrac{1}{2}(-1t_{2x} + 1t_{2y} - 1t_{2z}) \tag{15.73}$$

$$b(CH_4) = 0.055(1a_1) + 0.497(2a_1) + \tfrac{1}{2}(-1t_{2x} - 1t_{2y} + 1t_{2z})$$

$$i(C) = 0.994(1a_1) - 0.111(2a_1)$$

From (15.56) and (15.73), we have

$$i(C) = 1.002(C1s) - 0.040(C2s_\perp)$$

$$- 0.025(H_1 1s + H_2 1s + H_3 1s + H_4 1s)$$

$$b(CH_1) = 0.024(C1s) + 0.292(C2s_\perp) + 0.569(H_1 1s) \tag{15.74}$$

$$- 0.066(H_2 1s + H_3 1s + H_4 1s)$$

$$+ 0.277(C2p_x + C2p_y + C2p_z)$$

The carbon AO contribution to each energy-localized bonding MO is approximately an equal mixture of $2s$, $2p_x$, $2p_y$, and $2p_z$ orbitals, i.e., approximately an sp^3 hybrid. (See also the VB discussion of methane in Section 15.10.)

The optimized orbital exponents found by Pitzer are: H1s, 1.17; C1s, 5.68; C2s, 1.76; C2p, 1.76. These values may be compared with the values 1.0, 5.7, 1.625, 1.625 given by Slater's rules (Problem 15.27). (Several other SCF MO calculations have been done on methane.)

Next we consider ethane. The most fascinating property of ethane is the barrier to internal rotation about the carbon–carbon single bond. The staggered (equilibrium) conformation of C_2H_6 is more stable than the eclipsed conformation by

$$2.9 \text{ kcal/mole} = 0.13 \text{ eV/molecule} = 0.0047 \text{ hartree/molecule} \qquad \textbf{(15.75)}$$

This fact was discovered in 1936 by J. D. Kemp and Kenneth Pitzer in examining thermodynamic data for ethane. The experimental electronic energy (including nuclear repulsion) of ethane is -80 hartrees $= -2200$ eV. The correlation energy runs one-half to one percent of the total energy of an atom or molecule. Thus we expect the Hartree–Fock energy of ethane to differ by, say, 20 eV from the true molecular electronic energy; this difference is far greater than the barrier height. At first sight, it seems hopeless to expect an SCF MO calculation to give a meaningful result for the ethane barrier.

The minimal-basis-set AO's for ethane are the hydrogen $1s$ orbitals and the carbon $1s$, $2s$, and $2p$ orbitals, a total of $6(1) + 2(5) = 16$ basis AO's. To calculate the barrier in ethane, one must calculate the energy of the staggered and the eclipsed conformations, which requires two separate SCF calculations. One first forms appropriate linear combinations of the hydrogen AO's and of the carbon AO's to get symmetry-adapted orbitals. The Roothaan equations are then solved iteratively to give the orbital coefficients and orbital energies and the total molecular energy is found. We omit details and simply list the energy results from several SCF MO calculations (Table 15.2). All the calculations listed are many-center ones.

Table 15.2 SCF MO Calculations of Ethane

Reference[1]	Basis Functions	Eclipsed Energy (hartrees)	Staggered Energy (hartrees)	Barrier (kcal/mole)
Pitzer and Lipscomb	16 STO's	-78.98593	-78.99115	3.3
Pitzer	16 STO's	-79.09233	-79.09797	3.5
Clementi and Davis	86 GTO's	-79.10247	-79.10824	3.6
Fink and Allen	110 GTO's	-79.14377	-79.14778	2.5
Veillard	120 GTO's	-79.23410	-79.23899	3.07
Clementi and Popkie	150 GTO's	-79.25364	-79.25875	3.21
Experimental values			-79.84	2.93 ± 0.03

[1] R. M. Pitzer and W. N. Lipscomb, *J. Chem. Phys.*, **39**, 1995 (1963); R. M. Pitzer, *ibid.*, **47**, 965 (1967); E. Clementi and D. R. Davis, *ibid.*, **45**, 2593 (1966); W. H. Fink and L. C. Allen, *ibid.*, **46**, 2261 (1967); A. Veillard, *Theor. Chim. Acta*, **18**, 21 (1970); E. Clementi and H. Popkie, *J. Chem. Phys.*, **57**, 4870 (1972). Experimental barrier: S. Weiss and G. E. Leroi, *ibid.*, **48**, 962 (1968).

The pioneering ethane calculation is by Russell Pitzer (Kenneth Pitzer's son) and W. N. Lipscomb. They used a minimal basis set of 16 STO's; the orbital exponents were not optimized, but were chosen according to Slater's rules; all integrals were evaluated accurately. The Pitzer calculation is similar to the Pitzer–Lipscomb calculation, except that the orbital exponents used are those that minimize the energy of methane.

The first four calculations listed used the experimentally observed equilibrium geometry for staggered ethane and assumed the geometry of the eclipsed form to be that given by rigidly rotating one methyl group with respect to the other. Veillard varied the bond angles and the CC bond length for each conformation. He found an increase of 0.02 Å in the CC length and a decrease of $\frac{1}{2}°$ in the HCH angle on going from the staggered to the eclipsed form; this change affected the barrier by $\frac{1}{2}$ kcal/mole. Clementi and Popkie's near-Hartree–Fock calculation also uses geometry optimization.

All the SCF MO calculations give good values of the ethane rotational barrier. Why should this be so? The answer lies in the correlation energy. Electrons paired in the same localized orbital move through the same region of space. Hence the intraorbital correlation for such a pair should be substantially greater than the interorbital correlation energy for two electrons in different localized MO's. In line with this, it was formerly believed that the total interorbital molecular correlation energy was much less than the total intraorbital correlation energy. However, there are many more interorbital pair correlations than intraorbital correlations, and it is now recognized that the total interorbital correlation is not negligible, and in some cases can be of comparable magnitude to the total intraorbital correlation. [See E. Steiner, *J. Chem. Phys.*, **54**, 1114 (1971).] Hence we must consider both kinds of correlation in ethane. Rotation of a methyl group in ethane does not change any of the bonds and thus intraorbital correlation should be essentially the same in the staggered and eclipsed forms. Moreover, we expect most of the interorbital correlations to be essentially unchanged in the two forms. In particular, correlations between the C—H bonds within each methyl group should remain virtually the same, and so should correlations between the C—C and C—H bonding pairs. It is only the correlations between C—H pairs of different methyl groups that should change, and these make the smallest contributions to interorbital correlation. Thus we expect the total correlation energy to be only very slightly changed from staggered to eclipsed. Thus the energy error in an SCF calculation is about the same for the two forms, and the Hartree–Fock energy difference should yield a good estimate of the barrier. None of the SCF calculations listed in Table 15.2 have actually reached the Hartree–Fock limit, but they still yield good values for the barrier. (Recall that Hartree–Fock calculations give poor values for dissociation energies. This is because the number of electron pairs changes in forming a chemical bond from atoms, thereby changing the correlation energy substantially.)

Rotational barriers in other molecules have been studied by the MO method.[12] Allen and co-workers used the Gaussian-lobe SCF MO method to calculate barriers. Some of their results are (values in kcal/mole): C_2H_6, 2.5 calculated versus 2.9 experimental; C_2H_5F, 2.6 calculated versus 3.3 experimental; CH_3CHO, 0.8 calculated versus 1.2 experimental; CH_3NH_2, 2.4 calculated versus 2.0 experimental; CH_3OH, 1.06 calculated versus 1.07 experimental.

Table 15.2 shows that for ethane a reasonably accurate barrier can be gotten with an SCF calculation that has a minimal basis set and doesn't use geometry optimization, and this is true for most barriers investigated. For H_2O_2 such calculations give quite poor barrier results. However, when a large basis set and

---

[12] For summaries of SCF MO barrier calculations, see W. H. Fink, D. C. Pan, and L. C. Allen, *J. Chem. Phys.*, **47**, 895 (1967); L. C. Allen, *Chem. Phys. Letters*, **2**, 597 (1968).

geometry optimization are used, the H_2O_2 barriers can be calculated by the Hartree–Fock method, as shown by the following results [T. H. Dunning and N. W. Winter, *Chem. Phys. Letters*, **11**, 194 (1971)]: calculated *cis* barrier (0° dihedral angle) 8.4 kcal/mole versus 7.0–7.6 kcal/mole experimental; calculated *trans* barrier (180° dihedral angle) 1.1 kcal/mole versus 1.1 kcal/mole experimental; calculated equilibrium dihedral angle 114° versus 112° experimental.

The physical origin of the ethane rotational barrier appears to be due mainly to the Pauli exclusion principle repulsion (Section 10.4) between the eclipsing localized C—H bonding electron pairs in eclipsed ethane. [See O. J. Sovers, C. W. Kern, R. M. Pitzer, and M. Karplus, *J. Chem. Phys.*, **49**, 2592 (1968).] In contrast, in acetaldehyde the barrier seems to be due to loss of the attraction between the electronegative oxygen and the methyl group in the more stable H-eclipsing-O conformation. [W. L. Jorgensen and L. C. Allen, *J. Am. Chem. Soc.*, **93**, 567 (1971).]

Finally, consider the SCF MO treatment of ethylene. The ground-state equilibrium-geometry point group is $\mathcal{D}_{2h}$. The standard choice of coordinate axes is shown in Fig. 15.10. (Unfortunately, the standard convention has often been ignored, and one finds calculations with the molecular plane being the xz or the xy plane; this affects the naming of the MO symmetry species, so that different workers use different symbols for the same MO.)

There are eight symmetry operations for $\mathcal{D}_{2h}$. Each symmetry operation commutes with every other symmetry operation, so that the electronic wave function must be an eigenfunction of all the symmetry operators, and we have only nondegenerate (A and B) symmetry species. The three rotations, the three reflections, and the inversion operation each have their squares equal to the identity operation, so that these symmetry operations must have the eigenvalues ± 1. All eight symmetry operations can be expressed as the product of one, two, or three of the reflections (each reflection simply converts one coordinate to its negative):

$$\hat{E} = [\hat{\sigma}(xy)]^2, \qquad \hat{\imath} = \hat{\sigma}(xy)\,\hat{\sigma}(xz)\,\hat{\sigma}(yz)$$

$$\hat{C}_2(x) = \hat{\sigma}(xy)\,\hat{\sigma}(xz), \qquad \hat{C}_2(y) = \hat{\sigma}(xy)\,\hat{\sigma}(yz), \qquad \hat{C}_2(z) = \hat{\sigma}(xz)\,\hat{\sigma}(yz)$$

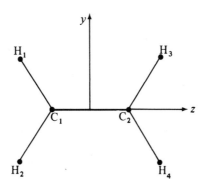

FIGURE 15.10 *Coordinate axes for ethylene. The x axis is perpendicular to the molecular plane.*

Since the symmetry eigenvalues multiply the same way the symmetry operations do, specification of the eigenvalues of the three reflections is sufficient to fix all eight symmetry eigenvalues. There are thus $2^3 = 8$ possible symmetry species. The standard notation for these is:

	$\hat{\sigma}(xy)$	$\hat{\sigma}(xz)$	$\hat{\sigma}(yz)$	
A_g	$+1$	$+1$	$+1$	
A_u	-1	-1	-1	
B_{1g}	$+1$	-1	-1	
B_{1u}	-1	$+1$	$+1$	(15.76)
B_{2g}	-1	$+1$	-1	
B_{2u}	$+1$	-1	$+1$	
B_{3g}	-1	-1	$+1$	
B_{3u}	$+1$	$+1$	-1	

The g or u subscript corresponds to eigenvalue $+1$ or -1 for $\hat{\imath}$. For $\mathscr{D}_{2h}$, the designation A is used only for symmetry species with eigenvalue $+1$ for all three $\hat{C}_2$ rotations.

There are 14 minimal-basis-set AO's. It it easy to set up symmetry orbitals by trial and error; the reader will readily verify the symmetry species of the following (unnormalized) symmetry orbitals:

Symmetry Orbital	Symmetry Species	
$H_1 1s + H_2 1s + H_3 1s + H_4 1s$	a_g	
$C_1 1s + C_2 1s$	a_g	
$C_1 2s + C_2 2s$	a_g	
$C_1 2p_z - C_2 2p_z$	a_g	
$H_1 1s + H_2 1s - H_3 1s - H_4 1s$	b_{1u}	
$C_1 1s - C_2 1s$	b_{1u}	
$C_1 2s - C_2 2s$	b_{1u}	(15.77)
$C_1 2p_z + C_2 2p_z$	b_{1u}	
$H_1 1s - H_2 1s + H_3 1s - H_4 1s$	b_{2u}	
$C_1 2p_y + C_2 2p_y$	b_{2u}	
$H_1 1s - H_2 1s - H_3 1s + H_4 1s$	b_{3g}	
$C_1 2p_y - C_2 2p_y$	b_{3g}	
$C_1 2p_x + C_2 2p_x$	b_{3u}	
$C_1 2p_x - C_2 2p_x$	b_{2g}	

The 14 lowest MO's thus include four a_g, four b_{1u}, two b_{2u}, two b_{3g}, one b_{3u}, and one b_{2g} MO. In the ground state, eight of these MO's are occupied. SCF calculations[13] yield the following configuration for the ^1A_g ground state:

$$(1a_g)^2 (1b_{1u})^2 (2a_g)^2 (2b_{1u})^2 (1b_{2u})^2 (3a_g)^2 (1b_{3g})^2 (1b_{3u})^2 \qquad (15.78)$$

[13] U. Kaldor and I. Shavitt, J. Chem. Phys., 48, 191 (1968).

Chemists traditionally classify each MO of a planar molecule as σ or π, according to whether its eigenvalue for reflection in the molecular plane is $+1$ or -1. (This usage is somewhat inconsistent with the $\sigma, \pi, \delta, \ldots$ classification of linear-molecule MO's. For linear molecules, the symbols σ and π signify an axial component of electronic orbital angular momentum of 0, and $\pm\hbar$, respectively; for nonlinear molecules, one cannot specify the component of **L** along an internuclear line. For linear molecules, σ MO's are nondegenerate and π MO's are doubly degenerate; for nonlinear molecules, the σ–π classification is unrelated to the degeneracy.) For the ground state of water, all the occupied MO's are σ MO's, except the lone-pair $1b_1$ MO, which is a π MO.

For ethylene, the only occupied π MO in the ground electronic state is the $1b_{3u}$ MO, the highest occupied MO. Since there is only one b_{3u} symmetry orbital in (15.77), the $1b_{3u}$ MO must be identical (apart from a normalization constant) to this symmetry orbital. One finds (using STO's):

$$1b_{3u} = 0.63(C_1 2p_x + C_2 2p_x) \tag{15.79}$$

This bonding MO formed by overlap of the $2p_x$ AO's of carbon resembles the π_u MO of Fig. 13.14. The $1b_{3u}$ pi MO accounts for the planarity of ethylene in its ground state. As one CH_2 group is rotated relative to the other, the overlap between the two carbon $2p_x$ AO's rapidly diminishes and the energy of the $1b_{3u}$ MO increases; hence the molecule shows a considerable resistance to torsion about the carbon–carbon bond.

The lowest-lying unoccupied MO of ethylene is the $1b_{2g}$ antibonding π MO:

$$1b_{2g} = 0.82(C_1 2p_x - C_2 2p_x) \tag{15.80}$$

It resembles the π_g MO in Fig. 13.14. The excited ethylene configuration

$$(1a_g)^2 \cdots (1b_{3g})^2 (1b_{3u})(1b_{2g}) \tag{15.81}$$

gives rise to two terms (a singlet and a triplet) and it is likely that these electronic states have a nonplanar configuration, with one CH_2 group rotated 90° with respect to the other.

The canonical σ MO's of ethylene each contain contributions from AO's of all six atoms and are delocalized over the whole molecule. By taking appropriate linear combinations of the canonical σ MO's, one can form localized σ MO's; we expect these MO's to consist of the following inner-shell and bonding MO's:

$$i(C_1), \quad i(C_2) \tag{15.82}$$

$$b(C_1C_2), \quad b(C_1H_1), \quad b(C_1H_2), \quad b(C_2H_3), \quad b(C_2H_4) \tag{15.83}$$

The MO's $b(C_1C_2)$ and $1b_{3u}$ constitute the familiar description of the carbon–carbon double bond as one sigma and one pi bond (Fig. 15.11). We still do not, however, have the equivalent MO's of ethylene, since the π MO $1b_{3u}$ is not equivalent to any of the σ MO's in (15.83), nor is it equivalent to itself—it goes into its negative upon a $\hat{C}_2(z)$ rotation. By adding and subtracting the $b(C_1C_2)$ and $1b_{3u}$ MO's, we can form two equivalent localized carbon–carbon bonding MO's:

$$b_1(C_1C_2) = 2^{-1/2}[b(C_1C_2) + 1b_{3u}] \tag{15.84}$$

$$b_2(C_1C_2) = 2^{-1/2}[b(C_1C_2) - 1b_{3u}] \tag{15.85}$$

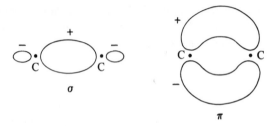

FIGURE 15.11 *σ–π description of the ethylene double bond. The cross sections are taken in the plane perpendicular to the molecular plane, which is a nodal plane for the pi* MO.

The MO's (15.84) and (15.85) lead to the description of the carbon–carbon bond as composed of two "banana" bonds (Fig. 15.12).

There has been considerable controversy as to whether the ethylene double bond is best described as two equivalent bent banana bonds or as a σ and a π bond. Kaldor[14] calculated the energy-localized MO's of ethylene from the minimal-basis-set canonical SCF MO's. Since there is no *a priori* necessity that the energy-localized MO's be equivalent orbitals, this calculation provides evidence as to which is the "better" description of the carbon–carbon double bond. Kaldor found the energy-localized carbon–carbon bond orbitals in ethylene to be the two equivalent banana bonds. For acetylene, he found the energy-localized carbon–carbon bond orbitals to be three equivalent banana bonds, and not one σ and two π bonds. Of course, although the electron densities in the individual MO's differ for the banana-bond versus σ–π descriptions, the total probability density for the 4 or 6 electrons in the double or triple bond is the same in either picture.

The energy-localized C_1H_1 bond MO in ethylene was found by Kaldor to be

$$0.373(C_1\,2s) + 0.414(C_1\,2p_y) - 0.257(C_1\,2p_z) + 0.494(H_1\,1s) + \cdots$$

where the dots indicate small contributions from other AO's. From Problem 15.61, the ratio of $2p_y$ to $2p_z$ orbital coefficients in an sp^2 hybrid atomic orbital is 1.73:1;

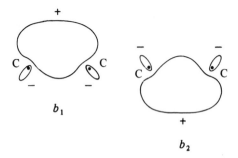

FIGURE 15.12 *Banana-bond description of the ethylene double bond. (Cross sections as in Fig. 15.11.)*

[14] U. Kaldor, *J. Chem. Phys.*, **46**, 1981 (1967).

for $b(C_1H_1)$ this ratio is $1.61:1$, so that the hybridization of carbon is very close to sp^2 in this MO. The angle made by $b(C_1H_1)$ with the C—C axis is $\pi - \arctan(1.61) = 122°$, essentially the same as the experimental angle; hence the localized C—H bond orbitals are not bent in planar ethylene.

Localized MO's for butadiene and benzene are discussed at the end of Section 15.8.

15.7 Molecular Geometry

Allen and co-workers did *ab initio* calculations to test the adequacy of SCF MO calculations for predicting molecular equilibrium geometries.[15] As basis functions, they used Gaussian-lobe representations of AO's; the AO's used were those found to give accurate representations of the Hartree–Fock wave functions of the atoms of the molecule.

The total molecular energy is found to be relatively insensitive to even large changes in molecular geometry. For example, the calculated SCF electronic energy (including nuclear repulsion) of F_2O as a function of the F—O—F angle is[16]

Bond Angle	60°	80°	102°	120°	180°
Energy (Hartrees)	−273.05	−273.36	−273.41	−273.39	−273.20

The variation in energy over the range of bond angles is 0.1 percent, as compared to an expected correlation energy of perhaps 1 percent. Similar small variations in SCF energy are found for changes in bond lengths. Moskowitz and Harrison found for water at the 105° bond angle:

Bond Distance (Å)	0.846	0.952	1.058
Energy (Hartrees)	−76.0054	−76.0336	−76.0123

Despite the smallness of these changes in total energy, as compared to the energy error (the correlation energy) inherent in the SCF method, SCF wave functions give good predictions (1–2% error) of equilibrium bond angles and distances. Some results are[16]:

Molecule	H_2O	F_2O	Li_2O	O_3	N_3^-
Predicted Angle	110°	102°	180°	$118\frac{1}{2}°$	180°
Observed Angle	104.5°	103°	180°	117°	180°

---

[15] For a summary, see "A New Approach to Many-Electron Theory," by L. C. Allen, in *Quantum Theory of Atoms, Molecules, and the Solid State*, P.-O. Löwdin, ed., Academic Press, New York, 1966, pp. 39–80.

[16] References for this work are given in footnote 12 of L. C. Allen, *Theor. Chim. Acta*, **24**, 117 (1972).

Evidently, the correlation energy remains approximately constant for bond angle and length variations in the region of the equilibrium geometry, and the SCF potential-energy surface, although lying above the true potential-energy surface, is approximately parallel to it.

A molecule of considerable interest to organic chemists is the reaction intermediate CH_2, the methylene radical. Experimental and theoretical work are in agreement that the CH_2 ground state is a triplet. The first spectroscopic observations on CH_2 were interpreted as indicating a linear ground state; however, accurate theoretical calculations indicated a bent molecule. Further experimental work showed that indeed the molecule is bent with a bond angle $138° \pm 10°$. A CI calculation on CH_2 using 617 configurations gives a ground-state triplet bond angle of $134°$, estimated to be reliable to within $2°$. [See D. R. McLaughlin, C. F. Bender, and H. F. Schaefer, *Theor. Chim. Acta*, **25**, 352 (1972) and references cited therein.]

Accurate SCF MO calculations for large molecules are difficult. We want a simple procedure that will give reasonably accurate predictions of bond angles. One such procedure is the *valence-shell electron-pair repulsion* (VSEPR) theory. This theory originated with Sidgwick and Powell in 1940. Gillespie has done much to extend and popularize it.[17] The VSEPR viewpoint is even displacing the traditional VB hybridization explanation (Section 15.10) in freshman-chemistry discussions of bond angles.

We saw in Section 15.5 that the energy-localized MO's for the 8 valence-shell electrons of water consist of two bonding orbitals $b(OH_1)$ and $b(OH_2)$ and two lone-pair MO's $l_1(O)$ and $l_2(O)$; roughly speaking, these four MO's are tetrahedrally disposed about the oxygen atom. (Actually, the bonding MO's are separated by $95°$ and the lone-pair MO's by $122°$.) Similarly, the energy-localized MO's found by Edmiston and Ruedenberg for the valence-shell electrons of NH_3 consist of three bonding MO's making angles of $104\frac{1}{2}°$ with each other, and a lone-pair MO making an angle of $114°$ with each bonding localized MO. Again, these four MO's are approximately tetrahedrally disposed.

The VSEPR method considers the bonding and lone-pair electrons of the central atom's valence shell and the bonding electrons of the attached ligands; these electrons are then paired and the electron pairs arranged in space so as to minimize the repulsions between the localized MO's of the various pairs. [Recall that the condition for the energy-localized MO's is the minimization of (15.43).] More important than the Coulombic repulsion between localized pairs is the Pauli repulsion (Section 10.4) which forces electrons with like spins to keep apart; each localized pair contains electrons with both possible spin values and thus excludes other electrons from the space it occupies. Note that the VSEPR method is based on electron pair–electron pair repulsions (where the pairs are bond or lone pairs) rather than ligand atom–ligand atom repulsions.

For 4 pairs of electrons, the minimum repulsion occurs with the 4 MO's disposed tetrahedrally about the central atom. The most favorable arrangements

[17] R. J. Gillespie, *J. Chem. Educ.*, **40**, 295 (1963); **47**, 18 (1970); *Can. J. Chem.*, **38**, 818 (1960); *Angew. Chem. Intern. Ed. Engl.*, **6**, 819 (1967).

for various numbers of electron pairs are (see Fig. 15.13):

2	3	4	5	6	8
straight line	equilateral triangle	tetrahedron	trigonal bipyramid	octahedron	square antiprism

Consider some examples. For water, there are 8 valence electrons, and we have two bonding pairs and two lone pairs arranged tetrahedrally. The bond angle should be close to the $109\frac{1}{2}°$ tetrahedral angle. To explain the deviation of the bond angle ($104\frac{1}{2}°$) from tetrahedral, the VSEPR approach points out that since lone-pair orbitals are under the influence of only one nucleus (rather than two), they are "fatter" (more spread out) than bonding orbitals; hence lone-pair electrons exert greater repulsions on neighboring pairs than bonding pairs exert on neighboring pairs. The angle between the lone pairs of water is thus greater than tetrahedral, while the angle between the bonding pairs is less than tetrahedral. This view is confirmed by the values of 122° and 95° found for the angles between the lone-pair and bonding energy-localized MO's of water. [The "fatness" of lone-pair MO's is illustrated by the greater contribution of the $2s$ oxygen AO to the lone-pair water MO's than to the bonding MO's—see Eq. (15.45).] For ammonia, the 4 valence pairs are arranged approximately tetrahedrally; since there is only one lone pair instead of two, the bonding pairs are not pushed together as much as in the case of water, and the observed bond angle (107°) is closer to tetrahedral than for water.

For IF_5, there are $\frac{1}{2}(7+5) = 6$ pairs arranged octahedrally. One pair is a lone pair, giving the observed square-pyramidal structure. For XeF_4, there are $\frac{1}{2}(8+4) = 6$ pairs arranged octahedrally; the two fat lone pairs are directed toward opposite vertices of the octahedron, giving the observed square-planar structure.

For ClF_3, there are $\frac{1}{2}(7+3) = 5$ pairs. The two "fat" lone pairs are placed so as to minimize the repulsions. A trigonal bipyramid has three equatorial and

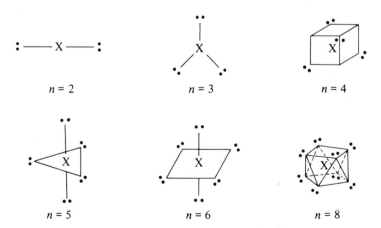

FIGURE 15.13 *Preferred arrangements for n electron pairs about a central atom* X.

two axial positions. An axial electron pair makes an angle of 90° with 3 neighboring pairs; an equatorial pair makes an angle of 90° with only two neighboring pairs and an angle of 120° with 2 other neighboring pairs. The repulsions fall off rapidly with increasing angle, so that the most favorable arrangement is with the two lone pairs of ClF_3 each in equatorial positions. This gives the molecule a (planar) T structure (Fig. 15.14). The observed slight distortion of $2\frac{1}{2}°$ from the T structure is explained by the fat lone pairs pushing the bonding axial pairs toward the bonding equatorial pair.

The $TaF_8{}^{3-}$ ion has $\frac{1}{2}(5+3+8) = 8$ valence-shell pairs and has the square-antiprism structure.

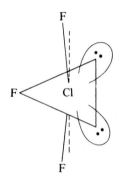

FIGURE 15.14   VSEPR *explanation of the structure of* ClF_3.

For molecules with multiple bonds, Gillespie recommends that for simplicity a double or triple bond be considered as a single electron pair. For example, for $CH_2\!=\!CH_2$, the expected bond angles are all 120°, since each carbon is to be considered as surrounded by 3 electron pairs. The observed H—C—H angle of about 116° can be explained by the double-bond electrons pushing together the single-bond pairs. An alternative view (which is more consistent with the energy-localized MO's of ethylene) is to consider the double bond as two electron pairs forming two banana bonds which start out from each carbon atom at roughly the tetrahedral angle (the angle between the energy-localized banana bonds in ethylene is 112°); with 4 pairs about each carbon, the expected H—C—H angle is $109\frac{1}{2}°$; the observed angle results from the banana double-bond orbitals exerting less repulsion on the bonding C—H pairs than would two ordinary tetrahedrally directed orbitals.

XeF_6 has $\frac{1}{2}(8+6) = 7$ valence-shell pairs about Xe. The most favorable arrangement for 7 electron pairs is not certain, since it depends on the specific form of the effective repulsive forces between the pairs. However, with 7 pairs, the VSEPR approach predicts that the molecule will certainly not be octahedral. Electron-diffraction results do indicate that XeF_6 is not octahedral, but the departure from the octahedral structure is less than would be expected on the VSEPR model. The final word on the XeF_6 structure is yet to be said. [See G. L. Goodman, *J. Chem. Phys.*, **56**, 5038 (1972); H. H. Claasen, G. L. Goodman, and H. Kim, *ibid.*, **56**, 5042; and references cited in these papers.] The molecule IF_7 is a somewhat deformed pentagonal bipyramid [W. J. James, H. B. Thompson, and L. S. Bartell, *J. Chem. Phys.*, **53**, 4040 (1970).]

The arrangements of Fig. 15.13 assume that the inner shells of the central atom are spherically symmetric and so do not affect the arrangement of the valence pairs. Recall (Section 11.1) that filled and half-filled subshells give spherically symmetric probability densities. Hence Fig. 15.13 applies to main-group elements (which all have filled inner subshells) and applies to those transition elements with d^0, d^5, or d^{10} subshells. In transition elements with nonspherical d subshells, distortions from the shapes of Fig. 15.13 may be observed.

The VSEPR model has a remarkably high batting average, but is not infallible. Thus $TeCl_6^{-2}$ has 7 electron pairs about Te, but its observed structure is octahedral. Other exceptions are some of the alkaline earth dihalides (e.g. BaF_2, $SrCl_2$) that are bent, rather than linear. Gillespie has discussed the probable reasons for these exceptions in *J. Chem. Educ.*, **47**, 18 (1970).

An alternative approach to predicting molecular geometry is the use of Walsh diagrams of orbital energy versus bond angle. This method is less comprehensive than the VSEPR approach and can be shown to be equivalent to VSEPR. See L. C. Allen, *Theor. Chim. Acta*, **24**, 117 (1972).

15.8 Semiempirical MO Treatments of Planar Conjugated Molecules

The canonical MO's of a planar unsaturated organic molecule can be divided into σ and π MO's (Section 15.6). Semiempirical treatments of planar conjugated organic compounds usually make the approximation of treating the π electrons separately from the σ electrons. This is sometimes justified by arguing that since the π MO's have a node in the molecular plane, the π-electron density is well separated from the σ-electron density. Actually this is false and the σ and π probability densities overlap appreciably. Coulson has stated that the justification for σ–π separability lies in the different symmetry of the σ and π orbitals and in the greater polarizability of the pi electrons, which makes them more susceptible to perturbations such as those occurring in chemical reactions.

In the *pi-electron approximation*, the n_π pi electrons are treated separately by incorporating the effects of the sigma electrons and the nuclei into some sort of effective pi-electron Hamiltonian $\hat{H}_\pi$ (recall the similar valence-electron approximation—Section 13.15):

$$\hat{H}_\pi = \sum_{i=1}^{n_\pi} \hat{H}_{core}(i) + \sum_{i=1}^{n_\pi} \sum_{j>i} \frac{1}{r_{ij}} \tag{15.86}$$

$$\hat{H}_{core}(i) = -\tfrac{1}{2}\nabla_i^2 + V_i \tag{15.87}$$

where V_i is the potential energy of the ith pi electron in the field produced by the nuclei and the σ electrons. The variational principle is then applied to find a pi-electron wave function ψ_π that minimizes the variational integral $\int \psi_\pi^* \hat{H}_\pi \psi_\pi \, d\tau$. The validity of the pi-electron approximation has been discussed by Lykos and

Parr.[18] Since (15.86) is not the true molecular Hamiltonian, the treatments of this section are semiempirical.

Perhaps the simplest semiempirical pi-electron theory is the *free-electron molecular-orbital* (FE MO) *treatment*, developed around 1950 by Kuhn, Bayliss, Platt, and Simpson. Here, the interelectronic repulsions $1/r_{ij}$ are ignored and the effect of the σ electrons is represented by a particle-in-a-box potential-energy function: $V = 0$ in a certain region, while $V = \infty$ outside this region. With the interelectronic repulsions omitted, $\hat{H}_\pi$ is the sum of Hamiltonians for each pi electron; hence (Section 6.2):

$$\hat{H}_\pi \psi_\pi = E_\pi \psi_\pi \tag{15.88}$$

$$\psi_\pi = \prod_{i=1}^{n_\pi} \varphi_i \tag{15.89}$$

$$\hat{H}_{\text{core}}(i)\,\varphi_i = e_i \varphi_i \tag{15.90}$$

$$E_\pi = \sum_{i=1}^{n_\pi} e_i \tag{15.91}$$

The wave function (15.89) takes no account of spin or the Pauli principle. To do so, we must put each electron in a spin-orbital $\lambda_i = \varphi_i \chi_i$ where χ_i is a spin function (either α or β). The wave function ψ_π is then written as an antisymmetrized product (Slater determinant) of spin-orbitals. Since $\hat{H}_{\text{core}}(i)$ doesn't involve spin, we have

$$\hat{H}_{\text{core}}(i)\,\lambda_i = e_i \lambda_i \tag{15.92}$$

Each term in the antisymmetrized product function ψ_π has each electron in a different spin-orbital (see for example 10.68). When $\hat{H}_\pi$, which is being approximated as the sum of the $\hat{H}_{\text{core}}(i)$'s, acts on each term in ψ_π it gives the sum of the e_i's. Hence $\hat{H}_\pi \psi_\pi$ equals $\sum_i e_i \psi_\pi$ and (15.91) still holds when spin and the Pauli principle are allowed for.

For conjugated chain molecules, the FE MO approximation takes the box in which the pi electrons move as one dimensional. We have

$$e_i = \frac{n_i^2 h^2}{8ml^2}, \qquad n_i = 1, 2, \ldots \tag{15.93}$$

The n_i's are restricted by the Pauli principle—no more than two electrons can be in a given spatial MO. In the ground electronic state, the pi electrons fill the $\frac{1}{2}n_\pi$ lowest free-electron pi MO's.

The pi-electron transition giving the lowest-frequency electronic absorption involves an electron going from the highest occupied to the lowest vacant MO—Fig. 15.15. (The particle-in-a-box selection rule allows the quantum number of an electron in the FE MO model to change by an odd integer, as shown in *Pilar*, p. 125; hence the transition of Fig. 15.15 is allowed.) For the wavelength λ of this transition, the FE MO model gives

$$\frac{1}{\lambda} = \frac{1}{hc}(e_{n_\pi/2+1} - e_{n_\pi/2}) = \frac{h}{8mcl^2}(n_\pi + 1) \tag{15.94}$$

---

[18] See *Parr*, pp. 41–45, 211–218; *Pilar*, Section 18-1.

$$n$$

5 ————

4 ——

3 ——•—•—

2 ——•—•—

1 ——•—•—

FIGURE 15.15   *The longest wavelength* FE MO *electronic transition in a conjugated molecule with six pi electrons.*

We shall apply the FE MO model to the conjugated polyenes

$$CH_2=[CH\!-\!CH=]_kCH_2 \tag{15.95}$$

We take l as the zig-zag length along the carbon chain. (Another possibility is to use the direct distance between the end carbons.) Let l_1 and l_2 be the carbon–carbon single- and double-bond lengths in (15.95). For *s-trans*-1,3-butadiene these values are[19] 1.46 and 1.34 Å. (The term "*s-trans*" refers to the configuration about the single bond:

s-trans   *s-cis*

The *s-trans* configuration is the one observed for 1,3-butadiene.[20]) We shall allow the π electrons to move a bit beyond the ends of the carbon chain by adding in a distance $\frac{3}{4}l_1+\frac{1}{4}l_2$ at each end. This is about one average bond length, and allows for the fact that the MO's are not confined to the regions between the bonding atoms. We have

$$l = kl_1 + (k+1)l_2 + \tfrac{3}{2}l_1 + \tfrac{1}{2}l_2 = (k+\tfrac{3}{2})(l_1+l_2)$$

$$= \tfrac{1}{2}(n_C+1)(l_1+l_2) \tag{15.96}$$

---

[19] K. Kuchitsu, F. Tsutomu, and Y. Morino, *J. Mol. Struct.*, **1**, 463 (1967).

[20] D. R. Lide, *J. Chem. Phys.*, **37**, 2074 (1962). *Ab initio* CI calculations [S. Shih, R. J. Buenker, and S. D. Peyerimhoff, *Chem. Phys. Letters*, **16**, 244 (1972)] indicate that the *s-trans* form is more stable by about 4.6 kcal/mole, which (if accurate) means that about 0.05% of the *s-cis* form is present at 25°C.

where n_C is the number of carbons. Using (15.94), (15.96), and $n_\pi = n_C$, we have

$$\frac{1}{\lambda} = \frac{h}{2mc(l_1+l_2)^2(n_C+1)} = \frac{1}{n_C+1} \times 155{,}000 \text{ cm}^{-1} \tag{15.97}$$

The observed[21] first electronic absorption bands for the conjugated polyenes (15.95) decrease monotonically from $1/\lambda = 61{,}500 \text{ cm}^{-1}$ to $1/\lambda = 22{,}400 \text{ cm}^{-1}$ as k goes from 0 to 9. The FE MO Eq. (15.97) does correctly predict the trend of increasing wavelength with increasing chain length, but quantitative agreement with experiment is quite poor; the predicted values have a whopping $15{,}000 \text{ cm}^{-1}$ standard deviation from observed polyene bands. This disagreement is hardly surprising in view of the crudity of the model. [The first excited FE MO configuration gives rise to two electronic terms, a singlet and a triplet. In the FE MO model, neglect of electronic repulsions gives the singlet and triplet terms the same energy. The observed longest wavelength electronic transition is a singlet-singlet transition, since singlet-triplet transitions are forbidden. Strictly speaking, one should compare (15.97) with the average of the singlet-singlet and singlet-triplet energy differences.]

The FE MO model of the polyenes can be improved. We expect the pi-electron probability density to be greater in the double-bond regions than in the single-bond regions. To allow for this, Kuhn replaced the $V = 0$ part of the free-electron potential-energy function by a sine curve with minima at the double-bond centers, maxima at the single-bond centers, and length given by (15.96); V goes to infinity at each end of the curve. For

$$V = V_0 \sin \frac{2\pi x}{l_1+l_2} \tag{15.98}$$

the Schroedinger equation can't be solved in analytic form. Kuhn used an analog computer to find numerical values of the energy levels; the values for the longest wavelength transitions of the polyenes (15.95) are accurately reproduced by the following formula[22]:

$$\frac{1}{\lambda} = \frac{1}{n_C+1} \times 155{,}000 \text{ cm}^{-1} + \frac{0.83V_0}{hc}\left(1 - \frac{1}{n_C}\right) \tag{15.99}$$

With $V_0 = 0$, Eq. (15.99) reduces to (15.97). With $V_0 = 2.4 \text{ eV}$, Eq. (15.99) gives a good fit to the polyene data; the standard deviation is only 1600 cm^{-1}.

Although the simple FE MO method fares poorly for the conjugated polyenes, it should work better for polymethine ions with the formula

$$(CH_3)_2\overset{+}{N}{=}CH({-}CH{=}CH)_k{-}\overset{..}{N}(CH_3)_2 \tag{15.100}$$

Here the carbon–carbon bond lengths are all equal. (There is an equivalent VB resonance structure with carbon–carbon single and double bonds interchanged and the charge on the other nitrogen.) We shall assume the carbon–carbon bond length

---

[21] See H. Suzuki, *Electronic Absorption Spectra*, Academic Press, 1967, p. 204.
[22] H. Kuhn, *Fortschritte der Chemie Organischer Naturstoffe*, **17**, 404 (1959)—this is a review article with many references; *J. Chem. Phys.*, **17**, 1198 (1949).

to be 1.40 Å as in benzene. We shall not worry about the small difference in carbon–nitrogen and carbon–carbon bond lengths. Adding in an extra bond length at each end of the chain, we set $l = (2k+4)(1.40 \text{ Å})$ and $n_\pi = 2k+4$ in (15.94) to get

$$\frac{1}{\lambda} = \frac{h}{8mc(1.96 \text{ Å}^2)}\frac{2k+5}{(2k+4)^2} = \frac{(2k+5)}{(2k+4)^2} \times 155{,}000 \text{ cm}^{-1} \qquad \textbf{(15.101)}$$

The observed [23] $1/\lambda$ values decrease monotonically from 44,600 cm^{-1} to 11,800 cm^{-1} as k goes from 0 to 6. Values calculated from (15.101) are in pretty good agreement with experiment, the standard deviation being 2300 cm^{-1}.

The FE MO model and its refined versions have been applied to conjugated ring hydrocarbons with reasonable success, but we omit any discussion (see Problem 15.32).

The most celebrated semiempirical pi-electron theory is the *Hückel molecular-orbital* (HMO) *method*, developed in the 1930's. Here, the pi-electron Hamiltonian (15.86) is approximated by the simpler form

$$\hat{H}_\pi = \sum_{i=1}^{n_\pi} \hat{H}^{\text{eff}}(i) \qquad \textbf{(15.102)}$$

where $\hat{H}^{\text{eff}}(i)$ somehow incorporates the effects of the pi-electron repulsions in an average way. This sounds rather vague, and in fact the Hückel method does not specify any explicit form for $\hat{H}^{\text{eff}}(i)$. Since the Hückel pi-electron Hamiltonian is the sum of one-electron Hamiltonians, a separation of variables is possible, as in FE MO theory. Equations (15.89) and (15.91) hold, where the Hückel MO's satisfy

$$\hat{H}^{\text{eff}}(i)\varphi_i = e_i\varphi_i \qquad \textbf{(15.103)}$$

Since $\hat{H}^{\text{eff}}$ is not specified, there is no point in trying to solve (15.103) directly. Instead, the variational method is used.

The next assumption in the HMO method is to approximate the pi MO's as LCAO's. In a minimal-basis-set calculation of a planar conjugated hydrocarbon, the only AO's of pi symmetry are the carbon $2p\pi$ orbitals, where by $2p\pi$ we mean the real $2p$ AO's that are perpendicular to the molecular plane. We thus write

$$\varphi_i = \sum_{r=1}^{n_C} c_{ir}f_r \qquad \textbf{(15.104)}$$

where f_r is a $2p\pi$ AO on the rth carbon atom and n_C is the number of carbon atoms. (15.104) is a linear variation function. The optimum values of the coefficients for the n_C lowest pi MO's satisfy Eq. (8.85):

$$\sum_{s=1}^{n_C} [(H_{rs}^{\text{eff}} - S_{rs}e_i)c_{is}] = 0, \qquad r = 1, 2, ..., n_C \qquad \textbf{(15.105)}$$

where the e_i's are the roots of the secular equation (8.88):

$$\det(H_{rs}^{\text{eff}} - S_{rs}e_i) = 0 \qquad \textbf{(15.106)}$$

The key assumptions in the Hückel theory involve the integrals in (15.106). The integral H_{rr} is assumed to have the same value for every carbon atom in the

---

[23] See Suzuki, *op. cit.*, p. 365.

molecule. (For benzene, the six carbons are equivalent and this is no assumption; for 1,3-butadiene, one would expect H_{rr} for an end carbon and a middle carbon to differ slightly.) Moreover, H_{rr} is assumed to be the same for carbon atoms in different planar hydrocarbons. The integral H_{rs} is assumed to have the same value for any two carbon atoms bonded to each other and to vanish for two nonbonded carbons. The integral S_{rr} is equal to 1, since the AO's are normalized. The overlap integral S_{rs} is assumed to vanish for $r \neq s$. We have

$$H_{rr}^{\text{eff}} = \int f_r^*(i)\, \hat{H}^{\text{eff}}(i)\, f_r(i)\, dv_i \equiv \alpha \qquad (15.107)$$

$$H_{rs}^{\text{eff}} = \int f_r^*(i)\, \hat{H}^{\text{eff}}(i)\, f_s(i)\, dv_i \equiv \beta \quad \text{for } C_r \text{ and } C_s \text{ bonded} \qquad (15.108)$$

$$H_{rs}^{\text{eff}} = 0 \quad \text{for } C_r \text{ and } C_s \text{ not bonded together} \qquad (15.109)$$

$$S_{rs} = \int f_r^*(i)\, f_s(i)\, dv_i = \delta_{rs} \qquad (15.110)$$

$$f_r \equiv C_r 2p\pi \qquad (15.111)$$

The integrals α and β are called the *Coulomb* and *bond integrals*, respectively. (Often β is called the *resonance integral*; however, the term "resonance" is more appropriate to the VB method than to the MO method.) Since carbons not bonded to each other are well separated in space, the assumption (15.109) is reasonable. However, taking the overlap integral as zero for carbons bonded to each other is a poor assumption; for Slater orbitals, S_{rs} for adjacent carbons ranges between 0.2 and 0.3, depending on the bond distance. Inclusion of overlap will be considered later.

To illustrate the HMO method, consider 1,3-butadiene. The only thing of significance in the simple HMO treatment of a planar hydrocarbon is the topology of the carbon-atom framework; by this we mean which carbons are bonded together. No distinction is made between the *s-cis* and *s-trans* forms of butadiene. The numbering of the carbon atoms is

$$\underset{1}{\text{CH}_2}=\underset{2}{\text{CH}}-\underset{3}{\text{CH}}=\underset{4}{\text{CH}_2}$$

The Hückel assumptions give

$$H_{11}^{\text{eff}} = H_{22}^{\text{eff}} = H_{33}^{\text{eff}} = H_{44}^{\text{eff}} = \alpha$$

$$H_{12}^{\text{eff}} = H_{23}^{\text{eff}} = H_{34}^{\text{eff}} = \beta$$

$$H_{13}^{\text{eff}} = H_{14}^{\text{eff}} = H_{24}^{\text{eff}} = 0$$

The secular equation (15.106) is:

$$\begin{vmatrix} \alpha - e_k & \beta & 0 & 0 \\ \beta & \alpha - e_k & \beta & 0 \\ 0 & \beta & \alpha - e_k & \beta \\ 0 & 0 & \beta & \alpha - e_k \end{vmatrix} = 0 \qquad (15.112)$$

We now divide each row of the determinant by β. This divides the determinant by β^4, and since $0/\beta^4 = 0$, Eq. (15.112) becomes

$$\begin{vmatrix} x & 1 & 0 & 0 \\ 1 & x & 1 & 0 \\ 0 & 1 & x & 1 \\ 0 & 0 & 1 & x \end{vmatrix} = 0 \qquad \text{(15.113)}$$

where

$$x \equiv \frac{\alpha - e_k}{\beta}, \qquad e_k = \alpha - \beta x \qquad \text{(15.114)}$$

The secular determinant is a continuant and Eq. (8.56) gives

$$\prod_{j=1}^{4} \left(x - 2 \cos \frac{j\pi}{5} \right) = 0$$

$$x = 2 \cos(j\pi/5), \qquad j = 1, 2, 3, 4 \qquad \text{(15.115)}$$

$$x = -1.618, -0.618, 0.618, 1.618 \qquad \text{(15.116)}$$

Alternatively, one can expand the secular determinant to yield an algebraic equation with the 4 roots

$$x = (3 \pm 5^{1/2})^{1/2}/2^{1/2}, \quad -(3 \pm 5^{1/2})^{1/2}/2^{1/2}$$

$$x = (5^{1/2} \pm 1)/2, \quad -(5^{1/2} \pm 1)/2 \qquad \text{(15.117)}$$

Corresponding to (15.113), the equations for the HMO coefficients of butadiene are

$$\begin{aligned} xc_{j1} + c_{j2} &= 0 \\ c_{j1} + xc_{j2} + c_{j3} &= 0 \\ c_{j2} + xc_{j3} + c_{j4} &= 0 \\ c_{j3} + xc_{j4} &= 0 \end{aligned} \qquad \text{(15.118)}$$

Substituting each of the roots (15.116) in turn, we find (see Section 8.4) as the normalized HMO's:

$$\begin{aligned} \varphi_1 &= 0.372f_1 + 0.602f_2 + 0.602f_3 + 0.372f_4 \\ \varphi_2 &= 0.602f_1 + 0.372f_2 - 0.372f_3 - 0.602f_4 \\ \varphi_3 &= 0.602f_1 - 0.372f_2 - 0.372f_3 + 0.602f_4 \\ \varphi_4 &= 0.372f_1 - 0.602f_2 + 0.602f_3 - 0.372f_4 \end{aligned} \qquad \text{(15.119)}$$

The HMO energies are

$$\begin{aligned} e_1 &= \alpha + 1.618\beta, & e_2 &= \alpha + 0.618\beta \\ e_3 &= \alpha - 0.618\beta, & e_4 &= \alpha - 1.618\beta \end{aligned} \qquad \text{(15.120)}$$

The MO φ_1 in (15.119) has no nodes (other than the molecular plane) and leads to maximum charge buildup between the atoms; clearly this must be the lowest-energy pi MO; its energy is $\alpha + 1.618\beta$ and, therefore, the bond integral β must be negative. [See also Eq. (13.58).] The HMO's and energy levels are sketched in Fig. 15.16. The pattern of nodes is the same as for the FE MO wave functions of butadiene; the number of vertical nodal planes is zero for the ground MO and increases by one for each higher MO. From the figure it is clear that these MO's are orthogonal. We can approximate the energy of an electron in a carbon $2p\pi$ AO by $\int f_i^* \hat{H}^{\mathrm{eff}} f_i \, dv = \alpha$; an HMO is classified as bonding or antibonding according to whether its energy is less than or greater than α.

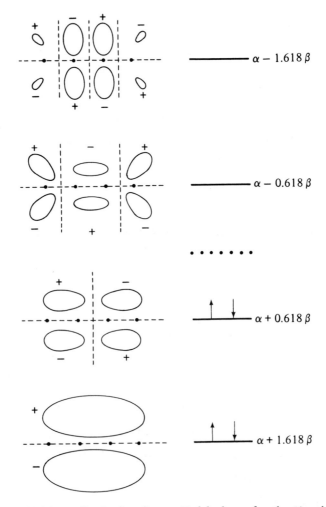

FIGURE 15.16 HMO's *for butadiene. Nodal planes for the pi MO's are indicated by dashed lines. Note the symmetry of the bonding and antibonding energy levels about α (dotted line). The ground-state pi-electron MO configuration is shown.*

For the conjugated polyene (15.95) with n_C carbon atoms, the HMO secular equation involves a continuant similar to (15.113), but of order n_C; Eq. (8.56) with $b = c = 1$, $a = x$, and $n = n_C$ gives $x = 2 \cos [j\pi/(n_C+1)]$, where $j = 1, ..., n_C$. Since the values of x for $j = k$ and for $j = n_C + 1 - k$ are simply the negatives of each other, we can write

$$x = -2 \cos \frac{j\pi}{n_C+1} \tag{15.121}$$

$$e_j = \alpha + 2\beta \cos \frac{j\pi}{n_C+1}, \qquad j = 1, 2, ..., n_C \tag{15.122}$$

Since β is negative, e_1 is the lowest pi energy level. All the pi-electron levels are nondegenerate. The HMO coefficients are (Problem 15.34):

$$c_{jr} = \left(\frac{2}{n_C+1}\right)^{1/2} \sin \frac{jr\pi}{n_C+1} \tag{15.123}$$

In the ground electronic state of (15.95), the highest occupied and lowest vacant pi MO's have $j = \frac{1}{2}n_C$ and $(\frac{1}{2}n_C + 1)$, respectively; HMO theory predicts the longest wavelength band of the electronic absorption spectrum of a conjugated polyene to occur at:

$$\frac{1}{\lambda} = -\frac{4\beta}{hc} \sin \frac{\pi}{2n_C+2} \tag{15.124}$$

where we used

$$\cos a - \cos b = -2 \sin \tfrac{1}{2}(a+b) \sin \tfrac{1}{2}(a-b) \tag{15.125}$$

The bond integral β is a semiempirical parameter and is adjusted to give the best fit to experimental data. If we use the observed butadiene absorption wavelength $\lambda = 2170$ Å, we find $|\beta|/hc = 37,300$ cm^{-1}, $|\beta| = 4.62$ eV. With this value of β we then calculate wavelengths for the polyenes (15.95). The predicted values do show the correct trend of increase in λ with increase in n_C, but agreement with experiment is poor; predicted $1/\lambda$ values show a standard deviation of 9600 cm^{-1} for the first several members of the series.

An obvious defect of the Hückel approximation for conjugated polyenes is the use of a single value of β for each pair of adjacent carbon atoms. The bond lengths in these molecules alternate, and we expect β for doubly bonded carbons to be larger than for singly bonded carbons. The refinement of using two polyene bond integrals β_1 and β_2 for C—C and C=C bonds, respectively, was introduced by Lennard-Jones.[24] With two β's the mathematics becomes complicated, so we shall omit it. With

$$\beta_1 = -3.32 \text{ eV}, \qquad \beta_2 = -4.20 \text{ eV}$$

agreement with experiment is much improved over the single-β predictions. The standard deviation of predicted values is reduced to 3300 cm^{-1}.

---

[24] J. E. Lennard-Jones, *Proc. Roy. Soc.*, **A158**, 280 (1937).

We now consider cyclic conjugated hydrocarbons. For benzene

the HMO secular equation is

$$\begin{vmatrix} x & 1 & 0 & 0 & 0 & 1 \\ 1 & x & 1 & 0 & 0 & 0 \\ 0 & 1 & x & 1 & 0 & 0 \\ 0 & 0 & 1 & x & 1 & 0 \\ 0 & 0 & 0 & 1 & x & 1 \\ 1 & 0 & 0 & 0 & 1 & x \end{vmatrix} = 0 \qquad \textbf{(15.126)}$$

where x is given by (15.114). Equation (8.53) gives

$$\prod_{k=1}^{6} (x + e^{2\pi i k/6} + e^{-2\pi i k/6}) = 0, \qquad i = \sqrt{-1}$$

where we used $\exp(2\pi i k \cdot 5/6) = \exp(-2\pi i k/6)$. We have

$$x = -2 \cos\left(\frac{2\pi k}{6}\right), \qquad k = 1, ..., 6 \qquad \textbf{(15.127)}$$

$$x = -1, +1, +2, +1, -1, -2$$

$$e_i = \alpha + 2\beta, \alpha + \beta, \alpha + \beta, \alpha - \beta, \alpha - \beta, \alpha - 2\beta \qquad \textbf{(15.128)}$$

There are two nondegenerate and two doubly degenerate Hückel levels. Figure 15.17 shows the HMO ground-state pi-electron configuration.

The HMO coefficients can be found by solving the usual set of simultaneous equations, but it is simpler to use molecular symmetry. The $\hat{O}_{C_6}$ symmetry operator

$$\underline{\qquad} \qquad \alpha - 2\beta$$

$$\underline{\qquad} \qquad \underline{\qquad} \qquad \alpha - \beta$$

$$\underline{\uparrow\downarrow} \qquad \underline{\uparrow\downarrow} \qquad \alpha + \beta$$

$$\underline{\uparrow\downarrow} \qquad \alpha + 2\beta$$

FIGURE 15.17   Hückel MO energies for benzene.

commutes with the pi-electron Hamiltonian, so that we can choose each MO to be an eigenfunction of this 60° rotation. Since $(\hat{O}_{C_6})^6 = \hat{1}$, the eigenvalues of $\hat{O}_{C_6}$ are the six sixth roots of unity (Problem 7.13):

$$e^{2\pi i k/6}, \qquad k = 0, 1, ..., 5 \tag{15.129}$$

(Since $\hat{O}_{C_6}$ has some complex eigenvalues, it certainly is not Hermitian; only operators representing physical quantities need be Hermitian, and $\hat{O}_{C_6}$ does not correspond to any physical property of the molecule.) We have [Eq. (15.104)]:

$$\hat{O}_{C_6} \varphi_j = e^{2\pi i k/6} \varphi_j$$

$$\sum_{r=1}^{6} c_{jr} \hat{O}_{C_6} f_r = \sum_{r=1}^{6} c_{jr} e^{2\pi i k/6} f_r$$

$$\sum_{r=1}^{6} c_{jr} f_{r-1} = \sum_{r=1}^{6} c_{jr} e^{2\pi i k/6} f_r$$

$$\sum_{r=1}^{6} c_{j,r+1} f_r = \sum_{r=1}^{6} c_{jr} e^{2\pi i k/6} f_r \tag{15.130}$$

where $f_0 \equiv f_6$ and $c_{j7} \equiv c_{j1}$. Equating the coefficients of corresponding AO's in (15.130), we have

$$c_{j,r+1} = e^{2\pi i k/6} c_{jr} \tag{15.131}$$

The normalization condition that follows from (15.110) is

$$\sum_{r=1}^{6} |c_{jr}|^2 = 1 \tag{15.132}$$

We see from (15.131) that each coefficient in the jth MO has the same absolute value. Hence

$$|c_{jr}| = 1/\sqrt{6}, \qquad r = 1, 2, ..., 6 \tag{15.133}$$

By setting $c_{j1} = 1/\sqrt{6}$ and using (15.131), we have the desired coefficients. To determine which coefficients go with which energy, we evaluate the variational integral:

$$\int \varphi_j^* \hat{H}^{\text{eff}} \varphi_j \, dv = \sum_{r=1}^{6} \sum_{s=1}^{6} c_{jr}^* c_{js} \int f_r^* \hat{H}^{\text{eff}} f_s \, dv$$

$$= \sum_{r=1}^{6} |c_{jr}|^2 \alpha + \sum_{r=1}^{6} c_{jr}^* c_{j,r+1} \beta + \sum_{r=1}^{6} c_{jr}^* c_{j,r-1} \beta$$

$$= \alpha + e^{2\pi i k/6} \sum_{r=1}^{6} |c_{jr}|^2 \beta + e^{-2\pi i k/6} \sum_{r=1}^{6} |c_{jr}|^2 \beta$$

$$= \alpha + 2\beta \cos(2\pi k/6), \qquad k = 0, ..., 5 \tag{15.134}$$

which agrees with (15.128). From (15.131), (15.133), and (15.134), the Hückel

MO's and energies for benzene are

$$\varphi_1 = 6^{-1/2}(f_1+f_2+f_3+f_4+f_5+f_6)$$

$$\varphi_2 = 6^{-1/2}(f_1+e^{\pi i/3}f_2+e^{2\pi i/3}f_3-f_4+e^{4\pi i/3}f_5+e^{5\pi i/3}f_6)$$

$$\varphi_3 = 6^{-1/2}(f_1+e^{-\pi i/3}f_2+e^{-2\pi i/3}f_3-f_4+e^{-4\pi i/3}f_5+e^{-5\pi i/3}f_6)$$

$$\varphi_4 = 6^{-1/2}(f_1+e^{2\pi i/3}f_2+e^{4\pi i/3}f_3+f_4+e^{2\pi i/3}f_5+e^{4\pi i/3}f_6)$$

$$\varphi_5 = 6^{-1/2}(f_1+e^{-2\pi i/3}f_2+e^{-4\pi i/3}f_3+f_4+e^{-2\pi i/3}f_5+e^{-4\pi i/3}f_6)$$

$$\varphi_6 = 6^{-1/2}(f_1-f_2+f_3-f_4+f_5-f_6)$$

$$e_1 = \alpha + 2\beta, \qquad e_2 = \alpha + \beta, \qquad e_3 = \alpha + \beta$$

$$e_4 = \alpha - \beta, \qquad e_5 = \alpha - \beta, \qquad e_6 = \alpha - 2\beta$$

(15.135)

The condition (15.131) determining the pi-MO coefficients for benzene was derived solely from symmetry considerations, without use of the Hückel approximations. Thus the MO's $\varphi_1, ..., \varphi_6$ are (except for normalization constants) the correct minimal-basis-set SCF pi-electron MO's for benzene. (The Hückel energies $e_1, ..., e_6$ are, however, not the true SCF orbital energies; the Hückel method ignores electron repulsions and takes the total pi-electron energy as the sum of orbital energies. The SCF method takes electron repulsions into account in an average way and the total SCF energy is not the sum of orbital energies.) A similar situation occurs for ethylene, where the minimal-basis-set pi MO's (15.79) and (15.80) are determined solely by symmetry. (An extended-basis-set benzene calculation would mix in $3p\pi$, $3d\pi$, etc., carbon AO's, and the contributions of these AO's must be determined by an explicit SCF calculation.)

The MO's in (15.135) for the degenerate pi levels are complex. Often, real forms of these MO's are used. The two MO's of each degenerate level are complex conjugates of each other; by adding and subtracting these MO's, we get the real forms:

$$\varphi_{2,\,real} = 2^{-1/2}(\varphi_2+\varphi_3) \qquad \varphi_{3,\,real} = -2^{-1/2}i(\varphi_2-\varphi_3)$$

$$\varphi_{2,\,real} = 12^{-1/2}(2f_1+f_2-f_3-2f_4-f_5+f_6)$$

$$\varphi_{3,\,real} = \tfrac{1}{2}(f_2+f_3-f_5-f_6)$$

(15.136)

$$\varphi_{4,\,real} = 12^{-1/2}(2f_1-f_2-f_3+2f_4-f_5-f_6)$$

$$\varphi_{5,\,real} = \tfrac{1}{2}(f_2-f_3+f_5-f_6)$$

Figure 15.18 shows the real benzene pi-electron MO's. Note the charge buildup between the nuclei for the bonding MO's.

The symmetry species of the benzene pi MO's are (*Schonland*, p. 210):

MO	φ_1	φ_2	φ_3	φ_4	φ_5	φ_6
Symmetry Species	a_{2u}	e_{1g}	e_{1g}	e_{2u}	e_{2u}	b_{2g}

The ground-state pi-electron configuration is $(1a_{2u})^2(1e_{1g})^4$.

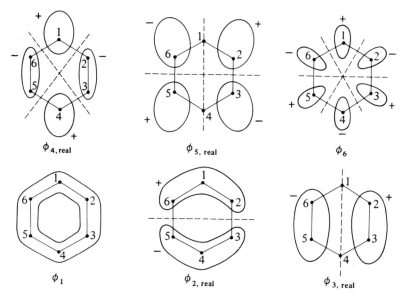

FIGURE 15.18   *Benzene pi* MO*'s (real form).   A top view is shown; the pi* MO*'s change sign on reflection in the molecular plane (which is a nodal plane for them).   Dashed lines indicate nodal planes perpendicular to the molecular plane.*

For the monocyclic planar conjugated polyene C_nH_n, we can use the same treatment as for benzene; replacing "6" by "n_C" in (15.134), (15.131), and (15.133), we find the HMO energies and coefficients:

$$e_k = \alpha + 2\beta \cos \frac{2\pi k}{n_C}, \qquad k = 0, ..., n_C - 1 \tag{15.137}$$

$$c_{kr} = \frac{1}{\sqrt{n_C}} \exp\left[\frac{2\pi i r k}{n_C}\right], \qquad i = \sqrt{-1} \tag{15.138}$$

$$\varphi_k = \frac{1}{\sqrt{n_C}} \sum_{r=1}^{n_C} \exp\left[\frac{2\pi i (r-1)k}{n_C}\right] f_r \tag{15.139}$$

where $f_r = C_r 2p\pi$.   Note that the index k in these equations does not correspond to the actual order of the MO's: the lowest MO has $k = 0$; next are the MO's with $k = 1$ and $k = n_C - 1$; next are the MO's with $k = 2$ and $k = n_C - 2$; and so on.   A most amusing mnemonic device[25] is available for the HMO energies (15.137).   One inscribes a regular polygon of n_C sides in a circle of radius $2|\beta|$, putting an apex at the bottom of the circle.   If a vertical scale of energy is set up with energy α coinciding with the center of the circle, then each polygon vertex is located at an HMO energy (Fig. 15.19).   The method gives the correct degeneracies and spacings of the Hückel levels of the ring hydrocarbon C_nH_n (Problem 15.37).

[25] A. A. Frost and B. Musulin, *J. Chem. Phys.*, **21**, 572 (1953).

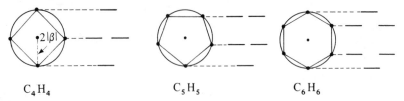

C$_4$H$_4$ C$_5$H$_5$ C$_6$H$_6$

FIGURE 15.19 *Mnemonic device for* HMO *energies of monocyclic planar hydrocarbons. The levels shown are for cyclobutadiene, the cyclopentadienyl radical, and benzene.*

Consider the Hückel energy levels for the monocyclic polyene C$_n$H$_n$. The lowest subshell consists of a nondegenerate level and holds 2 electrons. Each of the remaining low-lying subshells consists of a doubly degenerate level and holds 4 electrons. (If n_C is even, the highest pi energy level is nondegenerate, but this level is not occupied in the ground state.) To have a stable filled-subshell pi-electron configuration, the number of pi electrons must satisfy

$$n_\pi = 4m + 2, \qquad m = 0, 1, 2, \ldots \tag{15.140}$$

This is Hückel's famous $4m+2$ rule, which ascribes extra stability to monocyclic conjugated systems that satisfy (15.140). With $4m+1$ or $4m-1$ pi electrons, the compound is a free radical. With $4m$ pi electrons, there are two electrons in a subshell that can hold four electrons, and Hund's rule predicts a triplet (diradical) ground state.

Benzene satisfies the $4m+2$ rule. The cyclopentadienyl radical $\cdot$C$_5$H$_5$ is one electron short of satisfying (15.140); the cyclopentadienyl anion C$_5$H$_5^-$ satisfies the $4m+2$ rule; the cation C$_5$H$_5^+$ is predicted to have a triplet ground state and be highly reactive. These predictions are borne out; C$_5$H$_5^-$ is found to be considerably more stable than either C$_5$H$_5^+$ or $\cdot$C$_5$H$_5$. Similarly, C$_7$H$_7^+$ should be more stable than $\cdot$C$_7$H$_7$ or C$_7$H$_7^-$ as is verified experimentally; e.g., the salt C$_7$H$_7^+$Br$^-$ is readily prepared.

Cyclobutadiene is predicted to be a diradical.[26] After many unsuccessful efforts to produce C$_4$H$_4$, cyclobutadiene has been detected using a mass spectrometer. It turns out to be a highly reactive reaction intermediate with a very short lifetime at room temperature.[27] HMO theory predicts planar cyclooctatetraene to be a diradical; experimentally, C$_8$H$_8$ has a nonplanar "tub" structure, with alternating single and double bonds. Because of nonplanarity, the amount of conjugation between the double bonds is slight, and the delocalization energy (this term is defined later in this section) is small. The dianion C$_8$H$_8^{--}$ satisfies the $4m+2$ rule; the salt $[K_2]^{++}[C_8H_8]^{--}$ has been prepared and the evidence is that C$_8$H$_8^{--}$ is planar.

---

[26] *Ab initio* calculations indicate that the C$_4$H$_4$ ground state is a triplet with square-planar geometry; see A. Krantz, C. Y. Lin, and M. D. Newton, *J. Am. Chem. Soc.*, **95**, 2744 (1973).

[27] See references cited in L. T. Scott and M. Jones, *Chem. Rev.*, **1972**, 181. For the infrared spectrum, see the reference of footnote 26.

In the preceding discussion we used the same HMO's for a neutral compound and for its related ions. The Hückel method takes no account of electron repulsions and therefore the HMO's are unchanged when pi electrons are added or removed.

The $4m+2$ rule is sometimes applied to polycyclic systems; however, the pattern (15.137) of HMO levels holds only for a monocyclic system and use of the $4m+2$ rule for polycyclic systems is not justified.

The $4m+2$ rule actually does not depend on the Hückel assumptions (15.107)–(15.110). The C_nH_n pi MO's (15.139) were derived solely by symmetry considerations and are the correct SCF minimal-basis-set pi MO's. With $k = 0$, we have an MO with all plus signs in front of the AO's; clearly this MO has a lower energy than any of the others. For the remaining MO's, the pair with $k = j$ and $k = n_C - j$ are complex conjugates of each other and must have the same energy. (Since $\hat{H}$ is Hermitian, we have $\int \varphi^* \hat{H} \varphi \, dv = \int (\varphi^*)^* \hat{H} \varphi^* \, dv$.) Thus the excited MO's occur in pairs (except that when n_C is even, the MO with $k = \frac{1}{2} n_C$ is nondegenerate; with alternating plus and minus signs in front of the AO's, this is the highest energy MO). The pattern of a nondegenerate lowest pi level followed by doubly degenerate pi levels thus holds for the minimal-basis-set SCF MO's. Of course, the energies (15,137) are not the correct SCF orbital energies.

Now consider the HMO treatment of naphthalene. For butadiene and benzene, we set up the secular equation without bothering with the intermediate step of constructing symmetry orbitals from the $2p\pi$ AO's; for these molecules, the secular equation was easy enough to solve without the simplifications introduced by symmetry orbitals. For naphthalene, the 10×10 secular determinant is difficult to deal with, and we first find symmetry orbitals. The point group of naphthalene (Fig. 15.20) is $\mathscr{D}_{2h}$. The possible symmetry species are (15.76). The C2$p\pi$ AO's all have eigenvalue -1 for reflection in the molecular (yz) plane. Each symmetry orbital will be some linear combination of AO's that are permuted among one another by the symmetry reflections (recall ethylene). Hence to aid in finding the symmetry orbitals we examine the effects of the $\hat{\sigma}(xy)$ and $\hat{\sigma}(xz)$ operations on the pi AO's. We find the pi AO's to fall into three sets:

$$1, 4, 5, 8 \qquad 2, 3, 6, 7 \qquad 9, 10 \qquad \textbf{(15.141)}$$

where the members of each set are permuted among one another by the symmetry reflections. (Of course, these are also the chemically equivalent carbons.) Each

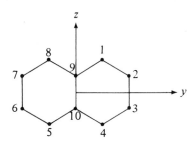

FIGURE 15.20 *Axes for naphthalene. The x axis is perpendicular to the molecular plane.*

symmetry orbital must be some linear combination of the AO's of a given set. Naphthalene and ethylene have the same point group, and the pattern of the hydrogen symmetry orbitals in (15.77) gives us the symmetry orbitals of the first two sets of AO's in (15.141). The symmetry orbitals and their readily verified symmetry species are then:

$$b_{3u}: g_1 = \tfrac{1}{2}(f_1+f_4+f_5+f_8) \qquad g_2 = \tfrac{1}{2}(f_2+f_3+f_6+f_7)$$
$$g_3 = 2^{-1/2}(f_9+f_{10})$$
$$a_u: g_4 = \tfrac{1}{2}(f_1-f_4+f_5-f_8) \qquad g_5 = \tfrac{1}{2}(f_2-f_3+f_6-f_7)$$
$$b_{2g}: g_6 = \tfrac{1}{2}(f_1-f_4-f_5+f_8) \qquad g_7 = \tfrac{1}{2}(f_2-f_3-f_6+f_7)$$
$$g_8 = 2^{-1/2}(f_9-f_{10})$$
$$b_{1g}: g_9 = \tfrac{1}{2}(f_1+f_4-f_5-f_8) \qquad g_{10} = \tfrac{1}{2}(f_2+f_3-f_6-f_7) \qquad \textbf{(15.142)}$$

The constants $\tfrac{1}{2}$ and $1/\sqrt{2}$ normalize the symmetry orbitals, provided the approximation (15.110) is used.

Instead of using the f_r's as basis functions, we set up the secular equation using the symmetry orbitals as basis functions:

$$\det[\langle g_p|\hat{H}^{\text{eff}}|g_q\rangle - \langle g_p|g_q\rangle e_k] = 0 \qquad \textbf{(15.143)}$$

The secular determinant in (15.143) is in block-diagonal form (Section 15.4), and we have two third-degree and two second-degree equations to solve. From (15.142) and (15.110), it follows that

$$\langle g_p|g_q\rangle = \delta_{pq} \qquad \textbf{(15.144)}$$

when g_p and g_q belong to the same symmetry species. Also

$$\langle g_1|\hat{H}^{\text{eff}}|g_1\rangle = \tfrac{1}{4}\langle f_1+f_4+f_5+f_8|\hat{H}^{\text{eff}}|f_1+f_4+f_5+f_8\rangle = \tfrac{1}{4}(\alpha+\alpha+\alpha+\alpha) = \alpha$$
$$\langle g_1|\hat{H}^{\text{eff}}|g_2\rangle = \tfrac{1}{4}\langle f_1+f_4+f_5+f_8|\hat{H}^{\text{eff}}|f_2+f_3+f_6+f_7\rangle = \tfrac{1}{4}(\beta+\beta+\beta+\beta) = \beta$$

Evaluating the remaining matrix elements, we find as the secular equation for the b_{3u} MO's:

$$\begin{vmatrix} \alpha-e_k & \beta & \sqrt{2}\beta \\ \beta & \alpha+\beta-e_k & 0 \\ \sqrt{2}\beta & 0 & \alpha+\beta-e_k \end{vmatrix} = 0 \qquad \textbf{(15.145)}$$

$$\begin{vmatrix} x & 1 & \sqrt{2} \\ 1 & x+1 & 0 \\ \sqrt{2} & 0 & x+1 \end{vmatrix} = 0$$

$$(x+1)(x^2+x-3) = 0$$

$$x = -1, \qquad -\tfrac{1}{2}\pm\tfrac{1}{2}\sqrt{13} \qquad \textbf{(15.146)}$$

Solution of the three remaining secular equations is left as an exercise (Problem 15.43).

The HMO coefficients are found by solving the appropriate sets of simultaneous equations. The resulting HMO's and energies for naphthalene are given in Table 15.3.

Table 15.3 The Hückel MO's of Naphthalene

$1b_{3u}$: $\varphi_1 = 0.301(f_1+f_4+f_5+f_8)$
$\qquad\qquad + 0.231(f_2+f_3+f_6+f_7) + 0.461(f_9+f_{10})$ $\qquad\qquad e_1 = \alpha + 2.303\beta$
$1b_{1g}$: $\varphi_2 = 0.263(f_1+f_4-f_5-f_8) + 0.425(f_2+f_3-f_6-f_7)$ $\qquad e_2 = \alpha + 1.618\beta$
$1b_{2g}$: $\varphi_3 = 0.400(f_1-f_4-f_5+f_8)$
$\qquad\qquad + 0.174(f_2-f_3-f_6+f_7) + 0.347(f_9-f_{10})$ $\qquad\qquad e_3 = \alpha + 1.303\beta$
$2b_{3u}$: $\varphi_4 = 0.408(f_2+f_3+f_6+f_7) - 0.408(f_9+f_{10})$ $\qquad\qquad e_4 = \alpha + \beta$
$1a_u$: $\varphi_5 = 0.425(f_1-f_4+f_5-f_8) + 0.263(f_2-f_3+f_6-f_7)$ $\qquad e_5 = \alpha + 0.618\beta$
$2b_{1g}$: $\varphi_6 = 0.425(f_1+f_4-f_5-f_8) - 0.263(f_2+f_3-f_6-f_7)$ $\qquad e_6 = \alpha - 0.618\beta$
$2b_{2g}$: $\varphi_7 = -0.408(f_2-f_3-f_6+f_7) + 0.408(f_9-f_{10})$ $\qquad\quad e_7 = \alpha - \beta$
$3b_{3u}$: $\varphi_8 = 0.400(f_1+f_4+f_5+f_8)$
$\qquad\qquad - 0.174(f_2+f_3+f_6+f_7) - 0.347(f_9+f_{10})$ $\qquad\qquad e_8 = \alpha - 1.303\beta$
$2a_u$: $\varphi_9 = 0.263(f_1-f_4+f_5-f_8) - 0.425(f_2-f_3+f_6-f_7)$ $\qquad e_9 = \alpha - 1.618\beta$
$3b_{2g}$: $\varphi_{10} = 0.301(f_1-f_4-f_5+f_8)$
$\qquad\qquad - 0.231(f_2-f_3-f_6+f_7) - 0.461(f_9-f_{10})$ $\qquad\qquad e_{10} = \alpha - 2.303\beta$

The predicted wavelength for a transition between the highest occupied and lowest vacant HMO's of a conjugated hydrocarbon is

$$\frac{1}{\lambda} = \frac{|\beta|}{hc}\Delta x \qquad (15.147)$$

where Δx is the difference in x values [Eq. (15.114)] for the two MO's. For naphthalene, $\Delta x = 1.236$ and the observed $1/\lambda$ is 34,700 cm^{-1}. Choosing β to fit the observed wavelength for naphthalene (because of the orbital degeneracy of its first excited term, benzene is atypical), we find

$$|\beta|/hc = 28,000 \text{ cm}^{-1}, \qquad |\beta| = 3.48 \text{ eV} \qquad (15.148)$$

Comparison of predicted and observed longest-wavelength absorptions for a large number of benzenoid hydrocarbons shows only fair agreement with experiment, with many deviations of a few thousand cm^{-1}.

Improved agreement can be obtained if we fit the frequencies to a straight line that does not pass through the origin; i.e., we use

$$\frac{1}{\lambda} = \frac{1}{hc}|\beta|\Delta x + a \qquad (15.149)$$

A least-squares fit of benzenoid hydrocarbon data gives [28]

$$a = 8200 \text{ cm}^{-1}, \qquad |\beta|/hc = 21,900 \text{ cm}^{-1}, \qquad |\beta| = 2.72 \text{ eV} \qquad (15.150)$$

---

[28] E. Heilbronner and J. N. Murrell, *J. Chem. Soc.*, **1962**, 2611.

These constants give a good fit to the data; the standard deviation is 600 cm^{-1}. (Of course, with two parameters instead of one, the agreement is bound to be improved. The fact that a semiempirical theory with several adjustable parameters gives a good fit to experimental data cannot be taken as overwhelming proof of the validity of the theory.)

We can partially justify the constant term in (15.149) as follows. The Hückel method neglects electron repulsions and therefore doesn't distinguish between singlet and triplet terms. Hence we should compare (15.147) with the energy difference between the ground state and the average of the energies of the singlet and triplet terms of the configuration with one electron excited to the lowest vacant HMO. The experimental frequencies are for singlet-singlet transitions. If we assume that the singlet-triplet splitting of the first excited configuration is reasonably constant for aromatic hydrocarbons, then $a = 8200$ cm$^{-1} = 1.0$ eV can be interpreted as one-half this singlet-triplet splitting. Experimental values[29] for this splitting are available for many aromatic hydrocarbons; typically, the value of half the singlet-triplet splitting is 0.7 to 0.8 eV, in reasonable agreement with $a = 1.0$ eV.

In applying HMO theory to conjugated hydrocarbons, planarity is assumed. Occasionally this assumption doesn't hold. In gas-phase biphenyl, the two rings are twisted at an angle of 40° with each other, due to steric interference between the *ortho* hydrogens.

From (15.105), it is clear that the order of the HMO secular determinant equals the number of conjugated carbons. (Students sometimes make the error of assuming that this order always equals the number of pi electrons.)

There are several properties of conjugated hydrocarbons that can be defined using HMO theory. We begin with *delocalization energy*. (The corresponding VB term is *resonance energy*.) The energy of the occupied pi HMO (15.79) of ethylene is

$$\int \frac{1}{\sqrt{2}}(f_1+f_2)^* \hat{H}^{\text{eff}} \frac{1}{\sqrt{2}}(f_1+f_2)\, dv = \alpha + \beta \tag{15.151}$$

There are two pi electrons in this MO, and the total Hückel pi-electron energy for ethylene is $2\alpha+2\beta$. For butadiene, the total Hückel pi-electron energy is

$$2(\alpha+1.618\beta) + 2(\alpha+0.618\beta) = 4\alpha + 4.472\beta \tag{15.152}$$

If butadiene had two isolated double bonds, its pi-electron energy would be twice that of ethylene, namely $4\alpha+4\beta$. The quantity

$$4\alpha + 4.472\beta - (4\alpha+4\beta) = 0.472\beta \tag{15.153}$$

is interpreted as the extra stability of butadiene arising from delocalization of the pi electrons, and is the delocalization energy.

For benzene, the pi-electron energy is

$$2(\alpha+2\beta) + 4(\alpha+\beta) = 6\alpha + 8\beta \tag{15.154}$$

which exceeds the energy of three isolated double bonds by 2β, the delocalization energy. An "experimental" delocalization energy for benzene can be calculated as

---

[29] G. B. Porter and M. W. Windsor, *Proc. Roy. Soc.*, **A245**, 238 (1958).

follows. The heat of hydrogenation of cyclohexene to cyclohexane is 28.6 kcal/mole. If benzene had three isolated double bonds, one would expect its heat of hydrogenation to be 3×28.6 kcal/mole $= 85.8$ kcal/mole. The observed value is only 49.8 kcal/mole, indicating that benzene is more stable by 36 kcal/mole than it would be if its double bonds were isolated. (A similar delocalization energy is arrived at by adding up the bond energies of six C—H bonds, three C—C bonds, and three C=C bonds, and comparing this to the heat of formation of benzene from its atoms; see Problem 15.41.) Setting $2|\beta| = 36$ kcal/mole, we get $|\beta| = 18$ kcal/mole $= 0.8$ eV/molecule. This is far less than the value 2.72 eV/molecule $= 63$ kcal/mole found by spectroscopic observations [Eq. (15.150)]. Part of the discrepancy is explainable as follows. In the hydrogenation of cyclohexene, the carbon–carbon double-bond length becomes a single-bond length; the figure of 85.8 kcal/mole applies to the hydrogenation of a hypothetical molecule with three isolated double bonds and three single bonds, with alternating bond lengths. We must therefore also consider the strain energy needed to compress three single bonds and stretch three double bonds to the benzene bond length. Even with this correction (Problem 15.40), the thermochemical value of β differs sharply from the spectroscopic value. The difference is to be attributed to the crudity of the HMO method. One finds that a different value of β is required for each different physical property that is being considered. Moreover, the optimum values of β differ for chain and ring conjugated hydrocarbons.

Another *defined* quantity is the *pi-electron (charge) density*. The probability density for an electron in the HMO (15.104) is

$$|\varphi_i|^2 = \sum_r \sum_s c_{ir}^* c_{is} f_r^* f_s \tag{15.155}$$

The normalization requirement for (15.155) gives

$$\sum_r |c_{ir}|^2 = 1 \tag{15.156}$$

where (15.110) was used. Since the HMO coefficients satisfy (15.156), it is natural to say that an electron in the MO φ_i has the probability $|c_{ir}|^2$ of being in the vicinity of the rth carbon atom. If n_i ($= 0$, 1, or 2) is the number of electrons in the MO φ_i, then the total pi-electron density q_r in the region of carbon-atom r is defined to be

$$q_r \equiv \sum_i n_i |c_{ir}|^2 \tag{15.157}$$

The name "pi-electron density" for q_r is misleading in that q_r is neither a charge density (which is measured in statcoul/cm^3) nor a probability density (which is measured in electrons/cm^3); rather q_r is a pure number, giving the approximate number of pi electrons near atom r. For butadiene:

$$q_1 = 2|c_{11}|^2 + 2|c_{21}|^2 = 2(0.372)^2 + 2(0.602)^2 = 1.000$$

$$q_2 = 2|c_{12}|^2 + 2|c_{22}|^2 = 1.000 \tag{15.158}$$

Let atoms r and s be bonded to each other. In (15.155), the quantity $c_{ir}^* c_{is}$ is a measure of the pi-electron probability density in the bond region between atoms r and s. The *pi-electron* (or *mobile*) *bond order* p_{rs} for the bond between atoms r and

s is *defined* as

$$p_{rs} \equiv \sum_i n_i \tfrac{1}{2}(c_{ir}^* c_{is} + c_{is}^* c_{ir}) \tag{15.159}$$

where the sum is over the pi MO's. The definition is such that the contribution to p_{rs} of each MO φ_i is real. Addition of the σ-electrons' single bond gives the *total bond order* P_{rs} as

$$P_{rs} = 1 + p_{rs} \tag{15.160}$$

For butadiene, we find $p_{12} = 0.894$, $p_{23} = 0.447$. The total bond orders are

$$CH_2 \overset{1.894}{\text{------}} CH \overset{1.447}{\text{------}} CH \overset{1.894}{\text{------}} CH_2 \tag{15.161}$$

The central bond has some double-bond character, and the end bonds have some single-bond character. (In VB theory, this is explained by contributions from such resonance structures as $\overset{-}{CH_2}$—CH=CH—$\overset{+}{CH_2}$.) The sum of the bond orders is 5.235, and exceeds 5. [This is because the pi-electron energy of butadiene exceeds that of two isolated double bonds—see Eq. (15.164).] For benzene, each carbon–carbon bond order is found to be $5/3 = 1.667$.

Naturally, we expect a relation between the bond order and the bond length R_{rs} for carbon–carbon bonds. The simplest assumption is a linear relation:

$$R_{rs} = a + bP_{rs} \tag{15.162}$$

where a and b are constants. The pi-electron MO coefficients for ethylene and for benzene are determined completely by symmetry, and are independent of the Hückel approximations. We therefore use the bond orders and bond lengths of ethylene (2; 1.335 Å) and benzene (5/3; 1.397 Å) to find a and b; we get

$$R_{rs} = [1.707 - 0.186 P_{rs}]\,\text{Å} = [1.521 - 0.186 p_{rs}]\,\text{Å} \tag{15.163}$$

Equation (15.163) works reasonably well. Thus, the predicted naphthalene 1–2, 2–3, 1–9, and 9–10 bond lengths (in Å) as compared to the experimental values (in parentheses) are: 1.386 (1.361), 1.409 (1.421), 1.418 (1.425), and 1.425 (1.410), respectively. Note that the rings are not regular hexagons. In phenanthrene, 6 of the 9 predicted bond lengths are correct to 0.01 Å, but the errors in the other 3 are 0.02, 0.04, and 0.05 Å.

Ab initio, all-electron SCF MO calculations on naphthalene and azulene have been carried out [R. J. Buenker and S. D. Peyerimhoff, *Chem. Phys. Letters*, **3**, 37 (1969); these monumental calculations required the evaluation of nearly 10^9 two-electron integrals]. The SCF MO bond orders for naphthalene correctly predict the observed order of increasing bond lengths (which the HMO bond orders do not quite do); however, the calculated SCF MO azulene bond orders bear little relation to the observed azulene bond lengths. Clearly other factors besides conjugation are important in determining bond lengths.[30]

A much-investigated question is whether the carbon–carbon bond lengths in very large conjugated linear and cyclic polyenes ($C_{2n}H_{2n+2}$ and $C_{4m+2}H_{4m+2}$

---

[30] For discussions on carbon-carbon bond lengths, see: D. R. Lide, Jr., *Tetrahedron*, **17**, 125 (1962); B. P. Stoicheff, *ibid.*, **17**, 135; L. S. Bartell, *ibid.*, **17**, 177; E. B. Wilson, Jr., *ibid.*, **17**, 191.

for m and n large) are equal or alternate in length. This question is still unsettled. [See J.-M. André and G. Leroy, *Int. J. Quantum Chem.*, **5**, 557 (1971), and references cited therein.]

The Hückel pi-electron energy E_π is related to the pi bond orders p_{rs} and pi-electron densities q_r; in fact (Problem 15.44):

$$E_\pi = \alpha \sum_r q_r + 2\beta \sum_{s-r} p_{rs} \tag{15.164}$$

where the first sum is over the carbon atoms and the second is over the carbon–carbon bonds. For example, for butadiene

$$E_\pi = \alpha(1+1+1+1) + 2\beta(0.894+0.447+0.894) = 4\alpha + 4.47\beta$$

which agrees with (15.152).

Another defined quantity is Coulson's *free-valence index* F_r, for carbon atom r in a planar conjugated organic compound:

$$F_r \equiv 3 + \sqrt{3} - {\sum_s}' P_{rs} = \sqrt{3} - {\sum_s}' p_{rs} \tag{15.165}$$

where the sum is over all atoms (including hydrogens) bonded to carbon atom r. The quantity $3+\sqrt{3}=4.732$ is the value of ${\sum}' P_{rs}$ for the central carbon of the diradical $C(CH_2)_3$, which was formerly believed to have the largest value for this sum. It is now realized that the central carbon of the diradical $HC{=}C{=}CH$ has the value $2+2^{3/2} = 4.828$ for this sum. [See Problem 15.47 and C. Finder, *J. Org. Chem.*, **32**, 1672 (1967).] For butadiene:

$$\begin{aligned}{\sum_s}' P_{1s} &= 1 + 1 + 1.89 = 3.89 \\ F_1 = F_4 &= 4.73 - 3.89 = 0.84 \\ F_2 = F_3 &= 4.73 - 4.34 = 0.39\end{aligned} \tag{15.166}$$

F_r is a measure of the unused bonding power of atom r, and serves as a rough indicator of the susceptibility of a given atom to attack by a neutral free radical; the end carbons in butadiene are attacked preferentially by free radicals.

An important concept is that of an *alternant hydrocarbon*, which is a planar conjugated hydrocarbon in which the carbon atoms can be divided into a starred set and an unstarred set, with starred carbons bonded only to unstarred carbons and vice versa (Fig. 15.21). All planar conjugated hydrocarbons are alternants except those containing a ring with an odd number of carbons. Alternants are divided into even-alternants (e.g., benzene) and odd-alternants (e.g., benzyl) according to whether n_C is even or odd.

FIGURE 15.21 *Some alternant hydrocarbons.*

The equations determining the HMO coefficients of the orbital φ_i with energy $e_i = \alpha - x_i\beta$ are:

$$(\alpha - e_i)c_{ir} + \beta \sum_{s \to r} c_{is} = 0$$

$$x_i c_{ir} + \sum_{s \to r} c_{is} = 0, \qquad r = 1, \ldots, n_C \qquad \textbf{(15.167)}$$

where the summation is over carbons bonded to carbon r. Let the hydrocarbon be an alternant. From the definition of an alternant it follows that if r is a starred atom, then s in (15.167) is unstarred, and vice versa. We shall use the left superscripts * and ° to denote coefficients of starred and unstarred carbons, respectively. For those atoms r that are unstarred, we rewrite (15.167) as

$$(-x_i)(-{}^\circ c_{ir}) + \sum_{s \to r} ({}^*c_{is}) = 0 \qquad \textbf{(15.168)}$$

For r starred, we multiply (15.167) by -1 to get

$$(-x_i)({}^*c_{ir}) + \sum_{s \to r} (-{}^\circ c_{is}) = 0 \qquad \textbf{(15.169)}$$

If we let

$$x_j = -x_i, \qquad {}^*c_{jr} = {}^*c_{ir}, \qquad {}^\circ c_{jr} = -{}^\circ c_{ir}, \qquad r = 1, \ldots, n_C \qquad \textbf{(15.170)}$$

we can combine (15.168) and (15.169) into the single equation

$$x_j c_{jr} + \sum_{s \to r} c_{js} = 0 \qquad \textbf{(15.171)}$$

Equation (15.171) has the same form as (15.167) and thus (15.171) shows that for each alternant HMO φ_i with x value x_i, there is an HMO φ_j with x value $-x_i$ and coefficients the same as φ_i except that the unstarred-atom coefficients are changed in sign. The HMO's of an alternant hydrocarbon are *paired*, with pairs having energies $\alpha + x\beta$ and $\alpha - x\beta$. The coefficients of an antibonding HMO of an alternant hydrocarbon can be obtained simply by changing the signs of the unstarred-atom coefficients in the paired bonding HMO. These results may be checked for butadiene, benzene, and naphthalene. For an odd-alternant hydrocarbon, the HMO with energy α is paired with itself and (15.170) implies that the coefficients of the unstarred atoms are zero for this HMO.

The preceding derivation may bother the reader in that we found both x_j and the c_{jr}'s from the simultaneous equations (15.167) [corresponding to (15.105)], whereas the usual procedure is to find x_j from the determinantal secular equation (15.106) and then solve the simultaneous equations (15.105) for the coefficients. Actually the procedure of finding both x_j and the c_{jr}'s from (15.105) is perfectly valid. The only values of x_j that allow a nontrivial solution of (15.105) are those that satisfy the secular equation (15.106). (See Section 8.4.) Having found an x_j value that allows the nontrivial solution (15.170) for the c_{jr}'s, we can be sure it satisfies (15.106). Equation (15.106) is simply a *device* which can be dispensed with if we are able to solve (15.105) another way.

Benzyl (Fig. 15.21) is an odd-alternant with 7 conjugated carbons and hence 7 HMO's; from the above discussion, three MO's are bonding, three are antibonding, and one is nonbonding ($e_i = \alpha$). The bonding MO's are filled with six pi electrons and the unpaired electron is in the nonbonding MO. We can find the nonbonding MO coefficients without solving the secular equation. With $x_i = 0$, Eq. (15.167) becomes

$$\sum_{s \to r} c_{is} = 0, \qquad r = 1, \dots, n_C \tag{15.172}$$

where the sum is over carbons bonded to carbon r. The CH_2 carbon of benzyl is bonded to carbon number 1 only, and (15.172) gives $c_{i1} = 0$ for the nonbonding MO. Since C_2 is bonded to C_1 and C_3, we have $c_{i3} = 0$; similarly, $c_{i5} = 0$. The remaining four coefficients are readily found—see Problems 15.45 and 15.63.

For the ground state of a *neutral* alternant hydrocarbon, all the pi-electron densities q_r are 1. (See *Pilar*, p. 600.)

So far, we have applied the HMO method to hydrocarbons only. For planar conjugated molecules that involve pi bonding to noncarbon atoms, the Coulomb and bond integrals for the heteroatoms must be modified from the carbon values. For heteroatoms X and Y, we write

$$\alpha_X = \alpha_C + h_X \beta_{CC}$$
$$\beta_{XY} = k_{XY} \beta_{CC} \tag{15.173}$$

where h_X and k_{XY} are certain constants. The best values for these constants vary, depending on which molecular property is being considered, and the values used are based on a mixture of theory and guesswork. One set of values (*Streitwieser*, Chapter 5) is:

Atom	—N=	—N̈—	=N̈⁺—	—Ö—	=O	—F	—Cl	—Br	
h_X	0.5	1.5	2	2	1	3	2	1.5	(15.174)

Bond	C—N̈—	aromatic CN	C=N̈⁺—	N—O—	C—O—	C=O	C—F	C—Cl	C—Br
k_{XY}	0.8	1	1	0.7	0.8	1.0	0.7	0.4	0.3

These values should not be taken too seriously—e.g., different workers recommend values for $h_{=O}$ ranging from 0.15 to 2.

Consider pyridine and pyrrole as examples. Pyridine

pyridine   pyrrole

has six pi electrons, one of which is contributed by nitrogen; pyrrole has six pi electrons, two of which are contributed by nitrogen. If we use the values (15.174), the HMO secular determinant for pyridine is the same as (15.126) for benzene, except that the element x in the first row and first column is replaced by $x+0.5$. For pyrrole the HMO secular equation is:

$$\begin{vmatrix} x+1.5 & 0.8 & 0 & 0 & 0.8 \\ 0.8 & x & 1 & 0 & 0 \\ 0 & 1 & x & 1 & 0 \\ 0 & 0 & 1 & x & 1 \\ 0.8 & 0 & 0 & 1 & x \end{vmatrix} = 0$$

We might also use different values of β for the carbon–carbon single and double bonds in pyrrole; Streitwieser recommends

$$\beta_{C-C} = 0.9\beta_{CC}, \qquad \beta_{C=C} = 1.1\beta_{CC} \tag{15.175}$$

where β_{CC} is for an aromatic carbon–carbon bond (e.g., benzene).

The HMO method can be applied to the ions (15.100); however, the FE MO method is simpler to use, and we omit the HMO calculation—see Problem 15.52. [The molecule (15.100) is not planar. However, the out-of-plane methyl protons are but a slight perturbation on an otherwise planar molecule, and the σ–π classification holds to a very good approximation.]

For molecules with heteroatoms, Eq. (15.164) becomes

$$E_\pi = \sum_{\text{atoms}} q_r \alpha_r + 2 \sum_{\text{bonds}} p_{rs} \beta_{rs} \tag{15.176}$$

Because of the simplicity of the method, carrying out HMO calculations has become a favorite pastime of organic chemists, and the results of HMO calculations have been tabulated for hundreds of compounds.[31] The HMO method has been widely used to rationalize and predict the course of organic reactions involving conjugated systems. In view of the crudity of the HMO approximations, the fact that the method works as well as it does is surprising and not yet fully explained.

Aside from using the one-electron Hamiltonian (15.102), perhaps the most serious approximation of the simple HMO method is that of taking all overlap integrals equal to zero. Wheland proposed using a nonzero value S for the overlap integral of carbons bonded together. Inclusion of overlap replaces each element β in the HMO secular equation (15.106) with $\beta - Se_i$. With overlap, the benzene HMO secular equation becomes

$$\begin{vmatrix} w & 1 & 0 & 0 & 0 & 1 \\ 1 & w & 1 & 0 & 0 & 0 \\ 0 & 1 & w & 1 & 0 & 0 \\ 0 & 0 & 1 & w & 1 & 0 \\ 0 & 0 & 0 & 1 & w & 1 \\ 1 & 0 & 0 & 0 & 1 & w \end{vmatrix} = 0 \tag{15.177}$$

[31] C. A. Coulson and A. Streitwieser, Jr., *Dictionary of π-Electron Calculations*, Freeman, San Francisco, 1965; A. Streitwieser, Jr., and J. I. Brauman, *Supplemental Tables of Molecular Orbital Calculations*, Pergamon Press, New York, 1965; Heilbronner and Straub, *Hückel Molecular Orbitals*, Springer-Verlag, New York, 1966.

where

$$w \equiv \frac{\alpha - e_i}{\beta - Se_i} \tag{15.178}$$

$$e_i = \alpha - \frac{w(\beta - S\alpha)}{1 - Sw} = \alpha - \frac{w}{1 - Sw}\gamma \tag{15.179}$$

$$\gamma \equiv \beta - S\alpha \tag{15.180}$$

Since (15.177) is identical in form to (15.126), the values of w are the same as the values (15.127) for x, and no additional calculation is required. Provided we use a common value of S for any two bonded carbons in a given molecule, this situation holds for any planar conjugated hydrocarbon. To get the HMO energy levels with overlap included, we use Eq. (15.179), where w takes on the same values as found for x when solving the HMO secular equation with overlap omitted. The HMO coefficients in the Wheland approximation differ only in the normalization constants from those obtained with zero overlap (Problem 15.57).

To estimate S, we use the following formula (Problem 15.24) for the overlap integral between two $2p\pi$ STO's with orbital exponent ζ:

$$S_{2p\pi - 2p\pi} = e^{-\zeta R}\left[1 + \zeta R + \frac{2\zeta^2 R^2}{5} + \frac{\zeta^3 R^3}{15}\right] \tag{15.181}$$

where R is the internuclear separation in bohrs. Slater's rules give $\zeta = 1.625$ for a carbon $2p$ AO. (Since Slater's ζ is the effective nuclear charge divided by n, this value corresponds to $Z_{eff} = 3.25$.) We have

R (Å)	1.20	1.335	1.397	1.53
S	0.338	0.272	0.246	0.195

$$\tag{15.182}$$

At the benzene bond distance 1.397 Å, the overlap integral is 0.25.

The Wheland orbital energies for benzene (with S taken as 0.25) are

$$\alpha + 1.33\gamma, \qquad \alpha + 0.80\gamma, \qquad \alpha + 0.80\gamma,$$

$$\alpha - 1.33\gamma, \qquad \alpha - 1.33\gamma, \qquad \alpha - 4.0\gamma$$

Inclusion of overlap destroys the symmetric spacing of the energy levels about α that holds for alternant hydrocarbons in the simple HMO theory.

Let w_{lv} and w_{ho} be the w values for the lowest vacant and highest occupied pi MO's. The transition frequency between these two Wheland MO's is:

$$\frac{hc}{\lambda} = \frac{\gamma w_{lv}}{1 - Sw_{lv}} - \frac{\gamma w_{ho}}{1 - Sw_{ho}}$$

$$\frac{1}{\lambda} = \frac{\gamma}{hc}\frac{(w_{lv} - w_{ho})}{[1 + S^2 w_{lv} w_{ho} - S(w_{lv} + w_{ho})]} \tag{15.183}$$

For alternant hydrocarbons $w_{lv} + w_{ho} = 0$, and (15.183) becomes

$$\frac{1}{\lambda} = \frac{|\gamma|}{hc} \times \frac{\Delta w}{1 - \frac{1}{4}S^2(\Delta w)^2} \qquad (15.184)$$

where the Δw values are identical to the Δx values calculated without overlap. Since most Δw values are close to 1, we have $\frac{1}{4}S^2(\Delta w)^2 \approx 1/64 \ll 1$, and (15.184) is very nearly the same formula as (15.147), except that the proportionality constant is interpreted as $\beta - S\alpha$, rather than β. Also, since the overlap correction is roughly the same ($\approx 64/63$) for most aromatic hydrocarbons, it is largely taken care of by using an empirical value of γ. Inclusion of overlap would thus give only slight changes in predicted transition frequencies.

With inclusion of overlap, the definitions (15.157) and (15.159) for the pi-electron densities and bond orders must be modified. With the modified definitions, it can be shown that inclusion of overlap gives the *same* charge densities and bond orders for hydrocarbons as found when overlap is neglected.[32] (This result doesn't hold for molecules with heteroatoms.)

Even though inclusion of overlap is not difficult, simple LCAO calculations on pi-electron systems usually omit overlap. This gives no error in calculated hydrocarbon bond orders and charge densities, and but little change in the predicted longest-wavelength transitions of alternant hydrocarbons. Hence there isn't much point in including overlap in simple semiempirical calculations. (However, inclusion of overlap does give better agreement between the spectroscopic and thermochemical values of γ than is found between the corresponding values of β when overlap is omitted; see Problem 15.50.)

Although the Hückel theory can be used to predict the longest-wavelength bands of aromatic hydrocarbons, it would be hopeless to try and use HMO theory to predict the complete electronic spectrum of an aromatic hydrocarbon. For example, Hückel theory, which neglects interelectronic repulsions, gives no separation between singlet and triplet electronic terms arising from the same configuration. Experimentally, separations of one or two eV are observed between such terms. Several semiempirical pi-electron theories have been developed to take electron repulsion into account and thereby improve on the Hückel method. The most widely used of these theories is the *Pariser–Parr–Pople* (PPP) *method*. Here, the pi-electron Hamiltonian (15.86) including electron repulsions is used, and the pi-electron wave function is written as an antisymmetrized product of spin-orbitals. The pi MO's are taken as LCAO's, using $2p\pi$ carbon orbitals for hydrocarbons. The Roothaan equations are used to find SCF pi MO's. However, instead of attempting a rigorous SCF calculation, the Pariser–Parr–Pople method makes certain approximations for some integrals and uses experimental data to evaluate other integrals. As in Hückel theory, overlap is neglected:

$$S_{rs} = \langle f_r(1)|f_s(1)\rangle = \delta_{rs} \qquad (15.185)$$

where δ_{rs} is the Kronecker delta. The bond integral

$$\beta_{rs}^{core} = \langle f_r(1)|\hat{H}_{core}(1)|f_s(1)\rangle \qquad (15.186)$$

---

[32] B. H. Chirgwin and C. A. Coulson, *Proc. Roy. Soc.*, **A201**, 196 (1950).

is taken as an empirical parameter for two bonded atoms; for nonbonded atoms, β_{rs}^{core} is assumed to vanish. The integrals

$$\alpha_r^{core} = \langle f_r | \hat{H}_{core} | f_r \rangle \qquad (15.187)$$

are allowed to differ for different atoms and are evaluated with a certain approximate formula. We also have electron repulsion integrals:

$$\int \int f_r^*(1) f_s(1) \frac{1}{r_{12}} f_t^*(2) f_u(2) \, dv_1 \, dv_2 \equiv (rs|tu) \qquad (15.188)$$

The widely used notation of (15.188) should not be misinterpreted as an overlap integral. Consistent with (15.185), the Pariser–Parr–Pople method makes the assumption of *zero differential overlap* (ZDO):

$$f_r(1) f_s(1) \, dv_1 = 0 \qquad \text{for } r \neq s \qquad (15.189)$$

From this approximation, it follows that

$$(rs|tu) = \delta_{rs} \delta_{tu} (rr|tt) = \delta_{rs} \delta_{tu} \gamma_{rt} \qquad (15.190)$$

where the notation of (15.188) is used, and γ_{rt} is defined as $(rr|tt)$. Thus the method ignores many, but not all, of the electron repulsion integrals. The integrals γ_{rt} are often treated as empirical parameters, rather than being evaluated theoretically. With these approximations, the Roothaan equations are solved iteratively until self-consistency is attained. For alternant hydrocarbons, the result $q_r = 1$ and the pairing properties of MO energies and coefficients hold in the PPP theory. Configuration interaction may be included to improve the results. The PPP treatment gives a good account of the electronic spectra of many, but not all, aromatic hydrocarbons.[33]

The literature on quantum-mechanical studies of pi-electron systems is huge, due mainly to the relative ease with which semiempirical treatments of such molecules can be carried out. Part of the great interest results from the biological importance of conjugated molecules.

Heredity and protein synthesis are controlled by the genes, whose active components are deoxyribonucleic acid (DNA) molecules. DNA is a long polymeric double helix, whose strands each contain a backbone of alternating sugar (deoxyribose) and phosphate groups; to each sugar is bonded a nitrogen base. The two strands are held together by hydrogen bonds between the bases. The bases that occur in DNA are adenine, guanine, cytosine, and thymine. Because of steric requirements, hydrogen bonds can be formed only between adenine and thymine and between guanine and cytosine. During cell division, the two strands of the DNA helix separate, and each strand serves as a template for the synthesis of a complementary strand, thereby passing on the hereditary material to each daughter cell. The DNA strands also separate to control protein synthesis; here, one strand of DNA serves as a template for the synthesis of messenger ribonucleic acid (mRNA), which is similar to a DNA strand, except that it contains ribose instead of deoxyribose and uracil instead of thymine. The mRNA then serves as a template to line up molecules

---

[33] For further discussion of the method, see *Parr*, Chapter III; *Pilar*, Chapter 19.

of transfer RNA (tRNA). At one end of a tRNA molecule is a sequence of three bases which must match the complementary triplet of bases in mRNA; at the other end is a corresponding amino acid. Thus the amino acids are lined up in proper sequence to form the desired protein. Each amino acid is "coded" by a certain sequence of three bases in DNA.[34].

The five bases that form the genetic code in DNA and RNA are conjugated pi-electron systems, as are many other biomolecules.

The carotenoid pigments contain systems of conjugated double bonds: β-carotene (the orange pigment in carrots) has 11 conjugated double bonds. The body cleaves β-carotene to produce vitamin A, which has 5 conjugated double bonds; vitamin A is converted by the body to 11-*cis*-retinal (retinene), which also has 5 conjugated double bonds; retinene combines with the protein opsin to form the photosensitive pigment rhodopsin found in the retinas of animals. When light strikes rhodopsin, it isomerizes 11-*cis*-retinal to all-*trans*-retinal, which doesn't "fit" the protein opsin and dissociates from it.

Most organic dyes owe their color to pi-electron transitions. If there is only one strong absorption band in the visible region, the observed color of a compound is related to the wavelength of the electronic absorption maximum as follows:

λ (Å)	4000	4250	4500	4900	5300	5900	6400	7300
observed color	greenish-yellow	yellow	orange	red	violet	blue	blue-green	green

Molecules related to porphin (which has a conjugated pi-electron system) are of widespread biological occurrence; substituted porphins are called porphyrins. The protein hemoglobin contains four heme groups; each heme group is an iron complex of a porphyrin. Chlorophyll is a magnesium complex of a porphyrin; the presence of low-lying vacant MO's, which is characteristic of conjugated pi-electron systems, allows chlorophyll to absorb visible light.

A. and B. Pullman have attributed the biological importance of conjugated molecules to two factors: the extra stability associated with electron delocalization, and the functional advantages conferred by conjugated pi-electron systems.

Löwdin suggested that naturally occurring mutations may be caused by tunneling of one or more protons of DNA hydrogen bonds from a base on one strand to the paired base on the other strand.

Clementi and co-workers did an *ab initio* all-electron SCF MO calculation on the guanine–cytosine ($C_5N_5H_5O$–$C_4N_3H_5O$) base pair of DNA. [E. Clementi, J. Mehl, and W. von Niessen, *J. Chem. Phys.*, **54**, 508 (1971).] Computations were done for 27 different geometries to determine the potential-energy function for motion of hydrogen atoms in the hydrogen bonds. For this 136-electron 29-nuclei system, the basis set used was 334 GTO's; 7×10^{10} two-electron repulsion integrals were evaluated and the computation took 8 days of computer time. Unfortunately, despite the enormous size of this computation, the basis set used was not large

---

[34] For further details, see J. Watson, *Molecular Biology of the Gene*, 2d ed., Benjamin, New York, 1970; *The Double Helix*, Atheneum, New York, 1968.

enough to approach the Hartree–Fock limit, and definitive conclusions about Löwdin's ideas could not be reached.

The carcinogenicity of certain aromatic hydrocarbons has been studied using pi-electron theory.

MO theory is being used to aid in the design of drugs. [See *Molecular Orbital Studies in Chemical Pharmacology*, L. B. Kier, ed., Springer-Verlag, 1970.]

Significant biological applications of quantum chemistry are on the increase.[35]

The relation between quantum mechanics and the mind has been the subject of much speculation. Wigner argued that the reduction of the wave function occurs when the result of a measurement enters the consciousness of an observer and thus "the being with consciousness must have a different role in quantum mechanics than the inanimate measuring device." He believes it likely that conscious beings obey different laws of nature than inanimate objects and proposes that scientists look for unusual effects of consciousness acting on matter. [E. P. Wigner, "Remarks on the Mind-Body Question," in *The Scientist Speculates*, I. J. Good, ed., Capricorn, 1965, p. 284; *Proc. Amer. Phil. Soc.*, **113**, 95 (1969); *Found. Phys.*, **1**, 35 (1970).] Schmidt constructed an electronic random-number generator based on the radioactive decay of Sr^{90} (a probabilistic quantum-mechanical process) and presented evidence for human precognition of and psychokinetic influence on the numbers generated by this device. However, a test for telepathy with a similar device yielded a negative result. [H. Schmidt, *New Scientist*, **50**, 757 (1971); *J. Parapsychol.*, **33**, 99 (1969); **34**, 175 (1970); J. Beloff and D. Bate, *J. Soc. Psych. Res.*, **46**, 21 (1971).]

For nonconjugated closed-subshell molecules (e.g., H_2O) we can view the electrons as residing either in the delocalized canonical MO's or in the energy-localized bond, inner-shell, and lone-pair orbitals. The latter picture allows one to accurately approximate the molecular binding energy as a sum of bond energies. For conjugated molecules (e.g., 1,3-butadiene, benzene), the molecular binding energy exceeds the sum of bond energies by the delocalization energy. We therefore expect that the energy-localized bonding MO's in conjugated systems are not as well localized as those in nonconjugated systems. Newton and Switkes calculated the energy-localized MO's for *s-trans*-butadiene and benzene, starting from all-electron minimal-basis-set SCF canonical MO's. [M. D. Newton and E. Switkes, *J. Chem. Phys.*, **54**, 3179 (1971).] In butadiene, they found the localized double bonds to be the bent banana bonds (as Kaldor found for ethylene), rather than σ–π bonds. They defined a percentage of delocalization d of an energy-localized bond MO that measures the degree to which orbitals centered on atoms other than the bonding pair of atoms contribute to the bond MO. For the butadiene energy-localized double-bond MO's, d is $8\frac{1}{2}\%$, only slightly more than the 6% value for the ethylene localized double-bond MO's. Thus conjugation in butadiene leads to only a slight increase in delocalization of the localized double-bond orbitals.

---

[35] Some references are: P.-O. Löwdin, *Advances in Quantum Chemistry*, vol. 2, Academic Press, New York, 1965, pp. 213–360; B. Pullman and A. Pullman, *Quantum Biochemistry*, Wiley, New York, 1963; A. Burger, ed., *Medicinal Chemistry*, 3rd ed., Wiley-Interscience, 1970, pp. 164–192; A. Pullman, *Fortschr. Chem. Forsch.*, **23**, 31 (1972).

For benzene, the energy-localization procedure led to two equivalent solutions, in each of which single and double bonds alternate (as in the Kekulé structures), with each double bond composed of two bent banana bonds. (The total electron density in a localized MO wave function must have the same symmetry as the density calculated from canonical MO's; for a Kekulé-like localized benzene wave function, the tails of the localized double-bond MO's are sufficiently large to maintain $\mathcal{D}_{6h}$ symmetry.) In benzene, each energy-localized double bond MO was found to have $d = 19\%$, indicating large contributions from AO's of atoms other than the bonding pair. The high degree of delocalization is, of course, expected. Another significant point was that for benzene, the bent banana double bonds were only slightly preferred (in terms of energy localization) to σ–π double-bond MO's.

15.9 Semiempirical MO Treatments of Nonplanar Molecules

Semiempirical MO theories fall into two categories: those using a Hamiltonian that is the sum of one-electron terms, and those using a Hamiltonian that includes two-electron repulsion terms, as well as one-electron terms. The Hückel method is a one-electron theory, whereas the Pariser–Parr–Pople method is a two-electron theory.

For nonplanar molecules, the simplifying approximation of treating the pi electrons separately is not available, and all the valence electrons must be considered together. The most important one-electron semiempirical MO method for nonplanar molecules is the *extended Hückel theory*; an early version was used by Wolfsberg and Helmholz in treating inorganic complex ions; the method was further developed and widely applied by Hoffmann.[36]

The extended Hückel (EH) method begins with the approximation of treating the valence electrons separately from the rest (Section 13.15). The valence-electron Hamiltonian is taken as the sum of one-electron Hamiltonians:

$$\hat{H}_{val} = \sum_i \hat{H}_{eff}(i) \tag{15.191}$$

where $\hat{H}_{eff}(i)$ is not specified explicitly. The MO's are approximated as linear combinations of the valence AO's f_j of the atoms:

$$\varphi_i = \sum_j c_{ij} f_j \tag{15.192}$$

In the simple Hückel theory of planar hydrocarbons, each pi MO contains contributions from one $2p\pi$ AO on each carbon atom; in the extended Hückel treatment of nonplanar hydrocarbons, each valence MO contains contributions from four AO's on each carbon atom (one $2s$ and three $2p$'s) and one $1s$ AO on each hydrogen atom. The AO's used are usually Slater-type orbitals with fixed orbital exponents. For the simplified Hamiltonian (15.191), the problem separates into several one-electron

[36] R. Hoffmann, *J. Chem. Phys.*, **39**, 1397 (1963); *ibid.*, **40**, 2745, 2474, 2480 (1964); *Tetrahedron*, **22**, 521, 539 (1966). M. Wolfsberg and L. Helmholz, *J. Chem. Phys.*, **20**, 837 (1952).

problems:

$$\hat{H}_{\text{eff}}(i)\,\varphi_i = e_i\varphi_i \qquad\qquad (15.193)$$

$$E_{\text{val}} = \sum_i e_i \qquad\qquad (15.194)$$

Application of the variation theorem to the linear trial function (15.192) gives as the secular equation and the equations for the MO coefficients:

$$\det\left(H_{jk}^{\text{eff}} - e_i S_{jk}\right) = 0 \qquad\qquad (15.195)$$

$$\sum_k \left(H_{jk}^{\text{eff}} - e_i S_{jk}\right)c_{jk} = 0, \qquad j = 1, 2, \dots \qquad\qquad (15.196)$$

All this is similar to simple Hückel theory. However, the extended Hückel theory does not neglect overlap. Rather *all* overlap integrals are explicitly evaluated using the forms chosen for the AO's and the internuclear distances at which the calculation is being done. (Formulas for overlap integrals of STO's are available.[37]) Thus, off-diagonal e_i's are present in the secular determinant. A computer is used to solve (15.195).

Since $\hat{H}_{\text{eff}}(i)$ is not specified, there is the problem of what to use for the integrals H_{jk}^{eff}. Generally, the integrals with $j = k$ are approximated by minus the appropriate atomic valence-state ionization potentials. (The justification is by analogy to Koopmans' theorem—*Pilar*, p. 350—of SCF theory.) Valence-state ionization potentials differ from ordinary atomic ionization potentials; they will be defined in Section 15.10. For carbon and hydrogen atoms, the valence-state ionization-potential parametrization gives

$$\langle C2s|\hat{H}_{\text{eff}}|C2s\rangle = -20.8\text{ eV}, \qquad \langle C2p|\hat{H}_{\text{eff}}|C2p\rangle = -11.3\text{ eV}$$

$$\langle H1s|\hat{H}_{\text{eff}}|H1s\rangle = -13.6\text{ eV} \qquad\qquad (15.197)$$

For the off-diagonal matrix elements H_{jk}^{eff}, $j \neq k$, Wolfsberg and Helmholz wrote

$$H_{jk}^{\text{eff}} = K\frac{H_{jj}^{\text{eff}} + H_{kk}^{\text{eff}}}{2}S_{jk} \qquad\qquad (15.198)$$

where K is a numerical constant (values ranging from 1 to 3 have been used) and the remaining quantities are evaluated as above. Since H_{jj}^{eff} and H_{kk}^{eff} are usually negative, (15.198) gives H_{jk}^{eff} as negative. The arithmetic and geometric means of two quantities of comparable magnitude do not differ greatly, and instead of (15.198), Ballhausen and Gray used

$$H_{jk}^{\text{eff}} = -K(H_{jj}^{\text{eff}} H_{kk}^{\text{eff}})^{1/2}S_{jk} \qquad\qquad (15.199)$$

Equations (15.199) and (15.198) are the most widely used approximations, but many others have been proposed. In contrast to the simple Hückel theory, H_{jk}^{eff} is non-zero for all pairs of orbitals (unless S_{jk} vanishes for symmetry reasons).

Once the H_{jk}^{eff} and S_{jk} integrals have been evaluated, the secular equation is

---

[37] D. M. Bishop, M. Randič, and J. R. Morton, *J. Chem. Phys.*, **45**, 1880 (1966); footnotes 12–18 of this paper give references to available tabulations.

solved for the orbital energies and then the MO coefficients are found. The total valence-electron energy is given by (15.194). To predict molecular geometry using the extended Hückel method, one carries out a series of calculations over a range of bond distances and angles and looks for the nuclear configuration that minimizes (15.194). Note that (15.194) omits both electron–electron repulsions and nuclear–nuclear repulsions, and it might be thought that such a theory would be useless for predicting molecular geometry, but this is not so.

Allen and Russell compared EH results with those of *ab initio* SCF calculations for 12 molecules. They used (15.199) with $K = 1.5$. They found that for compounds whose bonds are not highly polar, the extended-Hückel-theory graph of (15.194) versus bond angle and the graph of SCF MO total energy (including nuclear repulsion) versus bond angle have minima at essentially the same angles. Since the SCF MO method yields generally accurate bond angles, so does the extended Hückel method for compounds of low polarity. The cases where the extended Hückel method failed ($H_2O, Li_2O, LiOH, FOH$) all involve highly polar bonds. Theoretical arguments have been given to explain why the relatively crude extended Hückel method works so well in predicting bond angles.[38]

Allen and Russell found that the order of MO energies predicted by the extended Hückel method is generally reliable for compounds of low polarity. (Hoffmann's extended Hückel calculation of benzene predicted that the lowest pi MO, the $1a_{2u}$ MO, would lie below some of the occupied sigma MO's, namely, the $3e_{2g}$ and $1b_{2u}$ MO's. The near-Hartree–Fock calculation of benzene done by Ermler and Kern shows the $1a_{2u}$ pi MO to have higher energy than the $1b_{2u}$ MO, but very slightly lower energy than the $3e_{2g}$ pair of sigma MO's.[39] Thus Hoffmann's prediction is partly confirmed.)

For bond lengths, Allen and Russell state that empirical formulas involving bond radii are more reliable than the extended Hückel method.

The extended Hückel MO coefficients are found by Allen and Russell to deviate significantly from those of *ab initio* wave functions. Thus the extended Hückel method cannot be expected to give the accurate predictions of such properties as dipole moments and rotational barriers achieved by the SCF MO method.

The EH method has been widely applied to predict conformations of organic compounds and it was believed to be fairly reliable for such work. However, a careful EH study of benzene showed that the $\mathscr{D}_{6h}$ benzene geometry predicted by EH theory corresponds to a saddle point (rather than a true minimum) on the potential-energy surface for nuclear motion; in fact, EH theory erroneously predicts benzene to be unstable with respect to dissociation to three acetylenes. Hence the reliability of EH theory for conformational studies has come under question. [See W. L. Bloemer and B. L. Bruner, *Chem. Phys. Letters*, **17**, 452 (1972).]

Several two-electron semiempirical MO theories for nonplanar molecules have been developed; these are generalizations of the Pariser–Parr–Pople theory. The *complete neglect of differential overlap* (CNDO) *method* was developed by Pople, Santry, and Segal in 1965; the *intermediate neglect of differential overlap* (INDO)

---

[38] L. C. Allen and J. D. Russell, *J. Chem. Phys.*, **46**, 1029 (1967); S. D. Peyerimhoff, R. J. Buenker, and L. C. Allen, *ibid.*, **45**, 734 (1966).
[39] W. C. Ermler and C. W. Kern, *J. Chem. Phys.*, **58**, 3458 (1973).

method was developed by Pople, Beveridge, and Dobosh in 1967.[40] (If you learn enough abbreviations you can convince most people that you know quantum chemistry.) Both methods treat only the valence electrons explicitly. The valence-electron Hamiltonian has the same form as (15.86);

$$\hat{H}_{\text{val}} = \sum_{i=1}^{n} (-\tfrac{1}{2}\nabla_i^2 + V_i) + \sum_{i=1}^{n} \sum_{j>i} \frac{1}{r_{ij}} \tag{15.200}$$

where there are n valence electrons and V_i is the potential energy of valence electron i in the field of the nuclei and inner-shell electrons; the quantity in parentheses is $\hat{H}_{\text{core}}(i)$. Both methods are SCF methods that iteratively solve the Hartree–Fock–Roothaan equations using the Hamiltonian (15.200), subject to certain approximations for the integrals.

The CNDO method uses a minimal basis set of valence Slater AO's with fixed orbital exponents on each atom. When each MO is expressed as a linear combination of AO's, the molecular Coulomb and exchange integrals that occur in solving the Roothaan equations become linear combinations of two-electron repulsion integrals $(rs|tu)$ over atomic orbitals [Eq. (15.188)]. The CNDO method makes the zero differential overlap approximation [Eq. (15.189)] for all pairs of AO's in two-electron integrals. Thus the only nonvanishing repulsion integrals in CNDO are of the form $(rr|tt)$; since only two AO's occur in these integrals, all three- and four-center integrals are neglected. In the PPP treatment of conjugated hydrocarbons, there is only one basis AO per atom—the $2p\pi$ AO. In the CNDO method, there are several basis valence AO's on every atom (except hydrogens), and the ZDO approximation leads to neglect of electron repulsion integrals containing the product $f_r(1)f_s(1)$ where f_r and f_s are different AO's centered on the *same* atom. The CNDO method also neglects overlap integrals [Eq. (15.185)]. The core-Hamiltonian integrals (15.186) and (15.187) are approximated by using data such as atomic ionization potentials and electron affinities and by taking some of them as semiempirical parameters adjusted so that CNDO calculations will give a good overall fit with the results of minimal basis *ab initio* SCF calculations. The original version of CNDO is called CNDO/1; a version using an improved parametrization is called CNDO/2.

The INDO method is an improvement on CNDO; here, differential overlap between AO's on the same atom is not neglected in one-center electron-repulsion integrals, but is still neglected in two-center electron-repulsion integrals. Thus fewer two-electron integrals are neglected, as compared to CNDO; otherwise, the two methods are the same. The INDO method gives an improvement on CNDO results, especially where electron spin distribution is important (e.g., in calculating electron-spin-resonance spectra).

As to results, the CNDO and INDO methods give generally accurate molecular bond angles, fairly good bond lengths and dipole moments (with a few exceptions), but poor dissociation energies. (For full details on the CNDO and INDO methods, see *Pople and Beveridge*.)

The aim of Pople and co-workers in the CNDO and INDO methods was to

---

[40] J. A. Pople, D. P. Santry, and G. A. Segal, *J. Chem. Phys.*, **43**, S129 (1965); J. A. Pople and G. A. Segal, *ibid.*, **43**, S136; **44**, 3289 (1966); J. A. Pople, D. L. Beveridge, and P. A. Dobosh, *ibid.*, **47**, 2026 (1967).

reproduce as well as possible the results of *ab initio* SCF MO calculations with theories that require much less computational effort than an *ab initio* treatment. Thus, their results have the good and bad features of *ab initio* SCF wave functions: geometries and dipole moments are generally good, but binding energies are poor. Dewar and co-workers devised several semiempirical SCF MO theories which closely resemble the INDO theory. However, Dewar's aim was not to reproduce *ab initio* SCF wave functions, but to have a theory that would give molecular binding energies with chemical accuracy (i.e., to within 1 kcal/mole) and that would be applicable to large molecules without a lot of computation. It might seem unlikely that one could devise an SCF theory that involves approximations to the *ab initio* Hartree–Fock procedure, but that succeeds in an area (binding energies) where the Hartree–Fock theory fails. However, by proper choice of the parameters in the semiempirical SCF theory, one can actually get better results than *ab initio* SCF calculations, because the choice of suitable parameters can compensate for the partial neglect of electron correlation in *ab initio* SCF theory.

In 1967 Dewar and Klopman put forth the PNDO (partial neglect of ...) theory; in 1969, Baird and Dewar published the MINDO/1 (first version of modified INDO) theory.[41] The parameters in these theories were chosen so as to have calculated molecular heats of formation fit experimental data as well as possible. Although these theories worked well for heats of formation, they were quite poor for geometry. Therefore in 1970, Dewar and Haselbach proposed the MINDO/2 theory.[42] In MINDO/2 a very careful choice of parameters allows generally accurate calculations of molecular geometry, as well as quite accurate heats of formation. Since MINDO/2 gives large errors in dipole moments (about 50%) and in bond lengths to hydrogen atoms (0.1 or 0.15 Å too short), MINDO/2' was published in 1972 [N. Bodor, M. J. S. Dewar, and D. H. Lo, *J. Am. Chem. Soc.*, **94**, 5303 (1972)]. This improved version gives good C—H bond lengths and reduces the dipole-moment errors to around 20%.

The MINDO/2' method has been parametrized for compounds containing C, H, O, and N [and also for C, H, F compounds; see M. J. S. Dewar and D. H. Lo, *ibid.*, **94**, 5296 (1972)]. Calculations have been done on molecules as large as the steroid $C_{19}H_{28}O_2$. The typical error in predicted heats of formation ($\Delta H_{f, 298}^\circ$) is 3 kcal/mole. A MINDO calculation yields the molecular heat of atomization; one then uses experimental values of heats of formation of C, H, O, and N atoms from the elements in their standard states (graphite, H_2, O_2, N_2) to calculate $\Delta H_{f, 298}^\circ$. Note that $\Delta H_{f, 298}^\circ$ contains rotational and vibrational contributions (Section 13.1). Rather than being calculated explicitly, these contributions are allowed for by the choice of parameters used in the calculation. The 3 kcal/mole error is higher than Dewar was aiming for, but is still a significant achievement. (MINDO does not do so well with small-ring compounds; here ΔH may be in error by 10 or 20 kcal/mole due to the strain energy.) Bond lengths are typically in error by 0.01 Å, although errors in bonds to nitrogen and oxygen may be larger.

[41] M. J. S. Dewar and G. Klopman, *J. Am. Chem. Soc.*, **89**, 3089 (1967); N. C. Baird and M. J. S. Dewar, *J. Chem. Phys.*, **50**, 1262 (1969); N. C. Baird, M. J. S. Dewar, and R. Sustmann, *ibid.*, **50**, 1275 (1969).

[42] M. J. S. Dewar and E. Haselbach, *J. Am. Chem. Soc.*, **92**, 590 (1970); N. Bodor, M. J. S. Dewar, A. Harget, and E. Haselbach, *ibid.*, **92**, 3854.

Further applications of MINDO/2 and 2' include the following. A study of conformations of organic compounds gave good results [N. Bodor and M. J. S. Dewar, *J. Am. Chem. Soc.*, **92**, 4270 (1970)]. A calculation on cyclobutadiene predicted the ground state to be a singlet with rectangular geometry, in disagreement with the observed infrared spectrum—footnotes 26 and 27 [M. J. S. Dewar, M. C. Kohn, and N. Trinajstic, *ibid.*, **93**, 3437 (1971)]. Methylene (carbene) was predicted to have a triplet-ground-state bond angle of 142°, in pretty good agreement with the *ab initio* CI angle 134° ± 2° and the experimental angle 138° ± 10° (Section 15.7). [N. Bodor, M. J. S. Dewar, and J. S. Wasson, *ibid.*, **94**, 9095 (1972).]

Of course, all the semiempirical treatments of this section are applicable to planar (as well as nonplanar) compounds, and they represent improvements on semiempirical pi-electron theories, since they explicitly allow for the effects of the sigma valence electrons. The development of the MINDO, INDO, and CNDO semiempirical SCF theories has led Murrell and Harget to the conclusion that "Hückel theory has largely outlived its usefulness." A good survey of semiempirical SCF theories is the book by *Murrell and Harget*.

15.10 Valence-Bond Treatment of Polyatomic Molecules

The valence-bond treatment of polyatomic molecules is closely tied to chemical ideas of structure.[43] One begins with the atoms that form the molecule and pairs up the unpaired electrons to form chemical bonds. There are generally several ways of pairing up the electrons; each pairing scheme gives a VB *structure*. The molecular wave function is taken as a linear combination of Heitler–London-type functions (called *bond eigenfunctions*) for each structure, and the variation principle is applied. The VB wave function is said to be a *resonance hybrid* of the various structures; the weight of each resonance structure is usually taken as proportional to the square of its coefficient in the molecular wave function. Because the bond eigenfunctions are not mutually orthogonal, the electron probability density is not equal to the weighted sum of the probability densities of the various structures, and the weights of resonance structures are somewhat lacking in physical significance.

Consider water as an example. The ground-state configuration of oxygen is $1s^2 2s^2 2p^4$ with an unpaired electron in each of the AO's $2p_y$ and $2p_z$. We thus assume that these AO's along with the hydrogen $1s$ AO's will form electron-pair bonds. There are three possible ways of pairing these four AO's to get covalent structures:

$$
\begin{array}{ccccc}
\text{O}2p_y \quad \text{O}2p_z & \quad & \text{O}2p_y\text{——}\text{O}2p_z & \quad & \text{O}2p_y \quad \text{O}2p_z \\
| \qquad\quad | & & & & \diagdown\!\!\!\!\diagup \\
\text{H}_1 1s \quad \text{H}_2 1s & & \text{H}_1 1s\text{——}\text{H}_2 1s & & \text{H}_1 1s \quad \text{H}_2 1s \\
A & & B & & C
\end{array}
\qquad \textbf{(15.201)}
$$

---

[43] For a review of VB theory, see M. Simonetta, "Forty Years of Valence Bond Theory," in A. Rich and N. Davidson, eds., *Structural Chemistry and Molecular Biology*, Freeman, San Francisco, 1968.

Let

$$s_1 \equiv H_1 1s, \qquad s_2 \equiv H_2 1s, \qquad p_y = O2p_y, \qquad p_z = O2p_z$$

The normalized VB function corresponding to structure A is:

$$\Phi_A = N|\cdots \widehat{p_y s_1}\,\widehat{p_z s_2}| = N|\cdots \overline{p_y} s_1 \overline{p_z} s_2| - N|\cdots \overline{p_y} s_1 p_z \overline{s_2}|$$
$$- N|\cdots p_y \overline{s_1} \overline{p_z} s_2| + N|\cdots \overline{p_y} s_1 \overline{p_z} s_2| \qquad \textbf{(15.202)}$$

where the signs are determined by the rule in Section 13.13; the dots stand for $O1s\overline{O1s}O2s\overline{O2s}O2p_x\overline{O2p_x}$. Similarly,

$$\Phi_B = N|\cdots \widehat{p_y p_z}\,\widehat{s_1 s_2}|, \qquad \Phi_C = N|\cdots \widehat{p_y s_2}\,\widehat{p_z s_1}| \qquad \textbf{(15.203)}$$

We then take as a trial variation function ψ, a linear combination of the bond eigenfunctions of structures A, B, and C. However, the functions Φ_A, Φ_B, and Φ_C are not linearly independent; we have (Problem 15.59):

$$\Phi_C = -(\Phi_A + \Phi_B) \qquad \textbf{(15.204)}$$

It is wasted effort to include all three structures; we shall drop structure C, taking $\psi = c_A \Phi_A + c_B \Phi_B$.

For a molecule with n valence AO's to be paired, where n is even, Rumer showed in 1932 that the following procedure gives the linearly independent covalent structures for singlet states: The n AO's are arranged in a ring and lines are drawn between pairs of AO's; those structures where no lines cross are linearly independent. These are the VB *canonical* covalent structures of the molecule. Any structure with lines crossing is linearly dependent on the canonical structures and is omitted from the VB wave function. The number of ways of drawing $\frac{1}{2}n$ noncrossing lines between n points on a circle is [44]:

$$\frac{n!}{(\frac{1}{2}n)!(\frac{1}{2}n+1)!} \qquad \textbf{(15.205)}$$

For water there are $4!/2!\,3! = 2$ canonical covalent structures, and these are A and B. (Actually, which structures are taken as the canonical ones is arbitrary, since the orbitals can be arranged in various ways on the ring.) To use Rumer's method when the number of orbitals to be paired is odd, one adds a "phantom" orbital, whose contribution is subtracted at the end of the calculation.

Rumer's procedure is easily justified. Let $\Phi(|\ \ |)$, $\Phi(\frown)$, and $\Phi(\mathsf{X})$ be three bond eigenfunctions that involve any number of AO's, but that differ only in the way they pair up a certain subset of four AO's—each of these functions corresponds to one of the three different ways of pairing these four AO's [see (15.201)]. By a slight extension of (15.204), it follows that

$$\Phi(\mathsf{X}) = -[\Phi(|\ \ |) + \Phi(\frown)] \qquad \textbf{(15.206)}$$

Any pairing scheme involving lines that cross can be shown by repeated application of (15.206) to be a linear combination of structures with no lines crossing. For

---

[44] For a proof of (15.205), see J. Barriol, *Elements of Quantum Mechanics with Chemical Applications*, Barnes and Noble, 1971, pp. 281–282.

example, consider the following pairing scheme for six orbitals:

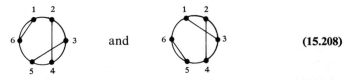

$$(15.207)$$

Application of (15.206) to the set of four AO's 1, 5, 3, 6, shows that (15.207) is a linear combination of

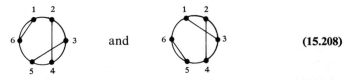

$$(15.208)$$

Use of (15.206) then shows each of the structures in (15.208) to be a linear combination of two structures with no lines crossing. Thus (15.207) has been reduced to a linear combination of canonical structures.

The structures corresponding to the pairing schemes A and B in (15.201) for water are

$$(15.209)$$

The separation between H_1 and H_2 is considerably greater than between O and each hydrogen; the small overlap between the hydrogen $1s$ AO's makes structure A far more significant than structure B. Since the $2p_y$ and $2p_z$ AO's are at 90° to each other, the VB structure A predicts a bond angle of 90°, since this allows maximum overlap between the bonding oxygen and hydrogen AO's. The observed angle of $104\frac{1}{2}°$ can be rationalized by considering electrostatic repulsions between the hydrogen atoms (ionic structures) and by allowing some mixing in (hybridization) of the $2s$ oxygen AO with the two bonding $2p$ AO's.

For H_2, the Heitler–London function was improved by inclusion of small contributions from ionic structures. Because of the considerable electronegativity difference between O and H, we expect ionic structures to be important in H_2O. [Recall, however, that the "covalent" structure A of (15.209) contains some ionic character—see Section 13.18.] Ionic structures for water include:

Because oxygen is much more electronegative than hydrogen, the contributions of G, H, and I should be negligible. A reasonable variation function for water is

$$c_A \Phi_A + c_B \Phi_B + c_D \Phi_D + c_E \Phi_E + c_F \Phi_F \qquad (15.210)$$

The ionic functions are written by analogy to (13.192); for example,

$$\Phi_D = |\cdots \widehat{p_y s_1} \, p_z \overline{p_z}| = |\cdots p_y \overline{s_1} \, p_z \overline{p_z}| - |\cdots \overline{p_y} s_1 \, p_z \overline{p_z}| \qquad (15.211)$$

The linear variation function (15.210) leads to a secular equation

$$\det(H_{ij} - ES_{ij}) = 0 \qquad (15.212)$$

The AO's are expressed as, say, STO's, and the matrix elements and overlap integrals between the functions $\Phi_A, \ldots, \Phi_F$ are calculated. The lowest root of the secular equation gives an approximation to the ground-state energy (higher roots correspond to excited singlet states); evaluation of the corresponding coefficients gives the VB ground-state wave function. The calculation can be done semiempirically using experimental data to evaluate some of the integrals. Calculation of the matrix elements is involved, and approximations are often made; for example, overlap integrals between different AO's (but *not* between different structures) are neglected and exchange integrals involving interchange of the coordinates of more than two electrons are neglected. Systematic procedures for evaluating the matrix elements have been developed.[45]

One of the rare *ab initio* all-electron VB calculations on polyatomic molecules is Peterson and Pfeiffer's calculation on H_2O (Table 15.1). They used a Gaussian-lobe AO basis set and included 10 covalent and 39 ionic VB structures in their wave function. (The large number of structures arises because they considered structures arising from such oxygen configurations as $1s^2 2s2p^5$ and $1s^2 2p^6$, as well as $1s^2 2s^2 2p^4$.) The contribution of ionic structures was found to be 62%. They also performed calculations on OH and O, so as to calculate the first and second bond dissociation energies of H_2O; the calculated dissociation energies were not in good agreement with experiment.

Consider the VB treatment of methane. The carbon ground-state configuration $1s^2 2s^2 2p^2$ has two unpaired electrons and would seem to indicate a valence of two. To get the well-known tetravalence of carbon, we assume that a $2s$ electron is promoted to the vacant $2p$ orbital giving the configuration $1s^2 2s2p^3$. If we then assume one bond is formed with the $2s$ electron and three bonds are formed with the $2p$ electrons, the bonds are not all equivalent as they are known to be. Hence Pauling proposed that the L-shell s and p functions be linearly combined to form *hybridized sp^3 orbitals*, of the form

$$b_i(C2s) + d_i(C2p_x) + e_i(C2p_y) + f_i(C2p_z), \qquad i = 1, \ldots, 4 \qquad (15.213)$$

For maximum overlap, we want each function to point to a vertex of a tetrahedron. From the discussion following Eq. (15.57), the constants d_i, e_i, f_i are proportional to the direction cosines in (15.68). Also, each orbital should have the same value of b_i, so that the four hybrid orbitals will be equivalent. Thus the orbitals (15.213) are of the form (15.69) with $a = 0$ and $2a_1, 1t_{2x}$, etc., replaced by $C2s$, $C2p_x$, etc. If we impose the requirement that the hybrid AO's be orthonormal, we have

$$b^2 + c^2 = 1, \qquad b^2 - \tfrac{1}{3}c^2 = 0 \qquad (15.214)$$

$$c = \tfrac{1}{2}\sqrt{3}, \qquad b = \tfrac{1}{2} \qquad (15.215)$$

[45] L. Pauling, *J. Chem. Phys.*, **1**, 280 (1933); M. Simonetta and V. Schomaker, *ibid.*, **19**, 649 (1951).

The four equivalent sp^3 hybrid carbon AO's are then:

$$te_1 = \tfrac{1}{2}[C2s + C2p_x + C2p_y + C2p_z]$$

$$te_2 = \tfrac{1}{2}[C2s + C2p_x - C2p_y - C2p_z]$$

$$te_3 = \tfrac{1}{2}[C2s - C2p_x + C2p_y - C2p_z]$$

$$te_4 = \tfrac{1}{2}[C2s - C2p_x - C2p_y + C2p_z]$$

(15.216)

where "te" stands for tetrahedral. A typical sp^3 hybrid AO contour is shown in Fig. 15.22. (The three-dimensional shape is obtained by rotation about a horizontal axis through carbon.) Carbon sp^2 and sp hybrid AO's have similar shapes. [See I. Cohen and T. Bustard, *J. Chem. Educ.*, **43**, 187 (1966).]

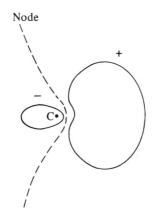

FIGURE 15.22 *Carbon sp^3 hybrid orbital.*

There are many canonical covalent VB structures for methane, as well as ionic structures; however, chemical intuition tells us that the main contribution to the wave function is from the following covalent structure:

$$|C1s\overline{C1s}s_1\,\widehat{te_1}\,\overline{s_2}\,\widehat{te_2}\,\widehat{s_3}\,te_3\,\widehat{s_4}\,\overline{te_4}|$$

(15.217)

where $s_1 = H_1 1s$, etc. The structure (15.217) is a linear combination of $2^4 = 16$ determinants.

For ethylene, the VB method uses sp^2-hybridized carbon AO's to form the sigma bonds by overlap with the $1s$ hydrogen AO's; this leaves a p orbital on each carbon to form the pi bond. The HCH bond angle is predicted to be 120°, in reasonable agreement with the observed value 116° or 117°. For acetylene, each carbon is sp hybridized.

Now consider benzene. We use the pi-electron approximation. The sigma bonds are formed by sp^2 carbon hybrid AO's and $1s$ hydrogen orbitals; this leaves a p orbital on each carbon to form pi bonds. There are 6!/3! 4! = 5 canonical covalent structures for pairing the pi orbitals, and these are:

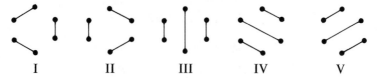

| I | II | III | IV | V |

Structures I and II are the Kekulé structures, and III, IV, and V are the Dewar structures. (The puckered compound bicyclo[2.2.0]hexa-2,5-diene has been

synthesized and is called "Dewar benzene." The VB Dewar "structures" of benzene are formal ways of pairing up electrons in AO's; each VB Dewar "structure" is based on a regular hexagonal arrangement of carbon atoms and is to be distinguished from the compound "Dewar benzene." Likewise, the structures I and II correspond to a regular hexagon of carbons, and differ from the hypothetical cyclohexatriene with alternating bond lengths. Each VB resonance "structure" is based on the same internuclear distances, but a different electron pairing scheme.)

The following types of singly polar ionic structures occur:

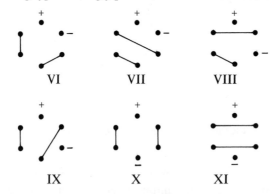

There are 12 structures of the form VI (the plus sign can be put on each of 6 carbons, and the minus sign can be put on the preceding or following carbon), 12 of the form VII, 12 of the form VIII, 12 of the form IX, 6 of the form X, and 6 of the form XI. There are also contributions from doubly polar and triply polar structures. Of course, we include only linearly independent ionic structures; an ionic structure that involves lines crossing is a linear combination of two ionic structures with no lines crossing and is omitted. To simplify things, we include only the ionic structures that make the largest contributions; thus we omit doubly and triply polar structures; also the 6 singly polar structures like XI will be omitted, since they involve two "long" bonds between nonadjacent carbons.

Simonetta[46] did a semiempirical calculation of benzene, including the 5 canonical covalent structures and 54 singly polar ionic structures (VI–X). As for

---

[46] M. Simonetta, *J. Chim. Phys.*, **49**, 68 (1952).

H_2 (Section 13.9), a VB calculation of polyatomic molecules involves Coulomb and exchange integrals. Simonetta took these integrals as empirical parameters whose values are adjusted to fit such experimental data as electronic spectra and thermodynamically determined resonance energies of pi-electron systems. He found for the ground-state pi-electron VB wave function of benzene:

$$0.56\,(I+II) + 0.24\,(III+IV+V) + 0.11\,(VI+11 \text{ others})$$

$$+ 0.05\,(VII+11 \text{ others}) + 0.02\,(VIII+11 \text{ others})$$

$$+ 0.02\,(IX+11 \text{ others}) + 0.02\,(X+5 \text{ others})$$

The Kekulé structures make the greatest contribution. Even though the coefficient of each ionic structure is small, the large number of ionic structures makes their contribution significant.

Recall that increasing the number of functions f_i in a linear variation function $\sum c_i f_i$ improves the variation function; i.e., lowers the value of the variational integral. If we were to consider structure I only, then the energy obtained would be considerably higher than when several VB structures are considered. The difference between the energy for structure I and that found when all VB structures are considered is the *resonance energy* of benzene; the resonance energy is the VB analog of the MO delocalization energy. One says that benzene is "stabilized by resonance," but of course resonance is not a real phenomenon.

Such concepts as "configuration interaction," "resonance," "exchange," "hybridization," etc., are not real physical phenomena, but only artifacts of the approximations used in the calculations. Even the concept of orbitals is but an approximation and, strictly speaking, orbitals do not exist. Around 1950, resonance theory came under attack by some Russian chemists as being "vicious," "perverse," "bourgeois," etc.; the basis for the attack was the fact that VB resonance structures and the resonance "phenomenon" have no physical reality; hence, resonance theory was deemed incompatible with Marxist–Leninist dialectical materialism.[47]

For cyclobutadiene, C_4H_4, a VB treatment including only the two canonical covalent pi-electron structures gives considerable resonance energy and thus predicts stability for the molecule; however, when singly and doubly polar ionic structures are included, the VB method does predict lack of stability.[48]

Using the pi-electron approximation for butadiene, we have $4!/2!\,3! = 2$ canonical covalent VB structures:

$$1: \quad CH_2{=}CH{-}CH{=}CH_2 \qquad 2: \quad \overline{CH_2{-}CH{=}CH{-}CH_2}$$

There are 12 singly polar ionic structures (Problem 15.64) of which two have a central double bond. Simonetta's 14-structure semiempirical calculation[49] gave the partial double-bond character of the central bond as due mainly to structure 2.

---

[47] For further discussion, see I. M. Hunsberger, *J. Chem. Educ.*, **31**, 504 (1954). For translations of Russian attacks on resonance, see I. S. Bengelsdorf, *J. Chem. Educ.*, **29**, 2, 13 (1952).

[48] R. McWeeny, *Proc. Roy. Soc.*, **A227**, 288 (1955).

[49] M. Simonetta, *J. Chim. Phys.*, **49**, 68 (1952); see also M. Simonetta, E. Gianinetti, and I. Vandoni, *J. Chem. Phys.*, **48**, 1579 (1968)—this paper formulates VB theory for nonsinglet states.

(a)

(b)

(c)   (d)

FIGURE 15.23   *Some* VB *pi-electron structures for naphthalene.   (a) The three Kekulé structures.   (b) Two Dewar structures.   (c) A doubly excited structure.   (d) A triply excited structure.*

Naphthalene has $10!/5!\,6! = 42$ canonical covalent structures for the pi electrons.   There are 3 Kekulé structures (no "long" bonds), 16 Dewar structures (one long bond), 19 structures with two long bonds, and 4 structures with three long bonds (Fig. 15.23).   The number of long bonds is called the *degree of excitation* of a VB structure; a Kekulé structure is unexcited, a Dewar structure singly excited, etc. (There is no connection between the degree of excitation of a VB structure and the excited electronic states of a molecule.)   The greater the degree of excitation, the smaller the contribution of a structure.   Each VB pi-electron structure of naphthalene is a linear combination of $2^5 = 32$ determinants and the calculation of matrix elements between the 42 covalent structures and perhaps some ionic structures as well is involved.   Obviously, the MO approach is computationally much simpler than the VB method for aromatic hydrocarbons.   The naphthalene ionic structures are usually omitted in calculations, not because their contribution is negligible, but because their inclusion makes the calculation quite difficult.   A semiempirical naphthalene calculation[50] that includes the 42 covalent structures and no ionic structures showed the first Kekulé structure in Fig. 15.23a to be the most important one.

As in the MO method, one can define VB pi-electron bond orders, free valences, etc.

Organic chemists have found the ideas of VB (resonance) theory valuable for rationalizing in a simple manner the facts of organic structure and reactions; no doubt the reader is familiar with such applications from organic-chemistry courses. However, quantitative application of the VB method is much harder than for the MO method.   In most cases, the single-determinant Hartree–Fock MO wave function (or an accurate SCF approximation to it) furnishes a good description of the molecular ground state; in contrast, the VB ground-state wave function frequently must be taken as a linear combination of many covalent and ionic structures.   For quantitative calculations, the MO method has overshadowed the VB method.   The VB resonance approach is perhaps best suited to qualitative discussion of molecular structure.[51]

[50] T. H. Goodwin, *Theor. Chim. Acta*, **2**, 315 (1964).
[51] See L. Pauling, *The Nature of the Chemical Bond*, Third Edition, Cornell University Press, Ithaca, 1960; G. W. Wheland, *Resonance in Organic Chemistry*, Wiley, New York, 1955.

The VB method is often described as having the advantage of being based on familiar chemical ideas of bonding and structure. While it is true that the canonical MO's are not related to chemical bonds, the energy-localized MO's (which are becoming available for an increasing number of molecules) do furnish a convenient description in terms of chemical bonds.

Finally, we consider the concept of the *valence state* of an atom. By the valence state of an atom for a given molecular electronic state, we mean the state in which the atom exists in the molecule. Since individual atoms don't really exist in molecules, the valence-state concept is an approximate one. The VB approximation constructs molecular wave functions from wave functions of the individual atoms; we use the VB wave function to define the valence state of an atom as the wave function obtained on removing all other atoms to infinity, while keeping the form of the molecular wave function invariant. (This process is purely hypothetical, and the valence state is not in general a stationary atomic state.)

The simplest example is the H_2 ground state. The Heitler–London function is

$$N|1s_a\overline{1s_b}| = N[|1s_a\overline{1s_b}| - |\overline{1s_a}1s_b|]$$

Removal of hydrogen atom b leaves (at large internuclear separation, the normalization constant for each Slater determinant becomes $1/\sqrt{2}$):

$$2^{-1/2}1s_a - 2^{-1/2}\overline{1s_a} \tag{15.218}$$

We have a hydrogen atom with a $1s$ spatial function and a 50 percent probability for having each of spin α or spin β. The valence-state ionization potential of hydrogen is thus 13.6 eV, as in (15.197).

A less trivial example is water. The largest contribution to the VB wave function is from the bond eigenfunction (15.202). Removal of the hydrogen atoms from (15.202) gives

$$N[|\cdots 2p_y 2p_z| - |\cdots \overline{2p_y} 2p_z| - |\cdots 2p_y \overline{2p_z}| + |\cdots \overline{2p_y} \overline{2p_z}|] \tag{15.219}$$

Each determinant in (15.219) belongs to the oxygen configuration $1s^2 2s^2 2p^4$. This configuration gives the terms ^3P, ^1D, and ^1S (Table 11.2). The first and last determinants are eigenfunctions of $\hat{S}_z$ with eigenvalues $+1\hbar$ and $-1\hbar$, respectively; hence these two determinants must correspond to states of the ^3P term (which has $S=1$). Analysis (which we omit) of the other two determinants shows each of them to be an equal mixture (coefficients $1/\sqrt{2}$) of states belonging to the ^1D and ^3P terms. Thus the valence state is a mixture of states of the terms ^1D and ^3P and is definitely not a stationary state of the atom. The valence-state wave function ψ_{vs} is not an eigenfunction of the atomic Hamiltonian; we can, however, calculate an average energy:

$$\langle E \rangle_{vs} = \int \psi_{vs}^* \hat{H}\psi_{vs}\, d\tau \Big/ \int \psi_{vs}^* \psi_{vs}\, d\tau$$

From $\psi_{vs} = c_1\psi(^3P) + c_2\psi(^1D)$, we have

$$\langle E \rangle_{vs} = \frac{|c_1|^2 E(^3P) + |c_2|^2 E(^1D)}{|c_1|^2 + |c_2|^2}$$

From the above arguments, we have for c_1 and c_2 in the unnormalized valence-state wave function:

$$|c_1|^2 = 1^2 + (2^{-1/2})^2 + (2^{-1/2})^2 + 1^2 = 3$$
$$|c_2|^2 = (2^{-1/2})^2 + (2^{-1/2})^2 = 1$$

The valence-state energy is then

$$\langle E \rangle_{vs} = \tfrac{3}{4}E(^3P) + \tfrac{1}{4}E(^1D) \tag{15.220}$$

$\langle E \rangle_{vs}$ can then be calculated from Moore's tables of atomic energy levels (Section 11.6).

If $2s$ hybridization is included in the $2p$ bonding oxygen orbitals of water, the oxygen valence state is found [52] to be a linear combination involving terms of the configurations $1s^2 2s^2 2p^4$, $1s^2 2s2p^5$, and $1s^2 2p^6$. Hybridization gives a mixing of configurations in the valence state.

The valence state of carbon in methane is of considerable importance. It is sometimes carelessly stated that the carbon sp^3 valence state corresponds to the ^5S term of the carbon atom $2s2p^3$ configuration. This is not correct. The $M_S = 2$ state of the $2s2p^3$ $^5S_2$ level has one $2s$ and three $2p$ electrons with all four of these electrons having spin α. It is true that we can use the procedure of Section 15.5 to form linear combinations of the $2s$ and $2p$ orbitals and thereby put each of the four outer electrons of the $^5S_2$ $M_S = 2$ state into an sp^3 hybrid AO without changing the wave function. However, each such hybrid AO would still have spin α. On the other hand, when we remove the hydrogen AO's from the CH_4 VB wave function (15.217), we are left with a linear combination of 16 determinants in which each sp^3 hybrid AO has spin α in 8 determinants and spin β in 8 determinants. Thus the carbon valence state differs from the $2s2p^3$ $^5S_2$ $M_S = 2$ state, and in fact differs from the other states of this term. The valence state obtained on removal of the H's from (15.217) turns out to be a mixture of states of the ^5S, ^3D, and ^1D terms of the $2s2p^3$ atomic configuration. [When other CH_4 VB structures besides (15.217) are included, we also get contributions from terms of the $2p^4$ and $2s^2 2p^2$ configurations to the C valence state.[53]] The valence-state energy of carbon is well above the energy of the ground ^3P term of the $2s^2 2p^2$ configuration, but the energy gained by forming four bonds instead of two, more than compensates for the energy needed to form the valence state.

Valence-state ionization potentials are used to estimate integrals in semi-empirical calculations, such as the extended Hückel and Pariser–Parr–Pople methods. The valence-state ionization potential for a $2p$ electron in an sp^3-hybridized carbon atom [Eq. (15.197)] is the energy difference between the valence state of sp^3-hybridized C and the valence state of sp^2-hybridized C^+. Tables of valence-state ionization potentials are available.[54] Valence-state ionization

[52] M. Kotani, K. Ohno, and K. Kayama, "Quantum Mechanics of Electronic Structure," in S. Flugge, ed., *Encyclopedia of Physics/Handbuch der Physik*, Springer, Berlin, 1961, vol. 37, pp. 110–115.

[53] H. H. Voge, *J. Chem. Phys.*, **4**, 581 (1936).

[54] J. Hinze and H. H. Jaffé, *J. Am. Chem. Soc.*, **84**, 540 (1962); G. Pilcher and H. A. Skinner, *J. Inorg. Nucl. Chem.*, **24**, 937 (1962); L. C. Cusachs, J. W. Reynolds, and D. Barnard, *J. Chem. Phys.*, **44**, 835 (1966).

potentials and electron affinities are also used to calculate electronegativities from Mulliken's definition of half the sum of the valence-state ionization potential and electron affinity.

15.11 Chemical Reactions

The course of a chemical reaction is determined by the potential-energy function for nuclear motion $U(q_\alpha)$ (Section 13.1), where q_α indicates the coordinates of the N nuclei of the reactant molecules. For two atoms coming together to form a diatomic molecule, U is a function of one variable, the internuclear distance R, and $U(R)$ is the usual potential-energy curve. For more interesting chemical reactions, U is a function of $3N-6$ variables; we subtract 6 because the 3 translational and 3 rotational degrees of freedom of the system leave U unchanged. (For a two-atom system, there are only 2 rotational degrees of freedom.) U gives what is called the *potential-energy surface* for the reaction. If U depends on two variables, then a plot of $U(q_1, q_2)$ in three dimensions gives a surface in ordinary three-dimensional space. Because of the large number of variables $U(q_\alpha)$ is a "surface" in an abstract "space" of $3N-5$ dimensions. To find $U(q_\alpha)$, we must solve the electronic Schroedinger equation at a large number of nuclear configurations, a truly formidable task.

Once U is found, we look for the path of minimum potential energy on U connecting reactants and products. This minimum-energy path is called the *reaction path* (or *reaction coordinate*). For the reverse reaction, the surface U is the same as for the forward reaction, but the reaction path is traversed in the reverse direction. The point of maximum potential energy U on the reaction path is called the *transition state* (or *activated complex*); this is a saddle point on the U surface, since it is a maximum point on a minimum-energy path. The transition state is not a stable molecule, and the transition from reactants to products is a smooth one. (However, in certain theories of reaction rates, it is convenient to ascribe molecular properties such as entropy, free energy, vibrational frequencies, etc., to the transition state.) The energy difference between the transition state and the reactants is called the *barrier height* for the forward reaction.

When the U surface is known, it is possible (at least in principle) to calculate the reaction rate constant k as a function of temperature. Such calculations are extremely difficult. One must allow for quantum-mechanical tunneling through the barrier. Moreover, there is significant probability for molecules to traverse the reaction surface on paths that deviate somewhat from the minimum-energy path. Thus one must perform averaging over the various possible paths. (In other words, we must consider different approaches of the reactant molecules, calculate the probability of reaction occurring for each approach, and then suitably average these probabilities.) The rate constant thus depends not only on the barrier height, but on the whole shape of the reaction potential-energy surface. (Speaking thermodynamically, one considers the activation entropy as well as the activation energy.) For qualitative discussion, we can use the fact that a large barrier height means a small rate constant, and a low barrier means a fast reaction.

By measuring the experimental rate constant k as a function of temperature, one can determine an experimental *activation energy* E_a, where $k = A \exp(-E_a/RT)$. The experimental quantity E_a *differs* from the barrier height on the U surface. [See I. Shavitt, *J, Chem. Phys.*, **49**, 4048 (1968); M. Menzinger and R. Wolfgang, *Angew. Chem. Int. Ed. Engl.*, **8**, 438 (1969).] However, the difference between these two quantities should usually be rather small, and we can use experimental activation energies as a check on calculated theoretical barrier heights.

The Hückel theory has been used to derive a variety of reactivity indices (e.g., free valence) for organic reactions. The results of such predictions are rather mixed, and we refer the reader elsewhere for details. (See Chapter 17 of *Murrell, Kettle, and Tedder*, Chapters 11–15 of *Streitwieser*.)

In the 1960's several workers applied orbital symmetry rules to predict the course of chemical reactions. The most fruitful applications have come from the *Woodward–Hoffmann rules*, which predict the preferred path and stereochemistry for many important classes of organic reactions. As an example of the application of these rules, we consider the cyclization of a substituted *s-cis*-butadiene to a substituted cyclobutene. There are two possible steric courses the reaction can take, described as *conrotatory* or *disrotatory*, depending on whether the terminal groups rotate in the same or opposite senses as the reaction proceeds. Note the difference in products in Fig. 15.24.

FIGURE 15.24 *Conrotatory and disrotatory cyclizations. All atoms lie in the same plane except those shown with dashed or heavy bonds.*

One finds that when the reaction is thermally induced, the butadiene cyclization process is conrotatory, but when the reaction is photochemically induced, the process is disrotatory. To explain these facts, Woodward and Hoffmann examined the symmetry of the highest occupied MO of the substituted *s-cis*-butadiene; this is the pi MO φ_2 in Fig. 15.16. Figure 15.25 shows that for φ_2, a conrotatory motion of the pi AO's on carbons 1 and 4 causes the positive lobe of $C_1 2p\pi$ to overlap the positive lobe of $C_4 2p\pi$; this overlap gives a bonding interaction of these AO's

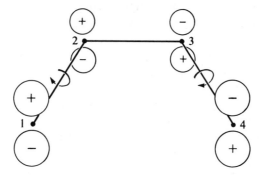

FIGURE 15.25   *Relative phases of* AO*'s in the highest occupied butadiene* MO.

and leads to formation of the 1–4 sigma bond of the cyclobutene. On the other hand, a disrotatory motion of these two AO's causes overlap of the positive lobe of one pi AO with the negative lobe of the other pi AO; this gives an antibonding interaction. Thus we expect the conrotatory process to have a lower activation energy than the disrotatory, and to be preferred over the disrotatory. As a further check, we note that conrotatory motion leads to an antibonding interaction between the carbon 1 and 4 pi AO's in the lowest pi MO φ_1; this leaves the pi AO's of carbons 2 and 3 in φ_1 to form the 2–3 pi bond in the cyclobutene. (Note that if the butadiene is less symmetrically substituted than in Fig. 15.24, clockwise and counterclockwise conrotatory motions lead to a mixture of two products.)

When the above reaction is induced photochemically, an absorbed photon excites an electron from φ_2 to the butadiene pi MO φ_3 (Fig. 15.16). The highest-occupied MO is now φ_3, in which the $2p\pi$ AO's on carbons 1 and 4 have the same phases (rather than opposite phases as in φ_2) and a disrotatory motion produces positive bonding overlap between these AO's. Thus we predict disrotatory ring closure, as observed. The same reasoning correctly predicts the courses of other polyene ring closures (Problem 15.71).

Provided the reactants and products do not differ greatly in energy, a high barrier for the forward reaction implies a high barrier for the reverse reaction (in which the reaction path is traversed in the opposite direction). Thus the above reasoning also applies in determining the course of the reverse, ring-opening, reactions.

For further details of the Woodward–Hoffmann rules and their application to a wide variety of organic reactions, see R. B. Woodward and R. Hoffmann, *Angew. Chem. Intern. Ed.*, **8**, 781 (1969); *The Conservation of Orbital Symmetry*, Academic Press, 1970; R. E. Lehr and A. P. Marchand, *Orbital Symmetry*, Academic Press, 1972.

Pearson has applied orbital symmetry concepts to inorganic reactions. As two reactant molecules approach, electrons begin to flow from the highest-occupied molecular orbital (HOMO) of one to the lowest-unoccupied MO (LUMO) of the other. These two MO's are called *frontier orbitals*. For a low activation energy, we require a positive overlap between these two MO's.

An example is the $H_2 + F_2 \to 2HF$ reaction. Consider a proposed mechanism in which the two molecules collide broadside to give a four-center transition state. The HOMO of H_2 is the $\sigma_g 1s$ MO; the LUMO of F_2 is the $\sigma_u^* 2p$ MO (Sections 13.5 and 13.6). Flow of electrons out of H_2 $\sigma_g 1s$ toward F_2 $\sigma_u^* 2p$ would lead to breaking of the H—H bond and formation of two H—F bonds. However, Fig. 15.26a shows that these two MO's do not have a positive overlap. Hence electron flow from H_2 to F_2 is forbidden by symmetry. Figure 15.26b shows the HOMO of F_2 and LUMO of H_2. Here there is a positive overlap, but flow of electrons out of the antibonding π_g^* MO would strengthen, rather than weaken the F—F bond. We conclude that this bimolecular one-step mechanism has a high activation energy and

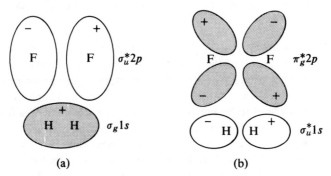

FIGURE 15.26 HOMO's and LUMO's for H_2 and F_2. Occupied MO's are shaded.

is not favored. The same reasoning applies to the famous $H_2 + I_2$ reaction. From 1898 to 1967 the world was under the misapprehension that this reaction had a simple one-step bimolecular mechanism. Careful work shows that in fact the mechanism involves initial dissociation of I_2 to I atoms which then react with H_2; see *Annual Review of Physical Chemistry*, 1970, pp. 376–380.

Further applications of orbital symmetry to inorganic reactions may be found in R. G. Pearson, *Chem. Eng. News*, Sept. 28, 1970, p. 66; *Accounts Chem. Res.*, **4**, 152 (1971); *J. Am. Chem. Soc.*, **94**, 8287 (1972).

We now consider *ab initio* calculation of reaction surfaces. As we have seen, the Hartree–Fock method does not generally describe correctly the process of molecular dissociation; hence (except in certain special cases), we must include CI in kinetics calculations. Together with the large number of variables, this makes calculation of $U(q_\alpha)$ a very difficult problem. Nevertheless, around 1970, meaningful *ab initio* kinetics calculations started to become available.

The $F + H_2 \to FH + H$ reaction has been studied experimentally using molecular beams and laser spectroscopy. Bender and co-workers did *ab initio* CI calculations for this reaction using a large basis set. Preliminary calculations had shown that the reaction path is linear, with the F atom approaching along the H—H internuclear line. Bender *et al.* determined the reaction path by investigating over 150 linear geometries. The saddle point was found to occur early in the course of the reaction, with the H—H distance slightly lengthened from its calculated equilibrium value of 0.75 Å to 0.77 Å; the saddle-point F—H distance is 1.53 Å, compared to 0.93 Å in HF. Thus the transition state resembles H_2 much more than HF. The experimental activation energy is 1.7 kcal/mole. A Hartree–Fock calculation gave a barrier of 34 kcal; the large error here is, of course, expected. With a 338-configuration wave function, Bender et al. found a barrier height of 1.7 kcal, in agreement with the experimental E_a. (The perfect agreement may be fortuitous, since these two quantities can be expected to differ somewhat, as we noted earlier.) These workers conclude that their potential surface is probably quite realistic. Since the reaction path is linear, $U(q_\alpha)$ is a function of two variables, which can be taken as the H—H and F—H distances, and U can be conveniently plotted in three dimensions. One can also make two-dimensional contour diagrams of U (as we did for orbitals). Bender and co-workers give some beautiful three-dimensional plots of U for this reaction. See C. F. Bender, P. K. Pearson, S. V. O'Neil, and H. F. Schaefer, J. Chem. Phys., **56**, 4626 (1972); Science, **176**, 1412 (1972); Schaefer, pp. 272–281.

Hsu, Buenker, and Peyerimhoff did an ab initio CI study of the interconversion of cyclobutene and s-cis-butadiene. Their wave functions contained up to 260 configurations, but because of the size of the molecule, their basis set was not as good as one would ideally want. The potential surface is 24-dimensional, so obviously they had to restrict the geometry variations to be considered. They calculated points corresponding to conrotatory (and disrotatory) rotations of the CH_2 groups and variations in R_{14}, the 1–4 carbon–carbon distance. These are clearly the geometrical parameters that undergo the greatest change in the course of the reaction. In agreement with experiment and the Woodward–Hoffmann rules, they found the conrotatory path to be the favored one; the disrotatory path had a barrier 14 kcal/mole higher than the conrotatory. The minimum-energy path they found has an interesting stepwise process. For ring opening, first R_{14} increases to a value about midway between cyclobutene and butadiene; then the CH_2 groups abruptly rotate 90° in a conrotatory manner; finally, R_{14} increases to its value in butadiene. It was previously believed that the CH_2 groups rotated gradually and continuously as R_{14} varied. [K. Hsu, R. J. Buenker, and S. D. Peyerimhoff, J. Am. Chem. Soc., **93**, 2117 (1971).]

Perhaps the most famous reaction surface is that for $H + H_2 \rightarrow H_2 + H$. The H_3 surface has been calculated to high accuracy with CI wave functions. From this surface, rate constants have been calculated. (See Schaefer, pp. 316–319.)

The semiempirical method that best reproduces molecular geometry, heats of formation, and force constants is MINDO/2 (and 2'). Hence this method may be useful for calculating reaction paths. Several MINDO/2 reaction studies have been done. Reaction paths and activation energies have been calculated for reactions of CH_2 with methane and with ethylene. [N. Bodor, M. J. S. Dewar, and J. S. Wasson, J. Am. Chem. Soc., **94**, 9095 (1972).] A MINDO/2 calculation gave a barrier height of 9.1 kcal/mole for the reaction of CH_3 with ethylene, compared to an observed activation energy of 7.8–8.9 kcal/mole. [J. R. Hoyland, Theor. Chim. Acta, **22**, 229 (1971).] A MINDO/2 study of the reaction cyclobutene → s-cis-butadiene gave a conrotatory barrier height of $49\frac{1}{2}$ kcal/mole, compared to the observed 32 kcal/mole activation energy; recall that MINDO/2 does not do well on small-ring compounds. [J. W. McIver and A. Komornicki, *J. Am. Chem. Soc.*, **94**, 2625 (1972).]

To improve the applicability of MINDO/2 to kinetics, Bingham and Dewar added a single excited configuration to the MINDO/2 ground-state wave function to give MINDO/CI. [R. C. Bingham and M. J. S. Dewar, *J. Am. Chem. Soc.*, **94**, 9107, (1972).] Because of the enormous difficulties involved in *ab initio* reaction-surface calculations, it would be very desirable to have a semiempirical method that gave reliable reaction-surface results. It is too early to tell whether MINDO/CI will meet this need.

15.12 Computers and Quantum Chemistry

An *ab initio* calculation of the wave function of a medium-sized molecule may involve evaluation of 10^6 integrals and solution of secular equations of high degree; a computer is clearly indispensable.

Digital computers use electronic circuits to perform arithmetic and logical operations. The advantages of a computer are the great speed and the accuracy with which they do arithmetic. Any task to be performed by a computer (whether it be evaluation of an integral or translation from one language to another) must be reduced to a problem in arithmetic or symbol manipulation. One must know how to solve a problem by hand calculation before it can be programmed for a computer.

A stored program provides for optimum use of a digital computer. A *program* is a series of instructions fed into the computer. After the program has been stored, the data required for the calculation are fed in and the desired calculations performed in accordance with the program's instructions. The computer can only "understand" instructions written in machine language, a language in which each step to be performed is explicitly specified according to a certain code. To write a machine-language program is extremely tedious and subject to error; moreover, machine language is peculiar to the type of computer being used. To avoid the difficulty of dealing with machine language, various other languages (e.g., FORTRAN, PL/1, ALGOL) have been devised; these are similar in appearance to ordinary algebra and enable complex programs to be written easily. In the United States, FORTRAN (*formula translation*) is the language commonly used for computer applications in the sciences. A FORTRAN program is usable (with perhaps minor changes) on most computers. Statements in FORTRAN cannot be understood by the computer; hence, after being read in, a FORTRAN program is translated by the computer (using an auxiliary program supplied by the manufacturer) to machine language.

Computer calculations are typically done to 7 or 8 significant figures (although provision for "double precision" 16-figure calculations is usually available). A calculation such as the solution of a high-degree secular equation involves many arithmetic steps, and although each step is performed to 8-place accuracy, the final answers may be accurate to, say, only 5 places, because of accumulated round-off errors.

Despite their high speed and accuracy, computers do only what they are instructed to do, and are not capable of exercising independent judgment to compensate for human errors in the program or input data. There is a tendency to consider a calculation that has been performed by a computer as having some special validity beyond what it would have if done by hand; however, every step of a computer calculation is performed in response to the directions given in the program, and the results can be no better or worse than the input data and program. A computer is no substitute for intelligent thought. (There are in the literature several quantum-chemistry computer calculations that are totally in error, due to errors in the programs used.) A favorite maxim of computer programmers is GIGO—garbage in, garbage out.

The reader interested in doing molecular calculations can (for a modest fee) obtain programs from the Quantum Chemistry Program Exchange, Chemistry Department, Indiana University, Bloomington, Indiana 47401. Available programs include the HMO, EH, PPP, CNDO, INDO, MINDO, and *ab initio* SCF MO methods.

The utility of computers for performing lengthy calculations is unquestioned. However, their capabilities in some other areas have sometimes been exaggerated. Despite considerable effort expended in devising programs for translating from one language to another, a 1966 review[55] of work in this field concluded that "There has been no [useful] machine translation of general scientific text...." Since then progress has been made and a 1973 *Newsweek* article[56] reported the imminent availability of useful programs for computer translation of scientific text; however, computer translation of nonscientific text is still an unsolved problem. A checker-playing computer program that plays the game better than all but a few humans has been developed.[57] Checkers, however, is a comparatively simple game, which has been largely "played out," i.e., essentially all plausible checker moves have been explored over the years by checker players, and the strongest moves in most positions are known. A game between two master checker players will almost always end in a draw. (To avoid this, the opening three moves in a checker game are drawn from a hat to force the players to use the less safe opening moves; even so, most master checker games are still drawn.) Chess is a much deeper game than checkers, and despite a 1957 prediction[58] that within 10 years a computer would be the chess champion of the world, present chess-playing programs play a good game, but one that is well below master standards.[59] This does not mean that computers will never play grandmaster chess or translate novels. Such achievements may come in time. They will, however, more likely be due to the people who devise the programs than to the supposed "intelligence" of computers.

---

[55] *Language and Machines*, National Academy of Sciences, National Research Council, Washington, D.C., 1966.

[56] *Newsweek*, Feb. 26, 1973, p. 49.

[57] A. L. Samuel, *IBM J. Res. Develop.*, **3**, 211 (1959); **11**, 601 (1967).

[58] H. A. Simon and A. Newell, *Operations Research*, **6**, 1 (1958).

[59] The computer chess program Mac Hack Six has a tournament record (against amateurs) of 3 wins, 12 losses, and 3 draws; for some of its games, see R. D. Greenblatt, D. E. Eastlake, and S. D. Crocker, *Proceedings of the Fall Joint Computer Conference*, **31**, 801 (1967). *Newsweek*, Aug. 28, 1972 reports on an all-computer chess tournament. See also A. L. Zobrist and F. R. Carlson, *Scientific American*, June 1973, p. 93; D. Levy, *Chess Life and Review*, **28**, 723 (1973).

Despite the so-far relatively unimpressive results of those working on artificial "intelligence" (AI), Marvin Minsky of MIT stated[60] in 1970 that "In from three to eight years we will have a machine with the general intelligence of an average human being.... After all, the human brain is just a computer that happens to be made out of meat." Whether machine intelligence will ever become a reality is a hotly debated question.[61] Objectivity in this area is hard to come by, since AI is related to the larger question: Are we machines?

A few people have deplored the introduction of computers into science and mathematics, claiming that creative thought is thereby stifled. While it is true that computers have sometimes been misused, they offer the only possibility for obtaining accurate molecular wave functions. Computers have also become important in processing the data of spectroscopy experiments.[62]

15.13 The Future of Quantum Chemistry

In the 1950's there was a general belief that meaningful *ab initio* calculation of molecular properties for all except very small molecules was out of the question. Quantum-chemistry books written in this period contain such statements as, "we cannot hope ever to make satisfactory *ab initio* calculations [for organic compounds]" and "It is wise to renounce at the outset any attempt at obtaining precise solutions of the Schroedinger equation for systems more complicated than the hydrogen molecule ion." In 1959, Mulliken and Roothaan identified the "bottleneck" holding up accurate quantum-mechanical calculations on polyatomic molecules as the difficulty in evaluating multicenter integrals.[63] This bottleneck has now been broken, and computer programs for accurate evaluation of three- and four-center integrals are available. The mood of many (but not all) quantum chemists has changed to one of cautious optimism. The remarkable success in *ab initio* calculations of such properties as rotational barriers in medium-sized molecules like ethane has justified this optimism. At present, the principal limitations on the size of a molecule for which one can do an accurate *ab initio* SCF MO calculation are those imposed by the storage capacity and speed of the available electronic computers; as larger and faster computers are developed, it will become feasible to treat larger molecules.[64] (Recall the *ab initio* treatments of naphthalene, azulene, and guanine-cytosine mentioned earlier.) Moreover, Dewar's MINDO method shows that by proper parametrization, a semiempirical SCF method can largely overcome the deficiencies of the Hartree–Fock method in calculating dissociation energies.

---

[60] *Life*, Nov. 20, 1970, p. 58B. Minsky was a technical adviser to the film *2001*, whose most interesting character was a computer named HAL.

[61] See H. Dreyfus, *What Computers Can't Do*, Harper and Row, 1972; I. Benson, *New Scientist*, **51**, 525 (1971); K. Gunderson, *Mentality and Machines*, Doubleday Anchor, 1971.

[62] See S. P. Perone and D. O. Jones, *Digital Computers in Scientific Instrumentation*, McGraw-Hill, 1973.

[63] R. S. Mulliken and C. C. J. Roothaan, *Proc. Natl. Acad. Sci. U.S.*, **45**, 394 (1959).

[64] For references to calculations done subsequent to the publication of this book, consult the review articles on quantum chemistry in volumes of the *Annual Review of Physical Chemistry*. A useful compilation is: W. G. Richards, T. E. H. Walker, and R. K. Hinkley, *A Bibliography of Ab Initio Molecular Wave Functions*, Oxford U. Press, 1971.

Although many-center integrals are computed rapidly and accurately using GTO's, the large number of GTO basis functions needed to represent an AO accurately leads to huge numbers of electron-repulsion integrals. Clementi noted that it is a waste of computer time to compute very small integrals to high accuracy. He implemented a procedure in which the computer tests electron-repulsion integrals to get their order of magnitude before computing them. Integrals less than 10^{-7} atomic units (a.u.) are neglected entirely; those in the range 10^{-7} to 10^{-5} a.u. are computed with intermediate accuracy; those larger than 10^{-5} a.u. are computed with full accuracy. This cuts computation time very substantially while leading to no significant loss in accuracy of the over-all SCF calculation. For example, suppose one is representing each of the four AO's in an electron-repulsion integral $(ij|kl)$ by a linear combination of 5 GTO's; one then has to compute $5^4 = 625$ integrals to evaluate $(ij|kl)$; however, if $(ij|kl)$ is in the range 10^{-7} to 10^{-5} a.u., Clementi approximates each AO by a single Gaussian and then has to compute only one integral to evaluate $(ij|kl)$ to the desired intermediate accuracy. These single Gaussians used to approximate the AO's form the *adjoined* basis set; the use of two basis sets (the adjoined set and the accurate set) in integral evaluation gives a *dynamical* basis set. Using a dynamical basis set, Clementi evaluated the integrals for $C_{25}N_4O_7H_{14}$ (the trinitrofluorenone-carbazole complex), a 50-atom 248-electron system in only $6\frac{1}{2}$ hours of computer time using a basis set of 618 GTO's contracted to 194 linear combinations. In addition to the cutting of computation time, the computer storage space needed is cut because integrals less than 10^{-7} a.u. are not stored and those between 10^{-7} and 10^{-5} a.u. are stored with fewer significant figures than those computed with full accuracy. [See E. Clementi, *Proc. Nat. Acad. Sci. USA*, **69**, 2942 (1972).]

An approach called the SCF Xα scattered-wave (SCF-Xα-SW) method uses numerical integration (rather than an analytic process as in the Roothaan equations) to find approximate solutions to Hartree–Fock-like equations. Evaluation of multicenter integrals is not required, so near-Hartree–Fock accuracy can be obtained with less computation time than in the conventional SCF method. An SCF-Xα-SW calculation on ethane gave a barrier of 2.9 kcal/mole in only a few minutes of computer time. The number of applications of this method is small so far, but it appears to be promising. [See U. Wahlgren and K. H. Johnson, *J. Chem. Phys.*, **56**, 3715 (1972) and references cited therein. For a different view, see E. Clementi, H. Kistenmacher, and H. Popkie, *ibid.*, **58**, 4699 (1973).]

Although a near-Hartree–Fock wave function allows accurate calculation of many equilibrium molecular properties (equilibrium geometry, dipole moment, rotational barrier), it must still deviate significantly from the true wave function. Computer programs to apply configuration interaction to medium-sized molecules have been developed, and significant CI wave functions for polyatomic molecules are now beginning to appear, at least for relatively small polyatomics. (Examples mentioned earlier include H_2O, CH_2, C_4H_6.) Chemical kinetics is beginning to benefit from *ab initio* CI calculations of reaction surfaces (Section 15.11).

Application of configuration interaction to a polyatomic-molecule SCF MO wave function is computationally difficult because of the many configurations that must be included to get significant improvement in the wave function. Hence, other techniques have been proposed to deal with electron correlation. The localized MO's are well separated from each other, thus minimizing repulsions between them; so, as noted earlier, correlation is greatest between two electrons in the same MO. Hurley, Lennard-Jones, and Pople therefore suggested the *separated-pair approximation*; here the molecular wave function is approximated not as an antisymmetrized product of one-electron functions (called orbitals by Mulliken) but as an antisymmetrized product of localized two-electron functions (called *geminals* by Shull); use of geminals takes account of much of the electron correlation omitted in an MO wave function. The geminal function for a given chemical bond (e.g., O—H) is expected to be approximately unchanged from molecule to molecule. Some applications of geminals have been made.[65] Geminals are a synthesis of the MO and VB approaches.

Linnett has proposed a method for constructing approximate molecular wave functions that differs from the MO and VB methods. His approach, the *non-paired-spatial-orbital* (NPSO) *method* has been very successful in calculations on several rather small molecules. However, there are formidable computational difficulties (connected with nonorthogonality) preventing application of the NPSO method to large molecules. Linnett has also developed an appealing qualitative description of chemical bonding (the *double-quartet theory*) based on the ideas of the NPSO method.[66]

The physicists Brueckner and Goldstone developed the *many-body perturbation theory* (MBPT) method to treat correlation in the calculation of nuclear wave functions. This method was extended to the calculation of atomic and molecular wave functions by Kelly. Such calculations are difficult and the first MBPT calculation on a triatomic molecule was the Miller–Kelly 1971 H_2O calculation (Table 15.1). A related approach is the *pair correlation theory* developed by Sinanoğlu and Nesbet. Pair correlation theory[67] assumes that atomic and molecular correlation energy can be well approximated as the sum of correlation energies over all pairs of electrons. (Thus for the Be $1s^2 2s^2$ configuration, the pair correlations are the $1s\alpha$–$1s\beta$ and $2s\alpha$–$2s\beta$ intraorbital correlations and the $1s\alpha$–$2s\alpha$, $1s\alpha$–$2s\beta$, $1s\beta$–$2s\alpha$, $1s\beta$–$2s\beta$ interorbital correlations.) One then attempts to calculate these pair correlation energies one at a time and then sums them to get the total correlation energy. (The separated-pair approximation described above allows for intraorbital correlation, but not interorbital correlation; it therefore omits a significant portion of the correlation.) Unfortunately, calculations on some small molecules (HF, CO, H_2O) indicate that the sum of the pair correlations overestimates the true correlation energy. (If localized, rather than canonical MO's are used, this overestimation may possibly be reduced.) For details on this work, see *Schaefer*, pp. 182–190, 323–325.

The electronic wave function depends on $3n$ spatial and n spin coordinates. Since the Hamiltonian (15.12) contains only one- and two-electron spatial terms, the

---

[65] *Pilar*, Section 17-8; *Parr*, Section 18; *Schaefer*, pp. 190–197.

[66] For the NPSO method, see R. Pauncz, *Alternant Molecular Orbital Method*, Saunders, Philadelphia, 1967, Chapter 10. For the double-quartet theory, see J. W. Linnett, *The Electronic Structure of Molecules*, Wiley, New York, 1964.

[67] *Parr*, Section 19; *Pilar*, pp. 373–374; *Time*, May 31, 1963, p. 39.

energy can be written in terms of integrals involving only six spatial coordinates (Problem 15.66). In a sense, the wave function of a many-electron molecule contains more information than is needed, and is lacking in direct physical significance. This has prompted the search for functions that involve fewer variables than the wave function and that can be used to calculate the energy and other properties. The molecular energy can be expressed in terms of the first-order spinless density matrix (which is a function of three spatial coordinates) and the second-order spinless density matrix (which is a function of six spatial coordinates). Unfortunately, no convenient principle (analogous to the variation principle used to calculate wave functions) has been developed that would allow direct calculation of these density matrices without first calculating the wave function.[68]

It has been proven that for the ground state of a molecule, the energy is uniquely determined by the electron density $\rho(x, y, z)$, a function of only three variables. [P. Hohenberg and W. Kohn, *Phys. Rev.*, **136**, B864 (1964).]

Clementi has proposed that the correlation energy be computed by an approximate statistical formula due to Wigner; this formula involves the integration of a certain function of the electron density ρ; the integration does not take an excessive amount of computer time. Clementi obtained encouraging results in initial applications. He believes that the use of contracted Gaussian basis sets, dynamical basis sets, and Wigner's formula is likely to make accurate *ab initio* calculations on large molecules "routinely possible and practicable." [See E. Clementi, *Proc. Nat. Acad. Sci. USA*, **69**, 2942 (1972).]

Before concluding, we indicate some areas of electronic structure that have not been discussed in this chapter. The application of MO theory to transition-metal complex ions is called *ligand-field theory* and has been successful in explaining the electronic absorption spectra of such ions. (See *Murrell, Kettle, and Tedder*, Chapter 13; *Offenhartz*, Chapter 9.) There is a tendency to consider ligand-field theory as a third branch of valence theory, separate from the MO and VB theories; actually, ligand-field theory is simply MO theory applied to compounds whose atoms have d (or f) valence electrons. Ligand-field theory has largely replaced the older VB approach, which described complex ions using such concepts as $d^2 sp^3$ hybridization of the metal orbitals.

MO theory provides a good description of the bonding in boron hydrides. These compounds have fewer than $2(n-1)$ valence electrons, where n is the number of atoms. Thus there are not enough electrons to form $(n-1)$ electron-pair bonds between the atoms; from the VB viewpoint such compounds are anomalous and have been termed electron deficient. However, it is only chemical prejudices (and not quantum-mechanical requirements) that lead one to expect $n-1$ electron-pair bonds. The MO treatment of boron hydrides shows all the bonding MO's to be completely filled in the ground state, and the term "electron deficient" is not really appropriate. Calculation of the localized bonding MO's in B_2H_6 shows that there are two localized MO's each of which extends over three nuclei (two borons and one hydrogen) giving two three-center bonds.[69] These three-center localized MO's

---

[68] For more on density matrices, see *Pilar*, Section 13-4.
[69] E. Switkes, R. M. Stevens, W. N. Lipscomb, and M. D. Newton, *J. Chem. Phys.*, **51**, 2085 (1969).

resemble the banana orbitals of the isoelectronic molecule ethylene; we can view B_2H_6 as obtained from C_2H_4 by removing a proton from each carbon nucleus and placing it in the midst of one of the banana orbitals. The higher boron hydrides have three-center bonds involving three boron atoms. (See *Murrell, Kettle, and Tedder,* Chapter 14.)

In 1929 Dirac wrote: "The underlying physical laws necessary for the mathematical theory of ... the whole of chemistry are thus completely known, and the difficulty is only that the exact application of these laws leads to equations much too complicated to be soluble." Application of high-speed digital computers to quantum chemistry has overcome to a significant degree the difficulties referred to by Dirac. Orbital symmetry rules are providing insight into the course of chemical reactions. Of course, just a small fraction of chemically important problems have been successfully treated by quantum mechanics, but future prospects are bright. To sum up, we quote Parr[70]: "Accurate descriptions of the electronic structure of molecules are upon us."

PROBLEMS

15.1 The following argument has occasionally been used to "prove" the impossibility of obtaining accurate wave functions for many-electron systems: The electronic wave function of an n-electron system depends on $3n$ spatial coordinates (and n spin coordinates). To accurately tabulate the wave function, we must specify ψ for, say, 100 different values of each spatial coordinate; for a 20-electron system, we need a table with $100^{60} = 10^{120}$ entries; this number is greater than the number of atoms in the observable universe (there are perhaps 10^{11} galaxies within 10^{10} light-years of us; a typical galaxy has 10^{11} stars; a typical star weighs 10^{33} g). Hence it is impossible to obtain accurate many-electron wave functions. Point out the fallacy in this argument.

15.2 Let $\hat{A} = n\,\delta(x_1 - x)\,\delta(y_1 - y)\,\delta(z_1 - z)$, where x_1, y_1, z_1 are the coordinates of electron 1, (x, y, z) is an arbitrary point in space, n is the number of electrons in the molecule, and δ is the Dirac delta function. If we evaluate $\langle \psi | \hat{A} | \psi \rangle$, what physically observable property is obtained?

15.3 Verify that (15.5) are the possible symmetry species for $\mathscr{C}_{2v}$.

15.4 Work out the possible symmetry species for $\mathscr{D}_2$.

15.5 For formaldehyde: (a) Work out the symmetry orbitals for a minimal-basis-set calculation; give the symmetry species of each symmetry orbital. (Choose the x axis perpendicular to the molecular plane.) (b) How many σ and how many π canonical MO's will result from a minimal-basis-set calculation? How many occupied σ and occupied π MO's are there for the ground state? (c) For each of the 8 energy-localized MO's, state which AO's will make significant contributions. (d) What is the maximum size secular determinant that occurs in finding the minimal-basis-set canonical MO's?

15.6 Work out the minimal-basis symmetry orbitals and their symmetry species for *cis*-1,2-difluoroethylene. (Choose the x axis perpendicular to the molecular plane.)

15.7 Sketch the $1a_1$, $3a_1$, $1b_1$, $4a_1$, and $2b_2$ MO's of water.

---

[70] *Parr,* p. 123.

15.8 Give the point group of: (a) staggered C_2H_6; (b) eclipsed C_2H_6; (c) a C_2H_6 conformation that is neither eclipsed nor staggered; (d) s-trans-butadiene; (e) s-cis-butadiene.

15.9 Give the point group of C_2H_4 for $0°$, $30°$, and $90°$ twist angles of one CH_2 group relative to the other.

15.10 Frequently the x and z axes of ethylene are interchanged as compared to Fig. 15.10. What change does this cause in the MO labeling? [The symmetry-species designations (15.76) are retained.]

15.11 Explain why the MO energies of a planar molecule generally lie in the order: bonding σ < bonding π < antibonding π < antibonding σ.

15.12 How many independent molecular wave functions correspond to: (a) a ^3E term? (b) a ^1E term?

15.13 Give the form of the normalization constants for the symmetry orbitals (15.18) and (15.19).

15.14 Suppose a ground-state calculation gives us some virtual orbitals for the molecule M. In which one of the following species, would an excited electron occupy an MO that was well approximated by a virtual orbital of ground-state M? (a) M; (b) M^+; (c) M^-. Explain.

15.15 (a) Does having the coefficient of $C1s$ greater than 1.0 in the $1a_1$ methane MO in (15.56) violate the condition that the MO be normalized? Explain. (b) Use the results of Problem 13.28 to express the $2a_1$ methane MO of (15.56) using a nonorthogonal $2s$ STO. (c) Verify that the $2a_1$ MO found in part (b) is normalized. [The needed overlap integrals can be found by interpolating in the tables of R. S. Mulliken, C. A. Rieke, D. Orloff, and H. Orloff, *J. Chem. Phys.*, **17**, 1248 (1949).]

15.16 Call the ethylene symmetry orbitals in (15.77) g_1 to g_{14}, in order. For each of the 8 canonical ethylene MO's in (15.78), decide, as best you can, which symmetry orbitals will make major contributions; give the sign of each such symmetry orbital in the MO expression. (*Hint*: Decide how many inner-shell and how many bonding canonical MO's there are; combine the symmetry orbitals so as to build up charge density between the nuclei for the bonding MO's. As a further hint, the third symmetry orbital in (15.77) makes no significant contribution to $3a_g$.) Sketch the canonical MO's. Assume an orthogonalized $2s$ orbital is used.

15.17 Given the following computed Hartree-Fock energies (in hartrees):

F	H_2	F_2	HF
-99.409	-1.1336	-198.768	-100.070

(a) Compute the dissociation energy of HF from the Hartree-Fock energies of the species in the reaction $H + F \rightarrow HF$. (b) The experimental HF dissociation energy is 6.11 eV. Explain why the procedure in (a) gives a substantial error. (c) Explain why using the Hartree-Fock energies to calculate the energy change in the reaction $H_2 + F_2 \rightarrow 2HF$ should give a smaller error than for the reaction in (a). Then using the above data and the experimental dissociation energies of H_2 and F_2 (4.747 and 1.65 eV), calculate D_e for HF and compare to the experimental result. (d) Explain why D_e as calculated by procedure (a) should be *less* than the true D_e.

15.18 Predict the ground-state geometry of: (a) $SnBr_2$; (b) $HgBr_2$; (c) $TeCl_2$; (d) OF_2; (e) XeF_2; (f) H_2S; (g) I_3^-; (h) HOCl.

15.19 Predict the ground-state geometry of: (a) GaI_3; (b) BrF_3; (c) PF_3; (d) BF_3; (e) H_3O^+.

15.20 Predict the ground-state geometry of: (a) BrF_4^-; (b) SnH_4; (c) SeF_4; (d) XeF_4; (e) BH_4^-.

15.21 Predict the ground-state geometry of: (a) PF_3Cl_2; (b) $SbCl_5$; (c) BrF_5; (d) SF_6; (e) S_2F_{10}.

15.22 Give the point group of each of the molecules in Problems 15.20 and 15.21.

15.23 Predict the ground-state geometry of each of the following molecules, considering the electrons in a multiple bond as a single pair occupying a "large orbital." (a) ONF; (b) NO_2^+; (c) SO_2; (d) CO_2; (e) ClO_2^-; (f) NO_2^-; (g) F_2CO; (h) SO_3; (i) HNO_2; (j) XeO_3; (k) $SOBr_2$; (l) POF_3; (m) $FClO_3$; (n) $F_2IO_2^-$; (o) XeO_4; (p) $XeOF_4$; (q) SOF_4; (r) IOF_5.

15.24 Derive Eq. (15.181). Use confocal elliptic coordinates, but note the difference in choice of axes between a diatomic and a planar polyatomic molecule.

15.25 Is Eq. (15.79) an accurate representation of the Hartree–Fock $1b_{3u}$ MO of ethylene? Explain.

15.26 When an extended STO basis set is used to calculate a near Hartree–Fock ψ for H_2O, one includes $3d$ functions on oxygen. Use symmetry species arguments to decide which of the following $3d$ oxygen AO's must make no contribution to the occupied ground-state H_2O MO's: $3d_{z^2}$, $3d_{xz}$, $3d_{yz}$, $3d_{x^2-y^2}$, $3d_{xy}$.

15.27 Slater's rules for finding approximate orbital exponents of K-, L-, and M-shell Slater AO's are as follows. The orbital exponent ζ is taken as $(Z - s_{nl})/n$, where n is the principal quantum number and Z is the atomic number. The screening constant s_{nl} is calculated as follows: The AO's are divided into the following groups:

$$(1s) \qquad (2s, 2p) \qquad (3s, 3p) \qquad (3d)$$

To find s_{nl}, the following contributions are summed: (a) Zero from electrons in groups outside the one being considered. (b) 0.35 from each other electron in the group considered, except that 0.30 is used in the $1s$ group. (c) For an s or p orbital, 0.85 from each electron with n one less than the orbital considered and 1.00 from each electron still further in. For a d orbital, 1.00 for each electron inside the group.

Calculate the orbital exponents according to Slater's rules for the atoms H, He, C, N, O, S, Ar. The optimum values of ζ to use when approximating an AO as a single STO have been calculated[71]; compare these values with the values found by Slater's rules.

15.28 The FE MO model usually takes the pi electrons of a conjugated polyene as moving in a one-dimensional box. A better picture would be a long, thin, rectangular three-dimensional box. Answer the following questions for a three-dimensional-box model. (a) What restriction must be imposed on the quantum numbers of an orbital to give it the required pi symmetry? (b) Show that this model still gives the expression (15.94) for the longest wavelength transition.

15.29 Calculate the longest wavelength electronic transition of:

(a) $CH_2{=}CH{-}CH{=}CH{-}\overset{-}{C}H_2$;

(b) $CH_2{=}CH{-}CH{=}CH{-}\overset{+}{C}H_2$;

[71] E. Clementi and D. L. Raimondi, *J. Chem. Phys.*, **38**, 2686 (1963); E. Clementi, D. L. Raimondi, and W. P. Reinhardt, *ibid.*, **47**, 1300 (1967). [For $n = 4$, Slater took ζ as $(Z - s_{nl})/3.7$; however, Slater's rules are generally unreliable for $n \geqslant 4$.]

(c) β-carotene. For each species use either the FE MO model or the FE MO model with a sinusoidal potential added, whichever is more appropriate. Predict the color of each species.

15.30 Calculate the limiting value of the longest wavelength transition of the polyene (15.95) as $n_C \to \infty$, using: (a) the simple FE MO model; (b) the FE MO model with a sinusoidal potential added.

15.31 Express the real forms of the spherical harmonics as linear combinations of the complex functions Y_l^m. Three separate equations are required.

15.32 Apply the FE MO model to benzene by solving the Schroedinger equation for a particle confined to move on a circle. (There is only one variable, the angle φ.) Draw the pattern of pi-electron FE MO energies and compare to the Hückel method. Pick a reasonable value for the radius and calculate the position of the longest wavelength band of benzene; compare with the experimental value 2038 Å.

15.33 Write down symmetry orbitals for a minimal-basis-set calculation of H_2.

15.34 (a) Verify that the HMO coefficients (15.123) satisfy the HMO set of simultaneous equations. [*Hint:* use the identity $\sin a + \sin b = 2 \sin \frac{1}{2}(a+b) \cos \frac{1}{2}(a-b)$.] (b) Verify that the coefficients (15.123) give a normalized HMO. [To evaluate the needed sum, express the sine function as exponentials and then use the formula for the sum of a geometric series.]

15.35 Calculate the HMO total bond orders and the pi-electron densities for the lowest excited state of butadiene.

15.36 Since only the topology of the carbon framework is of significance in the HMO method, the full symmetry of s-*trans*-butadiene need not be used to get the maximum simplification possible in the HMO method; instead, it is sufficient to use only the C_2 axis. (a) Write down the two possible symmetry species for the group $\mathscr{C}_2$. (b) Construct pi-electron symmetry orbitals for butadiene, classifying them according to the symmetry species of $\mathscr{C}_2$. (c) Set up and solve the two Hückel secular equations for butadiene using the symmetry orbitals of (b) as basis functions.

15.37 Verify that the geometric construction of Fig. 15.19 gives the correct HMO energies of the cyclic polyene $C_n H_n$.

15.38 For the allyl radical $\cdot CH_2 - CH = CH_2$, find: (a) the HMO's and energies; (b) the mobile bond orders; (c) the pi-electron densities; (d) the free valences; (e) the delocalization energy.

15.39 Calculate the quantities (a) through (e) of Problem 15.38 for the allyl cation and anion, $[CH_2CHCH_2]^+$ and $[CH_2CHCH_2]^-$. Which ion is predicted to be more stable?

15.40 (a) Calculate the energy needed to compress 3 carbon-carbon single bonds and stretch 3 carbon-carbon double bonds to the benzene bond length 1.397 Å. Assume a harmonic-oscillator potential-energy function for bond stretching and compression. Typical carbon-carbon single- and double-bond lengths are 1.53 and 1.335 Å; typical stretching force constants for carbon-carbon single and double bonds are 5 and 9.5 millidynes/Å. (b) Use the result of (a) to calculate an improved β value for benzene from the data following Eq. (15.154).

15.41 Typical bond energies (in kcal/mole) are:

C—H	C—C	C=C
99	83	146

The heat of formation of benzene from 6 hydrogen and 6 carbon atoms is 1323 kcal/mole. Calculate the "experimental" delocalization energy of benzene using these data, first omitting the strain-energy correction, then including it. (Because bond energies vary by several kcal from compound to compound, this procedure is very rough.)

15.42 Estimate the carbon-carbon bond length in: (a) $C_5H_5^-$; (b) $C_7H_7^+$; (c) $C_8H_8^{--}$.

15.43 (a) Set up and solve the a_u, b_{2g}, and b_{1g} HMO secular equations for naphthalene. (b) Find the coefficients of the lowest naphthalene HMO.

15.44 Derive Eq. (15.164). *Hint:* Start with E_π as the sum of the orbital energies and use $e_i = \langle \varphi_i| \hat{H}^{\text{eff}} |\varphi_i \rangle$.

15.45 Work out the coefficients of the nonbonding HMO of benzyl.

15.46 Sketch the HMO's of naphthalene; indicate the nodal planes by dashed lines.

15.47 (a) Calculate the quantities (a) through (e) of Problem 15.38 for the diradical trimethylenemethane $C(CH_2)_3$. (The degenerate MO's can be taken as either real or complex, similar to the benzene degenerate MO's.) (b) The same as (a) for the propargyl diradical $HC\!=\!C\!=\!CH$. Save time by using the results of Problem 15.38. Note that this linear molecule has two sets of spatially perpendicular pi MO's.

15.48 Use Table 15.3 to calculate the naphthalene bond orders, free valences, delocalization energy, and predicted bond lengths.

15.49 The ionization potentials (in eV) of the first few polyacenes are

benzene	naphthalene	anthracene	tetracene
9.4	8.3	7.6	7.0

(a) Use these data in conjunction with the HMO method to calculate values of α and β; compare the value of β obtained with (15.150). (b) Predict the ionization potential of pentacene. (The HMO Δx values for HOMO's and LUMO's of these polyacenes are 2.0, 1.236, 0.828, 0.590, 0.439.)

15.50 (a) Compute the pi-electron energy of ethylene when overlap is included in the HMO method. (b) Compute in terms of γ the delocalization energy of benzene when overlap is included in the HMO method. (c) Using the procedure of Problem 15.40, evaluate γ; compare with the spectroscopic value 2.72 eV [Eq. (15.150)].

15.51 Write down the simple HMO secular determinant for each of the following molecules. (a) phenol; (b) phenanthrene; (c) furan.

15.52 Find the HMO energies for the polymethine ion (15.100) with $k = 0$; use averages of the values in (15.174); to simplify the work, use symmetry orbitals. What value of β is required to fit the observed lowest energy transition?

15.53 (a) For P_{rs} equal to 1 and to 3, compare the bond-length predictions of Eq. (15.163) with experimental carbon-carbon single- and triple-bond lengths. (b) Look up (in one of the tabulations mentioned in Section 15.8) the Hückel bond orders of azulene and compare the predicted bond lengths with the experimental values. [The experimental data can be found in R. J. Buenker and S. D. Peyerimhoff, *Chem. Phys. Letters*, **3**, 37 (1969).]

15.54 (a) What is the HMO delocalization energy of cyclobutadiène? (b) Calculate the HMO total bond orders in cyclobutadiene.

15.55 Show that

$$\sum_r q_r = n_\pi$$

15.56 Calculate the Wheland pi MO energies of butadiene; use $S = 0.25$.

15.57 Prove that the Wheland MO coefficients b_{jr} for conjugated hydrocarbons are related to the HMO coefficients by

$$b_{jr} = \frac{c_{jr}}{(1 - Sw_j)^{1/2}}$$

15.58 Apply the extended Hückel method to H_2; use $K = 1.5$; use the expression from Chapter 13 of S as a function of R; plot the valence-electron energy as a function of R; compare the predicted value of R_e with the experimental value. (To avoid solving a secular equation, use symmetry orbitals.) Use 1.0 as the orbital exponent.

15.59 Verify Eq. (15.204).

15.60 (a) Set up the 8×8 extended Hückel secular determinant for methane at the equilibrium configuration; don't use symmetry orbitals. Take $K = 1.5$; use (15.198); use Slater's rules (Problem 15.27) for the orbital exponents; evaluate the overlap integrals from the reference of Problem 15.15. (b) The same as (a), but now use symmetry orbitals.

15.61 The three equivalent sp^2 hybrid AO's of carbon point to the corners of an equilateral triangle. Derive expressions for them, assuming orthonormality.

15.62 The two equivalent sp hybrid carbon AO's make an angle of 180° with each other. Derive them.

15.63 Draw VB resonance structures of the benzyl radical with the odd electron on the CH_2 carbon, on an *ortho* carbon, on a *meta* carbon, and on a *para* carbon. Explain why the contribution of the structure with the odd electron on a *meta* carbon should be quite small. Is this consistent with the MO results (Problem 15.45)?

15.64 Draw the 12 butadiene singly polar ionic structures.

15.65 (a) Which bonds in naphthalene does the resonance method predict to be the shortest? (b) Which bond in azulene does the resonance method predict to be the longest? (Consider only Kekulé structures.)

15.66 Express the electronic energy of a molecule in terms of integrals involving no more than six spatial coordinates.

15.67 Consider the following statement[72]: "Semiempirical quantum chemistry violates the fundamental canon of a *scientific theory* to the effect that statements have to be expressed in a manner that allows for the possibility of disproof." Give arguments for or against this statement.

15.68 Let the AO's i and k be on the same atom in a molecule and let the AO s be on a different atom. Which of the following integrals are neglected in the CNDO method? Which are neglected in the INDO method? (a) $(ii|kk)$; (b) $(ik|ik)$; (c) $(ii|ss)$; (d) $(is|is)$; (e) $(ii|is)$.

15.69 Four of the six calculated pair correlation energies for the Be ground state are 0.00081, 0.00212, 0.04183, 0.04535 hartrees. Each of the two pair correlation energies not given has the same value as one of the four listed. (a) Which of these numbers is the $1s\alpha$–$2s\beta$ pair correlation energy? (b) Which of these values is the $1s\alpha$–$2s\alpha$ pair correlation energy? (c) What are the values of the two pair correlation energies not given?

15.70 Consider a closed-shell wave function with n electrons occupying $n/2$ MO's. (a) How many intraorbital pair correlations are there? (b) How many interorbital pair correlations are there? (c) What is the total number of pair correlations?

---

[72] H. Primas, *Int. J. Quantum Chem.*, **1**, 493 (1967).

15.71 Consider the thermal reaction 1,3,5-hexatriene → 1,3-cyclohexadiene. (a) Use the symmetry of the polyene HOMO to predict whether the reaction path is conrotatory or disrotatory. (The HMO's need not be found explicitly; all that is needed is the signs of the AO's in the HOMO and these can be found by noting that the HMO nodal pattern is the same as the FE MO nodal pattern.) (b) The same as (a) when the reaction occurs photochemically. (c) State the general rules for the cyclization of the polyene (15.95) with n_π pi electrons.

15.72 Examine the frontier orbitals and decide whether each of the following elementary reactions should have a high or low activation energy for a 4-center broadside-collision reaction path. (a) $H_2 + D_2 \rightarrow 2HD$; (b) $N_2 + O_2 \rightarrow 2NO$; (c) $F_2 + Br_2 \rightarrow 2FBr$; (d) $H_2 + C_2H_4 \rightarrow C_2H_6$.

Appendix

Table A.1 Physical Constants [1]

Constant	Symbol	Value	Error Limit [2]
Speed of light in vacuum	c	$2.99792458 \times 10^{10}$ cm/sec	4
Proton charge	e	4.80324×10^{-10} statcoul	4
Avogadro's constant	N_0	6.02204×10^{23} mole^{-1}	9
Electron rest mass	m	9.10953×10^{-28} g	14
Proton rest mass	m_p	1.672648×10^{-24} g	26
Neutron rest mass	m_n	1.674954×10^{-24} g	26
Planck's constant	h	6.62618×10^{-27} erg sec	11
	$\hbar = h/2\pi$	1.054589×10^{-27} erg sec	17
Faraday	$F = N_0 e$	2.892534×10^{14} statcoul/mole	25
	F	9.64846×10^4 C/mole	8
Fine-structure constant	$\alpha = e^2/\hbar c$	7.297351×10^{-3}	18
	$1/\alpha$	137.03604	33
Bohr radius	$a_0 = \hbar^2/me^2$	0.5291771×10^{-8} cm	13
Bohr magneton	$\beta_e = e\hbar/2mc$	9.27408×10^{-21} erg/G	11
Nuclear magneton	$\beta_p = e\hbar/2m_p c$	5.05082×10^{-24} erg/G	6
Electron g value	g_e	2.002319313	11
Proton g value	g_p	5.585691	7
Gas constant	R	8.3144×10^7 erg/°K mole	8
Boltzmann constant	$k = R/N_0$	1.38066×10^{-16} erg/°K	13
Gravitational constant	G	6.672×10^{-8} dyn cm^2/g^2	12
Rydberg constant for infinite nuclear mass	$R_\infty = e^2/2a_0 hc$	$109{,}737.32$ cm^{-1}	2

[1] E. R. Cohen and B. N. Taylor, *J. Phys. Chem. Ref. Data*, **2**, 663 (1973).
[2] The error limit given is three standard deviations and applies to the final digits of the quoted value.

Table A.2   Definitions of Standards and Equivalents

Quantity	Definition
meter	1,650,763.73 times the vacuum wavelength of the orange-red line of Kr^{86}
kilogram	mass of the international kilogram at Sèvres, France
second	9,192,631,770 times the period of the hyperfine transition between the sublevels $F = 4$, $M_F = 0$ and $F = 3$, $M_F = 0$ of the $^2S_{1/2}$ ground level of Cs^{133}
degree Kelvin	defined in the thermodynamic scale by assigning 273.16°K to the triple point of water (freezing point of water = 273.15°K = 0°C)
Avogadro's number	the number of atoms in exactly 12 g of C^{12}
thermochemical calorie	4.1840×10^7 ergs
liter	1000 cm^3

Table A.3   Energy Conversion Factors

		erg	eV	cm^{-1}
1 erg	=	1	6.2415×10^{11}	5.0340×10^{15}
1 eV	=	1.6022×10^{-12}	1	8065.5
1 cm^{-1}	=	1.9865×10^{-16}	$1.2398_5 \times 10^{-4}$	1
1 kcal/mole	=	6.9478×10^{-14}	4.3364×10^{-2}	349.75
1 hartree	=	4.3598×10^{-11}	27.212	219,474.6

		kcal/mole	hartree
1 erg	=	1.4393×10^{13}	2.2937×10^{10}
1 eV	=	23.060	3.6749×10^{-2}
1 cm^{-1}	=	2.8591×10^{-3}	4.55634×10^{-6}
1 kcal/mole	=	1	1.5936×10^{-3}
1 hartree	=	627.51	1

Table A.4 gives equivalent quantities in the SI and Gaussian systems of units. Table A.5 allows one to convert an equation from SI to Gaussian units; the quantities in the SI column are replaced by those in the Gaussian column.   For example, Coulomb's law in SI units is

$$F = q_1 q_2/4\pi\varepsilon_0 r^2$$

Replacement of ε_0 by $1/4\pi$ gives for Coulomb's law in Gaussian units

$$F = q_1 q_2/r^2$$

Table A.4 Conversion Table for Units[1]

Quantity	SI	Gaussian
mass (m)	1 kg	$= 10^3$ g
length (l)	1 meter	$= 10^2$ cm
time (t)	1 sec	$= 1$ sec
force (**F**)	1 newton	$= 10^5$ dynes
energy (E)	1 joule	$= 10^7$ ergs
power (P)	1 watt	$= 10^7$ ergs/sec
charge (q)	1 coulomb	$= $ "3" $\times 10^9$ statcoulombs
current (I)	1 ampere	$= $ "3" $\times 10^9$ statamp
electric field (**E**)	1 volt/meter	$= (1/\text{"3"}) \times 10^{-4}$ statvolt/cm
electric potential (V)	1 volt	$= (1/\text{"3"}) \times 10^{-2}$ statvolt
electric displacement (**D**)	1 coul/m²	$= $ "3" $\times 4\pi \times 10^5$ statcoul/cm²
magnetic induction (**B**)	1 weber/m²	$= 10^4$ gauss
magnetic field strength (**H**)	1 amp/m	$= 4\pi \times 10^{-3}$ oersted

[1] The symbol "3" stands for 2.9979..., the digits in the speed of light.

Table A.5 Conversion Table for Symbols[1]

Quantity	SI	Gaussian
permittivity constant	ε_0	$1/4\pi$
permeability constant	μ_0	$4\pi/c^2$
electric field	**E**	**E**
electric displacement	**D**	**D**$/4\pi$
magnetic induction	**B**	**B**$/c$
magnetic field strength	**H**	c**H**$/4\pi$
electric potential	V	V
magnetic vector potential	**A**	**A**$/c$
Poynting vector	**S**	**S**
magnetization	**M**	c**M**
magnetic dipole moment	**μ**	c**μ**

[1] c is the speed of light.

Table A.6 Integrals

$$\int x \sin bx \, dx = \frac{1}{b^2} \sin bx - \frac{x}{b} \cos bx \tag{A.1}$$

$$\int xe^{bx} \, dx = \frac{e^{bx}}{b^2}(bx-1) \tag{A.2}$$

$$\int x^2 e^{bx} \, dx = e^{bx}\left(\frac{x^2}{b} - \frac{2x}{b^2} + \frac{2}{b^3}\right) \tag{A.3}$$

$$\int_0^\infty x^n e^{-qx} \, dx = \frac{n!}{q^{n+1}}, \qquad n > -1, \; q > 0 \tag{A.4}$$

$$\int_0^\infty e^{-bx^2} \, dx = \frac{1}{2}\left(\frac{\pi}{b}\right)^{1/2} \tag{A.5}$$

$$\int_0^\infty x^{2n} e^{-bx^2} \, dx = \frac{1 \cdot 3 \cdots (2n-1)}{2^{n+1}}\left(\frac{\pi}{b^{2n+1}}\right)^{1/2}, \qquad n = 1, 2, 3, \ldots \tag{A.6}$$

$$\int_t^\infty z^n e^{-az} \, dz = \frac{n!}{a^{n+1}} e^{-at}\left(1 + at + \frac{a^2 t^2}{2!} + \cdots + \frac{a^n t^n}{n!}\right), \qquad n = 0, 1, 2, \ldots \tag{A.7}$$

Selected Bibliography

Quantum Chemistry

Anderson, J. M., *Introduction to Quantum Chemistry*, Benjamin, New York, 1969. Uses both wave mechanics and matrix mechanics.

Atkins, P. W., *Molecular Quantum Mechanics*, Oxford University Press, London, 1970. Includes treatments of molecular electric and magnetic properties often omitted from other texts.

Bethe, H. A., and E. E. Salpeter, *Quantum Mechanics of One- and Two-Electron Atoms*, Academic Press, New York, 1957. A very thorough treatment of the nonrelativistic and relativistic quantum mechanics of hydrogen and helium.

Davis, J. C., Jr., *Advanced Physical Chemistry*, Ronald Press, New York, 1965. Discusses quantum chemistry, statistical mechanics, and spectroscopy.

Dewar, M. J. S., *Molecular Orbital Theory of Organic Chemistry*, McGraw-Hill, New York, 1969. A valuable presentation of semiempirical MO methods.

Eyring, H., J. Walter, and G. E. Kimball, *Quantum Chemistry*, Wiley, New York, 1944. A concise treatment of quantum chemistry, statistical mechanics, and the quantum-mechanical theory of reaction rates.

Gatz, C. R., *Introduction to Quantum Chemistry*, Merrill, Columbus, Ohio, 1971. A concise introduction to quantum chemistry and spectroscopy.

Hanna, M. W., *Quantum Mechanics in Chemistry*, Second Edition, Benjamin, New York, 1969. A good, short text for undergraduates; discusses electronic structure and molecular spectroscopy.

Karplus, M., and R. N. Porter, *Atoms and Molecules*, Benjamin, New York, 1970. An undergraduate-level treatment of quantum chemistry and spectroscopy.

Kauzmann, W., *Quantum Chemistry*, Academic Press, New York, 1957. Discusses electronic structure and the interaction of radiation with matter.

La Paglia, S. R., *Introductory Quantum Chemistry*, Harper and Row, New York, 1971. A good, concise treatment.

Murrell, J. N., and A. J. Harget, *Semi-empirical Self-Consistent-Field Molecular Orbital Theory of Molecules*, Wiley-Interscience, London, 1971. A fine review of the PPP, CNDO, INDO, and MINDO theories.

Murrell, J. N., S. F. A. Kettle, and J. M. Tedder, *Valence Theory*, Second Edition, Wiley, London, 1970. A nice presentation of the MO and VB methods for organic and inorganic compounds.

Offenhartz, P. O'D., *Atomic and Molecular Orbital Theory*, McGraw-Hill, New York, 1970. Covers Hartree–Fock, PPP, and CNDO theories.

Parr, R. G., *Quantum Theory of Molecular Electronic Structure*, Benjamin, New York, 1963. Contains an extensive discussion of pi-electron systems and a chapter on the correlation problem; includes reprints on electronic structure.

Pauling, L., and E. B. Wilson, Jr., *Introduction to Quantum Mechanics*, McGraw-Hill, New York, 1935. Despite its age, this pioneering quantum-chemistry text is still useful.

Pilar, F. L., *Elementary Quantum Chemistry*, McGraw-Hill, New York, 1968. A very extensive graduate-level treatment of electronic structure with many literature references.

Pople, J. A., and D. L. Beveridge, *Approximate Molecular Orbital Theory*, McGraw-Hill, New York, 1970. A good presentation of the CNDO and INDO methods.

Salem, L., *The Molecular Orbital Theory of Conjugated Systems*, Benjamin, New York, 1966. A good presentation of elementary and advanced methods of dealing with pi-electron systems; includes discussions of the results of NMR and ESR spectroscopy.

Schaefer, H. F., *The Electronic Structure of Atoms and Molecules*, Addison-Wesley, Reading, 1972. An excellent survey of results of *ab initio* calculations.

Slater, J. C., *Quantum Theory of Atomic Structure*, vols. I and II, McGraw-Hill, New York, 1960. A good treatment of atomic structure with many tables useful for reference; contains an extensive bibliography of research papers.

Slater, J. C., *Quantum Theory of Molecules and Solids*, vol. 1, *Electronic Structure of Molecules*, McGraw-Hill, New York, 1963. A fine discussion of the *ab initio* approach to molecular calculations; the main text emphasizes the physical ideas of chemical bonding with the mathematical details relegated to a series of appendixes.

Streitwieser, A., Jr., *Molecular Orbital Theory for Organic Chemists*, Wiley, New York, 1961. An extensive presentation of the Hückel MO method.

Quantum Mechanics

Bates, D. R., ed., *Quantum Theory*, 3 vols., Academic Press, New York, 1961. A comprehensive treatise. Volume I treats nonrelativistic quantum mechanics; volume II treats group theory, atoms, molecules, solids, and liquids; volume III treats relativistic quantum mechanics, radiation, and nuclear structure. Each chapter is by a different author.

Bethe, H. A., and R. W. Jackiw, *Intermediate Quantum Mechanics*, Second Edition, Benjamin, New York, 1968. Covers atomic structure, relativistic quantum mechanics, and atomic collisions.

Blokhintsev, D. I., *Principles of Quantum Mechanics*, Allyn and Bacon, Boston, 1964. A good general text.

Dicke, R. H., and J. P. Wittke, *Introduction to Quantum Mechanics*, Addison-Wesley, Reading, 1960. A concise text.

Dirac, P. A. M., *The Principles of Quantum Mechanics*, Fourth Edition, Oxford University Press, London, 1958. An elegant, abstract presentation; probably too difficult for most chemists.

Fong, P., *Elementary Quantum Mechanics*, Addison-Wesley, Reading, 1962. A good introductory text with emphasis on the physical interpretation of quantum mechanics.

Hameka, H. F., *Introduction to Quantum Theory*, Harper and Row, New York, 1967. A concise, useful treatment.

Landau, L. D., and E. M. Lifshitz, *Quantum Mechanics; Non-Relativistic Theory*, Second Edition, Addison-Wesley, Reading, 1965. An excellent text providing much physical insight; treats areas of molecular quantum mechanics usually neglected in books written by physicists.

Merzbacher, E., *Quantum Mechanics*, Second Edition, Wiley, New York, 1970. A well-written, widely used text.

Park, D., *Introduction to the Quantum Theory*, McGraw-Hill, New York, 1964. A thorough, illuminating treatment designed for undergraduate physics students.

Powell, J. L., and B. Crasemann, *Quantum Mechanics*, Addison-Wesley, Reading, 1961. A good treatment of the standard topics.

Schiff, L., *Quantum Mechanics*, Third Edition, McGraw-Hill, New York, 1968. A favorite text of physicists.

Group Theory

Cotton, F. A., *Chemical Applications of Group Theory*, Second Edition, Wiley, New York, 1970. A popular introduction with applications to MO theory and molecular vibrations.

Hall, L. H., *Group Theory and Symmetry in Chemistry*, McGraw-Hill, New York, 1969. A comprehensive treatment; contains stereoscopic figures of molecules.

Hamermesh, M., *Group Theory*, Addison-Wesley, Reading, Massachusetts, 1962. A nicely done, rather advanced treatment; the applications given are mainly of interest to physicists.

Jaffé, H. H., and M. Orchin, *Symmetry in Chemistry*, Wiley, New York, 1965. An elementary, nonmathematical treatment with applications to MO theory, molecular vibrations, and crystal symmetry.

Schonland, D. S., *Molecular Symmetry*, Van Nostrand, Princeton, New Jersey, 1965. An outstanding introductory text for chemists; careful discussions of difficult points; applications to MO theory, electronic spectra, and molecular vibrations.

Tinkham, M., *Group Theory and Quantum Mechanics*, McGraw-Hill, New York, 1964. The applications given are of interest to both chemists and physicists, but the treatment is a bit too advanced for many chemists.

Miscellaneous

Anderson, J. M., *Mathematics for Quantum Chemistry*, Benjamin, New York, 1966. A short book with chapters on orthogonal functions, matrices, and classical mechanics.

Annual Review of Physical Chemistry, Annual Reviews, Palo Alto, California. Excellent review articles of the previous year's progress in physical chemistry.

Coulson, C. A., *Electricity*, Fourth Edition, Oliver and Boyd, Edinburgh, 1956. A compact treatment of electricity and magnetism.

Davidson, N., *Statistical Mechanics*, McGraw-Hill, New York, 1962. A good, thorough treatment.

Halliday, D., and R. Resnick, *Physics*, parts I and II, Wiley, New York, 1966. A widely used introductory general-physics text.

Jammer, M., *The Conceptual Development of Quantum Mechanics*, McGraw-Hill, New York, 1966. A scholarly discussion of the origins and ideas of quantum mechanics.

Margenau, H., and G. M. Murphy, *The Mathematics of Physics and Chemistry*, Second Edition, Van Nostrand, Princeton, New Jersey, 1956. A comprehensive presentation of advanced mathematical topics useful in theoretical chemistry and physics; also contains chapters on quantum mechanics and statistical mechanics.

Mathews, J., and R. L. Walker, *Mathematical Methods of Physics*, Second Edition, Benjamin, New York, 1970. Covers roughly the same topics as *Margenau and Murphy*, but with emphasis on problem-solving.

Sokolnikoff, I. S., and R. M. Redheffer, *Mathematics of Physics and Modern Engineering*, Second Edition, McGraw-Hill, New York, 1966. A large book dealing with areas of mathematics useful for physical applications; a notable omission is group theory.

Taylor, A. E., and W. R. Mann, *Advanced Calculus*, Second Edition, Xerox, Lexington, 1972. A standard text.

Answers to Selected Problems

1.1 (a) g cm/sec^2; (b) g cm^2/sec^2; (c) g$^{1/2}$ cm$^{3/2}$/sec.   **1.2** 4.0×10^4 dynes.
1.3 (a) 3.32 Å; (b) relativistic.   **1.4** $x = F(t-t_0)^2/2m + v_0(t-t_0) + x_0$.   **1.6** none.
1.7 2.24, 0.0126.   **1.8** 13/25.   **1.9** 2.22×10^{-6} deg.   **1.10** 3.1 Å.   **1.13** (a) 1,
$\pi/2$; (c) $5^{1/2}$, 296.6°.

2.1 $y = ae^x + be^{-2x}$.   **2.2** (b) $y = ae^x + bxe^x$.   **2.3** 3.0×10^{26}.   **2.4** (b) 3;
(c) $\frac{1}{4}$.   **2.5** (b) 1.1×10^2 Å; (c) uv.

3.3 (b) $\hat{A}$ and $\hat{B}$ linear and commute.   **3.4** $\hat{1}$.   **3.5** (a) linear; (b) nonlinear;
(c) linear; (d) nonlinear; (e) linear.   **3.6** (a) complex conjugation; (b) *hint:* consider an
operator that is the product of operators.   **3.9** $2a + (4ax + 2b) \, d/dx$.   **3.11** (a) $i\hbar$;
(b) $2\hbar^2 \, \partial/\partial x$; (c) 0; (d) 0; (e) $(\hbar^2/m) \, \partial/\partial x$.   **3.12** (a) Yes; (b) $1/p$; (c) $1/(p-a)$.   **3.13**
(a) Yes; (b) $1-2x$.   **3.15** (a) Yes, 1; (b) no; (c) yes, -1; (d) yes, -1; (e) yes, -1.
3.16 (a) $a/2$; (b) $b/2, c/2$; (c) 0; (d) $(1 - 3/2n_x^2\pi^2)(a^2/3)$, no, yes.   **3.17** (a) nondegenerate;
(b) 6; (c) 4.   **3.19** (a) cm$^{-1/2}$.   **3.20** (a), (c), (d), (g).   **3.21** (b), (c).   **3.22** (a)
No; (b) yes; (c) yes; (d) yes; (e) no.   **3.26** (a) $i\hbar^3 \, \partial^3/\partial y^3$.

4.1 $hv/4, hv/4$.   **4.2** (a) odd; (b) even; (c) odd; (d) neither.   **4.5** $(v_x + \frac{1}{2})hv_x +$
$(v_y + \frac{1}{2})hv_y + (v_z + \frac{1}{2})hv_z$.   **4.13** (a) 4.77 mdyn/Å.   **4.16** Use parity considerations.
4.19 (c) Yes.

5.2 $\Delta x = (h/8\pi^2 mv)^{1/2}$, $\Delta p_x = (mhv/2)^{1/2}$.   **5.5** $|\mathbf{A}| = 7$, $\mathbf{A} \cdot \mathbf{B} = 13$, $\mathbf{A} \times \mathbf{B} =$
$-32\mathbf{i} - 18\mathbf{j} + 10\mathbf{k}$.   **5.8** $\nabla^2 f = 6$.   **5.9** 3.   **5.12** 35.3°, 65.9°, 90°, 114.1°, 144.7°.
5.13 1, 0.707.

6.1 (a) 1.13 Å.   **6.2** (a) 0.24; (c) 2.66a.   **6.3** 14.   **6.4** (a) $3a/2Z$; (b) a/Z; (c) $5a/Z$.   **6.5** at the origin (nucleus).   **6.8** $-e^2/a$, $e^2/2a$, $-\frac{1}{2}$.   **6.9** -6.8 eV. **6.14** Yes.   **6.16** 1/137.0.   **6.17** Yes.   **6.19** s states.   **6.20** -108.8 eV.   **6.21** (a) spheres centered at the origin; (b) m.   **6.23** (f) 1, 3, 6.   **6.28** (a) all; (b) $\hat{H}$, $\hat{L}^2$; (c) all.

7.1 (a) F; (b) T; (c) F; (d) F; (e) F; (f) T; (g) F; (h) F.   **7.4** id/dx, $4d^2/dx^2$. **7.8** $\pi^3/32 = 1 - 1/3^3 + 1/5^3 - 1/7^3 + \cdots$.   **7.10** (c) Yes. No.   **7.13** The nth roots of 1. **7.14** (b) and (c).   **7.17** (c) and (d).   **7.21** (a) 0, 1, 0; (b) $\frac{1}{2}$, 0, $\frac{1}{2}$.   **7.23** (a) 1; (b) 0; (c) 1; (d) 0.   **7.28** Possible outcomes: $n^2h^2/8ml^2$. Probabilities: 0 for n even, $960/n^6\pi^6$ for n odd.   **7.29** $\pi^6/960$.

8.3 $3h^2/2\pi^2ml^2$.   **8.5** (a) $c = 8/9\pi$, 15% error; (b) $c = 8/729\pi$.   **8.7** -84. **8.9** (a) $x = y = z = 0$.   **8.10** $n!$ **8.13** 1.3%, 6.4%.

9.2 -12.86 eV.   **9.4** $3b$, $15b$, where $b = dh^2/64\pi^4v^2m^2$.   **9.6** $1s3s$, two non-degenerate levels; $1s3p$, two triply degenerate levels; $1s3d$, two fivefold degenerate levels. **9.7** $E^{(0)} = -77.5$ eV; $E^{(1)} = 0$.   **9.9** -27.2 eV.   **9.10** first.   **9.11** 0, 0, $\pm 3e\mathscr{E}a_0$; $2p_{+1}$, $2p_{-1}$, $2^{-1/2}(2s \mp 2p_0)$.   **9.14** 1.2×10^{-8} eV.

10.1 ground state: $1s(1)1s(2)1s(3)$.   **10.3** (a) $2^{-1/2}(\hat{1} - \hat{P}_{12})$.   **10.6** $2J_{1s2s} + J_{1s1s}$.   **10.8** 54.7° (Note that the component in the xy plane exceeds the z component.) **10.9** (1) neither; (2) antisymmetric; (3) symmetric.   **10.11** (a) $\pm\frac{1}{2}\hbar$.

11.1 (a) $2n^2$; (b) $4l+2$; (c) 2; (d) 1.   **11.2** $^2S_{1/2}$, $^1S_0$, $^2S_{1/2}$, $^1S_0$, $^2P_{1/2}$, $^3P_0$, $^4S_{3/2}$, $^3P_2$, $^2P_{3/2}$, $^1S_0$.   **11.3** ^1F, ^1G, ^1H, ^3F, ^3G, ^3H.   **11.8** (a) 45°.   **11.10** No. **11.11** $15\hbar^2/4$, $\frac{1}{2}\hbar$.   **11.13** 22.   **11.16** cobalt.   **11.17** (a) 15; (b) 36.   **11.18** 4.5×10^{-5} eV.   **11.19** 7.7×10^{-6} eV.   **11.20** There are at least 5 such configurations. **11.22** B, N, F.

12.1 After solving this problem, consider the case where cigars (blunt at one end, pointed at the other end) are used instead of coins.   **12.2** (a) $2\sigma_v$, C_2; (b) $3\sigma_v$, C_3; (g) none.   **12.3** (a) Yes; (b) No; (c) Yes.   **12.4** (b) lies along the C_3 axis; (e) is zero; (g) no information.   **12.6** (a) the regular tetrahedron.   **12.8** $\mathscr{C}_1$, $\mathscr{C}_s$, $\mathscr{C}_n$, $\mathscr{C}_{nv}$.   **12.9** $\mathscr{C}_1$, $\mathscr{C}_n$, $\mathscr{D}_n$, $\mathscr{T}$, $\mathscr{O}$, $\mathscr{I}$.   **12.10** (b) 2, 6, 10, 14, ...; (c) 3, 5, 7, ...   **12.11** (a) $\mathscr{T}_d$; (b) $\mathscr{C}_{3v}$; (c) $\mathscr{C}_{2v}$; (d) $\mathscr{C}_{3v}$; (e) $\mathscr{O}_h$; (f) $\mathscr{C}_{4v}$; (g) $\mathscr{D}_{4h}$; (h) $\mathscr{C}_{3v}$.   **12.13** (a) $\mathscr{D}_{6h}$; (b) $\mathscr{C}_{2v}$; (c) $\mathscr{C}_{2v}$; (d) $\mathscr{C}_{2v}$; (e) $\mathscr{D}_{2h}$.   **12.15** (a) $\mathscr{O}_h$; (b) $\mathscr{C}_{4v}$; (c) $\mathscr{D}_{2d}$; (d) $\mathscr{O}_h$; (e) $\mathscr{C}_{3v}$; (f) $\mathscr{D}_{2h}$.   **12.17** The answer is not $\mathscr{D}_2$.   **12.18** (a) $\mathscr{C}_{4v}$; (b) $\mathscr{C}_{\infty v}$; (c) $\mathscr{D}_{4h}$; (d) $\mathscr{C}_{4v}$; (e) $\mathscr{D}_{\infty h}$; (j) The answer is not $\mathscr{C}_{2v}$.   **12.19** (b) No, since its eigenvalues are not all real.   **12.23** $\overline{10}$, $\overline{3}$, $\overline{14}$.

13.1 (a) 1836.1; (b) -1; (c) 2π; (d) -2; (e) 4.134×10^{16} (one atomic unit of time $= \hbar a_0/e^2 = 2.419 \times 10^{-17}$ sec); (f) 137.04; (g) -0.49973; (h) 0.3934.   **13.4** (a) ellipsoids of revolution; (c) half planes.   **13.9** $-(3k^3/\pi)^{1/2}e^{-kr}\cos\theta$.   **13.11** $R^4/(1-e^{-R})$. **13.14** (a) Li_2; (b) C_2; (c) O_2^+; (d) F_2^+. (Actually, the dissociation energy of Li_2^+ is greater than that of Li_2.)   **13.15** (b) 3; (d) 2.   **13.17** $j+k$ even.   **13.24** (a) F; (b) F.   **13.26** VB.

14.1 (b) 0; (c) -2; (d) $\frac{3}{2}$.   **14.2** state 1.   **14.8** $\langle V \rangle = 3\frac{1}{3}$ eV.   **14.10** 1.8, 4.1, 6.9, and 10 Å. General formula: $R_e[(Z_aZ_b)^{1/2} - Z_a]$.

15.5 (a) a_1: $H_1 1s + H_2 1s$, $C1s$, $C2s$, $C2p_z$, $O1s$, $O2s$, $O2p_z$. b_1: $C2p_x$, $O2p_x$. b_2: $C2p_y$, $O2p_y$, $H_1 1s - H_2 1s$. (b) 10 sigma, 2 pi; 7 sigma, 1 pi. (d) 7×7. **15.6** There are nine a_1, nine b_2, two b_1, and two a_2 orbitals. **15.8** (c) $\mathscr{D}_3$; (d) $\mathscr{C}_{2h}$; (e) $\mathscr{C}_{2v}$. **15.10** Interchanges the subscripts 1 and 3 for the b symmetry species. **15.12** (b) 2. **15.14** (c). **15.15** (a) No. **15.18** (a) bond angle somewhat less than 120°; (b) linear; (c) bond angle somewhat less than $109\frac{1}{2}°$. **15.19** (a) planar, bond angles 120°; (b) planar, T shaped, two bond angles somewhat less than 90°. **15.20** (a) square planar; (b) tetrahedral. **15.22** SeF_4—$\mathscr{C}_{2v}$; XeF_4—$\mathscr{D}_{4h}$. **15.23** (a) bond angle near 120°; (b) linear; (g) FCF angle somewhat less than 120°. **15.25** No. **15.26** $3d_{xy}$. **15.27** N: $1s$—6.7; $2s$—1.95; $2p$—1.95. **15.29** (a) 30,100 cm^{-1}, colorless; (b) 21,500 cm^{-1}, orange-red; (c) 22,000 cm^{-1}, orange. **15.30** (a) 0 cm^{-1}; (b) 16,100 cm^{-1}. **15.32** $E = J^2 h^2/2ml^2$, where $J = 0, \pm 1, \pm 2, \ldots$ and l is the circumference; 51,800 cm^{-1}. **15.38** (a) $\alpha + 2^{1/2}\beta$, α, $\alpha - 2^{1/2}\beta$; (b) 0.707, 0.707; (c) 1, 1, 1; (d) 1.025, 0.318, 1.025; (e) 0.828β. **15.39** (a) same as previous problem; (b) 0.707, 0.707; 0.707, 0.707. **15.40** (a) 27 kcal/mole; (b) 1.4 eV. **15.41** 42 kcal/mole, 69 kcal/mole. **15.42** (a) 1.40_1 Å. **15.45** *ortho* and *para* carbons, $7^{-1/2}$; CH_2 carbon, $2/7^{1/2}$; others, 0. **15.48** free valences: 1, 0.452; 2, 0.404; 9, 0.104; delocalization energy, $3.683|\beta|$. **15.49** (a) $\alpha = -6$ eV; $\beta = -4$ eV. **15.58** predicted $R_e = 0$. **15.61** $(\frac{1}{3})^{1/2}2s + (\frac{2}{3})^{1/2}2p_z$, $(\frac{1}{3})^{1/2}2s - (\frac{1}{6})^{1/2}2p_z \pm (\frac{1}{2})^{1/2}2p_y$. **15.62** $2^{-1/2}(2s \pm 2p_z)$. **15.65** (a) 1–2, 7–8, 3–4, 5–6. **15.68** CNDO: (b), (d), (e); INDO: (d), (e). **15.70** (a) $n/2$; (b) $\frac{1}{2}n^2 - n$; (c) $\frac{1}{2}n(n-1)$. **15.71** (a) disrotatory; (b) conrotatory. **15.72** (a) high.

Index

Dipole-moment operator, 339
Dirac, P. A. M., 125, 215, 235, 476
Dirac delta function, 145–147, 176
Direction cosines, 408–409
Discontinuity, 45, 175–176
Dissociation energy, 291, 329–330,
    352–353, 397, 477
  table, 321
Divergence, 68
Dobosh, P. A., 453
Dot product of vectors, 66–67
Double-quartet theory, 474
Drugs, 449
Dummy variable, 49–50
Dynamical basis set, 473

Edmiston, C., 401, 403, 418
Effective nuclear charge, 191, 301
Ehrenfest's theorem, 155
Eigenfunctions, 29–30 (*see also*
    Harmonic oscillator, etc.)
  angular momentum, 74–81
  of commuting operators, 61–64
  of Hermitian operators, 128–130,
    133–134, 149
  of momentum operator, 33, 143–144
  of parity operator, 138–139
  of position operator, 145–147
Eigenvalues, 29
  of Hermitian operators, 127–128
Einstein, A., 2, 151
Electric field, 339
Electron, 1, 3, 8, 98, 118, 215–216,
    222–223, 234–235
Electron-deficient compounds, 475
Electronegativity, 465
Electronic Hamiltonian, 290
Electron repulsion integrals, 389, 447,
    453, 473
Electron volt, 107
Electrostatic theorem, 374–380
Elliptic coordinates, 295
Energy:
  kinetic, 30–32, 307, 361–371, 380
  potential, 7, 51–52, 68, 186, 307,
    361–371
Energy levels:
  free particle, 24–25
  harmonic oscillator, 54–55

hydrogen atom, 100, 104–106, 107
  particle in a box, 20–21
  rigid rotor, 97
Energy-localized orbitals, 400–405,
    407–410, 416, 449–450, 463,
    475–476
Energy operator, 32, 64 (*see also*
    Hamiltonian operator)
Equivalent electrons, 255, 325
Equivalent orbitals, 400, 407–410,
    415–416, 458
Ermler, W. C., 397
Ethane, 405, 410–412, 413
  table of MO calculations, 411
Ethylene, 413–417, 420, 438, 459
Euler's theorem, 362
Even function, 55, 139
Ewen, H. I., 267
Exchange, 210, 461
Exchange degeneracy, 209
Exchange integral, 205, 207, 309, 332
Exchange operator, 347, 359
Exclusion principle, 220–224, 229–230
Expansion of functions, 130–134
Expectation value (*see* Average value)
Extended basis set, 349
Extended Hückel method, 450–452

Factorization, 106
Feinberg, M. J., 307
Fermi, E., 223
Fermi hole, 247
Fermions, 223
Ferrocene, 287
Feynman, R. P., 375
Fine structure, 215, 261, 264
Fine-structure constant, 235
Finkelstein, B. N., 302
Fluorine molecule, 320, 350–351, 352,
    353
Fock, V., 242
Force, 51, 88, 377–380
Force constant, 51
FORTRAN, 470
Fourier series, 130–133
Fourier transform, 134
Free-electron molecular-orbital
    (FE MO) method, 421–425
Free particle, 24–25, 143–144

Machine translation, 471
Magnetic field, 118–120, 261, 265
Magnetic moment, 119–120
Magnetic moment, spin, 234–235
Magnetic monopole, 119
Magnetic quantum number, 120
Many-body perturbation theory, 474
Margenau, H., 151
Matrix, 125, 386
Matrix element, 125
Measurement:
    and eigenvalues, 32–35, 141–145,
        149–150
    of position, 7–8, 151 (*see also* Born
        postulate)
    and superposition of states, 141–145,
        150, 236, 316
    and uncertainty principle, 3–5,
        61–64, 71
Merrifield, D. P., 393
Methane:
    scf mo treatment, 405–410
    vb treatment, 458–459
Methylene, 418, 455
Meyer, W., 397
Microwave spectroscopy, 98
Mind, 449
MINDO method, 453–454, 469–470, 472
Minimal basis set, 349
Minor, 164, 165
Minsky, M., 472
Molecular-orbital (mo) method:
    for diatomic molecules, 300–329,
        333–336, 337–338, 341–346,
        347–356
    for H_2, 327–329, 333–336, 338
    for polyatomic molecules, 387–390
        (*see also under individual*
        molecules)
    and vb method, 333–336, 462–463
Molecular-orbital nomenclature:
    diatomic molecules, 299, 317, 353
    polyatomic molecules, 386, 387
Moment of inertia, 96–97
Momentum, 3–5, 30–31, 69
Momentum eigenfunctions, 33, 143–144
Momentum operator, 31, 68, 143–144
Montgomery, H. E., 397
Moore, C. E., 264
Moskowitz, J. W., 417

Mulliken, R. S., 336, 465, 472, 474
Multiconfiguration scf method,
    352–353
Multiplet, 264
Multiplicity, 254, 322, 326, 384–385
Muon, 237
Murrell, J. N., 455
Mutations, 448

Naphthalene:
    hmo treatment, 435–437, 440
    scf mo treatment, 440
    vb treatment, 462
Nesbet, R. K., 474
Neutron, 1, 216
Newton, M. D., 449
Newton's second law, 6, 155
Nitrogen molecule, 320, 344, 352,
    353–354, 404
Nodes, 21, 57, 106, 122, 241, 428
Nonequivalent electrons, 254, 323
Nonpaired spatial orbital (npso)
    theory, 474
Normalization, 13, 21, 37, 44, 75–76,
    130, 217–218
    of spherical harmonics, 80–81, 111,
    236–237
Normal state, 55
Nuclear motion:
    in atoms, 107, 214, 267
    in molecules, 292
Null operator, 27

Observables, 64
Odd function, 55, 140
One-center expansion method, 388–389
Operators, 26–35, 148–149
    angular momentum, 70, 74, 82, 249
    antisymmetrization, 235
    commutation of, 27–28, 61–64
    Hamiltonian (*see* Hamiltonian
        operator)
    Hermitian, 125–130, 219, 431
    ladder (*see* Ladder operators)
    linear, 28, 149
    momentum, 31, 68, 143–144
    permutation, 221–222
    potential-energy, 31–32